HUMOROUS STORIES

HUMOROUS STORIES

INTRODUCED BY
RONNIE BARKER

Original edition published in 1984
This revised and expanded edition published in 1985 by

Octopus Books Limited
59 Grosvenor Street
London W1

Copyright © 1984, 1985 Introduction and arrangement
Octopus Books Limited

Editor: Moira Eminton
Designer: Design 23

ISBN 0 86273 164 X

Printed and bound in Great Britain by Collins, Glasgow

CONTENTS

Contents

Contents

Contents

Contents

Introduction

The first thing any collection of funnies is likely to do is set off some sort of argument. Either you start haggling with your husband/wife/friend (delete as applicable) over whether chapter three is funnier than chapter thirty or you complain bitterly because the clown who compiled it hasn't included your favourite bit of wit. Anthologies are like that.

No two ribs tickle in the same way and one man's guffaw is another man's frosty face. It's even more chancy than that: you can treasure the memory of some hilarious snippet for years, only to dig it out again and find it's silly or pretentious or just plain boring. Humour is such a personal business that the best you can ever do is present what makes you laugh right now and hope that it makes enough other people do the same. The upshot is that there's only a very general rule of thumb for any collection of humorous stories – it should be big enough to use as a missile if the argument gets out of hand but not so weighty that you can't read it in the bath without sinking in a fizz of bubbles.

Between these covers you can have a spiffing romp with the upper crust (P. G. Wodehouse: *The Rummy Affair of Old Biffy*) or wallow in the rural byres (James Herriot: *Let Sleeping Vets Lie*), you can find fun in the Cameroons (Gerald Durrell: *The King and the Conga*) or in Lady Astor's back garden (Basil Boothroyd: *Why Dogs Bite Gardeners*). Some of the pieces will be so familiar that the very title starts your mouth twitching happily. Others come in a new explosion of laughter. And if the list of contents still leaves you hankering after that side-splitting story by Whosit or that witty little tale by Whatsit and sends you ferreting through the library to check on what Whosit wrote or who Whatsit was – well, that's just one more favour this book has done for you.

I can see only three reasons why, as its owner, you might fail to chortle over it: a) you haven't opened it b) you've broken your reading specs c) your mother-in-law has just moved in. Of course, there are those unfortunate folk who Take Life Seriously (capitals come naturally to them) and frequently mutter that 'there's nothing much to laugh at in this world'. But they just aren't looking. Comedy is a looking-glass world: you turn pomposity, vanity or greed back to front and there's the laugh.

Most humour is based on fear. When you laugh at a man upended by a banana skin, you laugh because you're so jolly glad it wasn't you. It's safe enough to enjoy a vision of the luckless Sheila hoisted upside down up the mast in Michael Green's *The Art of Coarse Sailing* or the members of the Post-Cardiac City Cricket Club keeling over at the moment of victory in Richard Stilgoe's *The Cricket Match*. You are safe in your comfy armchair and it couldn't possibly happen to you – or could it?

Mind you, if there's one thing in the world that always has to be taken seriously, it's writing comedy. Performing is a doddle by comparison. As a performer you do the best you can and that's that. It's rather like diving from the high board – you just hope you don't bang your head on the bottom. Writing is more like creeping in at the shallow end: every step is chilly misery and any progress you make is horribly slow. A glance at the names we give the two skills shows you the difference immediately. Someone who tells funny stories calls himself a comedian; someone who writes them calls himself a humorist – and that sounds like a weightier, more substantial business altogether.

I've had the chance – some might say the cheek – to browse on both sides of the fence and I tell you sincerely that comedy writing is *no joke*. You sit there, gazing at a blank sheet of paper, convinced that you'll never manage a funny thought again. Typewriters and waste-paper baskets don't rate too high, as audiences go – and they never clap. When you've wrung every drop of humour out of your bones and your elbows have gone floppy, you're left with the awful thought that perhaps no one out there will laugh. I much prefer hiding behind another character – even if it's only Ronnie Barker, buffoon. Years ago, when I started writing scripts for *The Two Ronnies*, I invented a new name for myself and I only owned up when all the excuses about Gerald Wiley being an aged recluse with a phobia about phones, living at the end of a five mile mud track, wore out. I liked it better when we were two different people. I was only too willing to share the responsibility with the other fellow if a sketch fell flat on its face. Both Wiley and I take off imaginary hats to professional humorists who never have anyone to front for them.

As the reader, you get all the luck: sheer pleasure without any of the pain. But before you turn the page and get on with the real business of the book, give a thought or two to making the most of it. For instance, loud laughers should try reading it in the garden, where their guffaws can scare the birds off the vegetable patch, and silent gigglers should try a crowded train – it's amazing how mute shakes can clear a carriage and leave you with a comfy spread of seats. (A word of warning to the deep chuckler: last thing at night reading causes marital discord in direct proportion to the bounce of the bed).

Reading the whole thing at once is like eating a box of chocs at one guzzle. Connoisseurs will dip in over and over again, sample the wit here, the waggery there, the subtle satire or the slapstick, so that every delicious chapter has a special taste of its own. Happy dipping!

Ronnie Barker

The Hangover in Question

Alan Coren

4.17 A.M, light from fridge snaps on, reverberates through head like noise, can *hear* pupils contracting, shut fridge door, little polychrome rhomboids continue to kaleidoscope about in brain.

Or I am dead. This is Elysian fridge, I have snuffed it and gone to Kitchen, God's final jest, doomed to an eternity standing on jammy lino in bare feet, unable to find bottle opener, parched for Coke.

Would He be this tough on drinkers? Cannot recall pentateuchal injunctions against alcohol, is there an XIth Commandment somewhere in small print, *Thou shalt not booze?* Are there parables in minor prophet texts, *And Jeroboam came home legless, and fell over the cat, and uttered oaths; and the LORD God brought forth thunderbolts and smote him in that place where he was, saying: Henceforth shall the floor of thy mouth be as a wadi, and thine eyeballs as twin coals, and the fruit of thy loins go about on all fours, even unto the tenth generation?*

Amazing what a few minutes of natural sleep can do for you. Such as maim. Came home at 3.15, not tight, loosened, if anything, one or two joints unbolted, no more than that, perfectly capable of sticking key in letter-box and walking into Christmas tree, got glass ball off ear at only third attempt, negotiated staircase easily as falling over a log, found bedroom door handle well before 3.30, removed clothes with nothing more than minor pause to work out best way of pulling trousers over head, climbed athletically up onto bed, stubbed fag out on clock, sank into oblivion.

Rose from oblivion 4.13, not tea-time already, surely? No, clock still smouldering, faint smell of plastic molecules reorganizing their domestic arrangements.

Tongue lying on mouth-floor like felled cactus.

Got up, carrying head carefully in both hands, groped for dressing-gown, dressing-gown totally incapacitated, arms flapping, belt treble-knotted, dressing-gown obviously just got in from even wilder New Year's Eve party

than mine, crawled downstairs together like, like – who was it used to sing
Me an' My Shadow, plump man, white tie, face of some kind?

4.20, now, by kitchen clock; brave fridge searchlights again. Guy Gibson's
voice crackling on ectoplasmic intercom as we go in low over the bacon,
something registers a hit on hand, grab Coke bottle from back of fridge, slam
door, and we are away before gunners can even get range.

What hit hand? Hand got egg-white on it. Two possibilities: either I bleed
albumen, or else wife still pursuing mad habit, despite previous incidents, of
leaving egg-whites in cup after using yokes, standing cup on top shelf, and
awaiting results.

Cannot bring self to open fridge again, know what it looks like, seen it
before, it looks like giant snail has run amok; not generally known fact that
average hen's egg contains up to eighteen miles of mucus if allowed to drip
long enough.

Put it behind me, other things on what's left of mind, how, for example, to
open Coke bottle? By light chiaroscuring in from street lamp, as in
Caravaggio's immortal *Parched Drunk Looking For Coke Bottle Opener*, begin
tugging at utensil drawers, forgetting Second Law of Ergodynamics which
states that all drawers stick during small hours, also forgetting Third Law of
Ergodynamics which states that all drawers *only stick for a bit*.

Said bit having elapsed, all drawers leap from their cavities and vomit
cake-cutters, used batteries, bent screwdrivers, half a scissor, corks, spare
fuses, knife handles, flea collars, pieces of gas bill, empty Sparklets, flints,
two-pin bakelite plugs you brought from your last house just in case, Good
Boy drops, cup handles, matchboxes (empty), matchboxes (with screws in;
or, after drawer flies open, with screws out), doll's heads, and seventy-one
keys you brought from you last house just in case.

No bottle-openers, though.

4.26.

Think.

Have seen John Wayne open bottles with teeth. Or, no doubt, John
Wayne's double's teeth. Probably special teeth, though, enamelled steel
props built at San Diego Navy Yard. *John Wayne's double lies a-mouldering in the
grave, but his teeth go marching on...*

Shall not chance own vulnerable choppers, though, last time I chomped an
incautious cobnut, mouth resembled tiny Temple of Dagon, crumbling
masonry everywhere, crown dust rising, bits of bridge, World War Two
fillings – God knows what Coke bottle would do, whole skull might come off.

Ah.

Remember seeing someone open Coke bottle in door-jamb.

Ah.

Look at foot.

Foot still hissing slightly, Coke bubbles dying among instep hair. Must be special trick in opening horizontal Coke bottle in door jamb. Must be *two* special tricks, since large sliver of door jamb now lying beside Coked foot.

4.31.

No more Coke in house.

Water, squash, milk, no use, need something aerated, no good simply departing tongue, am Very Aware of need to shift something lying sideways across oesophagus. Seem to have swallowed large plank. Could be case for Red Adair, long experience assures me only megacharge of bubbles will do trick, no point ringing Dyno-Rod at 4.33, *You must be joking, squire, couldn't touch anything till February earliest, we're up to here with paperwork, not to mention staff shortages, unofficial strike up Northampton, black ice, Good Friday looming, etc...*

If plank *is* lying across oesophagus.

Aorta? Vasa cava inferior? Duodenum? Ventriculus dexter? Pulmo?

Stop, in larder, hand on bicarb packet; reflect.

All down to Jonathan Miller, this. We live in post-*Body In Question* Age. Used to know nothing about what goes on past tonsils. Now know three per cent. Point-three per cent. Know it looks like Rotorua mud-spring, in constant state of peristaltic glug; know about referred pain, i.e. if feel sudden stabbing pain in shin, could mean going deaf. To layman – to 0.3 per cent expert – entire nervous system is result of giant connective cock-up, nothing hurts where it's supposed to, everything where it isn't. If Dalston Junction like that, Central Line tube to Chancery Lane ends up in East Kilbride.

Prior to Miller, all my anatomical information came from Arthur Mee. *Children's Encylopaedia* used to have big sepia illustrations of human body in section, showing little men in overalls shovelling food into tin boiler (stomach), little men in head with Box Brownies (eyes), little men in lungs with footpumps. Very nice. Liked to think of them all down there, contented work force beavering away; felt like benevolent mill-owner, loyal workers, whistling as they shovelled, pumped, treadled, ticked carbohydrates off clipboard check-list, stoked furnaces.

Pleasant, having anthropomorphic view of own insides; every time I ate breakfast, thought of little men in spotless gumboots carrying egg away in buckets.

Impossible, now. Post-Miller, see myself as not even human, merely large biochemical complex or permanent germ-warfare battlefield. A great itinerant skin bag of blood and offal, horribly vulnerable. Never used to worry about smoking, drinking, guzzling, little men would take care of all that, scouring lungs, washing down intestinal tract, buffing liver to spotless health.

4.38.

Bicarb packet still in hand, plank still across throbbing insides. Eyes (not Box Brownies) focus on minuscule print: $NaHCO_3$.

Yes. Could be anything, really, could well combine with whatever I am to produce $SO_9C_4Pb_8Th_2Nb_6H_3Sb_2Zn_7$ ... without unease, post-Jonathan, bunging assorted valences down into the pulsing tripes, what if wedged-plank-plus-aching-eye-plus-metal-tongue syndrome is actually referral of neurological complaints about dislocated spleen, could be $NaHCO_3$ is worst possible treatment for dislocated spleen, could end up quitting vale of tears on one terminal burp.

Appalling way to go.

Return bicarb to shelf, shut larder door, hobble across floor on Coke-gummy foot, fuses, screws, Good Boy drops sticking to sole, wedged plank grinding in chest cavity, possibly indicating grit behind patella, mastoid sprouting in left ear, onset of silicosis.

4.56.

Shameful, tragic, terrifying how body gets abused, body only thing I have (gave up idea of soul 1967, following TV programme by glib atheist), New Year less than five hours old, good time to make New Year Resolution, must stop punishing tissues, must give up fags, liquor, toast, fatty...

Hang on.

Wonder if hair of dog good for wedged oesophagal plank?

Where scotch?

The Art of Coarse Sailing

Michael Green

Once more it was a disturbed night, this time due to Harry's snoring. It really was the most dreadful noise. My old car once made a similar sound shortly before expiring on Ealing Common. That was rather an unusual experience because the car simply dissolved. All the parts wore out at the same time and it disintegrated, swerved across the road and hit a tree. The headlights, which had not worked for six months, promptly blazed on and refused to go out. I remember the policeman asking me why I was wearing one trouser clip on the left leg while driving, and I explained that whenever the car went through a puddle a jet of water used to shoot up by the handbrake, so I had to take this precaution. He thought I was trying to be funny.

However, enough of the car. Yachtsmen, who find snoring a menace in the confined quarters of a cabin, have several ways of trying to stop snoring and we tried them all. My own theory is to give the offender a short, sharp shock, for example by clapping your hands loudly in his ear. I did this for five minutes until someone in the next boat called out, 'I don't mind your friend snoring, but do you have to blasted well applaud him?' So we gave this up and tried Beaver's solution. He believes that one should whisper continually 'Stop snoring' in the ear of the offender. This message would eventually penetrate the subconscious, he said, and the snoring would cease. So he knelt by Harry, looking rather as if he were praying by the side of a catafalque, and whispered gently at him. This had no effect and he gradually whispered louder and louder until eventually he was bellowing 'STOP SNORING!' at the top of his voice. Harry promptly woke up and asked what all the noise was about.

Ten minutes later, when we had all settled down, he was as bad as ever. I thought he would bring the mast down. I was still convinced a sharp shock would do the trick so I sprinkled a few drops of water on Harry's face. The snoring rose to a nightmarish crescendo and then he woke up. This time we made him promise not to try to sleep until we were all asleep. Twice he fell asleep first and we woke him up and told him to wait, and then we all fell into deep slumber.

During the night I had a dream about my old ancestor Jem Green. I was sinking in a storm-tossed ketch when Jem appeared in a lifeboat, wearing an enormous set of Victorian oilskins, and called on me to jump. I tried to vault the boat's rail and couldn't. Lead weights were tied to my feet. Just as the boat foundered, Jem gave a great shout and I woke up. Then I became aware that the noise was still going on.

It took a few moments to orientate myself. When fully conscious I realized the noise was coming from Beaver, who was sitting bolt upright in his bunk with his arms outstretched and his eyes tightly closed and shouting his head off. He was calling out, 'Jump for it . . . Jump for it . . .' and then lapsing into a direful burble. Finally he gave a great shout, fell back on his bunk and slept like a babe.

The noise had awoken Arthur, who loves to spend the night wandering abroad, and he arrived, clumping about in heavy boots and thoroughly disturbing everyone. He nodded sagely when we told him what had happened and recalled that many years ago, when he and Beaver had gone sailing, they had moored over a submerged stake which went straight through the bottom of the boat as the tide fell. They awoke in the middle of the night to find water lapping all round. Beaver had made a gallant effort to salvage something and was still in the cabin when the boat gave its final lurch. He swam out clutching a toothbrush. Ever since he had been subject to nightmares while afloat.

The only person undisturbed by all the commotion was Beaver himself, whose heavy breathing showed that he, at least, was having a good night.

We awoke at seven-thirty to a glorious, sunny morning. The storm had blown itself out and for the first time I felt I was on holiday. I even got up first, it being my turn to make the early-morning tea. By an extraordinary coincidence Joan was also making the tea on *Quiet Dawn*.

When I took Beaver his cup he demanded to know what all the row had been about in the middle of the night. He complained that he had been awakened by me and Arthur arguing about something. Told he was the centre of the commotion, he refused to believe it.

'Nonsense,' he said. 'I was asleep all the time until you woke me up.'

He lowered his voice confidentially.

'Actually, old man, I reckon it was Sheila who disturbed you. These preggers women get strange fancies, y'know. I've been watching her closely. She's got that faraway look in her eyes. I wouldn't trust her on the helm like that.'

By nine o'clock we were on the move. It should have been an easy sail on a broad stretch of the River Bure but so many anglers were out that it was like sailing up a tube. Anglers can never understand why a yacht has to zig-zag up the river and as for some reason they believe it is easier to move a five-ton yacht than haul in a two-ounce line, a clash is inevitable.

We were soon faced with a trial of wills, heading straight on the starboard tack for an angler who refused to draw in his line and just shouted, 'Why can't you sail straight?' There wasn't time to tell him although behind us, Arthur, who does a little fishing himself, was in fact trying to defy the wind in an effort to avoid his fellow-anglers. The only result of his kindness was that he inevitably luffed and paid off straight into a sort of nest of anglers, who judging by the litter around them hadn't moved for a month.

Tact isn't Arthur's strong point and while the fishermen pranced up and down and abused him, he started handing out simple advice, things like, 'Actually old boy, you'll never catch anything here, you want to try ledgering with a bit of herring further downstream...' When he sailed off, puffing contentedly at his pipe, I was surprised to see he was followed by a stream of anglers running along the bank, shaking their canvas stools in rage and hurling loaves of stale bread at the boat while Arthur nodded and hummed to himself. It took him five minutes to discover he had a complete rod and line wrapped round the front of the boat. When he did so, he was far too scared to land and threw the whole lot on to the bank and fled.

What with the anglers and the fact that it was the Broads morning rush-hour, things were rather difficult. The river was filled with six yachts tacking to and fro and something like a dozen motor-cruisers trying to get through in both directions. These included a mobile orchestra of guitar-playing youths who roared straight through the whole fleet at top speed sending two yachts into the bank and drenching half a dozen fishermen with their wash.

The cruisers seem to get bigger and bigger every year, and there are more and more of them. I can't think why they don't regulate the size and numbers. Since anyone without experience is entitled to hire a forty-foot boat and drive it down the river without reference to the rules of navigation, some of these boats can be a menace to cruisers and yachts alike.

Yachts, of course, are the most vulnerable craft especially when tacking.

The ideal cruiser helmsman creeps up close and sneaks round the stern of the yacht as it comes about, or when signalled to do so. Unfortunately, a Broads yacht skipper frequently can't signal his intentions because what with the variable wind and the crowded river he doesn't know what they are. A new marine signal is needed: 'I do not know what is going to happen in this blasted wind', perhaps a question-mark hoisted in the shrouds.

However, I must not be unjust to cruisers. Whenever I am on one I never cease to be amazed at the calm sanity of the motor-boat crews and the lunacy of the yacht helmsmen. It's just when I'm on a yacht that all cruiser skippers seem to be blind and deaf malcontents. And every time I have been given a tow by a cruiser I have felt nothing but admiration for the consistent courtesy and navigational skill displayed. This feeling lasts at least five minutes.

Beaver handed over the tiller for a time and vanished below while I took over. Even when Beaver gives up the helm one never feels one is really in command. At times of minor crisis he is liable to seize it from your grasp and blame you for the subsequent collision. This time I was just congratulating myself that I had the boat on my own for a few minutes when the hatch over the lavatory opened, and Beaver stuck his head out and shouted: 'Stop pinching her. Put your helm up a bit.'

Having discovered this novel position of command, Beaver was in high glee, and he spent a full half-hour sitting there distributing orders.

At Acle Bridge, *Quiet Dawn*, which was ahead, stopped to take down the mast to pass under the bridge. To gain an advantage Beaver decided to shoot the bridge, i.e. take the mast down under way, glide through and raise the mast on the other side in midstream.

The mast on a Broads boat is pivoted with a heavy weight at the bottom. In theory it is easy enough to raise or lower, taking the strain on the forestay, but in practice the effect of the forestay is lost as the mast becomes nearly horizontal and you have to be careful the mast doesn't crash down.

All went suspiciously well at first. We took sail off and about a hundred yards from the bridge Harry grasped the forestay, and I kept both feet firmly planted on the counterweight at the bottom of the mast as an additional precaution against accidents while Beaver tugged gently at the mast to start it moving. It had just started to come down when a motor-cruiser passed us flat out and the wash knocked Harry off his feet. Beaver lost his balance as well, and instinctively clung to the mast for support, which merely pulled it down faster. The only things exerting force in the other direction were the weight at the bottom of the mast and me standing on it.

Sometime I should like an engineer to work out the exact forces to which I was subjected in terms of foot pounds per square inch as the mast came down. They would probably be sufficient to do something unlikely, such as lift two dozen eggs a distance of three hundred feet. Anyway, they were powerful enough to hurl me upwards and outwards. I had a fleeting glimpse of Harry's startled face on the deck beneath and then I was four feet under the River Bure. I recall being surprised at how salty the water was, considering we were a dozen miles from the sea.

I have a horror of coming up underneath a boat so I swam lustily under water while my trousers ballooned about me with the air trapped inside before becoming soaked and pulling me down like lead weights. As usual on these occasions, I was swimming in the wrong direction and I surfaced just by the stern. From what I could see, unhappy though my predicament was, I was well out of things by being overboard. The tiller swung unattended as Sheila, who had been on the helm, sat helpless in a cocoon of ropes and rigging (heaven knows why the mast didn't hit her on the head). Beaver lay apparently lifeless on the cabin-top. Harry was kicking feebly at the wreckage.

As I hauled myself inboard. Beaver raised his head and said, 'Good God, what happened?'

A familiar voice called from the bank. 'Boyur,' came the rustic accents of Arthur, 'yew got that there mast down a bit quick didn't yew?'

In fact, despite the chaos, we had achieved what we set out to do and were now drifting through the bridge in a haphazard fashion, watched by the inevitable crowd of bloodthirsty ghouls. The simplest way of clearing the mess was to raise the mast again, but it had to be done quickly. One doesn't drift around sideways near Acle Bridge for long without someone hitting you.

Harry heaved on the forestay, I stood on the counterweight again and Beaver lifted from the cabin-top. The mast groaned up a few inches and then stuck as the shrouds caught the corners of the cabin. Beaver got them free, called for a mighty effort, and we all heaved. This time we were stopped by a shrill scream from Sheila, who under Beaver's strict instructions had been sitting passive under the tangled rigging, not daring to move in case she made matters worse.

A rope had somehow wound itself round her ankle and she was being dragged up the mast upside down. I have never seen a woman being dragged upside down up a mast before, and I must say that the spectacle was most interesting. In fact if it hadn't been for the others I would have seen if we could have got her to the top.

Eventually the mast swung upright, the base thumped into the socket and I rammed home the piece of metal which secured it.

'Hoist sail,' shouted Beaver.

This was easier said than done. All the ropes had tied themselves into obscure knots that would have taken hours to tie deliberately (why is it that left to its own devices a rope ties a knot much more complicated than anyone could invent?). I was just trying to unravel the jib halyard when Beaver called, 'Stand by to fend off.' We were drifting gently into a motorized wherry moored by the bank.

We struck the wherry a soft glancing blow. A red-faced man in a blue jersey appeared and created as much fuss as if we had rammed her at full speed, demanding why we came 'down here' barging all over the river and scraping people's paint. I notice that this type of person always makes his criticism from a vessel fitted with a nice twenty-horsepower engine. I have never met one actually sailing. It is one thing to shout at people in yachts and wear a blue jersey and look professional and quite another to sail a yacht yourself. Yachtsmen themselves rarely abuse each other (unless racing, of course).

Unfortunately, we couldn't get away from the man, because in the confusion of raising the mast we appeared to have lost a vital rope and while we gently rocked alongside him he just stood there and shouted insults. In the end we couldn't stand it any longer. Harry waited until we were ready to sail, kicked off our bows, and thinking we were safe shouted a remark which translated into pure English was: 'Why do you not go away, oh Illegitimate One.'

How we all roared! 'That'll teach him' chuckled Beaver as we came about. 'The bloke's a raving lunatic.' The next moment our mirth was cut short. The wind died and we found ourselves drifting back helplessly towards the wherry.

The red-faced man was still there. 'Call me that foul name would you?' he bellowed. 'I'll give you language I will.'

Once more we gently struck the wherry. It was as if we had released a hidden spring in the man because he didn't stop insulting us for five minutes while all the time we feebly tacked to and fro, making no ground and receiving fresh abuse every time we came about. In the end we got clear and as we drew ahead Beaver had the last word.

'Do you mind repeating all that?' he called. 'I'm afraid I'm rather deaf.'

The incident cost us our lead over Arthur, who sneaked past on a freak catspaw of wind, but we caught him up round the bend and then followed a grim battle for the lead. Arthur sailed by the book, demanding his rights according to the rules of racing.

'Give way to me Beaver you old clot!' he shouted, 'don't you know Rule 38 forbids a windward vessel to curtail a luff?'

Beaver didn't, but he used to invent a few rules of his own ('Give way, Arthur, can't you see I'm fore-reaching') and when those failed he simply got out a boathook and pushed Arthur's stern round. Occasionally as we swung close together I could see into the cabin, where Joan was beating up eggs in a bowl.

These little frolics passed the time pleasantly enough until we came to the little riverside village of Stokesby, two miles downstream, and Beaver shouted to Arthur that we ought to stop for a drink.

Arthur agreed and started to manoeuvre *Quiet Dawn* to the bank. And then an astonishing thing happened. As he came alongside he passed close to a motor-cruiser going in the opposite direction and Dennis's cat, which had been mewing piteously in the bows, leaped on to the other boat.

It was all over in a moment and I was the only one who noticed. I shouted to the cruiser and to Arthur, but the cruiser was speeding out of earshot and by the time Arthur and Dennis understood what I was saying he was past the bend and heading for Acle at six knots with the cat washing itself on the stern.

There was only one thing that could be done. Arthur swung *Quiet Dawn* round, and with the wind behind him headed forlornly upstream after the cruiser, Dennis in the bows shouting loudly, 'You've got our cat on board, give us back our pussy.'

They, too, disappeared round the bend. The sun shone and all was silent except for the lapping of water and the diminishing banshee howls of 'Pussy, Pussy' in the distance. We went for a midday pint with great peace in our hearts.

The Night the Ghost Got In

James Thurber

The ghost that got into our house on the night of November 17, 1915, raised such a hullabaloo of misunderstandings that I am sorry I didn't just let it keep on walking, and go to bed. Its advent caused my mother to throw a shoe through a window of the house next door and ended up with my grandfather shooting a patrolman. I am sorry, therefore, as I have said, that I ever paid any attention to the footsteps.

They began about a quarter past one o'clock in the morning, a rhythmic, quick-cadenced walking around the dining-room table. My mother was asleep in one room upstairs, my brother Herman in another; grandfather was in the attic, in the old walnut bed which, as you will remember, once fell on my father. I had just stepped out of the bathtub and was busily rubbing myself with a towel when I heard the steps. They were the steps of a man walking rapidly around the dining-table downstairs. The light from the bathroom shone down the back-steps, which dropped directly into the dining-room; I could see the faint shine of plates on the plate-rail; I couldn't see the table. The steps kept going round and round the table; at regular intervals a board creaked, when it was trod upon. I supposed at first that it was my father or my brother Roy, who had gone to Indianapolis but were expected home at any time. I suspected next that it was a burglar. It did not enter my mind until later that it was a ghost.

After the walking had gone on for perhaps three minutes, I tiptoed to Herman's room. 'Psst!' I hissed, in the dark, shaking him. 'Awp,' he said, in the low, hopeless tone of a despondent beagle – he always half suspected that something would 'get him' in the night. I told him who I was. 'There's something downstairs!' I said. He got up and followed me to the head of the back staircase. We listened together. There was no sound. The steps had ceased. Herman looked at me in some alarm: I had only the bath towel around my waist. He wanted to go back to bed, but I gripped his arm.

'There's something down there!' I said. Instantly the steps began again, circled the dining-room table like a man running, and started up the stairs towards us, heavily, two at a time. The light still shone palely down the stairs; we saw nothing coming; we only heard the steps. Herman rushed to his room and slammed the door. I slammed shut the door at the stairs top and held my knee against it. After a long minute, I slowly opened it again. There was nothing there. There was no sound. None of us ever heard the ghost again.

The slamming of the doors had aroused mother: she peered out of her room. 'What on earth are you boys doing?' she demanded. Herman ventured out of his room. 'Nothing,' he said, gruffly, but he was, in colour, a light green. 'What was all that running around downstairs?' said mother. So she had heard the steps, too! We just looked at her. 'Burglars!' she shouted, intuitively. I tried to quiet her by starting lightly downstairs.

'Come on, Herman,' I said.

'I'll stay with mother,' he said. 'She's all excited.'

I stepped back onto the landing.

'Don't either of you go a step,' said mother. 'We'll call the police.' Since the phone was downstairs, I didn't see how we were going to call the police – nor did I want the police – but mother made one of her quick, incomparable decisions. She flung up a window of her bedroom which faced the bedroom windows of the house of a neighbour, picked up a shoe, and whammed it through a pane of glass across the narrow space that separated the two houses. Glass tinkled into the bedroom occupied by a retired engraver named Bodwell and his wife. Bodwell had been for some years in rather a bad way and was subject to mild 'attacks'. Most everybody we knew or lived near had *some* kind of attacks.

It was now about two o'clock of a moonless night; clouds hung black and low. Bodwell was at the window in a minute, shouting, frothing a little, shaking his fist. 'We'll sell the house and go back to Peoria,' we could hear Mrs Bodwell saying. It was some time before mother 'got through' to Bodwell. 'Burglars!' she shouted. 'Burglars in the house!' Herman and I hadn't dared to tell her that it was not burglars but ghosts, for she was even more afraid of ghosts than of burglars. Bodwell at first thought that she meant there were burglars in his house, but finally he quieted down and called the police for us over an extension phone by his bed. After he had disappeared from the window, mother suddenly made as if to throw another shoe, not because there was further need of it but, as she later explained, because the thrill of heaving a shoe through a window glass had enormously taken her fancy. I prevented her.

The police were on hand in a commendably short time: a Ford sedan full of them, two on motorcycles, and a patrol wagon with about eight in it and a few reporters. They began banging at our front door. Flashlights shot streaks of gleam up and down the walls, across the yard, down the walk between our house and Bodwell's. 'Open up!' cried a hoarse voice. 'We're men from Headquarters!' I wanted to go down and let them in, since there they were, but mother wouldn't hear of it. 'You haven't a stitch on,' she pointed out. 'You'd catch your death.' I wound the towel around me again. Finally the cops put their shoulders to our big heavy front door with its thick bevelled glass and broke it in: I could hear a rending of wood and a splash of glass on the floor of the hall. Their lights played all over the living-room and crisscrossed nervously in the dining-room, stabbed into hallways, shot up the front stairs and finally up the back. They caught me standing in my towel at the top. A heavy policeman bounded up the steps. 'Who are you?' he demanded. 'I live here,' I said. 'Well, whattsa matta, ya hot?' he asked. It was, as a matter of fact, cold; I went to my room and pulled on some trousers. On my way out, a cop stuck a gun into my ribs. 'Whatta you doin' here?' he demanded. 'I live here,' I said.

The officer in charge reported to mother. 'No sign of nobody, lady,' he said. 'Musta got away – whatt'd he look like?' 'There were two or three of them,' mother said, 'whooping and carrying on slamming doors.' 'Funny,' said the cop. 'All ya windows and doors was locked on the inside tight as a tick.'

Downstairs, we could hear the tromping of the other police. Police were all over the place; doors were yanked open, drawers were yanked open, windows were shot up and pulled down, furniture fell with dull thumps. A half-dozen policemen emerged out of the darkness of the front hallway upstairs. They began to ransack the floor: pulled beds away from walls, tore clothes off hooks in the closets, pulled suitcases and boxes off shelves. One of them found an old zither that Roy had won in a pool tournament. 'Looky here, Joe,' he said, strumming it with a big paw. The cop named Joe took it and turned it over. 'What is it?' he asked me. 'It's an old zither our guinea pig used to sleep on,' I said. It was true that a pet guinea pig we once had would never sleep anywhere except on the zither, but I should never have said so. Joe and the other cop looked at me a long time. They put the zither back on a shelf.

'No sign o' nuthin',' said the cop who had first spoken to mother. 'This guy,' he explained to the others, jerking a thumb at me, 'was nekked. The lady seems hysterical.' They all nodded, but said nothing; just looked at me. In the small silence we all heard a creaking in the attic. Grandfather was turning over in bed. 'What's 'at?' snapped Joe. Five or six cops sprang for the attic door before I could intervene or explain. I realized that it would be bad if they burst in on grandfather unannounced, or even announced. He was going through a phase in which he believed that General Meade's men, under steady hammering by Stonewall Jackson, were beginning to retreat and even desert.

When I got to the attic, things were pretty confused. Grandfather had evidently jumped to the conclusion that the police were deserters from Meade's army, trying to hide away in his attic. He bounded out of bed wearing a long flannel nightgown over long woollen underwear, a nightcap, and a leather jacket around his chest. The cops must have realized at once that the indignant white-haired old man belonged in the house, but they had no chance to say so. 'Back, ye cowardly dogs!' roared grandfather. 'Back t' the lines, ye goddam lily-livered cattle!' With that, he fetched the officer who found the zither a flat-handed smack alongside his head that sent him sprawling. The others beat a retreat, but not fast enough; grandfather grabbed Zither's gun from its holster and let fly. The report seemed to crack the rafters; smoke filled the attic. A cop cursed and shot his hand to his shoulder. Somehow, we all finally got downstairs again and locked the door against the old gentleman. He fired once or twice more in the darkness and then went back to bed. 'That was grandfather,' I explained to Joe, out of breath. 'He thinks you're deserters.' 'I'll say he does,' said Joe.

The cops were reluctant to leave without getting their hands on somebody besides grandfather; the night had been distinctly a defeat for them. Furthermore, they obviously didn't like the 'layout'; something looked – and I can see their viewpoint – phony. They began to poke into things again. A reporter, a thin-faced, wispy man, came up to me. I had put on one of mother's blouses, not being able to find anything else. The reporter looked at me with mingled suspicion and interest. 'Just what the hell is the real lowdown here, Bud?' he asked. I decided to be frank with him. 'We had ghosts,' I said. He gazed at me a long time as if I were a slot machine into which he had, without results, dropped a nickel. Then he walked away. The cops followed him, the one grandfather shot holding his now-bandaged arm, cursing and blaspheming. 'I'm gonna get my gun back from that old bird,' said the zither-cop. 'Yeh,' said Joe. 'You – and who else?' I told them I would bring it to the station house the next day.

'What was the matter with that one policeman?' mother asked, after they had gone. 'Grandfather shot him,' I said. 'What for?' she demanded. I told her he was a deserter. 'Of all things!' said mother. 'He was such a nice-looking young man.'

Grandfather was fresh as a daisy and full of jokes at breakfast next morning. We thought at first he had forgotten all about what had happened, but he hadn't. Over his third cup of coffee, he glared at Herman and me. 'What was the idee of all them cops tarryhootin' round the house last night?' he demanded. He had us there.

A la Douane

Miles Kington

Official: Vous avez quelque chose à déclarer?

Voyageur: Non. Rien. Pas une saucisse.

Official: Les saucisses sont duty-free.

Voyageur: Ah. En ce cas, je me souviens soudain que j'ai quelques saucisses dans ma valise. Pas beaucoup. Presque rien.

Official: Combien?

Voyageur: 15 lb chipolates de porc, 15 lb thick Irish et 15 lb black pudding. C'est un cadeau pour Tante Emily.

Official: Black Pudding n'est pas tax-free.

Voyageur: Quand je dis black pudding, je suis inexact. Ce n'est pas noir, c'est gris, presque vert.

Official: Ce n'est pas un black pudding alors. On vous a vendue un concombre.

Voyageur: Ah. Bon. C'est tax-free?

Official: Oui. Les légumes sont tax-free.

Voyageur: Sans blague? Alors je veux déclarer 10 kg de carottes, 15 kg de choufleurs, et un navet, dans ce carrier bag ici.

Official: Un navet? Pourquoi un seul turnip?

Voyageur: Parce qu'il a les dimensions 2 m × 1.5 m × 1.3 m.

Official: Ce n'est guère une légume, c'est plutôt une arme offensive.

Voyageur: C'est tax-free, les armes offensives?

Official: Oui.

Voyageur: Alors, j'ai l'intention d'employer le navet dans un booby-trap.

Official: Mais pourquoi un *turnip* dans un booby-trap?

Voyageur: Pour divertir les enquêtes de la police à l'IRA, naturellement.

Official: Bonne idée. En passant, les autres légumes sont seulement tax-free s'ils sont pour consommation immédiate.

Voyageur: C'est le cas.
J'invite quelques amis à un
souper ce soir. Environ 150.
Official: Ah, oui. Et ils sont
teetotallers?
Voyageur: Les vins sont tax-
free?
Official: Un litre pour chaque
personne.
Voyageur: Bon! J'ai exactement
150 litres.
Official: Un litre pour chaque
voyageur, non pas pour chaque
ami.
Voyageur: J'ai dit 150 litres?
Silly moi! Je voulais dir 1.50
litres! Je dois payer le duty sur
un demi-litre, alors.

Official: Oui, monsieur. Je vous
souhaite bon appétit, et
amusez-vous bien.
Voyageur: Oui, on va s'amuser
bien! . . . A propos, les
drogues, elles sont tax-free?
Official: Les drogues? Comme
cocaïne?
Voyageur: Oui, exactement
comme cocaïne.
Official: Non, les impositions
sur les drogues sont *très* lourdes.
Très, très lourdes. Pourquoi?
Voyageur: Pour rien. Aucune
raison. Curiosité, seulement.
Au revoir.
Official: Au revoir, monsieur.

Dans le Health Food Shop

Miles Kington

Client: Bonjour. Je cherche un plain strong white flour.

Assistant: Ne cherchez pas ici, monsieur. White flour est toxique et deadly. Nous sommes un magasin sérieux.

Client: Oh. Quelle sorte de farine vous avez?

Assistant: Nous avons wholemeal, wheatmeal, mealwhole, 110% fullwheat, 120% wheat-of-the-loom ou 150% millstone grit.

Client: Et la différence?

Assistant: Nulle. Elles sont toutes organically grown avec real dung et hand ground dans notre mill à Buckminster Fuller. Elles sont transportées ici dans un organically built farm wagon.

Client: Et les sacs sont rangés sur les shelves ici par ruddy-cheeked yokels dans smocks traditionnels?

Assistant: Of course.

Client: Hmm. Je prends un 1 lb sac de 200% stonewheat.

Assistant: Ça fait £4.80.

Client: C'est cher.

Assistant: Health food est toujours cher. C'est le wholepoint. Nous ne voulons pas avoir chaque Tom, Dick and Harry dans le shop.

Client: Hmm. Et je veux acheter un carrier bag.

Assistant: Quelle sorte de carrier?

Client: Il y a différentes sortes?

Assistant: Oui, bien sûr. Wholeweave, brownbag recycle, Third Worldweave, Arty Dartington ou Jethrotwill.

Client: On peut les manger?

Assistant: Non. On peut manger les Chinese rice paper bags, mais ils ne sont pas très forts.

Client: OK. Un sac de stone-wheat et un Chinese paper bag.

Assistant: Un moment, je vais calculer sur mon abacus. £4.80 + 60p, c'est ... c'est ...

Client: £5.40.

Assistant: £5.80.

Client: Votre abacus est sur le blink.

Assistant: Un abacus ne va jamais sur le blink. J'ai simplement ajouté 40p pour le Save The Honeybee Appeal.

Client: Le honeybee est en danger?

Assistant: Non. Pas encore. Mais il faut anticiper. Sauvons le honeybee maintenant.

The King and the Conga

Gerald Durrell

Gerald Durrell's travels to Africa take him to the mountain world of Bafut. Here, where the forest gives way to the great grasslands, he befriends the Fon, a delightful old rogue, 'the sort of Nero' of the region, who has, he soon discovers, a weakness for liquor...

The great day of the grass-gathering ceremony arrived at last. Before dawn, when the stars had only just started to fade and dwindle, before even the youngest and most enthusiastic village cockerel had tried his voice, I was awakened by the gentle throb of small drums, laughter and chatter of shrill voices, and the soft scuff of bare feet on the dusty road below the house. I lay and listened to these sounds until the sky outside the window was faintly tinged with the green of the coming day, then I went out on to the veranda to see what was happening.

The mountains that clustered around Bafut were mauve and grey in the dim morning light, striped and patterned with deep purple and black in the valleys, where it was still night. The sky was magnificent, black in the West where the last stars quivered, jade green above me, fading to the palest kingfisher blue at the eastern rim of hills. I leant on the wall of the veranda where a great web of bougainvillaea had grown, like a carelessly flung cloak of brick-red flowers, and looked down the long flight of steps to the road below, and beyond it to the Fon's courtyard. Down the road, from both directions, came a steady stream of people, laughing and talking and beating on small drums when the mood took them. Over their shoulders were long wooden poles, and tied to these with creepers were big conical bundles of dried grass. The children trotted along carrying smaller bundles of their saplings. They made their way down past the arched opening into the Fon's courtyard and deposited their grass in heaps under the trees by the side of the road. Then they went through the arch into the courtyard, and there they stood about in chattering groups: occasionally a flute and a drum would make up a brief melody, and then some of the crowd would break into a shuffling dance, amid handclaps and cries of delight from the onlookers. They were a happy, excited and eager throng.

By the time I had finished breakfast the piles of grass bundles by the roadside were towering skywards, and threatening to overbalance as each new lot was added: the courtyard was now black with people and they overflowed through the arched door and out into the road. The air was full of noise as the first arrivals greeted the late-comers and chaffed them for their laziness. Children chased each other in and out of the crowd, shrieking with laughter, and hordes of thin and scruffy dogs galloped joyfully at their heels, yelping enthusiastically. I walked down the seventy-five steps to the road to join the crowd, and I was pleased and flattered to find that they did not seem to resent my presence among them, but greeted me with quick welcoming smiles that swiftly turned to broad grins of delight when I exchanged salutations in pidgin English. I eventually took up a suitable position by the roadside, in the shade of a huge hibiscus bush, scarlet with flowers and filled with the drone of insects. I soon had round me an absorbed circle of youths and children, who watched me silently as I sat and smoked and gazed at the gay crowd that surged past us. Eventually I was run to earth by a panting Ben, who pointed out reproachfully that it was long past lunchtime, and that the delicacy the cook had prepared would undoubtedly be ruined. Reluctantly I left my circle of disciples (who all stood up politely and shook my hand) and followed the grumbling Ben back to the house.

Having eaten, I descended once more to my vantage point beneath the hibiscus, and continued my anthropological survey of the Bafut people as they streamed steadily past. Apparently during the morning I had been witnessing the arrival of the common or working man. He was, as a rule, dressed in a gaudy sarong twisted tightly round the hips; the women wore the same, though some of the very old ones wore nothing but a dirty scrap of leather at the loins. This, I gathered, was the old style of costume: the tight sarong was a modern idea. Most of the older women smoked pipes, but not the short, stubby pipes of the lowland tribes, but ones with long, slender stems, like old-fashioned clay pipes; and they were black with use. This was how the lower orders of Bafut dressed. In the afternoon the council members, the petty chiefs, and other men of substance and importance started to arrive, and there was no mistaking them for just ordinary creatures of the soil. They all wore long, loose-fitting robes of splendid colours, which swished and sparkled as they walked, and on their heads were perched the little flat skull-caps I had noticed before, each embroidered with an intricate and colourful design. Some of them carried long, slender staves of dark brown wood, covered with a surprisingly delicate tracery of carving. They were all middle-aged or elderly, obviously very conscious of their high office, and each greeted me with great solemnity, shaking me by the hand and waving 'Welcome' several times very earnestly. There were many of these aristocrats and they added a wonderful touch of colour to the proceedings. When I went back to the house for tea I paused at the top of the steps and looked down at the great courtyard: it was a solid block of humanity, packed so tightly together that the red earth was invisible, except in places where some happy dancers cleared a small circle by their antics. Dotted among the crowd I could see the colourful robes of the elders like flowers scattered across a bed of black earth.

Towards evening I was in the midst of the thickest part of the throng, endeavouring to take photographs before the light got too bad, when a resplendent figure made his appearance at my side. His robes glowed with magenta, gold and green, and in one hand he held a long leather switch. He was the Fon's messenger, he informed me, and, if I was quite ready, he would take me to the Fon for the grass ceremony. Hastily cramming another film into the camera, I followed him through the crowd, watching with admiration as he cut a way through the thickest part by the simple but effective method of slicing with his switch across the bare buttocks that presented themselves so plentifully on all sides. To my surprise the crowd did not seem to take exception to this treatment but yelped and screamed in mock fear, and pushed and stumbled out of our way, all laughing with delight. The messenger led me across the great courtyard, through the arched doorway, along a narrow passage, and then through another arched doorway that brought us out into a honeycomb of tiny courtyards and passages. It was as complicated as a maze, but the messenger knew his way about, and ducked and twisted along passages, through courtyards, and up and down small flights of steps until at length we went through a crumbling brick archway and came out into an oblong courtyard about a quarter of an acre in extent, surrounded by a high red brick wall. At one end of this courtyard grew a large mango tree, and around its smooth trunk had been built a circular raised dais; on this was a big heavily carved chair, and in it sat the Fon of Bafut.

His clothing was so gloriously bright that, for the moment, I did not recognize him. His robe was a beautiful shade of sky blue, with a wonderful design embroidered on it in red, yellow and white. On his head was a conical red felt hat, to which had been stitched vast numbers of hairs from elephants' tails. From a distance it made him look as though he were wearing a cone-shaped haystack on his head. In one hand he held a fly-whisk, the handle of delicately carved wood and the switch made from the long, black-and-white tail of a colobus monkey – a thick silky plume of hair. The whole very impressive effect was somewhat marred by the Fon's feet: they were resting on a huge elephant tusk – freckled yellow and black with age – that lay before him, and they were clad in a pair of very pointed piebald shoes, topped off by jade-green socks.

After he had shaken me by the hand and asked earnestly after my health, a chair was brought for me and I sat down beside him. The courtyard was lined with various councillors, petty chiefs and their half-naked wives, all of them squatting along the walls on their haunches, drinking out of carved cow-horn flasks. The men's multicoloured robes made a wonderful tapestry along the red stone wall. To the left of the Fon's throne was a great pile of black calabashes, their necks stuffed with bunches of green leaves, containing mimbo or palm wine, the most common drink in the Cameroons. One of the Fon's wives brought a glass for me, and then lifted a calabash, removed the plug of leaves, and poured a drop of mimbo into the Fon's extended hand. He rolled the liquid round his mouth thoughtfully, and then spat it out and shook his head. Another flask was broached with the same result, and then two more. At last a calabash was found that contained mimbo the Fon considered fine enough to share with me, and the girl filled my glass. Mimbo looks like well-watered milk, and has a mild, faintly sour, lemonade taste which is most deceptive. A really good mimbo tastes innocuous, and thus lures you on to drink more and more, until suddenly you discover that it is not so harmless as you had thought. I tasted my glass of wine, smacked my lips, and complimented the Fon on the vintage. I noticed that all the councillors and petty chiefs were drinking out of flasks made from cows' horn, whereas the Fon imbibed his mimbo from a beautifully carved and polished buffalo horn. We sat until it was almost dark, talking and gradually emptying the calabashes of mimbo.

Eventually the Fon decided that the great moment for feeding the masses had arrived. We rose and walked down the courtyard between the double ranks of bowing subjects, the men clapping their hands rhythmically, while the women held their hands over their mouths, patting their lips and hooting, producing a noise that I, in my ignorance, had thought to be the prerogative of the Red Indian. We made our way through the doors, passages and tiny courtyards, the concourse filing behind, still clapping and hooting. As we came out of the archway into the main courtyard there arose from the multitude a deafening roar of approval, accompanied by clapping and drumming. Amid this tumultuous reception the Fon and I walked along the wall to where the Fon's throne had been placed on a leopard skin. We took our seats, the Fon waved his hand, and the feast began.

Through the archway came an apparently endless stream of young men, naked except for small loin-cloths, carrying on their shining and muscular shoulders the various foods for the people. There were calabashes of palm wine and corn beer, huge bunches of plantain and bananas, both green and golden yellow; there was meat in the shape of giant Cane Rats, mongooses, bats and antelope, monkeys and great hunks of python, all carefully smoked and spitted on bamboo poles. Then there were dried fish, dried shrimps and fresh crabs, scarlet and green peppers, mangoes, oranges, pawpaws, pineapples, coconuts, cassava and sweet potatoes. While this enormous quantity of food was being distributed, the Fon greeted all the headmen, councillors and chiefs. They would each approach him, then bend double before him and clap their hands three times. The Fon would give a brief and regal nod, and the man would retire backwards. If anyone wanted to address the Fon they had to do so through their cupped hands.

I had by now absorbed quite a quantity of mimbo and was feeling more than ordinarily benign; it seemed to have much the same effect on the Fon. He barked a sudden order, and, to my horror, a table was produced on which reposed two glasses and a bottle of gin, a French brand that I had never heard of, and whose acquaintance I am not eager to renew. The Fon poured out about three inches of gin into a glass and handed it to me; I smiled and tried to look as though gin, neat and in large quantities, was just what I had been wanting. I smelt it gingerly, and found that it was not unlike one of the finer brands of paraffin. Deciding that I really could not face such a large amount undiluted, I asked for some water. The Fon barked out another order, and one of his wives came running, clutching a bottle of Angostura bitters in her hand.

'Beeters!' said the Fon proudly, shaking about two teaspoonfuls into my gin; 'you like gin wit beeters?'

'Yes,' I said with a sickly smile, 'I love gin with bitters.'

The first sip of the liquid nearly burnt my throat out: it was quite the most filthy raw spirits I have ever tasted. Even the Fon, who did not appear to worry unduly about such things, blinked a bit after his first gulp. He coughed vigorously and turned to me, wiping his streaming eyes.

'Very strong,' he pointed out.

Presently, when all the food had been brought out and arranged in huge piles in front of us, the Fon called for silence and made a short speech to the assembled Bafutians, telling them who I was, why I was there and what I wanted. He ended by explaining to them that they had to procure plenty of animals for me. The crowd listened to the speech in complete silence, and when it had ended a chorus of loud 'Arhhh's!' broke loose, and much hand-clapping. The Fon sat down looking rather pleased with himself, and carried away by his enthusiasm, he took a long swig at his gin. The result was an anxious five minutes for us all as he coughed and writhed on his throne, tears streaming down his face. He recovered eventually and sat there glaring at the gin in his glass with red and angry eyes. He took another very small sip of it, and rolled it round his mouth, musing. Then he leant over to confide in me.

'Dis gin strong too much,' he said in a hoarse whisper; 'we go give dis strong drink to all dis small-small men, den we go for my house and we drink, eh?'

I agreed that the idea of distributing the gin among the petty chiefs and councillors – the small-small men as the Fon called them – was an excellent one.

The Fon looked cautiously around to make sure we were not overheard, and as there were only some five thousand people wedged around us he felt that he could tell me a secret in complete safety. He leant over and lowered his voice to a whisper once more.

'Soon we go for my house,' he said, gleefully; 'we go drink White Horshe.'

He sat back to watch the effect of his words on me. I rolled my eyes and tried to appear overcome with joy at the thought of this treat, while wondering what effect whisky would have on top of mimbo and gin. The Fon, however, seemed satisfied, and presently he called over the small-small men, one by one, and poured the remains of the gin into their cow-horn drinking cups, which were already half-filled with mimbo. Never have I given up a drink so gladly. I wondered at the cast-iron stomachs that could face with equanimity, and even pleasure, a cocktail composed of that gin and mimbo. I felt quite sick at the mere thought of it.

Having distributed his rather doubtful largesse among his following, the Fon rose to his feet, amid handclaps, drumbeats and Red Indian hootings, and led the way back through the intricate web of passages and courts, until we came to his own small village, almost hidden among the wives' many grass huts, like a matchbox in an apiary. We went inside, and I found myself in a large, low room furnished with easy-chairs and a big table, the wooden floor covered with fine leopard skins and highly coloured, locally made grass mats. The Fon, having done his duty to his people, relaxed in a long chair, and the White Horse was produced; my host smacked his lips as the virginal bottle was uncorked, and gave me to understand that, now the boring duties of state were over, we could start to drink in earnest. For the next two hours we drank steadily, and discussed at great length and in the most complicated detail such fascinating topics as the best type of gun to use on an elephant, what White Horse was made of, why I didn't attend dinners at Buckingham Palace, the Russian question, and so on. After this neither the Fon's questions nor my answers had the skill and delicate construction that we would have liked, so the Fon called for his band, being under the misguided impression that the ravages of strong drink could be dissipated by sweet music. The band came into the courtyard outside and played and danced for a long time, while the Fon insisted that another bottle of White Horse be broached to celebrate the arrival of the musicians. Presently the band formed a half-circle, and a woman did a swaying, shuffling dance and sang a song in a shrill and doleful voice. I could not understand the words, but the song was strangely mournful, and both the Fon and I were deeply affected by it. Eventually the Fon, wiping his eyes, sharply informed the band that they had better play something else. They had a long discussion among themselves and finally broke into a tune which was the most perfect Conga rhythm imaginable. It was so bright and gay that it quickly revived our spirits, and very soon I was tapping the rhythm out with my feet, while the Fon conducted the band with a glass of White Horse clutched in one hand. Flushed with the Fon's hospitality, and carried away by the tune, an idea came to me.

'The other night you done show me native dance, no be so?' I asked the Fon.

'Na so,' he agreed, stifling a hiccup.

'All right. Tonight you like I go teach you European dance?'

'Ah! my friend,' said the Fon, beaming and embracing me; 'yes, yes, foine, you go teach me. Come, we go for dancing house.'

We rose unsteadily to our feet and made our way to the dance-hall. When we reached it, however, I found that the effort of walking fifty yards had told on my companion; he sank on to his ornate throne with a gasp.

'You go teach all dis small-small men first,' he said, gesturing wildly at the throng of chiefs and councillors, 'den I go dance.'

I surveyed the shuffling, embarrassed crowd of council members that I was supposed to teach, and decided that the more intricate parts of the Conga – which was the jig I proposed to tutor them in – would be beyond them. Indeed, I was beginning to feel that they might even be beyond me. So I decided that I would content myself showing them the latter part of the dance only, the part where everyone joins into a line and does a sort of follow-my-leader around the place. The whole dance-hall was hushed as I beckoned the two-and-twenty council members to join me on the floor, and in the silence you could hear their robes swishing as they walked. I made them tag on behind me, each holding on to his predecessor's waist; then I gave a nod to the band, who, with great gusto, threw themselves into the Conga rhythm, and we were off. I had carefully instructed the pupils to follow my every movement, and this they did. I soon discovered, however, that everything I knew about the Conga had been swamped by the Fon cellars: all I could remember was the somewhere, some time, one gave a kick. So off we went, with the band playing frenziedly, round and round the dance-hall: one, two three, kick; one, two, three, kick. My pupils had no difficulty in following this simple movement and we went round the floor in great style, all their robes swishing in unison. I was counting the beats and shouting 'Kick' at the appropriate moment, in order to make the thing simpler for them to follow; apparently they took this to be part of the dance, a sort of religious chant that went with it, for they all started shouting in unison. The effect on our very considerable audience was terrific: screeching with delight, various other members of the Fon's retinue, about forty of his wives, and several of his older offspring, all rushed to join on to the column of dancing councillors, and as each new dancer joined on to the tail he or she also joined the chant.

'One, two, three, keek!' yelled the councillors.

'One, two, three, YARR!' yelled the wives.

'Oh, doo, ree, YARR!' screeched the children.

The Fon was not going to be left out of this dance. He struggled up from his throne and, supported by a man on each side, he tagged on behind; his kicks did not altogether coincide with the rhythmic movement of the rest of us, but he enjoyed himself none the less. I led them round and round the dance-hall until I grew giddy and the whole structure seemed to vibrate with the kicks and yells. Then, feeling that a little fresh air was indicated, I led them out of the door and into the open. Off we went in a tremendous, swaying line, up and down steps, in and out of courtyards, through strange huts – in fact everywhere that offered a free passage. The band, not to be outdone, followed us as we danced, running behind, sweating profusely, but never for one moment losing the tune. At last, more by luck than a sense of direction, I led my followers back into the dance-hall, where we collapsed in a panting, laughing heap. The Fon, who had fallen down two or three times during our tour, was escorted back to his chair, beaming and gasping.

'Na foine dance, dis,' he proclaimed; 'foine, foine!'

'You like?' I asked, gulping for air.

'I like too much,' said the Fon firmly; 'you get plenty power; I never see European dance like dis.'

I was not surprised; few Europeans in West Africa spend their spare time teaching the Conga to native chieftains and their courts. I have no doubt that, if they could have seen me doing that dance, they would have informed me that I had done more damage to the White Man's prestige in half an hour than anyone else had done in the whole history of the West Coast. However, my Conga appeared to have increased my prestige with the Fon and his court. 'One, two, three, keek!' murmured the Fon reminiscently, 'na fine song dis.'

'Na very special song,' said I.

'Na so?' said the Fon, nodding his head; 'na foine one.'

He sat on his throne and brooded for a while; the band struck up again and the dancers took the floor; I regained my breath and was beginning to feel rather proud of myself, when my companion woke up suddenly and gave an order. A young girl of about fifteen left the dancers and approached the dais where we sat. She was plump and shining with oil, and clad in a minute loin-cloth which left few of her charms to the imagination. She sidled up to us, smiling shyly, and the Fon leant forward and seized her by the wrist. With a quick pull and a twist he catapulted her into my lap, where she sat convulsed with giggles.

'Na for you, dis woman,' said the Fon, with a lordly wave of one enormous hand, 'na fine one. Na my daughter. You go marry her.'

To say that I was startled means nothing; I was horror-stricken. My host was by now in that happy state that precedes belligerency, and I knew that my refusal would have to be most tactfully put so that I should not undo the good work of the evening. I glanced around helplessly and noticed for the first time what a very large number of the crowd had spears with them. By now the band had stopped playing, and everyone was watching me expectantly. My host was regarding me glassy-eyed. I had no means of telling whether he was really offering me the girl as a wife, or whether this term was used as an euphemism for a more indelicate suggestion. Whichever it was, I had to refuse: quite apart from anything else, the girl was not my type. I licked my lips, cleared my throat, and did the best I could. First, I thanked the Fon graciously for the kind offer of his well-oiled daughter, whose eleven odd stone were at that moment making my knees ache. However, I knew that he was well versed in the stupid customs of my countrymen, and that being so, he knew it was impossible (however desirable) for a man in England to have more than one wife. The Fon nodded wisely at this. Therefore, I went on, I would be forced to refuse his extremely generous offer, for I already had one wife in England, and it would be unlawful, as well as unsafe, to take a second one back with me. If I had not already been married, I went on fluently, there would have been nothing I would have liked better than to accept his gift, marry the girl and settle down in Bafut for the rest of my life.

To my great relief a loud round of applause greeted my speech, and the Fon wept a bit that this lovely dream could never be realized. During the uproar I eased my dusky girl friend off my lap, gave her a slap on the rump and sent her giggling back to the dance-floor. Feeling that I had undergone quite enough for one night in the cause of diplomatic relations, I suggested that the party break up. The Fon and his retinue accompanied me to the great courtyard and here he insisted on clasping me round the waist and doing the Durrell Conga once more. The crowd fell in behind and we danced across the square, kicking and yelling, frightening the Fruit Bats out of the mango trees, and setting all the dogs barking for miles around. At the bottom of the steps the Fon and I bade each other a maudlin farewell, and I watched them doing an erratic Conga back across the courtyard. Then I climbed up the seventy-five steps, thinking longingly of bed.

Why Dogs Bite Gardeners

Basil Boothroyd

You mustn't think I'm not sorry for Lady Astor of Hever, because I am. It's no joke to break your foot and have to crawl about the estate, accompanied by three barking French whippets, until gardeners come to the rescue and wheel you to safety in a barrow. On the other hand, if you're a gardener loading a lady into a barrow, it's no joke to be bitten by three French whippets 'apparently thinking the gardeners were abducting their mistress'. Lord Astor, even, was moved to comment: 'It was hard luck to be bitten ... but the men seemed to understand. We hadn't the heart to scold the dogs.'

My source of information is one of the more nobility-fancying Press gossips, and as this particular piece carried news not only of the Astors but of the Queen, Prince Philip, Princess Birgitta of Sweden, Prince Johan of Hohenzollern, Sir Guy and Lady Shaw-Stewart, Sir Timothy Eden, Lord Downe, Lord Combermere and the Earl of Leicester, it was obviously impossible to introduce any sort of statement from mere gardeners. As Lord Astor said – avoiding any degrading suggestion of direct spokesmanship – they seemed to understand. The point I want to make is that the dogs didn't. They barked for help, and when help came they attacked it. It now gives me great pleasure to attack the dogs. The Astors may not have had the heart to scold them. I have.

These dogs, like all dogs, were fools. Admirers of the canine intelligence, so-called, tweedy folk of the 'he-understands-every-word-we-say' school, will be shocked to read this. And not before time. 'How lucky,' they have been saying to each other, 'that the dogs were there to bark for help. And of *course* when those great rough gardener men came stamping round in their horrid gaiters they bit them. Why, poor little things, they must have been in an awful state.' I don't take this view. I take one or two others.

(a) The dogs weren't barking for help at all. They were just barking. This is the average dog's contribution to any already exasperating situation, and is one of many pointers to the essential dimness of the species. If the dog had any whit of the intelligence ascribed to him he would know that, for instance, any domestic crisis involving say, dropped crockery or a bird catching fire on removal from the oven, would be a good time to get out of sight under the table and stay there. How many dogs have the intelligence to see this? Instead, they go into fits of yelping hysterics, showing the whites of their eyes and plunging into the storm-centre, where they trip people up and get their feet wedged in the vegetable-rack. Lady Astor's dogs were instinctively making a confounded nuisance of themselves. Either they resented her being on all fours, trying to get into their act, or they felt intuitively that she was in trouble, and that a concerted bout of shrill barking would stand a good chance of making things more difficult than they were already. Intelligence didn't come into it.

(b) Supposing, just for the sake of argument, that it did. Supposing they worked this thing out rationally.

1st FRENCH WHIPPET: (*in French, but never mind*) Look chaps, Mistress has fallen down.

2nd F.W.: How come? I wasn't watching.

3rd F.W.: Tripped, I think. What's she saying?

1st F.W. Sounds like, 'oo, my foot.' She's starting to crawl. Ought we to get help?

2nd F.W.: Pardon? Sorry, interesting smell here. Well, she won't get far at that rate. What about a good bark? Might fetch the gardeners.

3rd F.W.: Not a bad idea. All set then?

All: Row-row! Row-row-row! Row-row-row-row! Row-row-row (Etc.)

How's that for a reconstruction, dog-lovers? Chime in with your theories all right, does it? Good. Then let's move forward in time about ten minutes. Dimly, above the canine SOS, feet are heard approaching through the undergrowth.

All F.W.'s: (*as before*) Row-row! Row-row-row-row! (Etc.)

1st F.W.: Here come the gardeners, chaps.

2nd F.W.: They've spotted her.

3rd F.W.: They're lifting her up. Row-row-row!

1st F.W.: Row-row!

2nd F.W.: They've fetched a barrow. Row-row-row!

3rd F.W.: Ready boys? They're putting her into it. Stand by to bite gardeners.

1st F.W.: Bags I first. Grrr-rr-rr!

All: Grrr!

They sink teeth into gardeners' calves, ankles, wrists, etc.

Of course, I realize I haven't a chance of swaying dog-lovers. They'll soon find a way to explain and defend this sudden lapse from rational Good Samaritan into berserk fangster. One of the gardeners, no doubt, was wearing a jumble-sale hat, formerly the property of a Russian agent. Or the dogs had been following the Lady Chatterley case, and feared the worst as soon as they saw a coarse hand laid on their stricken mistress.

Well, I'm sorry. I've nothing against dogs, any more than I've anything against the Astors. I just want to explode the intelligence myth, that's all. I've even got a dog of my own. His name's Spot, and you only have to mention a word that rhymes with it, such as clot or guillemot, and he's up from the hearthrug trying to get an imaginary biscuit out of the hand you're holding your glass in. Other indications of his having no sense whatsoever include seeing off the goldfish, thinking it's bedtime and cringing into his kennel in mid-afternoon when all you've suggested is a strategic walk around the garden, trying to go upstairs when two men are coming down with a wardrobe, jumping up for twenty minutes at a tennis-ball on a string plainly two feet out of range, not being able to find a bit of cheese-rind he's standing with his foot on, and barking his head off every night at six when I come home, still not knowing my footsteps from a Broadmoor fugitive's after seven years of hearing them every night at six.

Dogs are fools, but at least I know it. When mine finds me crawling home on all fours with a broken foot it won't surprise me at all if he sinks his teeth in the rescue party. The real surprise will be if he doesn't sink them in me.

Tea

George Mikes

The trouble with tea is that originally it was quite a good drink.

So a group of the most eminent British scientists put their heads together, and made complicated biological experiments to find a way of spoiling it.

To the eternal glory of British science their labour bore fruit. They suggested that if you do not drink it clear, or with lemon or rum and sugar, but pour a few drops of cold milk into it, and no sugar at all, the desired object is achieved. Once this refreshing, aromatic, oriental beverage was successfully transformed into a colourless and tasteless gargling-water, it suddenly became the national drink of Great Britain and Ireland – still retaining, indeed usurping, the high-sounding title of tea.

There are some occasions when you must not refuse a cup of tea, otherwise you are judged an exotic and barbarous bird without any hope of ever being able to take your place in civilized society.

If you are invited to an English home, at five o'clock in the morning you get a cup of tea. It is either brought in by a heartily smiling hostess or an almost malevolently silent maid. When you are disturbed in your sweetest morning sleep you must not say: 'Madame (or Mabel), I think you are a cruel, spiteful and malignant person who deserves to be shot.' On the contrary, you have to declare with your best five o'clock smile: 'Thank you so much. I do adore a cup of early morning tea, especially early in the morning.' If they leave you alone with the liquid, you may pour it down the washbasin.

Then you have tea for breakfast; then you have tea at eleven o'clock in the morning; then after lunch; then you have tea for tea; then after supper and again at eleven o'clock at night.

You must not refuse any additional cups of tea under the following circumstances: if it is hot; if it is cold; if you are tired; if anybody thinks that you might be tired; if you are nervous; if you are gay; before you go out; if you are out; if you have just returned home; if you feel like it; if you do not feel like it; if you have had no tea for some time; if you have just had a cup.

You definitely must not follow my example. I sleep at five o'clock in the morning; I have coffee for breakfast; I drink innumerable cups of black coffee during the day; I have the most unorthodox and exotic teas even at tea-time.

The other day, for instance – I just mention this as a terrifying example to show you how low some people can sink – I wanted a cup of coffee and a piece of cheese for tea. It was one of those exceptionally hot days and my wife (once a good Englishwoman, now completely and hopelessly led astray by my wicked foreign influence) made some cold coffee and put it in the refrigerator, where it froze and became one solid block. On the other hand, she left the cheese on the kitchen table, where it melted. So had a piece of coffee and a glass of cheese.

Cheese in Transit

Jerome K. Jerome

The writer and his friends George and Harris agree that
they are overworked and need a holiday. This is to take the
form of a boating trip on the River Thames, but before the
travellers set off there are certain practical questions to be
tackled – notably what *not* to take with them...

Then we discussed the food question. George said:

'Begin with breakfast.' (George is so practical.) 'Now for breakfast we shall
want a frying-pan' (Harris said it was indigestible; but we merely urged him
not to be an ass, and George went on) 'a teapot and a kettle, and a
methylated-spirit stove.'

'No oil,' said George, with a significant look; and Harris and I agreed.

We had taken up an oil-stove once, but 'never again.' It had been like
living in an oil-shop that week. It oozed. I never saw such a thing as paraffin
oil is to ooze. We kept it in the nose of the boat, and, from there, it oozed
down to the rudder, impregnating the whole boat and everything in it on its
way, and it oozed over the river, and saturated the scenery and spoilt the
atmosphere. Sometimes a westerly oily wind blew, and at other times an
easterly oily wind, and sometimes in blew a northerly oily wind, and maybe a
southerly oily wind; but whether it came from the Arctic snows, or was raised
in the waste of the desert sands, it came alike to us laden with the fragrance of
paraffin oil.

And that oil oozed up and ruined the sunset; and as for the moonbeams,
they positively reeked of paraffin.

We tried to get away from it at Marlow. We left the boat by the bridge,
and took a walk through the town to escape it, but it followed us. The whole
town was full of oil. We passed through the churchyard, and it seemed as if
the people had been buried in oil. The High Street stunk of oil; we wondered

how people could live in it. And we walked miles upon miles out Birmingham
way; but it was no use, the country was steeped in oil.

At the end of that trip we met together at midnight in a lonely field, under
a blasted oak, and took an awful oath (we had been swearing for a whole
week about the thing in an ordinary, middle-class way, but this was a swell
affair) – an awful oath never to take paraffin oil with us in a boat again –
except, of course, in case of sickness.

Therefore, in the present instance, we confined ourselves to methylated
spirit. Even that is bad enough. You get methylated pie and methylated cake.
But methylated spirit is more wholesome when taken into the system in large
quantities than paraffin oil.

For other breakfast things, George suggested eggs and bacon, which were
easy to cook, cold meat, tea, bread and butter, and jam. For lunch, he said,
we could have biscuits, cold meat, bread and butter, and jam – but *no cheese*.
Cheese, like oil, makes too much of itself. It wants the whole boat to itself. It
goes through the hamper, and gives a cheesy flavour to everything else there.
You can't tell whether you are eating apple-pie or German sausage, or
strawberries and cream. It all seems cheese. There is too much odour about
cheese.

I remember a friend of mine buying a couple of cheeses at Liverpool.
Splendid cheeses they were, ripe and mellow, and with a two hundred horse-
power scent about them that might have been warranted to carry three miles,
and knock a man over at two hundred yards. I was in Liverpool at the time,
and my friend said that if I didn't mind he would get me to take them back
with me to London, as he should not be coming up for a day or two himself,
and he did not think the cheeses ought to be kept much longer.

'Oh, with pleasure, dear boy,' I replied, 'with pleasure.'

I called for the cheeses, and took them away in a cab. It was a ramshackle
affair, dragged along by a knock-kneed, broken-winded somnambulist,
which his owner, in a moment of enthusiasm, during conversation, referred
to as a horse. I put the cheeses on the top, and we started off at a shamble
that would have done credit to the swiftest steam-roller ever built, and all
went merry as a funeral bell, until we turned the corner. There, the wind
carried a whiff from the cheeses full on to our steed. It woke him up, and,
with a snort of terror, he dashed off at three miles an hour. The wind still
blew in his direction, and before we reached the end of the street he was
laying himself out at the rate of nearly four miles an hour, leaving the
cripples and stout old ladies simply nowhere.

It took two porters as well as the driver to hold him in at the station; and I do not think they would have done it, even then, had not one of the men had the presence of mind to put a handkerchief over his nose, and to light a bit of brown paper.

I took my ticket, and marched proudly up the platform, with my cheeses, the people falling back respectfully on either side. The train was crowded, and I had to get into a carriage where there were already seven other people. One crusty old gentleman objected, but I got in, notwithstanding; and putting my cheeses upon the rack, squeezed down with a pleasant smile, and said it was a warm day. A few moments passed, and then the old gentleman began to fidget.

'Very close in here,' he said.

'Quite oppressive,' said the man next to him.

And then they both began sniffing, and, at the third sniff, they caught it right on the chest, and rose up without another word and went out. And then a stout lady got up, and said it was disgraceful that a respectable married woman should be harried about in this way, and gathered up a bag and eight parcels and went. The remaining four passengers sat on for a while, until a solemn-looking man in the corner, who, from his dress and general appearance, seemed to belong to the undertaker class, said it put him in mind of a dead baby; and the other three passengers tried to get out of the door at the same time, and hurt themselves.

I smiled at the black gentleman, and said I thought we were going to have the carriage to ourselves; and he laughed pleasantly and said that some people made such a fuss over a little thing. But even he grew strangely depressed after we had started, and so, when we reached Crewe, I asked him to come and have a drink. He accepted, and we forced our way into the buffet, where we yelled, and stamped, and waved our umbrellas for a quarter of an hour; and then a young lady came and asked us if we wanted anything.

'What's yours?' I said, turning to my friend.

'I'll have half a crown's worth of brandy, neat, if you please, miss,' he responded.

And he went off quietly after he had drunk it and got into another carriage, which I thought mean.

From Crewe I had the compartment to myself, though the train was crowded. As we drew up at the different stations, the people, seeing my empty carriage, would rush for it. 'Here y' are, Maria; come along, plenty of room.' 'All right, Tom; we'll get in here,' they would shout. And they would run along, carrying heavy bags, and fight round the door to get in first. And one would open the door and mount the steps and stagger back into the arms of the man behind him; and they would all come and have a sniff, and then droop off and squeeze into other carriages, or pay the difference and go first.

From Euston I took the cheeses down to my friend's house. When his wife came into the room she smelt round for an instant. Then she said:

'What is it? Tell me the worst.'

I said: 'It's cheeses. Tom bought them in Liverpool, and asked me to bring them up with me.'

And I added that I hoped she understood that it had nothing to do with me; and she said that she was sure of that, but that she would speak to Tom about it when he came back.

My friend was detained in Liverpool longer than he expected; and three days later, as he hadn't returned home, his wife called on me. She said:

'What did Tom say about those cheeses?'

I replied that he had directed they were to be kept in a moist place, and that nobody was to touch them.

She said: 'Nobody's likely to touch them. Had he smelt them?'

I thought he had, and added that he seemed greatly attached to them.

'You think he would be upset,' she queried, 'if I gave a man a sovereign to take them away and bury them?'

I answered that I thought he would never smile again.

An idea struck her. She said:

'Do you mind keeping them for him? Let me send them round to you.'

'Madam,' I replied, 'for myself I like the smell of cheese, and the journey the other day with them from Liverpool I shall ever look back upon as a happy ending to a pleasant holiday. But, in this world, we must consider others. The lady under whose roof I have the honour of residing is a widow, and, for all I know, possibly an orphan too. She has a strong, I may say an eloquent, objection to being what she terms "put upon." The presence of your husband's cheeses in her house she would, I instinctively feel, regard as a "put upon"; and it shall never be said that I put upon the widow and the orphan.'

'Very well, then,' said my friend's wife, rising, 'all I have to say is, that I shall take the children and go to an hotel until those cheeses are eaten. I decline to live any longer in the same house with them.'

She kept her word, leaving the place in charge of the charwoman, who, when asked if she could stand the smell, replied, 'What smell?' and who, when taken close the cheeses and told to sniff hard, said she could detect a faint odour of melons. It was argued from this that little injury could result to the woman from the atmosphere, and she was left.

The hotel bill came to fifteen guineas; and my friend, after reckoning everything up, found that the cheeses had cost him eight-and-sixpence a pound. He said he dearly loved a bit of cheese, but it was beyond his means; so he determined to get rid of them. He threw them into the canal; but had to fish them out again, as the bargemen complained. They said it made them feel quite faint. And, after that, he took them one dark night and left them in the parish mortuary. But the coroner discovered them, and made a fearful fuss.

He said it was a plot to deprive him of his living by waking up the corpses.

My friend got rid of them, at last, by taking them down to a seaside town, and burying them on the beach. It gained the place quite a reputation. Visitors said they had never noticed before how strong the air was, and weak-chested and consumptive people used to throng there for years afterwards.

Fond as I am of cheese, therefore, I hold that George was right in declining to take any.

The Cricket Match

Richard Stilgoe

Ever since a life assurance company began to sponsor Test matches, the City of London has taken a renewed interest in cricket. Of course, the City has had for years the oddity of its own cricket field. It lies between the City Road and Bunhill Row, and since 1538 the Honourable Artillery Company have played cricket on it, despite the fact that if they stopped playing cricket on it and sold it to a developer, they could probably buy another twenty million pounds worth of artillery.

You might think it surprising that a group of part-time soldiers enjoy such expansive and expensive sporting facilities, in view of the fact that the City's other major cricket club has no home ground at all. But the City's other club is of recent formation. The H.A.C. annexed its oval before property prices passed through the false ceiling, the insulation and the roof in the 'sixties. The P.C.C.C.C. had no chance to show such foresight, as this is their first season. They are the Post-Cardiac City Cricket Club. To join, you have to be a City businessman who has survived both a major heart-attack and the ministrations of a particular heart specialist whose sworn opinion it is that heart sufferers should thenceforward play cricket, since it gives gentle exercise and cannot possibly excite. This, anyway, is his theory. At first, all went well. The P.C.C.C.C. turned up gently and punctually at eleven villages on eleven Saturdays, and each time managed to engineer the result most dear to the true cricket-lover's heart – a draw interrupted by rain.

In truth, the itinerant nature of the team is their own choice, spurred on by their doctor. He feels that these trips to havens of rural peace are as therapeutic as the game, serving to remove his ex-patients from the City with its associations of competition and stress. Had he decided otherwise – that the team must grasp the nettle and play always within the City, to exorcise their ghost by meeting it first bounce and despatching it over long-on – then the H.A.C.'s ground might have been under threat. For the P.C.C.C.C.'s dozen or so founder-members were among the richest men in the City, in England, in Europe, probably in the World, and raising twenty million pounds between them would have been the work of the few moments it takes to oversubscribe a new share issue. But their specialist had doomed them to wander the village greens of England and so they did as they were bid, for they believed it made them able to carry on juggling seven different burning currencies with two hands from Monday to Friday in the City, not half a mile from the H.A.C. ground.

The twelfth Saturday of their existence found the P.C.C.C.C. at TOILCHARD REGIS in Wiltshire, not far from Marlborough and not far from Hungerford, but not very near to either. Too far from London to commute, but too near to escape its influence. Much of Toilchard Regis is thatched unnaturally well, as second-home buyers have moved in and improved the houses to the point where no native of Toilchard Regis can afford them any more. Luckily, a large group of speculative post-war houses was built to attract people to the village. These now house the locals, who got them quite cheaply, the newcomers having eyes only for the thatch, the beams, the bread oven and the inglenook. Toilchard Regis's cricket team divides roughly half and half – well, exactly, not roughly, since most Saturdays either ten or twelve turn up and insist on playing – between seven-day-a-week residents and two-day-a-week residents. Of a Saturday they meet before lunch at the Bull and Bear on the village green, where they have a clear view of the cricket pitch and usually the opposition – for visiting cricket teams also tend to sniff out the nearest pub to soothe the effects of the journey, to try and catch a glimpse of the home side, to ask the landlord what they might expect in the way of fast bowling, reliable batting or (worst of all) a proper wicket-keeper, and generally to analyse the atmosphere of the alien planet on whose surface they find themselves.

Thus it was that Joe Painter, Alan Tremoyne, Ned Deering, Tom Deering, Jim Trance and the others sat and watched while the Bull and Bear's car park filled with two Daimler Double-Sixes, two Range Rovers, a Maserati Bora, a Porsche Turbo, a black Renault 5 with a telephone in it and four Silver Shadows (three of them with race-horse mascots replacing the flying lady). These, instead of the more normal motor-coach, represented the team transport of the eleven heart patients who now stood in the saloon bar, holding eleven neat tonic waters in eleven slightly shaking hands.

The rules of village cricket decree that, at about 1.30, the two teams shall set off from the pub to the pavilion, and on the way shall pretend to have seen each other for the first time. So it was that at 1.32, halfway across the village green, Alan Tremoyne of Toilchard Regis turned to a man who had walked with him for the last hundred yards or so and said, 'You'll be the chaps from London, I suppose. My name's Tremoyne. I'm the village captain, for my sins.' He smiled, and stuck out a hand.

His walking companion took it in a larger, redder hand, and shook it briefly. 'Hogdirt,' he said, 'Alec Hogdirt. Well, Sir Alec Hogdirt, if you insist. Not ashamed of it. It was these hands got it for me.'

'Are you the captain, er, Sir Alec?' asked Tremoyne.

'I am not, son, though there are those as says I should be. Oh yes. Alec, they say, you should be captain. Well, *Sir* Alec, in fact, they say, but I don't stand on ceremony. But I'm not captain, and that's that, so I pull my weight and bide my time, Sir Alec or no. You want the General, Sir Eric.' And he indicated a tall, brown husk of a man with a grey toothbrush tethered to his upper lip.

'Are you all Sir Something?' Tremoyne asked.

'Nay lad,' said Sir Alec. 'Just three of us. Eric over there, Tag, of course, and me. Sir Alec. I got mine eight years ago. Tag's is only two years old. Eric got his for being in the army. It didn't cost him a penny, so it doesn't really count. But they still made him captain. There are those who say that this country's decline is due to that kind of thinking, and I'm not saying I'm not one of them. But that's how it is. General!' he shouted, and the long, pale linen jacket ahead stiffened, and turned slowly. 'This is the home team's captain. He thought I was the captain. Easy mistake to make. I told him you were captain. For the moment.' Sir Alec looked belligerently at the general, who stared past him at Tremoyne, and offered a desiccated hand.

'Sir Eric Goldhat is my name,' he said, pleasantly enough. Alan Tremoyne took the hand. 'Tremoyne,' he said. 'Alan Tremoyne.'

The General looked interested. 'Tremoyne, eh? Any relation to D.R.T. Tremoyne? Green Jackets?'

'Not that I know of,' said Alan. 'Sorry.'

'B.J.M.?' said the General.

'I beg your pardon?'

'B.J.M.,' repeated the General. 'B.J.M. Tremoyne. Younger brother of D.R.T. Got a D.S.O. in Burma.'

'I don't think any of my family was in the army, sir,' Alan explained.

The General looked at him suspiciously. 'You're not Welsh, are you?' he asked after a pause.

Alan pretended not to hear and changed the subject. 'Don't you think we ought to toss, sir?' he said. The two teams were now moving into the pavilion in dribs and drabs, and it was getting late.

The General agreed, and asked his players if any of them had any money. They all denied possession of the smallest sou, as they did regularly to all inquiries. No really rich man ever admits to having any money. 'Liquidity problem,' said Sir Eric. 'What would you do if you won the toss?'

Alan hesitated. 'Put you into bat, sir,' he said.

'Set yourself a target, eh!' barked Sir Eric. 'Good ploy. I always bat first meself. Not saying you're not right. No need to toss, though. We bat first. Good decision, young Tremoyne. Tell me, were your father's initials S.E.J.?'

'No sir, T.K.A.' replied Alan.

'T.K.A., eh?' mused the General.

'No, just one "A",' said Alan.

The General looked at him, and again wondered if he was Welsh.

It was only five minutes past two when, to the surprise of the Toilchard Regis faithful, the umpires came out. By the standards of village cricket, this is punctuality almost to the point of pedantry. But the P.C.C.C., for all their lack of a coin to toss up with, were not men who had earned their millions by turning up late. Each one, invalid or no, was in his office every morning before his secretary, to sort through the mail and see which letters were for her to pass to him, and which for her to pass on to the groundlings. So the P.C.C.C. batting order was already on a typed slip of paper. The presence of a scorer and two umpires had been checked by phone and confirmed by letter (by one of the secretaries who arrived at the office after the team members). Indeed, the delay of five minutes was only due to the absence of a wicket-keeper's glove, which had been borrowed by the wife of the wicket-keeper to remove the vol-au-vents from the oven, so they would have plenty of time to go cold before the tea interval. The glove having been returned, Alan Tremoyne (an efficient, if rather harassed, person and a trainee estate manager) led his ten men on to the field, full of hope that the eleventh would arrive when he saw the rigours of fielding waning, and the chance of a bowl and a bat waxing.

The opening pair of millionaires were Sir Alec Hogdirt (whom we have

met, who had progressed from Pigs to Bacon to Pork Pies to Wholesale and
Retail until he controlled all food that grunted from squealing piglet to
smoky-bacon-flavoured crisps and pork scratchings) and GILES T. HAIR-
CORD, whose capacity for seeing carpet in terms of acres rather than yards had
made him at thirty-four very rich and very worried. His carpets had made
him a pile, his friends said. He had piles, his enemies said. Either way, his
incipient angina had greatly strengthened the team's batting, as had the fact
that, though ambitious and greedy, he was hardly mad at all. As the
Toilchard Regis clock struck eight, he looked at his digital watch. It was
2.06.00 (and 10.06.00 in Perth, Western Australia. It was that sort of watch).
Sir Alec took middle and leg from the local magistrate, looked round the field
and began to pat Wiltshire with his bat.

In village cricket, each bowler's first ball is special. The batsman has no
idea whether the new bowler is fast, medium slow, an absolute rabbit, keen
but mediocre, a man with a grudge against batsmen, or worst of all, a
halfway competent cricketer. The batsman finds out all these things during
the first few seconds. This makes that first ball harder than anything Test
cricket has to offer. In Test cricket the bowler is Lever, left-arm fast-medium,
tending to swing the ball in. In village cricket the bowler is the grocer, and
the umpire thinks he's right-handed from the way he works the bacon slicer.

So with trepidation Sir Alec Hogdirt faced the first ball from the Toilchard
Regis grocer, Joe Painter. It turned out to be a fast in-swinger, but only the
square-leg umpire could see whether or not it swung before it whistled past
him. The magistrate signalled four wides. Two German tourists in deck
chairs consulted each other on what this might mean. Giles T. Haircord
walked over to the point where the ball had bounced – a point about fifteen
yards away from the pitch – and prodded it. He was wondering whether to
open more branches of Ambience, a chain of shops he had successfully
started which sold uncomfortable knotty-pine beds and corduroy curtains, or
merely to take over Environ, his principal rival. He was still wondering when
the grocer bowled his second ball, a mirror image of the first, which hit cover
point in the kidneys on its way to the boundary. 'Next one should be bang on
middle stump,' said the umpire cheerfully, lowering his arms once the scorer
had acknowledged four more wides. It was, and it duly bowled Sir Alec
Hogdirt, who stood his ground firmly until the umpire raised his finger, then
glared at him and walked sullenly towards the pavilion, crossing as he did so
the incoming batsman, who was the frozen-food magnate, HAROLD ICEGRIST.

A small, dogged man with a healthy doormat of grey hair, Harold Icegrist came from Barnsley and therefore believed himself invincible at all forms of sport. This belief generally stood him in good stead, since self-confidence daunts an opponent more than almost anything else. He and Giles T. Haircord took the score to 31 before Giles T. Haircord was run out. Well, hardly run out, because he made no effort to run at all, standing instead deep in concentration. (It had just occurred to him that to bring the South Korean occasional tables in through Ireland might avoid the tariff controls – if not even attracting a subsidy.) He smiled sheepishly, collected his pocket calculator from the umpire and departed. The two German tourists clapped politely, and checked their rule book.

Harold Icegrist lasted not much longer, giving his wicket away in order to be back in the pavilion for a three o'clock transatlantic phone call. By the time he had hung up the P.C.C.C.C. had scored 65 for 4 with LORD A.G. CHRISTIE not out 11 and Sir Eric Goldhat not out 9, the innings of ARISTIDE GLORCH, the shipping magnate, having lasted only two balls. It should be said that the first of these went for six over square-leg. The second went to the same place, but this time square-leg did not get out of the way in time and was forced to catch the ball to save himself serious injury.

It is a fine thing to watch two old English patricians at the wicket. Arthur Gervaise Christie, six foot three of him from his grey socks to his bald head, like a Georgian folly topped by a dome, and Sir Eric Goldhat, nearly as tall but with an Old Wellingtonian tie holding up his trousers in contrast to Lord A. G. Christie's Etonian one. As they cantered their sweetly stroked runs, they looked like a pair of threadbare greyhounds with striped girths. Lord Christie's fifty was followed by Sir Eric's and their success so demoralized the Toilchard Regis team that the batsmen who followed them were also able to score freely – apart, that is, from the merchant banker HEROD GILTRAISE, whose company, GIRO CASHIER LTD, had doubled its value in the previous weeks thanks to judicious investment in the Middle East. Thinking of the Middle East, Herod Giltraise remembered that he should not be playing cricket on a Saturday and his concentration suffered. When the post-cardiac team's innings ended at 4.28, the score sheet read like this:

Sir Alec Hogdirt b. Painter 0
Giles T. Haircord run out 14
Harold Icegrist c. Trance b. Tremoyne 16
Lord A.G. Christie not out 77
Aristide Glorch c. Deering N. b. Deering T 6

So it was in cheerful mood that the team sat down to tea (well, LORD
CIGAR-HEIST didn't sit down, the wild stumping attempt from Jim Trance
having hit him firmly on the coccyx), for 240 is a formidable score in village
cricket. They might even win! The Post-Cardiac City Cricket Club had never
yet won a match. Normally they batted for a gentle couple of hours, scored
ninety or so, had a frugal tea, misfielded for an hour while the home team
approached their score, got rained on, shook hands with everyone and drove
home. But today – well, it was obviously the arrival in the team of Lord
Christie (promoted on the death of SIR GODRIC LEATH, the Governor of the
Bank of England, who had been run over while trying to pick up a penny that
had rolled into the middle of the North Circular Road) which had
strengthened the side. None of them knew him well. He was not a City man
generally, but he came up from the country occasionally to try and attract
sponsorship for the ballet festival he ran at his house, Glen Underboy, and
several of them had been approached in this capacity. Well, none of them
was averse to sponsoring art if the return was reasonable, and if he went on
playing his late cut as sweetly, Lord Christie could look forward to an easier
passage in the future. 'Perhaps he might be able to bowl as well,' they said to
one another. And with this pleasing thought in mind, they sat down to tea.
    The wives of the Toilchard Regis team had excelled themselves. They had
not only cooled the vol-au-vents, but had curled the sandwiches and dried
the tops with a hair-dryer. The biscuits had been dampened, the fairy cakes'
chocolate icing had been melted, then allowed to set again. Scones of a
weight to rival uranium – and roughly as beneficial to the human body – had
been buttered with butter whose sell-by date had long passed. There were
flapjacks of a consistency to challenge the whole falseteeth fixative industry
and sticky things made of Weetabix and cocoa, while the sandwich fillings –

the work of Mrs Deering (N) – were a tour de force: white of egg with cress and earth, cheese and mould, hundreds and thousands with lemon curd, and ham fat; each one a noble complement for the furry aluminium pot of already sugared tea. With 240 on the board, the P.C.C.C.C. tucked in – so much that when the four strongest ladies carried in the fruit cake, the magnates could manage scarcely two slices each. The remainder had to be sold to the two German tourists, who gave every sign of approval at being charged only 94p a slice, for they too had been to London.

When the teams returned to the field, it turned out that Lord Christie could indeed bowl. Sir Eric Goldhat invited him to take the second over instead of Sir Alec Hogdirt, who had expended so much energy in telling everyone how he had been unfairly dismissed that he was now too tired to bowl. The first over had been bowled by SIR TAG CHLORIDE, founder and managing director of DIGITAL SCHROER, a multinational whose purpose was clear to very few people below presidential rank. Sir Tag had conceded four wides and two runs, from a lucky snick by Ichabod Jordan over the head of the P.C.C.C.C.'s other Giles, GILES R. RICHTOAD, who was to assets what Nitromors is to paint. His concentration at what the rest of the team called 'first strip' was impaired by his listening throughout the game to a long memo from a New York colleague on his miniature earphone.

Lord A. G. Christie's first over was bowled at a speed which would not have disgraced Larwood himself (on whose style it was based). The effect was the more terrifying for the loud grunt that accompanied the delivery of the ball, and for the fact that Lord Christie did not stop when the ball left his hand, but carried on running down the wicket as if helpless without a braking parachute. This so surprised the opening batsman that he watched the progress of the galloping peer rather than the ball, which whistled unheeded past him and dislodged his off stump. His successor was less distracted, and played carefully forward – only to find himself caught by the bowler who had got within five feet of overhauling the ball. At the end of two overs the Toilchard Regis team were 6 for 2 and even some of the wives had come out of the pavilion to watch. They stood, ranged directly behind the bowler's arm, drying plates with flapping white tea-cloths.

The city cricketers clapped Lord Christie warmly on the back, and took their places for Sir Tag Chloride's next over. A new spirit was abroad. Better, a new spirit was in Wiltshire, which isn't abroad at all. Sir Tag's over conceded but one run, and that should have been a boundary but for Aristide Glorch throwing himself – nay, hurling himself – into the path of the ball, and returning it to the wicket-keeper with a smile his face had not seen since the invention of flags of convenience.

That same wicket-keeper's moment of glory was yet to come. After six overs, with the score at 29 for 6, Sir Eric Goldhat felt emboldened to change the bowling and allow his off-breaks their weekly outing. As he ran up he saw to his surprise that the wicket-keeper was standing right behind the stumps, not twenty yards back as he usually did. HORST I. CLARIDGE, hotelier and restaurateur, was remembering the happy days at G. CARRIDI's HOTEL, when he was reception clerk. And now, again, he had moved from the office at the back to the front door. Let no cricket ball try to pass *him* without a tie! Sir Eric duly bowled, the demoralized batsman duly played and missed and Horst I. Claridge, sweating a little, gathered the ball and removed the bails as if spinning a visitor's book round to face a guest. 'Porter!' he cried, forgetting himself for a moment. And the umpire, who was very deaf, raised his finger. Sir Eric Goldhat ran to congratulate the keeper, his Adam's apple bobbing furiously.

From then on, as each wicket fell, the Post-Cardiac Cricket Club ran excitedly to whoever was responsible and patted him, talking volubly, congratulating each other and giving little jumps. They were going to win. They liked winning. They were used to winning from Mondays to Fridays, but not used to winning at cricket. They were going to win, and it wasn't even going to rain.

When Alan Tremoyne came out to bat, his side had 43 runs on the board for the loss of nine wickets. The faces of the fielders were almost derisive as he took guard and looked around him. Four slips, a gully, silly mid-off, silly mid-on, leg-slip and a square-leg, all crouching with eyes unnaturally bright. The capillaries popped in their cheeks, the veins throbbed in their temples. Lord Christie, whose figures stood at 6 for 17 after ten high-speed overs, ignored the silver flecks that danced before his eyes as he walked back to bowl.

Alan Tremoyne had decided to have a tonk. He might as well. He wasn't really a batsman. Nobody expected him to score the 198 necessary for victory. So, at what he judged the appropriate moment, he shut his eyes and carved the air massively with his bat. The ball shot straight up in the air, followed by the gleaming eyes of the fielders. This was it. It would be caught. They had won. It was falling towards Sir Alec Hogdirt at square leg. 'Yours, Alec!' cried one of the fielders. '*Sir* Alec!' shouted Sir Alec, but didn't take his eyes from the red ball descending towards him. It was getting bigger. It was very red indeed, and huge. The whole sky was red and flaming. Why was somebody pulling a piano wire tight around his chest? Why were they hitting the backs of his legs with hammers? As Sir Alec pitched forward the ball hit him in the small of the back and bounced away. One by one the entire City eleven rolled his eyes, clutched at his throat and fell. The Toilchard Regis team ran on to the field, and with commendable unself-consciousness began giving their prone opponents the kiss of life. The Toilchard Regis wives ran on to the field as well, with the remains of the tea and a plate of headless gingerbread men.

The two German tourists, who had thought they were just getting the hang of it, looked at the eleven flannelled couples kissing on the ground and reflected that cricket was indeed a game hard to understand. But they took a photograph of it anyway.

Jots and Tittles

Lawrence Durrell

'In Diplomacy,' said Antrobus, 'quite small things can be One's Undoing; things which in themselves may be Purely Inadvertent. The Seasoned Diplomat keeps a sharp eye out for these moments of Doom and does what he can to avert them. Sometimes he succeeds, but sometimes he fails utterly – and then Irreparable Harm ensues.

'Foreigners are apt to be preternaturally touchy in small ways and I remember important negotiations being spoilt sometimes by a slip of the tongue or an imagined slight. I remember an Italian personage, for example (let us call him the Minister for Howls and Smells), who with the temerity of ignorance swarmed up the wrong side of the C.-in-C. Med.'s Flagship in Naples harbour with a bunch of violets and a bottle of Strega as a gift from the Civil Servants of Naples. He was not only ordered off in rather stringent fashion but passes were made at him with a brass-shod boathook. This indignity cost us dear and we practically had to resort to massage to set things right.

'Then there was the Finnish Ambassador's wife in Paris who slimmed so rigorously that her stomach took to rumbling quite audibly at receptions. I suppose she was hungry. But no sooner did she walk into a room with a buffet in it than her stomach set up growls of protest. She tried to pass it off by staring hard at other people but it didn't work. Of course, people not in the know simply thought that someone upstairs was moving furniture about. But at private dinner parties this characteristic was impossible to disguise; she would sit rumbling at her guests who in a frenzy of politeness tried to raise their voices above the noise. She soon lost ground in the Corps. Silences would fall at her parties – the one thing that Diplomats fear more than anything else. When silences begin to fall, broken only by the rumblings of the lady's entrails, it is The Beginning of the End.

'But quite the most illuminating example of this sort of thing occurred on the evening when Polk-Mowbray swallowed a moth. I don't think I ever told you about it before. It is the sort of thing one only talks about in the strictest confidence. It was at a dinner party given to the Communist People's Serbian Trade and Timber Guild sometime during Christmas week back in '52. Yugoslavia at that time had just broken with Stalin and was beginning to feel that the West was not entirely populated by 'capitalist hyenas' as the press said. They were still wildly suspicious of us, of course, and it was a very hot and embarrassed little group of peasants dressed in dark suits who accepted Polk-Mowbray's invitation to dinner at the Embassy. Most of them spoke only their mother tongue. Comrade Bobok, however, the leader of the delegation, spoke a gnarled embryonic English. He was a huge sweating Bosnian peasant with a bald head. His number two, Pepic, spoke the sort of French that one imagines is learned in mission houses in Polynesia. From a diplomatist's point of view they were Heavy Going.

'I shall say nothing about their messy food habits; Drage the butler kept circling the table and staring at them as if he had gone out of his senses. We were all pretty sweaty and constrained by the time the soup plates were removed. The conversation was early cave-man stuff consisting of growls and snarls and weird flourishes of knife and fork. Bobok and Pepic sat on Polk-Mowbray's right and left respectively; they were flanked by Spalding the Commercial Attaché and myself. We were absolutely determined to make the evening a success. De Mandeville for some curious reason best known to himself had decreed that we should eat turkey with mustard and follow it up with plum pudding. I suppose it was because it was Christmas week. Comrade Bobok fell foul of the mustard almost at once and only quenched himself by lengthy potations which, however, were all to the good as they put him into a good temper.

'The whole thing might have been carried off perfectly well had it not been for this blasted moth which had been circling the Georgian candlesticks since the start of the dinner-party and which now elected to get burnt and crawl on to Polk-Mowbray's side-plate to die. Polk-Mowbray himself was undergoing the fearful strain of decoding Comrade Bobok's weighty pleasantries which were full of corrupt groups and he let his attention wander for one fatal second.

'As he talked he absently groped in his side-plate for a piece of bread. He rolls bread balls incessantly at dinner, as you know. Spalding and I saw in a flash of horror something happen for which our long diplomatic training had not prepared us. Mind you, I saw a journalist eat a wine-glass once, and once in Prague I saw a Hindu diplomat's wife drain a glass of vodka under the impression that it was water. She let out a moan which still rings in my ears. But never in all my long service have I seen an Ambassador eat a moth – and this is precisely what Polk-Mowbray did. He has a large and serviceable mouth and into it Spalding and I saw the moth disappear. There was a breathless pause during which our poor Ambassador suddenly realized that something was wrong; his whole frame stiffened with a dreadful premonition. His large and expressive eye became round and glassy with horror.

'This incident unluckily coincided with two others; the first was that Drage walked on with a blazing pudding stuck with holly. Our guests were somewhat startled by this apparition, and Comrade Bobok, under the vague impression that the blazing pud must be ushering in a spell of diplomatic toasts, rose to his feet and cried loudly: "To Comrade Tito and the Communist People's Serbian Trade and Timber Guild. *Jiveo!*" His fellow Serbs rose as one man and shouted: "*Jiveo!*"

'By this time, however, light had begun to dawn on Polk-Mowbray. He let out a hoarse jarring cry full of despair and charred moth, stood up, threw up his arms and groped his way to the carafe on the sideboard, shaken by a paroxysm of coughing. Spalding and I rocked, I am sorry to say, with hysterical giggles, followed him to pat him on the back. To the startled eyes of the Yugoslavs we must have presented the picture of three diplomats laughing ourselves to death and slapping each other on the back at the sideboard, and utterly ignoring the sacred toast. Worse still, before any of us could turn and explain the situation Spalding's elbow connected with Drage's spinal cord. The butler missed his footing and scattered the pudding like an incendiary bomb all over the table and ourselves. The Yugoslav delegation sat there with little odd bits of pudding blazing in their laps or on their waistcoats, utterly incapable of constructive thought. Spalding, I am sorry to say, was racked with guffaws now which were infectious to a degree. De Mandeville who was holding the leg of the table and who had witnessed the tragedy also started to laugh in a shrill feminine register.

'I must say Polk-Mowbray rallied gamely. He took an enormous gulp of wine from the carafe and led us all back to table with apologies and excuses which sounded, I must say, pretty thin. What Communist could believe a capitalist hyena when he says that he has swallowed a moth? Drage was flashing about snuffing out pieces of pudding.

'We made some attempt to save the evening, but in vain. The awful thing was that whenever Spalding caught De Mandeville's eye they both subsided into helpless laughter. The Yugoslavs were in an Irremediable Huff and from then on they shut up like clams, and took their collective leave even before the coffee was served.

'It was quite clear that Spalding's Timber Pact was going to founder in mutual mistrust once more. The whole affair was summed up by the *Central Balkan Herald* in its inimitable style as follows: "We gather that the British Embassy organized a special dinner at which the Niece de Resistance was Glum Pudding and a thoroughly British evening was enjoyed by all." You couldn't say fairer than that, could you?'

The Rummy Affair of Old Biffy

P. G. Wodehouse

'Jeeves,' I said, emerging from the old tub, 'rally round.'

'Yes, sir.'

I beamed on the man with no little geniality. I was putting in a week or two in Paris at the moment, and there's something about Paris that always makes me feel fairly full of *espièglerie* and *joie de vivre*.

'Lay out our gent's medium-smart raiment, suitable for Bohemian revels,' I said. 'I am lunching with an artist bloke on the other side of the river.'

'Very good, sir.'

'And if anybody calls for me, Jeeves, say that I shall be back towards the quiet evenfall.'

'Yes, sir. Mr Biffen rang up on the telephone while you were in your bath.'

'Mr Biffen? Good heavens!'

Amazing how one's always running across fellows in foreign cities – coves, I mean, whom you haven't seen for ages and would have betted weren't anywhere in the neighbourhood. Paris was the last place where I should have expected to find old Biffy popping up. There was a time when he and I had been lads about town together, lunching and dining together practically every day; but some eighteen months back his old godmother had died and left him that place in Herefordshire, and he had retired there to wear gaiters and prod cows in the ribs and generally be the country gentleman and landed proprietor. Since then I had hardly seen him.

'Old Biffy in Paris? What's he doing here?'

'He did not confide in me, sir,' said Jeeves – a trifle frostily, I thought. It sounded somehow as if he didn't like Biffy. And yet they had always been matey enough in the old days.

'Where's he staying?'

'At the Hotel Avenida, Rue du Colisée, sir. He informed me that he was about to take a walk and would call this afternoon.'

'Well, if he comes when I'm out, tell him to wait. And now, Jeeves, *mes gants, mon chapeau, et le whangee de monsieur.* I must be popping.'

It was such a corking day and I had so much time in hand that near the Sorbonne I stopped my cab, deciding to walk the rest of the way. And I had hardly gone three steps and a half when there on the pavement before me stood old Biffy in person. If I had completed the last step I should have rammed him.

'Biffy!' I cried. 'Well, well, well!'

He peered at me in a blinking kind of way, rather like one of his Herefordshire cows prodded unexpectedly while lunching.

'Bertie!' he gurgled, in a devout sort of tone. 'Thank God!' He clutched my arm. 'Don't leave me, Bertie. I'm lost.'

'What do you mean, lost?'

'I came out for a walk and suddenly discovered after a mile or two that I didn't know where on earth I was. I've been wandering round in circles for hours.'

'Why didn't you ask the way?'

'I can't speak a word of French.'

'Well, why didn't you call a taxi?'

'I suddenly discovered I'd left all my money at my hotel.'

'You could have taken a cab and paid it when you got to the hotel.'

'Yes, but I suddenly discovered, dash it, that I'd forgotten its name.'

And there in a nutshell you have Charles Edward Biffen. As vague and woollen-headed a blighter as ever bit a sandwich. Goodness knows – and my Aunt Agatha will bear me out in this – I'm no master-mind myself; but compared with Biffy I'm one of the great thinkers of all time.

'I'd give a shilling,' said Biffy wistfully, 'to know the name of that hotel.'

'You can owe it me. Hotel Avenida, Rue du Colisée.'

'Bertie! This is uncanny. How the deuce did you know?'

'That was the address you left with Jeeves this morning.'

'So it was. I had forgotten.'

'Well, come along and have a drink, and then I'll put you in a cab and send you home. I'm engaged for lunch, but I've plenty of time.'

We drifted to one of the eleven cafés which jostled each other along the street and I ordered restoratives.

'What on earth are you doing in Paris?' I asked.

'Bertie, old man,' said Biffy solemnly, 'I came here to try and forget.'

'Well, you've certainly succeeded.'

'You don't understand. The fact is, Bertie, old lad, my heart is broken. I'll tell you the whole story.'

'No, I say!' I protested. But he was off.

'Last year,' said Biffy, 'I buzzed over to Canada to do a bit of salmon fishing.'

I ordered another. If this was going to be a fish story, I needed stimulants.

'On the liner going to New York I met a girl.' Biffy made a sort of curious gulping noise not unlike a bulldog trying to swallow half a cutlet in a hurry so as to be ready for the other half. 'Bertie, old man, I can't describe her. I simply can't describe her.'

This was all to the good.

'She was wonderful! We used to walk on the boat-deck after dinner. She was on the stage. At least, sort of.'

'How do you mean, sort of?'

'Well, she had posed for artists and been a mannequin in a big dressmaker's and all that sort of thing, don't you know. Anyway, she had saved up a few pounds and was on her way to see if she could get a job in New York. She told me all about herself. Her father ran a milk-walk in Clapham. Or it may have been Cricklewood. At least, it was either a milk-walk or a boot-shop.'

'Easily confused.'

'What I'm trying to make you understand,' said Biffy, 'is that she came of good, sturdy, respectable middle-class stock. Nothing flashy about her. The sort of wife any man might have been proud of.'

'Well, whose wife was she?'

'Nobody's. That's the whole point of the story. I wanted her to be mine, and I lost her.'

'Had a quarrel, you mean?'

'No, I don't mean we had a quarrel. I mean I literally lost her. The last I ever saw of her was in the Customs sheds at New York. We were behind a pile of trunks, and I had just asked her to be my wife, and she had just said she would and everything was perfectly splendid, when a most offensive blighter in a peaked cap came up to talk about some cigarettes which he had found at the bottom of my trunk and which I had forgotten to declare. It was getting pretty late by then, for we hadn't docked till about ten-thirty, so I told Mabel to go on to her hotel and I would come round next day and take her to lunch. And since then I haven't set eyes on her.'

'You mean she wasn't at the hotel?'

'Probably she was. But—'

'You don't mean you never turned up?'

'Bertie, old man,' said Biffy, in an overwrought kind of way, 'for Heaven's sake don't keep trying to tell me what I mean and what I don't mean! Let me tell this my own way, or I shall get all mixed up and have to go back to the beginning.'

'Tell it your own way,' I said hastily.

'Well, then, to put it in a word, Bertie, I forgot the name of the hotel. By the time I'd done half an hour's heavy explaining about those cigarettes my mind was a blank. I had an idea I had written the name down somewhere, but I couldn't have done, for it wasn't on any of the papers in my pocket. No, it was no good. She was gone.'

'Why didn't you make inquiries?'

'Well, the fact is, Bertie, I had forgotten her name.'

'Oh, no, dash it!' I said. This seemed a bit too thick even for Biffy. 'How could you forget her name? Besides, you told it to me a moment ago. Muriel or something.'

'Mabel,' corrected Biffy coldly. 'It was her surname I'd forgotten. So I gave it up and went to Canada.'

'But half a second,' I said. 'You must have told her your name. I mean, if you couldn't trace her, she could trace you.'

'Exactly. That's what makes it all seem so infernally hopeless. She knows my name and where I live and everything, but I haven't heard a word from her. I suppose when I didn't turn up at the hotel, she took it that that was my way of hinting delicately that I had changed my mind and wanted to call the thing off.'

'I suppose so,' I said. There didn't seem anything else to suppose. 'Well, the only thing to do is to whizz around and try to heal the wound, what? How about dinner to-night, winding up at the Abbaye or one of those places?'

Biffy shook his head.

'It wouldn't be any good. I've tried it. Besides I'm leaving on the four o'clock train. I have a dinner engagement to-morrow with a man who's nibbling at that house of mine in Herefordshire.'

'Oh, are you trying to sell that place? I thought you liked it.'

'I did. But the idea of going on living in that great, lonely barn of a house after what has happened appals me, Bertie. So when Sir Roderick Glossop came along—'

'Sir Roderick Glossop! You don't mean the loony-doctor?'

'The great nerve specialist, yes. Why, do you know him?'

It was a warm day, but I shivered.

'I was engaged to his daughter for a week or two,' I said, in a hushed voice. The memory of that narrow squeak always made me feel faint.

'Has he a daughter?' said Biffy absently.

'He has. Let me tell you all about—'

'Not just now, old man,' said Biffy, getting up. 'I ought to be going back to my hotel to see about my packing.'

Which, after I had listened to his story, struck me as pretty low-down. However, the longer you live, the more you realize that the good old sporting spirit of give-and-take has practically died out in our midst. So I boosted him into a cab and went off to lunch.

It can't have been more than ten days after this that I received a nasty shock while getting outside my morning tea and toast. The English papers had arrived, and Jeeves was just drifting out of the room after depositing *The Times* by my bed-side, when, as I idly turned the pages in search of the sporting section, a paragraph leaped out and hit me squarely in the eyeball. As follows:–

FORTHCOMING MARRIAGES

Mr C. E. Biffen and Miss Glossop

The engagement is announced between Charles Edward, only son of the late Mr E. C. Biffen, and Mrs Biffen, of 11, Penslow Square, Mayfair, and Honoria Jane Louise, only daughter of Sir Roderick and Lady Glossop, of 6b, Harley Street, W.

'Great Scott!' I exclaimed.

'Sir?' said Jeeves, turning at the door.

'Jeeves, you remember Miss Glossop?'

'Very vividly, sir.'

'She's engaged to Mr Biffen!'

'Indeed, sir?' said Jeeves. And, with not another word, he slid out. The blighter's calm amazed and shocked me. It seemed to indicate that there must be a horrible streak of callousness in him. I mean to say, it wasn't as if he didn't know Honoria Glossop.

I read the paragraph again. A peculiar feeling it gave me. I don't know if you have ever experienced the sensation of seeing the announcement of the engagement of a pal of yours to a girl whom you were only saved from marrying yourself by the skin of your teeth. It induces a sort of – well, it's difficult to describe it exactly; but I should imagine a fellow would feel much the same if he happened to be strolling through the jungle with a boyhood chum and met a tigress or a jaguar, or what not, and managed to shin up a tree and looked down and saw the friend of his youth vanishing into the undergrowth in the animal's slavering jaws. A sort of profound, prayerful relief, if you know what I mean, blended at the same time with a pang of pity. What I'm driving at is that, thankful as I was that I hadn't had to marry Honoria myself, I was sorry to see a real good chap like old Biffy copping it. I sucked down a spot of tea and began to brood over the business.

Of course, there are probably fellows in the world – tough, hardy blokes with strong chins and glittering eyes – who could get engaged to this Glossop menace and like it; but I knew perfectly well that Biffy was not one of them. Honoria, you see, is one of those robust, dynamic girls with the muscles of a welterweight and a laugh like a squadron of cavalry charging over a tin bridge. A beastly thing to have to face over the breakfast table. Brainy, moreover. The sort of girl who reduces you to pulp with sixteen sets of tennis and a few rounds of golf and then comes down to dinner as fresh as a daisy, expecting you to take an intelligent interest in Freud. If I had been engaged to her another week, her old father would have had one more patient on his books; and Biffy is much the same quiet sort of peaceful, inoffensive bird as me. I was shocked, I tell you, shocked.

And, as I was saying, the thing that shocked me most was Jeeves's frightful lack of proper emotion. The man happening to float in at this juncture, I gave him one more chance to show some human sympathy.

'You got the name correctly, didn't you, Jeeves?' I said. 'Mr Biffen is going to marry Honoria Glossop, the daughter of the old boy with the egg-like head and the eyebrows.'

'Yes, sir. Which suit would you wish me to lay out this morning?'

And this, mark you, from the man who, when I was engaged to the

Glossop, strained every fibre in his brain to extricate me. It beat me. I couldn't understand it.

'The blue with the red twill,' I said coldly. My manner was marked, and I meant him to see that he had disappointed me sorely.

About a week later I went back to London, and scarcely had I got settled in the old flat when Biffy blew in. One glance was enough to tell me that the poisoned wound had begun to fester. The man did not look bright. No, there was no getting away from it, not bright. He had that kind of stunned, glassy expression which I used to see on my own face in the shaving-mirror during my brief engagement to the Glossop pestilence. However, if you don't want to be one of the What is Wrong With This Picture brigade, you must observe the conventions, so I shook his hand as warmly as I could.

'Well, well, old man,' I said. 'Congratulations.'

'Thanks,' said Biffy wanly, and there was rather a weighty silence.

'Bertie,' said Biffy, after the silence had lasted about three minutes.

'Hallo?'

'Is it really true—'

'What?'

'Oh, nothing,' said Biffy, and conversation languished again. After about a minute and a half he came to the surface once more.

'Bertie.'

'Still here, old thing. What is it?'

'I say, Bertie, is it really true that you were once engaged to Honoria?'

'It is.'

Biffy coughed

'How did you get out – I mean, what was the nature of the tragedy that prevented the marriage?'

'Jeeves worked it. He thought out the entire scheme.'

'I think, before I go,' said Biffy thoughtfully, 'I'll just step into the kitchen and have a word with Jeeves.'

I felt that the situation called for complete candour.

'Biffy, old egg,' I said, 'as man to man, do you want to oil out of this thing?'

'Bertie, old cork,' said Biffy earnestly, 'as one friend to another, I do.'

'Then why the dickens did you ever get into it?'

'I don't know. Why did you?'

'I – well, it sort of happened.'

'And it sort of happened with me. You know how it is when your heart's broken. A kind of lethargy comes over you. You get absent-minded and cease to exercise proper precautions, and the first thing you know you're for it. I don't know how it happened, old man, but there it is. And what I want you to tell me is, what's the procedure?'

'You mean, how does a fellow edge out?'

'Exactly. I don't want to hurt anybody's feelings, Bertie, but I can't go through with this thing. The shot is not on the board. For about a day and a half I thought it might be all right, but now – You remember that laugh of hers?'

'I do.'

'Well, there's that, and then all this business of never letting a fellow alone – improving his mind and so forth—'

'I know. I know.'

'Very well, then. What do you recommend? What did you mean when you said that Jeeves worked a scheme?'

'Well, you see, old Sir Roderick, who's a loony-doctor and nothing but a loony-doctor, however much you may call him a nerve specialist, discovered that there was a modicum of insanity in my family. Nothing serious. Just one of my uncles. Used to keep rabbits in his bedroom. And the old boy came to lunch here to give me the once-over, and Jeeves arranged matters so that he went away firmly convinced that I was off my onion.'

'I see,' said Biffy thoughtfully. 'The trouble is there isn't any insanity in my family.'

'None?'

It seemed to me almost incredible that a fellow could be such a perfect chump as dear old Biffy without a bit of assistance.

'Not a loony on the list,' he said gloomily. 'It's just like my luck. The old boy's coming to lunch with me to-morrow, no doubt to test me as he did you. And I never felt saner in my life.'

I thought for a moment. The idea of meeting Sir Roderick again gave me a cold shivery feeling; but when there is a chance of helping a pal we Woosters have no thought of self.

'Look here, Biffy,' I said, 'I'll tell you what. I'll roll up for that lunch. It may easily happen that when he finds you are a pal of mine he will forbid the banns right away and no more questions asked.'

'Something in that,' said Biffy, brightening. 'Awfully sporting of you, Bertie.'

'Oh, not at all,' I said. 'And meanwhile I'll consult Jeeves. Put the whole thing up to him and ask his advice. He's never failed me yet.'

Biffy pushed off, a good deal braced, and I went into the kitchen.

'Jeeves,' I said, 'I want your help once more. I've just been having a painful interview with Mr Biffen.'

'Indeed, sir?'

'It's like this,' I said, and told him the whole thing.

It was rummy, but I could feel him freezing from the start. As a rule, when I call Jeeves into conference on one of these little problems, he's all sympathy and bright ideas; but not to-day.

'I fear, sir,' he said, when I had finished, 'it is hardly my place to intervene in a private matter affecting—'

'Oh, come!'

'No, sir. It would be taking a liberty.'

'Jeeves,' I said, tackling the blighter squarely, 'what have you got against old Biffy?'

'I, sir?'

'Yes, you.'

'I assure you, sir!'

'Oh, well, if you don't want to chip in and save a fellow-creature, I suppose I can't make you. But let me tell you this. I am now going back to the sitting-room, and I am going to put in some very tense thinking. You'll look pretty silly when I come and tell you that I've got Mr Biffen out of the soup without your assistance. Extremely silly you'll look.'

'Yes, sir. Shall I bring you a whisky-and-soda, sir?'

'No. Coffee! Strong and black. And if anybody wants to see me, tell 'em that I'm busy and can't be disturbed.'

An hour later I rang the bell.

'Jeeves,' I said with hauteur.

'Yes, sir?'

'Kindly ring Mr Biffen up on the phone and say that Mr Wooster presents his compliments and that he has got it.'

I was feeling more than a little pleased with myself next morning as I strolled round to Biffy's. As a rule the bright ideas you get overnight have a trick of not seeming quite so frightfully fruity when you examine them by the light of day; but this one looked as good at breakfast as it had done before dinner. I examined it narrowly from every angle, and I didn't see how it could fail.

A few days before, my Aunt Emily's son Harold had celebrated his sixth birthday; and, being up against the necessity of weighing in with a present of some kind, I had happened to see in a shop in the Strand a rather sprightly little gadget, well calculated in my opinion to amuse the child and endear him to one and all. It was a bunch of flowers in a sort of holder ending in an ingenious bulb attachment which, when pressed, shot about a pint and a half of pure spring water into the face of anyone who was ass enough to sniff at it. It seemed to me just the thing to please the growing mind of a kid of six, and I had rolled round with it.

But when I got to the house I found Harold sitting in the midst of a mass of gifts so luxurious and costly that I simply hadn't the crust to contribute a thing that had set me back a mere elevenpence-ha'penny; so with rare presence of mind – for we Woosters can think quick on occasion – I wrenched my Uncle James's card off a toy aeroplane, substituted my own, and trousered the squirt, which I took away with me. It had been lying around in my flat ever since, and it seemed to me that the time had come to send it into action.

'Well?' said Biffy anxiously, as I curveted into his sitting-room.

The poor old bird was looking pretty green about the gills. I recognized the symptoms. I had felt much the same myself when waiting for Sir Roderick to turn up and lunch with me. How the deuce people who have anything wrong with their nerves can bring themselves to chat with that man, I can't imagine; and yet he has the largest practice in London. Scarcely a day passes without his having to sit on somebody's head and ring for the attendant to bring the strait-waistcoat: and his outlook on life has become so jaundiced through constant association with coves who are picking straws out of their hair that I was convinced that Biffy had merely got to press the bulb and nature would do the rest.

So I patted him on the shoulder and said: 'It's all right, old man!'

'What does Jeeves suggest?' asked Biffy eagerly.

'Jeeves doesn't suggest anything.'

'But you said it was all right.'

'Jeeves isn't the only thinker in the Wooster home, my lad. I have taken over your little problem, and I can tell you at once that I have the situation well in hand.'

'You?' said Biffy.

His tone was far from flattering. It suggested a lack of faith in my abilities, and my view was that an ounce of demonstration would be worth a ton of explanation. I shoved the bouquet at him.

'Are you fond of flowers, Biffy?' I said.

'Eh?'

'Smell these.'

Biffy extended the old beak in a careworn sort of way, and I pressed the bulb as per printed instructions on the label.

I do like getting my money's-worth. Elevenpence-ha'penny the thing had cost me, and it would have been cheap at double. The advertisement on the outside of the box had said that its effects were 'indescribably ludicrous,' and I can testify that it was no over-statement. Poor old Biffy leaped three feet in the air and smashed a small table.

'There!' I said.

The old egg was a trifle incoherent at first, but he found words fairly soon and began to express himself with a good deal of warmth.

'Calm yourself, laddie,' I said, as he paused for breath. 'It was no mere jest to pass an idle hour. It was a demonstration. Take this, Biffy, with an old friend's blessing, refill the bulb, shove it into Sir Roderick's face, press firmly, and leave the rest to him. I'll guarantee that in something under three seconds the idea will have dawned on him that you are not required in his family.'

Biffy stared at me.

'Are you suggesting that I squirt Sir Roderick?'

'Absolutely. Squirt him good. Squirt as you have never squirted before.'

'But—'

He was still yammering at me in a feverish sort of way when there was a ring at the front-door bell.

'Good Lord!' cried Biffy, quivering like a jelly. 'There he is. Talk to him while I go and change my shirt.'

I had just time to refill the bulb and shove it beside Biffy's plate, when the door opened and Sir Roderick came in. I was picking up the fallen table at the moment, and he started talking brightly to my back.

'Good afternoon. I trust I am not—Mr Wooster!'

I'm bound to say I was not feeling entirely at my ease. There is something about that man that is calculated to strike terror into the stoutest heart. If ever there was a bloke at the very mention of whose name it would be excusable for people to tremble like aspens, that bloke is Sir Roderick Glossop. He has an enormous bald head, all the hair which ought to be on it seeming to have run into his eyebrows, and his eyes go through you like a couple of Death Rays.

'How are you, how are you, how are you?' I said, overcoming a slight desire to leap backwards out of the window. 'Long time since we met, what?'

'Nevertheless, I remember you most distinctly, Mr Wooster.'

'That's fine,' I said. 'Old Biffy asked me to come and join you in mangling a bit of lunch.'

He waggled the eyebrows at me.

'Are you a friend of Charles Biffen?'

'Oh, rather. Been friends for years and years.'

He drew in his breath sharply, and I could see that Biffy's stock had dropped several points. His eye fell on the floor, which was strewn with things that had tumbled off the upset table.

'Have you had an accident?' he said.

'Nothing serious,' I explained. 'Old Biffy had some sort of fit or seizure just now and knocked over the table.'

'A fit!'

'Or seizure.'

'Is he subject to fits?'

I was about to answer, when Biffy hurried in. He had forgotten to brush his hair, which gave him a wild look, and I saw the old boy direct a keen glance at him. It seemed to me that what you might call the preliminary spade-work had been satisfactorily attended to and that the success of good old bulb could be in no doubt whatever.

Biffy's man came in with the nose-bags and we sat down to lunch.

It looked at first as though the meal was going to be one of those complete frosts which occur from time to time in the career of a constant luncher-out. Biffy, a very C-3 host, contributed nothing to the feast of reason and flow of soul beyond an occasional hiccup, and every time I started to pull a nifty, Sir Roderick swung round on me with such a piercing stare that it stopped me in my tracks. Fortunately, however the second course consisted of a chicken fricassee of such outstanding excellence that the old boy, after wolfing a plateful, handed up his dinner-pail for a second instalment and became almost genial.

'I am here this afternoon, Charles,' he said, with what practically amounted to bonhomie, 'on what I might describe as a mission. Yes, a mission. This is most excellent chicken.'

'Glad you like it,' mumbled old Biffy.

'Singularly toothsome,' said Sir Roderick, pronging another half ounce. 'Yes, as I was saying, a mission. You young fellows nowadays are, I know, content to live in the centre of the most wonderful metropolis the world has seen, blind and indifferent to its many marvels. I should be prepared – were I a betting man, which I am not – to wager a considerable sum that you have never in your life visited even so historic a spot as Westminster Abbey. Am I right?'

Biffy gurgled something about always having meant to.

'Nor the Tower of London?'

No, nor the Tower of London.

'And there exists at this very moment, not twenty minutes by cab from Hyde Park Corner, the most supremely absorbing and educational collection of objects, both animate and inanimate, gathered from the four corners of the Empire, that has ever been assembled in England's history. I allude to the British Empire Exhibition now situated at Wembley.'

'A fellow told me one about Wembley yesterday,' I said, to help on the cheery flow of conversation. 'Stop me if you've heard it before. Chap goes up to deaf chap outside the exhibition and says, "Is this Wembley?" "Hey?" says deaf chap. "Is this Wembley?" says chap. "Hey?" says deaf chap. "Is this Wembley?" says chap. "No, Thursday," says deaf chap. Ha, ha, I mean, what?'

The merry laughter froze on my lips. Sir Roderick sort of just waggled an eyebrow in my direction and I saw that it was back to the basket for Bertram. I never met a man who had such a knack of making a fellow feel like a waste-product.

'Have you yet paid a visit to Wembley, Charles?' he asked. 'No? Precisely as I suspected. Well, that is the mission on which I am here this afternoon. Honoria wishes me to take you to Wembley. She says it will broaden your mind, in which view I am at one with her. We will start immediately after luncheon.'

Biffy cast an imploring look at me.

'You'll come too, Bertie?'

There was such agony in his eyes that I only hesitated for a second. A pal is a pal. Besides, I felt that, if only the bulb fulfilled the high expectations I had formed of it, the merry expedition would be cancelled in no uncertain manner.

'Oh, rather,' I said.

'We must not trespass on Mr Wooster's good nature,' said Sir Roderick, looking pretty puff-faced.

'Oh, that's all right,' I said. 'I've been meaning to go to the good old exhibish for a long time. I'll slip home and change my clothes and pick you up here in my car.'

There was silence. Biffy seemed too relieved at the thought of not having to spend the afternoon alone with Sir Roderick to be capable of speech, and Sir Roderick was registering silent disapproval. And then he caught sight of the bouquet by Biffy's plate.

'Ah, flowers,' he said. 'Sweet peas, if I am not in error. A charming plant, pleasing alike to the eye and the nose.'

I caught Biffy's eye across the table. It was bulging, and a strange light shone in it.

'Are you fond of flowers, Sir Roderick?' he croaked.

'Extremely.'

'Smell these.'

Sir Roderick dipped his head and sniffed. Biffy's fingers closed slowly over the bulb. I shut my eyes and clutched the table.

'Very pleasant,' I heard Sir Roderick say. 'Very pleasant indeed.'

I opened my eyes, and there was Biffy leaning back in his chair with a ghastly look, and the bouquet on the cloth beside him. I realized what had happened. In that supreme crisis of his life, with his whole happiness depending on a mere pressure of the fingers, Biffy, the poor spineless fish, had lost his nerve. My closely-reasoned scheme had gone phut.

Jeeves was fooling about with the geraniums in the sitting-room window-box when I got home.

'They make a very nice display, sir,' he said, cocking a paternal eye at the things.

'Don't talk to me about flowers,' I said. 'Jeeves, I know now how a general feels when he plans out some great scientific movement and his troops let him down at the eleventh hour.'

'Indeed, sir?'

'Yes,' I said, and told him what had happened.

He listened thoughtfully.

'A somewhat vacillating and changeable young gentleman, Mr Biffen,' was his comment when I had finished. '—Would you be requiring me for the remainder of the afternoon, sir?'

'No. I'm going to Wembley. I just came back to change and get the car.

Produce some fairly durable garments which can stand getting squashed by the many-headed, Jeeves, and then phone to the garage.'

'Very good, sir. The grey cheviot lounge will, I fancy, be suitable. Would it be too much if I asked you to give me a seat in the car, sir? I had thought of going to Wembley myself this afternoon.'

'Eh? Oh, all right.'

'Thank you very much, sir.'

I got dressed, and we drove round to Biffy's flat. Biffy and Sir Roderick got in at the back and Jeeves climbed into the front seat next to me. Biffy looked so ill-attuned to an afternoon's pleasure that my heart bled for the blighter and I made one last attempt to appeal to Jeeves's better feelings.

'I must say, Jeeves,' I said, 'I am dashed disappointed in you.'

'I am sorry to hear that, sir.'

'Well, I am. Dashed disappointed. I do think you might rally round. Did you see Mr Biffen's face?'

'Yes, sir.'

'Well, then.'

'If you will pardon my saying so, sir, Mr Biffen has surely only himself to thank if he has entered upon matrimonial obligations which do not please him.'

'You're talking absolute rot, Jeeves. You know as well as I do that Honoria Glossop is an Act of God. You might just as well blame a fellow for getting run over by a truck.'

'Yes, sir.'

'Absolutely yes. Besides, the poor ass wasn't in a condition to resist. He told me all about it. He had lost the only girl he had ever loved, and you know what a man's like when that happens to him.'

'How was that, sir?'

'Apparently he fell in love with some girl on the boat going over to New York, and they parted at the Customs sheds, arranging to meet next day at her hotel. Well, you know what Biffy's like. He forgets his own name half the time. He never made a note of the address, and it passed clean out of his mind. He went about in a sort of trance, and suddenly woke up to find that he was engaged to Honoria Glossop.'

'I did not know of this, sir.'

'I don't suppose anybody knows of it except me. He told me when I was in Paris.'

'I should have supposed it would have been feasible to make inquiries, sir.'

'That's what I said. But he had forgotten her name.'

'That sounds remarkable, sir.'

'I said that, too. But it's a fact. All he remembered was that her Christian name was Mabel. Well, you can't go scouring New York for a girl named Mabel, what?'

'I appreciate the difficulty, sir.'

'Well, there it is, then.'

'I see, sir.'

We had got into a mob of vehicles outside the Exhibition by this time, and, some tricky driving being indicated, I had to suspend the conversation. We parked ourselves eventually and went in. Jeeves drifted away, and Sir Roderick took charge of the expedition. He headed for the Palace of Industry, with Biffy and myself trailing behind.

Well, you know, I have never been much of a lad for exhibitions. The citizenry in the mass always rather puts me off, and after I have been shuffling along with the multitude for a quarter of an hour or so I feel as if I were walking on hot bricks. About this particular binge, too, there seemed to me a lack of what you might call human interest. I mean to say, millions of people, no doubt, are so constituted that they scream with joy and excitement at the spectacle of a stuffed porcupine-fish or a glass jar of seeds from Western Australia – but not Bertram. No; if you will take the word of one who would not deceive you, not Bertram. By the time we had tottered out of the Gold Coast village and were working towards the Palace of Machinery, everything pointed to my shortly executing a quiet sneak in the direction of that rather jolly Planter's Bar in the West Indian section. Sir Roderick had whizzed us past this at a high rate of speed, it touching no chord in him; but I had been able to observe that there was a sprightly sportsman behind the counter mixing things out of bottles and stirring them up with a stick in long glasses that seemed to have ice in them, and the urge came upon me to see more of this man. I was about to drop away from the main body and become a straggler, when something pawed at my coat-sleeve. It was Biffy, and he had the air of one who has had about sufficient.

There are certain moments in life when words are not needed. I looked at Biffy, Biffy looked at me. A perfect understanding linked our two souls.

'?'

'!'

Three minutes later we had joined the Planters.

I have never been in the West Indies, but I am in a position to state that in certain of the fundamentals of life they are streets ahead of our European civilization. The man behind the counter, as kindly a bloke as I ever wish to meet, seemed to guess our requirements the moment we hove in view. Scarcely had our elbows touched the wood before he was leaping to and fro, bringing down a new bottle with each leap. A planter, apparently, does not consider he has had a drink unless it contains at least seven ingredients, and I'm not saying, mind you, that he isn't right. The man behind the bar told us the things were called Green Swizzles; and, if ever I marry and have a son, Green Swizzle Wooster is the name that will go down on the register, in memory of the day his father's life was saved at Wembley.

After the third, Biffy breathed a contented sigh.

'Where do you think Sir Roderick is?' he said.

'Biffy, old thing,' I replied frankly, 'I'm not worrying.'

'Bertie, old bird,' said Biffy, 'nor am I.'

He sighed again, and broke a long silence by asking the man for a straw.

'Bertie,' he said, 'I've just remembered something rather rummy. You know Jeeves?'

I said I knew Jeeves.

'Well, a rather rummy incident occurred as we were going into this place. Old Jeeves sidled up to me and said something rather rummy. You'll never guess what it was.'

'No. I don't believe I ever shall.'

'Jeeves said,' proceeded Biffy earnestly, 'and I am quoting his very words – Jeeves said, "Mr Biffen" – addressing me, you understand –'

'I understand.'

'"Mr Biffen," he said, "I strongly advise you to visit the—"'

'The what?' I asked as he paused.

'Bertie, old man,' said Biffy, deeply concerned, 'I've absolutely forgotten!'

I stared at the man.

'What I can't understand,' I said, 'is how you manage to run that Herefordshire place of yours for a day. How on earth do you remember to milk the cows and give the pigs their dinner?'

'Oh, that's all right. There are divers blokes about the places – hirelings and menials, you know – who look after all that.'

'Ah!' I said. 'Well, that being so, let us have one more Green Swizzle, and then hey for the Amusement Park.'

When I indulged in those few rather bitter words about exhibitions, it must be distinctly understood that I was not alluding to what you might call the more earthy portion of these curious places. I yield to no man in my approval of those institutions where on payment of a shilling you are permitted to slide down a slippery run-way sitting on a mat. I love the Jiggle-Joggle, and I am prepared to take on all and sundry at Skee Ball for money, stamps, or Brazil nuts.

But, joyous reveller as I am on these occasions, I was simply not in it with old Biffy. Whether it was the Green Swizzles or merely the relief of being parted from Sir Roderick, I don't know, but Biffy flung himself into the pastimes of the proletariat with a zest that was almost frightening. I could hardly drag him away from the Whip, and as for the Switchback, he looked like spending the rest of his life on it. I managed to remove him at last, and he was wandering through the crowd at my side with gleaming eyes, hesitating between having his fortune told and taking a whirl at the Wheel of Joy, when he suddenly grabbed my arm and uttered a sharp animal cry.

'Bertie!'

'Now what?'

He was pointing at a large sign over a building.

'Look! Palace of Beauty!'

I tried to choke him off. I was getting a bit weary by this time. Not so young as I was.

'You don't want to go in there,' I said. 'A fellow at the club was telling me about that. It's only a lot of girls. You don't want to see a lot of girls.'

'I do want to see a lot of girls,' said Biffy firmly. 'Dozens of girls, and the more unlike Honoria they are, the better. Besides, I've suddenly remembered that that's the place Jeeves told me to be sure and visit. It all comes back to me. "Mr Biffen," he said, "I strongly advise you to visit the Palace of Beauty." Now, what the man was driving at or what his motive was, I don't know; but I ask you, Bertie, is it wise, is it safe, is it judicious ever to ignore Jeeves's lightest word? We enter by the door on the left.'

I don't know if you know this Palace of Beauty place? It's a sort of aquarium full of the delicately-nurtured instead of fishes. You go in, and there is a kind of cage with a female goggling out at you through a sheet of plate glass. She's dressed in some weird kind of costume, and over the cage is written 'Helen of Troy.' You pass on to the next, and there's another one doing jiu-jitsu with a snake. Sub-title, Cleopatra. You get the idea – Famous

Women Through the Ages and all that. I can't say it fascinated me to any great extent. I maintain that lovely woman loses a lot of her charm if you have to stare at her in a tank. Moreover, it gave me a rummy sort of feeling of having wandered into the wrong bedroom at a country house, and I was flying past at a fair rate of speed, anxious to get it over, when Biffy suddenly went off his rocker.

At least, it looked like that. He let out a piercing yell, grabbed my arm with a sudden clutch that felt like the bite of a crocodile, and stood there gibbering.

'Wuk!' ejaculated Biffy, or words to that general import.

A large and interested crowd had gathered round. I think they thought the girls were going to be fed or something. But Biffy paid no attention to them. He was pointing in a loony manner at one of the cages. I forget which it was, but the female inside wore a ruff so it may have been Elizabeth or Boadicea or someone of that period. She was rather a nice-looking girl, and she was staring at Biffy in much the same pop-eyed way as he was staring at her.

'Mabel!' yelled Biffy, going off in my ear like a bomb.

I can't say I was feeling my chirpiest. Drama is all very well, but I hate getting mixed up in it in a public spot; and I had not realized before how dashed public this spot was. The crowd seemed to have doubled itself in the last five seconds, and, while most of them had their eye on Biffy, quite a goodish few were looking at me as if they thought I was an important principal in the scene and might be expected at any moment to give of my best in the way of wholesome entertainment for the masses.

Biffy was jumping about like a lamb in the springtime – and, what is more, a feeble-minded lamb.

'Bertie! It's her! It's she!' He looked about him wildly. 'Where the deuce is the stage-door?' he cried. 'Where's the manager? I want to see the house-manager immediately.'

And then he suddenly bounded forward and began hammering on the glass with his stick.

'I say, old lad!' I began, but he shook me off.

These fellows who live in the country are apt to go in for fairly sizeable clubs instead of the light canes which your well-dressed man about town considers suitable for metropolitan use; and down in Herefordshire, apparently, something in the nature of a knob-kerrie is *de rigueur*. Biffy's first slosh smashed the glass all to a hash. Three more cleared the way for him to go into the cage without cutting himself. And, before the crowd had time to realize what a wonderful bob's-worth it was getting in exchange for its entrance-fee, he was inside, engaging the girl in earnest conversation. And at the same moment two large policemen rolled up.

You can't make policemen take the romantic view. Not a tear did these two blighters stop to brush away. They were inside the cage and out of it and marching Biffy through the crowd before you had time to blink. I hurried after them, to do what I could in the way of soothing Biffy's last moments, and the poor old lad turned a glowing face in my direction.

'Chiswick, 60873,' he bellowed in a voice charged with emotion. 'Write it down, Bertie, or I shall forget it. Chiswick, 60873. Her telephone number.'

And then he disappeared, accompanied by about eleven thousand sightseers, and a voice spoke at my elbow.

'Mr Wooster! What – what – what is the meaning of this?'

Sir Roderick, with bigger eyebrows than ever, was standing at my side.

'It's all right,' I said. 'Poor old Biffy's only gone off his crumpet.'

He tottered.

'What?'

'Had a sort of fit or seizure, you know.'

'Another!' Sir Roderick drew a deep breath. 'And this is the man I was about to allow my daughter to marry!' I heard him mutter.

I tapped him in a kindly spirit on the shoulder. It took some doing, mark you, but I did it.

'If I were you,' I said, 'I should call that off. Scratch the fixture. Wash it out absolutely, is my advice.'

He gave me a nasty look.

'I do not require your advice, Mr Wooster! I had already arrived independently at the decision of which you speak. Mr Wooster, you are a friend of this man – a fact which should in itself have been sufficient warning to me. You will – unlike myself – be seeing him again. Kindly inform him, when you do see him, that he may consider his engagement at an end.'

'Right-ho,' I said, and hurried off after the crowd. It seemed to me that a little bailing-out might be in order.

It was about an hour later that I shoved my way to where I had parked the car. Jeeves was sitting in the front seat, brooding over the cosmos. He rose courteously as I approached.

'You are leaving, sir?'

'I am.'

'And Sir Roderick, sir?'

'Not coming. I am revealing no secrets, Jeeves, when I inform you that he and I have parted brass-rags. Not on speaking terms now.'

'Indeed, sir? And Mr Biffen? Will you wait for him?'

'No. He's in prison.'

'Really, sir?'

'Yes. I tried to bail him out, but they decided on second thoughts to coop him up for the night.'

'What was his offence, sir?'

'You remember that girl of his I was telling you about? He found her in a tank at the Palace of Beauty and went after her by the quickest route, which was *via* a plate-glass window. He was then scooped up and borne off in irons by the constabulary.' I gazed sideways at him. It is difficult to bring off a penetrating glance out of the corner of your eye, but I managed it. 'Jeeves,' I said, 'there is more in this than the casual observer would suppose. You told Mr Biffen to go to the Palace of Beauty. Did you know the girl would be there?'

'Yes, sir.'

This was more remarkable and rummy to a degree.

'Dash it, do you know everything?'

'Oh, no, sir,' said Jeeves with an indulgent smile. Humouring the young master.

'Well, how did you know that?'

'I happen to be acquainted with the future Mrs Biffen, sir.'

'I see. Then you knew all about that business in New York?'

'Yes, sir. And it was for that reason that I was not altogether favourably disposed towards Mr Biffen when you were first kind enough to suggest that I might be able to offer some slight assistance. I mistakenly supposed that he had been trifling with the girl's affections, sir. But when you told me the true facts of the case I appreciated the injustice I had done to Mr Biffen and endeavoured to make amends.'

'Well, he certainly owes you a lot. He's crazy about her.'

'That is very gratifying, sir.'

'And she ought to be pretty grateful to you, too. Old Biffy's got fifteen thousand a year, not to mention more cows, pigs, hens and ducks than he knows what to do with. A dashed useful bird to have in any family.'

'Yes, sir.'

'Tell me, Jeeves,' I said, 'how did you happen to know the girl in the first place?'

Jeeves looked dreamily out into the traffic.

'She is my niece, sir. If I might make the suggestion, sir, I should not jerk the steering-wheel with quite such suddenness. We very nearly collided with that omnibus.'

The Darling Buds of May

H. E. Bates

Pop Larkin, his wife and six children are confronted by Mr
Charlton from the office of the Inspector of Taxes. Mr
Charlton has called about an income tax form which Mr
Larkin has failed to submit – but finds himself somewhat
distracted...

When Mariette and Mr Charlton came down from the bluebell wood an hour
later, Mariette carrying a bunch of bluebells and pink campion, Mr Charlton
bearing in his palm, with the tenderest care, two blue thrushes' eggs a bird
had dropped in the grass at the woodside, Pop was washing pig-buckets
under the tap in the yard.

'Pigs look well,' Pop said. 'I think we'll kill one. Hear the nightingales?'

Mr Charlton had not a second in which to answer this question before Pop
said:

'Wondering where you two had got to, Mister Charlton. Tea's ready. Just
in time.'

A searching odour of frying kippers cut almost savagely through the warm
May air.

'I thought we just had tea,' Mr Charlton said.

'That was dinner.'

'I ought to catch my bus,' Mr Charlton said. 'I must. The last one goes at
eight o'clock.'

'Ma won't hear of that,' Pop said. 'Will she, Mariette? Daresay Mariette
won't either. Like to wash your hands? What you got there?'

Mr Charlton revealed the thrushes' eggs, brilliant blue in his office-pale
hands, and Mariette gave him a small dark smile of fascination that held him
once more transfixed and speechless.

'Always run you home in the truck,' Pop said. 'Next time you come out you must bring your car. What kind of car you got, Mister Charlton?'

Mr Charlton confessed that he had no car. Pop was stunned.

'No car, no car?' he said. 'That'll never do. Can't have that. Hear that, Mariette? Mister Charlton ain't got no car.'

'I don't think I'll have the time to come out again,' Mr Charlton said. 'Do you think we could go into the question of the tax form before I go? It's very important.'

'Tea first,' Pop said. 'Must have a cuppa tea first. Don't want to make Ma mad, do you?'

Pop finished drying his hands and gave Mr Charlton the towel. Mr Charlton put the two thrushes' eggs into his pocket and ran tap water over his hands, washing them with a gritty cake of purple soap. Mariette gave him another intimate, flashing smile and then went towards the house, calling that she was going to powder her nose, and Mr Charlton, completely captivated by the delicate vision of green shantung retreating in the golden evening sunshine, forgot the thrushes' eggs and said:

'I don't know if you appreciate how severe the penalties are for not making a tax return, Mr Larkin.'

'Ma's calling,' Pop said.

Mr Charlton listened but couldn't hear a sound.

'I shall have to make some sort of report to my office,' Mr Charlton said. 'Then if you don't cooperate it'll be taken out of my hands and after that—'

'Beautiful evening, ain't it?' Pop said. Once again, caught in his own web of enchantment, he turned to stare at an evening distilled now into even deeper gold by the lower angle of light falling across still seas of buttercups and long-curled milky waves of may.

'I strongly recommend you—'

'Pair o' goldfinches,' Pop said, but Mr Charlton was too slow to see the birds, which darted past him like dipping sparks of scarlet, black, and gold.

In the kitchen Ma was frying a third batch of four fat tawny kippers in a brand new aluminium pan while Mariette powdered her face over the sink, looking into a heart-shaped mirror stuck about with little silver, pink, and violet seashells.

'How'd you get on with Mr Charlton, duckie?'

'Slow,' Mariette said. 'He's very shy.'

'Well, he mustn't be shy,' Ma said. 'That won't get you nowhere.'

'He would talk about horses.'

'You'll have to find something a bit better than that to talk about, won't you?' Ma said. 'Bit more stimulating.'

Mariette, who was busy making up her lips with a tender shade of pink, not at all unlike the pink of the rose campion, that went well with her dress of cool lime shantung, did not answer.

'I think he looks half-starved,' Ma said. 'No blood in him. Wants feeding up. I'll find him a good fat kipper.'

Mariette was wetting small wisps of short hair with her finger-tips and winding them about her ears like black watch-springs.

'Put some of my Goya on,' Ma said. 'The gardenia. Or else the Chanel. They both stand by my jewel-box in our bedroom.'

While Mariette went upstairs to dab perfume behind her ears and in soft hollows of her legs, Mr Charlton and Pop came in from the yard to join Montgomery, Primrose, Victoria and the twins, who sat at the table licking thick bars of choc-ice and watching a television programme in which three men, a clergyman, and a woman were discussing prostitution and what should be done about it all.

'Strawberry-picking on Monday over at Benacre, Pop,' Montgomery said. 'I heard from Fred Brown.'

'That's early,' Pop said. 'Earliest we've ever been. I said this wevver'd soon put the paint on 'em.'

Ma came in bearing a big dish of stinging hot kippers running with fat dabs of butter and on the television screen the woman shook a condemnatory finger at the gaping children and said: 'The women are, on the whole, less to be blamed than pitied. It is largely the fault of man.'

'Ma,' Pop said. 'Strawberry-picking Monday. Better get that deep-freeze, hadn't we?'

'Sooner the better,' Ma said. 'Better go in first thing tomorrow. It's Saturday.' She began to serve kippers. 'Start pouring tea, Primrose. Kipper, Mister Charlton? Here we come. Nice fat one. Help yourself to more butter if you want to.'

While Ma served kippers and Primrose poured tea Pop rose from the table and fetched a bottle of whisky from the cocktail cabinet.

'Milk?' he said to Ma.

'Please,' Ma said. 'Just what I need.'

Pop poured whisky into Ma's tea, then into his own, and then turned to Mr Charlton, the bottle upraised.

'Drop o' milk, Mister Charlton?'

'No, no, no. No really. Not for me. No really not for me.'

'Relieves the wind, frees the kidneys, and opens the bowels,' Pop said blandly.

'No, no. No really. Not at this time of day.'

'Do you all the good in the world, Mister Charlton.'

Pop, after filling up Mr Charlton's tea-cup with whisky, stood for a moment staring at the television screen and said:

'What the ruddy 'ell are they talking about? Kids, how much money you make on the stall?'

'Eighteenpence. There was a policeman on a motor-bike come along.'

'Pity he hadn't got summat else to do,' Pop said.

With elbows on the table Victoria, who was trying to eat kipper with a spoon, said in a shrill quick voice:

'I don't like kippers. They're made of combs.'

'Now, now,' Pop said. 'Now, now. Manners, manners. Elbows!'

'Pop has 'em at a word,' Ma said.

Mr Charlton sat held in a new constriction of bewilderment made more complex by the arrival of Mariette, fresh and lovely with new pink lipstick, face powder, and a heavy fragrance of gardenias that overwhelmed him in a cloud of intoxication as she came and sat at his side.

As if this were not enough she had brought with her the bluebells and the rose campion, arranged in an orange and crimson jar. She set the jar in the centre of the table, where the flowers glowed in the nightmare marine glow of the television light like a strange sheaf of sea-weed. The bluebells too smelt exquisitely.

'Sorry I'm late,' she whispered to Mr Charlton and he could have sworn, in another moment of shimmering agony, that her silky legs had brushed his own. 'Just had to make myself presentable.'

'By the way, Mister Charlton,' Pop said, 'what's your other name? Don't like this mistering.'

'Cedric.'

Ma started choking.

'Kipper bone!' Pop said. 'Happened once before.'

He rose from the table and struck Ma a severe blow in the middle of the back. She boomed like a drum.

'Better?' Pop said and hit her a second time, rather more robustly than the first.

Except for bouncing slightly Ma did not seem to mind at all.

'Worst of kippers,' Pop said. 'Too much wire-work. Fetched it up?'

On the television screen a man in close-up stared with steadfast earnestness at Mr Charlton and the eight Larkins and said: 'Well, there it is. We leave it with you. What do you think? What is to be done about these women? Is it their fault? Is it the fault of men? If not, whose fault is it?' and once again, for the third time, Ma started laughing like a jelly.

'Play crib at all, Mister Charlton?' Pop said.

Mr Charlton had to confess he had never heard of crib.

'Card game,' Pop said. 'We all play here. Learns you figures. Mariette plays. Mariette could show you how.'

Mr Charlton turned to look shyly at Mariette and found his vision, already blurred by the curious light from the television screen, clouded into more numbing and exquisite confusion by the thick sweet fragrance of gardenia. In return she gazed at him with dark silent eyes, so that he could not help trembling and was even glad when Pop said:

'Like billiards? Or snooker? Got a nice table out the back there. Full size. We could have a game o' snooker after tea.'

'You know,' Mr Charlton said, 'I'm really awfully sorry, but I must catch this eight o'clock bus.'

'No eight o'clock bus now,' Montgomery said. 'They knocked it off soon after petrol rationing started.'

'That's right,' Ma said. 'They never put it back again.'

Mr Charlton half-rose from the table, agitated.

'In that case I must start walking. It's eight miles.'

'Walking my foot,' Pop said. 'I said I'll run you home in the truck. Or else Mariette can take you in the stationwagon. Mariette can drive. Mariette'll take you, won't you, Mariette?'

'Of course.'

Mr Charlton sat down, mesmerized.

'Why don't you stay the night?' Pop said. 'That's all right, ain't it, Ma?'

'More the merrier.'

'Perfick,' Pop said. 'Ma'll make you a bed up on the billiard table.'

'No, really—'

'It's so simple,' Mariette said. 'After all tomorrow's Saturday. You don't have to go to the office Saturday, do you?'

'Course he don't,' Pop said. 'Offices don't work Saturdays. They don't none of 'em know what work is no more.'

'That's settled then,' Ma said. 'I'll put him on that new super-foam mattress Mariette has for sun-bathing.'

'Oh! that mattress is marvellous,' Mariette said. 'You sink in. Your body simply dreams into that mattress.'

In another unnerving moment Mr Charlton saw the girl, hands raised to her bare shoulders, luxuriously enact for him the attitudes of dreaming into the mattress. As her eyes closed and her lips parted gently he struggled to bring himself back to reality, firmness, and a state of resistance and he said:

'No, I'm sorry. I really must be adamant—'

Pop stared with open mouth, powerfully stunned and impressed by this word. He could not ever remember having heard it even on television.

'Quite understand,' he said.

In a single moment Mr Charlton was raised greatly in his estimation. He looked at him with awe.

'Oh! won't you stay?' Mariette said. 'We could ride tomorrow.'

Groping again, struggling against the dark eyes and the fragrance of gardenia, powerful even above the penetrating sting of kippers, Mr Charlton began to say:

'No, really. For one thing I've nothing with me. I've no pyjamas.'

'Gawd Almighty,' Pop said. 'Pyjamas?'

His admiration and awe for Mr Charlton now increased still further. He was held transfixed by the fact that here was a man who spoke in words of inaccessible meaning and wore pyjamas to sleep in.

'Sleep in your shirt, old man,' he said. 'Like I do.'

Pop had always slept in his shirt; he found it more convenient that way. Ma, on the other hand, slept in nylon nightgowns, one of them an unusual pale petunia-pink that Pop liked more than all the rest because it was light, delicate, and above all completely transparent. It was wonderful for seeing through. Under it Ma's body appeared like a global map, an expanse of huge explorable mountains, shadowy valleys, and rosy pinnacles.

'I wear pyjamas,' Mariette said. 'I'll lend you a pair of mine.'

'No, really—'

Mr Charlton became utterly speechless as Ma got up, went into the kitchen and brought back four tins of whole peaches, which she began to open with an elaborate tin-opener on the sideboard.

'Save some of the juice, Ma,' Pop said. 'I'll have it later with a drop o' gin.'

'I think you're about my size,' Mariette said, as if everything were now completely settled, so that Mr Charlton found himself in the centre of a shattering vortex, trapped there by the torturing and incredible thought that presently he would be sleeping in Mariette's own pyjamas, on her own dreaming bed of foam.

Before he could make any further protest about this Primrose poured him a second cup of tea and Pop, leaning across the table, filled it up with whisky.

'You ought to come strawberry-picking,' Pop said. Mr Charlton suddenly remembered the tax form. It mustn't be forgotten, he thought, the tax form. On no account must it be forgotten. 'This is very like the last summer we'll ever go strawberry-picking, Mister Charlton. We, you, anybody. You know why?'

Tax form, tax form, tax form, Mr Charlton kept thinking. Tax form. 'No. Why?'

On the television screen a voice announced: 'We now take you to Fanshawe Castle, the home of the Duke of Peele,' and Ma, ladling out the last of the peaches, crowned by thick ovals of cream, said:

'Turn up the contrast. I want to see this. It's got dark again.'

'Because,' Pop said, 'the strawberry lark's nearly over.'

Tax form, tax form, tax form, Mr Charlton thought again. How was it the strawberry lark was nearly over? Tax form.

'Disease,' Pop said. 'Sovereigns are finished. Climax is finished. Huxleys are finished. Soon there won't be no strawberries nowhere.'

Tax form. 'You mean that in this great strawberry-growing district–'

'This districk. Every districk. In two years the strawberry lark'll be over.'

'Well, myself, I actually prefer raspberries–'

'The raspberry lark's nearly over as well,' Pop said. 'Mosaic. Weakening strain. And the plum lark. And the cherry lark. And the apple lark. They can't sell apples for love nor–'

'We're in the library,' Ma said. 'Pop, look at the library.'

Tax form – Mr Charlton, with piteous desperation, struggled with the power of all his declining concentration to see that the tax form was remembered. 'I've got to go home,' he thought. 'I've got to start walking.' Something brushed his leg. 'I must remember the tax form.' He was startled into a sudden shivering catch of his breath and a moment later the white kitten was on his knee.

'Gawd Almighty,' Pop said. 'What are all them on the walls?'

'Must be books,' Ma said.

In mute staring concentration Pop sat involved by the picture on the television screen, noisily eating peaches and taking an occasional quick-sucked gulp of whisky and tea.

'Never,' he said. 'Can't be.'

'Beautiful home,' Ma said. 'I like the pelmets. That's what we want. Pelmets like that.'

Tax form! Mr Charlton's mind shouted. Tax form–!

'Books?' Pop said. '*All* books?'

'I'll go and find the pyjamas and get them aired,' Mariette said. Mr Charlton emerged from a moment of acute hypnosis to feel her hand reach out, touch him softly, and then begin to draw him away. 'Coming? We could try them against you for size.'

'The man who owns that owes five million tax,' Mr Charlton said desperately and for no reason at all. 'Mr Larkin, that reminds me – we mustn't forget that form–'

'Perfick place,' Pop said. 'On the big side though. Suppose they need it for the books.'

'Oh! the carpets. Look at the carpets,' Ma said. 'There must be miles of carpets. Acres.'

'He'll have to give it all up,' Mr Charlton said. 'The State will take it for taxes. You see what can happen–'

'Come on,' Mariette said and Mr Charlton, struggling for the last time against the flickering, rising tides of sea-green light rolling across the table in mesmeric, engulfing flow, followed the girl blunderingly into the kitchen, the white kitten softly brushing his legs as he went, the thick night-sweet scent of gardenia penetrating to his blood, seeming to turn it as white as the flower from which it sprang.

At half past ten, just before television closed down for the night, Pop, Ma, and Mariette were still trying to teach Mr Charlton the mysteries and arithmetic of crib. Utterly baffled – the only coherent thing he had been able to do all evening was to telephone his landlady to say that he wouldn't be coming home that night – Mr Charlton found it quite impossible to understand the elements of the game, still less its language and figures.

'Fifteen-two, fifteen-four, fifteen-six, pair's eight, three's eleven, three's fourteen, and one for his nob's fifteen.'

Pop dealt the cards very fluidly; he counted like a machine.

'I don't understand one for his nob.'

'Jack,' Pop said. 'I told you – one for his nob. Two for his heels. Your deal, Ma.'

Ma dealt very fluidly too.

'Got to use your loaf at this game, Mister Charlton,' Pop said. 'I thought you was office man? I thought you was good at figures?'

'Rather different sort of figures,' Mr Charlton said.

'Oh?' Pop said. 'Really? They look all the same to me.'

Pop picked up the cards Ma had dealt him, took a quick look at them, and said smartly:

'Mis-deal. Seven cards. Bung in.'

'Pick 'em up!' Ma said and threatened him with a hand as large as a leg of lamb. 'Don't you dare.'

'Wanted a Parson's Poke,' Pop said.

'No more Parson's Pokes,' Ma said. 'Get on with it. Make the best with what you've got.' Ma kicked Mr Charlton playfully on the shins under the table, laughing. 'Got to watch him, Mister Charlton, playing crib. Parson's Poke, my foot. Sharp as a packet o' pins.'

'Twenty-two, nine'll do. Twenty-five, six's is alive. Twenty-eight, Billy Wake. Twenty-seven, four's in heaven. Twenty-three, eight's a spree.'

In the combined turmoil of counting and the glare of the television Mr Charlton felt a certain madness coming back.

'What you got, Pop?'

'Terrible. What Paddy shot at.'

'See what I mean?' Ma said. She kicked Mr Charlton a second time on the shins, just as playfully as the first. 'Mis-deal my foot! No wonder he says you got to use your loaf at this game. Your deal next, Mr Charlton. Your box.'

Mr Charlton, as he picked up the cards, was beginning to feel that he had no loaf to use. He felt awful; his loaf was like a sponge.

'Let's have a Parson's Poke!' Pop said.

'No more Parson's Pokes,' Ma said. 'Too many Parson's Pokes are bad luck.'

'Your box, Mr Charlton. Give yourself a treat.'

'Let him play his own game!' Ma said. 'Play your own hand, Mr Charlton. Use your own loaf. What's on telly now?'

'Something about free speech,' Mariette said. 'Freedom of the press or something.'

Pop turned his head, looking casually at the flickering screen. On it four heated men were, it seemed, about to start fighting.

'Wherever conditions of uniform tolerance may be said to obtain–'

'Barmy,' Ma said. 'Want their heads testing.'

'The trouble with telly,' Pop said, 'it don't go on long enough.'

'You miss it when you're talking,' Ma said. 'You feel lost, somehow. Don't you think you feel lost, Mr Charlton?'

Mr Charlton had to confess he felt lost.

'I like this set better than the other,' Ma said. 'Better contrast.'

'Thirsty, Ma?' Pop said. 'I'm thirsty.'

During the evening Pop had drunk the remainder of the peach-juice, laced with gin, two bottles of Guinness, and a light ale. Mr Charlton had drunk two glasses of beer. Ma and Mariette had been drinking cider.

'I'll mix a cocktail,' Pop said. 'Mister Charlton, what about a cocktail?'

'You don't want no more,' Ma said. 'You'll want to get out in the night.'

'I'm thirsty,' Pop said. 'I'm parched up.'

'You'll be pickled.'

Pop was already on his feet, moving towards the expensive glass and chromium cocktail cabinet that stood in one corner. 'Sit down and play your hand.'

Pop stood by the cabinet, his pride hurt and offended.

'Never been pickled in me life,' he said. 'Anyway not more than once or twice a week. And then only standin'-up pickled.'

Was there some difference between that and other forms? Mr Charlton wondered.

'Layin'-down pickled,' Pop said, 'of course.'

'I'm getting tired of crib,' Mariette said. 'It's hot in here. I'm going to cool off in the yard, Mr Charlton.' Like her father she found it difficult to call Mr Charlton by his Christian name. 'Like to come?'

'After he's had a cocktail,' Pop said. 'I'm going to mix everybody a special cocktail.'

While Mariette packed up the cards, the pegs, and the pegboard Pop stood by the cocktail cabinet consulting a book, *A Guide to Better Drinking*, given him by Montgomery for Christmas. It was the only book he had ever read.

'Here's one we never tried,' Pop said. 'Rolls-Royce.'

'That sounds nice,' Ma said.

'Half vermouth, quarter whisky, quarter gin, dash of orange bitters.'

'Dash you will too,' Ma said, 'with that lot. It'll blow our heads off.'

'Blow summat off,' Pop said. 'Not sure what though.'

Once again Ma started laughing like a jelly.

'How do you like our cocktail cabinet, Mister Charlton?' Pop said. 'Only had it at Christmas. Cost us a hundred and fifty.'

'Hundred and eighty,' Ma said. 'We had that other model in the end. The one with the extra sets of goblets. The brandy lot. You remember. And the silver bits for hot punch and all that.'

With confusion and awe Mr Charlton stared at the cocktail cabinet, over which Pop hovered, mixing the drinks, in his shirt sleeves. The cabinet, he realized for the first time, seemed shaped like an elaborate glass and silver ship.

'Am I mistaken?' he said. 'Or is it a ship?'

'Spanish galleon,' Pop said. 'Heigh-ho and a bottle o' rum and all that lark.'

When the cocktail was mixed Pop poured it into four large cut-glass tumblers embellished with scarlet cockerels. He had mixed it double, he said. It saved a lot of time like that.

'Try it first,' Ma said. 'We don't want it if it's no good, Rolls-Royce or no Rolls-Royce. Besides, you might fall down dead.'

Pop drained the shaker.

'Perfick,' he said. 'This'll grow hair.'

'By the way,' Ma said, 'talking about Rolls-Royce, did you do anything about that one?'

'Sunday,' Pop said. 'The chap's a stock-broker. Colonel Forbes. He's only down week-ends.'

'Pop's mad on a Rolls,' Ma explained to Mr Charlton.

'By the way, Mister Charlton,' Pop said, 'what was that about that feller on telly owing five million tax? Was that right?'

'Perfectly correct.'

'What for?'

'Death duties.'

'Deaf duties!' Pop said. 'Deaf duties! I feel like murder every time I hear deaf duties!'

Pop, snorting with disgust and irritation, struck the table with the palm of his hand and as if by a pre-arranged signal the light in the television went out. Ma uttered a sudden cry as if something terrible had happened. Mariette got up suddenly and switched the set off and there floated by Mr Charlton's face, as she passed, a fresh wave of gardenia, warm as the evening itself, disturbed and disturbing as she moved.

'That made my head jump,' Ma said. 'I thought a valve had gone.'

'Closing down, that's all,' Pop said. 'Eleven o'clock and they're closing down. Hardly got started.'

Pop, giving another snort of disgust about death duties and the brief and contemptible daily compass of television, handed round the cocktails.

'Cheers, everybody,' he said, raising glass. 'Here's to the strawberry lark. Roll on Monday.'

Mr Charlton drank. A wave of pure alcohol burned the roots off his tongue. He was utterly unable to speak for some moments and could only listen with undivided and searing agony to a question, first from Pop and then from Mariette, about whether he could be with them on Monday for the strawberry lark.

'I-I-I-'

A sensation as of a white-hot stiletto descending rapidly towards Mr Charlton's navel prevented the sentence from developing beyond a single choking word.

'Make yourself fifteen or twenty quid in no time,' Pop said. 'All the strawberries you can eat. And a pound free every day. You can gather a hundred and fifty pounds a day.'

'I-I-I-'

Burning tears came into Mr Charlton's eyes. He succeeded in murmuring at last, with a tongue cauterized of all feeling and in a voice that did not belong to him, something about work, office, and having no leave.

'You could always come in the evenings,' Mariette said. 'Plenty of people do.'

As she said this she again turned and looked at him. The eyes seemed more tenderly, intensely, darkly penetrative than ever and he began flushing deeply.

'It's lovely in the evenings,' Mariette said. 'Absolutely lovely.'

Another draught of alcohol, snatched by Mr Charlton in another desperate moment of speechlessness, injected fire into remote interior corners of his body that he did not know existed.

'My God, this is a perfick pick-me-up,' Pop said. 'We must all have another one of those.'

Mr Charlton despaired and passed a groping hand over his face. His mouth burned, as from eating ginger. He heard Ma agree that the cocktail was a beauty. He actually heard her say that they owed everybody in the neighbourhood a drink. 'What say we have a cocktail party and give them this one? This'll get under their skin.'

That, Mr Charlton heard himself saying, was what was happening to him, but nobody seemed to hear a voice that was already inexplicably far away, except that Ma once again began laughing, piercingly, the salmon jumper shaking like a vast balloon.

'A few more of these and you won't see me for dust,' she said.

'A few more?' Mr Charlton heard himself saying. 'A few more?'

'First re-fill coming up, Mister Charlton. How do you like it? Ma, I bet this would go well with a bloater-paste sandwich.'

Something about this remark made Mr Charlton start laughing too. This enlivening development was a signal for Pop to strike Mr Charlton a severe blow in the back, exactly as he had done Ma, and call him a rattlin' good feller. 'Feel you're one of the family. Feel we've known you years. That right, Ma?'

That was right, Ma said. That was the truth. That was how they felt about him.

'Honest trufe,' Pop said. 'Honest trufe, Mister Charlton.'

A wave of unsteady pleasure, like a flutter of ruffling wind across water on a summer afternoon, ran through Mr Charlton's veins and set them dancing. He drank again. He felt a sudden lively and uncontrollable desire to pick strawberries on warm midsummer evenings, no matter what happened. 'My God, this is great stuff,' he told everybody. 'This is the true essence–'

Nobody knew what Mr Charlton was talking about. It was impossible to grasp what he meant by the true essence, but it set Ma laughing again. Somewhere behind the laughter Mr Charlton heard Pop mixing a third, perhaps a fourth, re-fill, saying at the same time, 'Only thing it wants is more ice. More ice, Ma!'

Mr Charlton, for no predetermined reason, suddenly rose and struck himself manfully on the chest.

'I'll get it,' he said. 'That's me. I'm the ice-man.'

When Mr Charlton came back from the kitchen carrying trays of ice, Pop mixed the new drink and tasted it with slow, appraising tongue and eye.

'More perfick than ever!'

Everything was more perfick, Mr Charlton kept telling himself. The scent of gardenia was more perfick. It too was stronger than ever. He laughed immoderately, for no reason, and at length, looking for the first time straight into the dark searching eyes of Mariette with neither caution nor despair.

'Mariette,' he said, 'what is the scent you're wearing?'

'Come and sit over here and I'll tell you.'

Mr Charlton moved to sit on the other side of the table. Rising abruptly, he stood stunned. It seemed to him that something remarkable had happened to Pop. Pop, it seemed to him, had disappeared.

'I didn't see Pop go out,' he said. 'Where's Pop gone?'

Ma began shrieking.

'I'm under here!' Pop said.

'Under me! I'm sitting on his lap,' Ma said. 'Why don't you ask Mariette if she'll sit on yours?'

Mariette, who needed no asking, sat on Mr Charlton's lap. The illusion of being caressed in a silken, sinuous, maddening way by the goose's neck returned to Mr Charlton as he felt her silken legs cross his own. A sensation that for the second time his blood was turning white, while being at the same time on fire, coursed completely through him. The soles of his feet started tingling. The scent of gardenia overwhelmed him like a drug.

'Tell me what the scent is,' Mr Charlton said.

'Gardenia.'

'Gardenia? Gardenia? What's Gardenia?'

'It's a flower. Do you like it?'

'Like it? Like it?' Mr Charlton said madly. 'Like it?'

With extraordinarily soft hands Mariette took his own and held them high round her waist, just under her breasts. With stupefying tenderness she started to rock backwards and forwards on his knee, with the result that Mr Charlton could not see straight. His eyes were simply two quivering balls revolving unrestrainedly in the top of his head.

'Well, getting late,' Pop said. 'Hitch up a bit, Ma, and I'll mix another before we go to shut-eye.'

Pop reappeared presently from underneath the salmon canopy of Ma and announced that he was going to mix a new one this time.

'How about a Chauffeur? Dammit, the Rolls has to have a Chauffeur,' he said. He stood earnestly consulting the *Guide to Better Drinking*. 'One third vermouth, one third whisky, one third gin, dash of angostura. Sounds perfick. Everybody game?'

Everybody was game. Mr Charlton was very game. He said so over and over again. Mariette held his hands more closely against her body and a little higher than before and Mr Charlton let his head rest against the velvety, downy nape of her dark neck.

'You're my goose. My gardenia,' he said.

'Wouldn't you think,' Mariette said, 'that it was soon time to go to bed?'

Some moment later Mr Charlton had drained the Chauffeur in two gulps and was addressing Ma and Pop in what he thought were solid, steadfast tones of gratitude.

'Can never thank you. Never thank you. Never be able to thank you.'

He shook on his feet, grasped at air with aimless hands, and started jiggling like a fish.

'Should be a cocktail called gardenia! A sweet one–'

'I'll make one,' Pop said. 'I'll think one up.'

'And one called Mariette,' Mr Charlton said. 'Sweet one too!–'

He staggered violently and some time later was vaguely aware of walking arm in arm to the billiard-room with Mariette. There was no light in the billiard-room. He felt filled with inconsolable happiness and laughed with wild immoderation, once again feeling her legs brush against him like the goose-neck, in the darkness. Once again too he called her a gardenia and stretched out groping hands to touch her.

Instead, unsurprised, he found himself kneeling by the billiard table, caressing in the corner pocket a solitary, cool abandoned ball.

'Where are you? Where are you?' he said. 'Mariette–'

Mr Charlton got up and fell down, breaking the thrushes' eggs in his pocket as he fell.

'Climb up,' Mariette said. Mr Charlton found it impossible to climb up and Mariette started pushing him. 'Upsadaisy. Up you go. I'll get your collar off.'

Meanwhile Pop, who was sitting up in bed in his shirt, thinking of the evening sunshine, the meadows shining so beautifully and so golden with buttercups and the prospect of summer growing to maturity all about his paradise, decided that the only thing to make the day more perfick was a cigar.

'I'm the same as Churchill,' he said. 'Like a good cigar.'

He lit the cigar and sat watching Ma undress herself. The thing he really loved most about Ma, he had long since decided, was that she didn't have to wear corsets. She didn't need them; her figure was all her own; pure and natural as could be.

'Ma, I've been thinking,' he said, 'when does Mariette expect this baby?'

'She can't make up her mind.'

'Well, she'd better,' Pop said.

'Why?' Ma said.

From the depths of her transparent petunia canopy, as it floated down over the global map of her white, wide territory, Ma spoke with her customary air of unconcern.

Smoking his cigar, gazing thoughtfully through the open window to a night of warm May stars, as if pondering again on summer and the way it would soon embroider with its gold and green his already perfick paradise, Pop made a pronouncement.

'I'm a bit worried about Mister Charlton. I don't think that young man's got it in 'im,' he said. 'At least not yet.'

No Kaddish for Weinstein

Woody Allen

Weinstein lay under the covers, staring at the ceiling in a depressed torpor. Outside, sheets of humid air rose from the pavement in stifling waves. The sound of traffic was deafening at this hour, and in addition to all this his bed was on fire. Look at me, he thought. Fifty years old. Half a century. Next year, I will be fifty-one. Then fifty-two. Using this same reasoning, he could figure out his age as much as five years in the future. So little time left, he thought, and so much to accomplish. For one thing, he wanted to learn to drive a car. Adelman, his friend who used to play dreidel with him on Rush Street, had studied driving at the Sorbonne. He could handle a car beautifully and had already driven many places by himself. Weinstein had made a few attempts to steer his father's Chevy but kept winding up on the sidewalk.

He had been a precocious child. An intellectual. At twelve, he had translated the poems of T. S. Eliot into English, after some vandals had broken into the library and translated them into French. And as if his high I.Q. did not isolate him enough, he suffered untold injustices and persecutions because of his religion, mostly from his parents. True, the old man was a member of the synagogue, and his mother, too, but they could never accept the fact that their son was Jewish. 'How did it happen?' his father asked, bewildered. My face looks Semitic, Weinstein thought every morning as he shaved. He had been mistaken several times for Robert Redford, but on each occasion it was by a blind person. Then there was Feinglass, his other boyhood friend: a Phi Beta Kappa. A labor spy, ratting on the workers. Then a convert to Marxism. A Communist agitator. Betrayed by the Party, he went to Hollywood and became the offscreen voice of a famous cartoon mouse. Ironic.

Weinstein had toyed with the Communists, too. To impress a girl at Rutgers, he had moved to Moscow and joined the Red Army. When he called her for a second date, she was pinned to someone else. Still, his rank of sergeant in the Russian infantry would hurt him later when he needed a security clearance in order to get the free appetizer with his dinner at Longchamps. Also, while at school he had organized some laboratory mice and led them in a strike over work conditions. Actually, it was not so much the politics as the poetry of Marxist theory that got him. He was positive that collectivization could work if everyone would learn the lyrics to 'Rag Mop.' 'The withering away of the state' was a phrase that had stayed with him, ever since his uncle's nose had withered away in Saks Fifth Avenue one day. What, he wondered, can be learned about the true essence of social revolution? Only that it should never be attempted after eating Mexican food.

The Depression shattered Weinstein's Uncle Meyer, who kept his fortune under the mattress. When the market crashed, the government called in all mattresses, and Meyer became a pauper overnight. All that was left for him was to jump out the window, but he lacked the nerve and sat on a window sill of the Flatiron Building from 1930 to 1937.

'These kids with their pot and their sex,' Uncle Meyer was fond of saying. 'Do they know what it is to sit on a window sill for seven years? There you see life! Of course, everybody looks like ants. But each year Tessie – may she rest in peace – made the Seder right out there on the ledge. The family gathered round for Passover. Oy, nephew! What's the world coming to when they have a bomb that can kill more people than one look at Max Rifkin's daughter?'

Weinstein's so-called friends had all knuckled under to the House Un-American Activities Committee. Blotnick was turned in by his own mother. Sharpstein was turned in by his answering service. Weinstein had been called by the committee and admitted he had given money to the Russian War Relief, and then added, 'Oh, yes, I bought Stalin a dining-room set.' He refused to name names but said if the committee insisted he would give the heights of the people he had met at meetings. In the end he panicked, and instead of taking the Fifth Amendment, took the Third, which enabled him to buy beer in Philadelphia on Sunday.

Weinstein finished shaving and got into the shower. He lathered himself, while steaming water splashed down his bulky back. He thought, Here I am at some fixed point in time and space, taking a shower. I, Isaac Weinstein.

One of God's creatures. And then, stepping on the soap, he slid across the floor and rammed his head into the towel rack. It had been a bad week. The previous day, he had got a bad haircut and was still not over the anxiety it caused him. At first the barber had snipped judiciously, but soon Weinstein realized he had gone too far. 'Put some back!' he screamed unreasonably.

'I can't,' the barber said. 'It won't stick.'

'Well, then give it to me, Dominic! I want to take it with me!'

'Once it's on the floor of the shop it's mine, Mr Weinstein.'

'Like hell! I want my hair!'

He blustered and raged, and finally felt guilty and left. Goyim, he thought. One way or another, they get you.

Now he emerged from the hotel and walked up Eighth Avenue. Two men were mugging an elderly lady. My God, thought Weinstein, time was when one person could handle that job. Some city. Chaos everyplace. Kant was right: The mind imposes order. It also tells you how much to tip. What a wonderful thing, to be conscious! I wonder what the people in New Jersey do.

He was on his way to see Harriet about the alimony payments. He still loved Harriet, even though while they were married she had systematically attempted to commit adultery with all the *R*'s in the Manhattan telephone directory. He forgave her. But he should have suspected something when his best friend and Harriet took a house in Maine together for three years, without telling him where they were. He didn't *want* to see it – that was it. His sex life with Harriet had stopped early. He slept with her once on the night they first met, once on the evening of the first moon landing, and once to test if his back was all right after a slipped disc. 'It's no damn good with you, Harriet,' he used to complain. 'You're too pure. Every time I have an urge for you I sublimate it by planting a tree in Israel. You remind me of my mother.' (Molly Weinstein, may she rest in peace, who slaved for him and made the best stuffed derma in Chicago – a secret recipe until everyone realized she was putting in hashish.)

For lovemaking, Weinstein needed someone quite opposite. Like LuAnne, who made sex an art. The only trouble was she couldn't count to twenty without taking her shoes off. He once tried giving her a book on existentialism, but she ate it. Sexually, Weinstein had always felt inadequate. For one thing, he felt short. He was five-four in his stocking feet, although in someone else's stocking feet he could be as tall as five-six. Dr Klein, his analyst, got him to see that jumping in front of a moving train was more hostile than self-destructive but in either case would ruin the crease in his pants. Klein was his third analyst. His first was a Jungian, who suggested they try a Ouija board. Before that, he attended 'group,' but when it came time for him to speak he got dizzy and could only recite the names of all the planets. His problem was women, and he knew it. He was impotent with any woman who finished college with higher than a B-minus average. He felt most at home with graduates of typing school, although if the woman did over sixty words a minute he panicked and could not perform.

Weinstein rang the bell to Harriet's apartment, and suddenly she was standing before him. Swelling to maculate giraffe, as usual, thought Weinstein. It was a private joke that neither of them understood.

'Hello, Harriet,' he said.

'Oh, Ike,' she said. 'You needn't be so damn self-righteous.'

She was right. What a tactless thing to have said. He hated himself for it.

'How are the kids, Harriet?'

'We never had any kids, Ike.'

'That's why I thought four hundred dollars a week was a lot for child support.'

She bit her lip, Weinstein bit his lip. Then he bit her lip. 'Harriet,' he said, 'I ... I'm broke. Egg futures are down.'

'I see. And can't you get help from your *shiksa*?'

'To you, any girl who's not Jewish is a *shiksa*.'

'Can we forget it?' Her voice was choked with recrimination. Weinstein had a sudden urge to kiss her, or if not her, somebody.

'Harriet, where did we go wrong?'

'We never faced reality.'

'It wasn't my fault. You said it was north.'

'Reality *is* north, Ike.'

'No, Harriet. Empty dreams are north. Reality is west. False hopes are east, and I think Louisiana is south.'

She still had the power to arouse him. He reached out for her, but she moved away and his hand came to rest in some sour cream.

'Is that why you slept with your analyst?' he finally blurted out. His face was knotted with rage. He felt like fainting but couldn't remember the proper way to fall.

'That was therapy,' she said coldly. 'According to Freud, sex is the royal road to the unconscious.'

'Freud said *dreams* are the road to the unconscious.'

'Sex, dreams – you're going to nit-pick?'

'Goodbye, Harriet.'

It was no use. *Rien à dire, rien à faire.* Weinstein left and walked over to Union Square. Suddenly hot tears burst forth, as if from a broken dam. Hot, salty tears pent up for ages rushed out in an unabashed wave of emotion. The problem was, they were coming out of his ears. Look at this, he thought; I can't even cry properly. He dabbed his ear with Kleenex and went home.

Let Sleeping Vets Lie

James Herriot

There is more to the life of a vet than meets the eye, and the care of animals is sometimes only a minor consideration. Often it is the characters in charge who seem a little unusual...

'Them masticks,' said Mr Pickersgill judicially, 'is a proper bugger.'

I nodded my head in agreement that his mastitis problem was indeed giving cause for concern; and reflected at the same time that while most farmers would have been content with the local word 'felon' it was typical that Mr Pickersgill should make a determined if somewhat inaccurate attempt at the scientific term.

Sometimes he got very wide of the mark as one time long after this when Artificial Insemination or A.I. was gaining a foothold in the Dales he made my day by telling me he had a cow in calf to the I.C.I.

However he usually did better than this – most of his efforts were near misses or bore obvious evidence of their derivation – but I could never really fathom where he got the masticks. I did know that once he fastened on to an expression it never changed; mastitis had always been 'them masticks' with him and it always would be. And I knew, too, that nothing would ever stop him doggedly trying to be right.

Because Mr Pickersgill had what he considered to be a scholastic background. He was a man of about sixty and when in his teens he had attended a two week course of instruction for agricultural workers at Leeds University. This brief glimpse of the academic life had left an indelible impression on his mind, and it was as if the intimation of something deep and true behind the facts of his everyday work had kindled a flame in him which had illumined his subsequent life.

No capped and gowned don ever looked back to his years among the spires of Oxford with more nostalgia than did Mr Pickersgill to his fortnight at Leeds and his conversation was usually laced with references to a godlike Professor Malleson who had apparently been in charge of the course.

'Ah don't know what to make of it,' he continued. 'In ma college days I was allus told that you got a big swollen bag and dirty milk with them masticks but this must be another kind. Just little bits of flakes in the milk off and on – neither nowt nor something, but I'm right fed up with it, I'll tell you.'

I took a sip from the cup of tea which Mrs Pickersgill had placed in front of me on the kitchen table. 'Yes, it's very worrying the way it keeps going on and on. I'm sure there's a definite factor behind it all – I wish I could put my finger on it.'

But in fact I had a good idea what was behind it. I had happened in at the little byre late one afternoon when Mr Pickersgill and his daughter Olive were milking their ten cows. I had watched the two at work as they crouched under the row of roan and red backs and one thing was immediately obvious; while Olive drew the milk by almost imperceptible movements of her fingers and with a motionless wrist, her father hauled away at the teats as though he was trying to ring in the new year.

This insight coupled with the fact that it was always the cows Mr Pickersgill milked that gave trouble was enough to convince me that the chronic mastitis was of traumatic origin.

But how to tell the farmer that he wasn't doing his job right and that the only solution was to learn a more gentle technique or let Olive take over all the milking?

It wouldn't be easy because Mr Pickersgill was an impressive man. I don't suppose he had a spare penny in the world but even as he sat there in the kitchen in his tattered, collarless flannel shirt and braces he looked, as always, like an industrial tycoon. You could imagine that massive head with its fleshy cheeks, noble brow and serene eyes looking out from the financial pages of *The Times*. Put him in a bowler and striped trousers and you'd have the perfect chairman of the board.

I was very chary of affronting such natural dignity and anyway, Mr Pickersgill was fundamentally a fine stocksman. His few cows, like all the animals of that fast-dying breed of small farmer, were fat and sleek and clean. You had to look after your beasts when they were your only source of income and somehow Mr Pickersgill had brought up a family by milk production eked out by selling a few pigs and the eggs from his wife's fifty hens.

I could never quite work out how they did it but they lived, and they lived graciously. All the family but Olive had married and left home but there was still a rich decorum and harmony in that house. The present scene was typical. The farmer expounding gravely, Mrs Pickersgill bustling about in the background, listening to him with quiet pride. Olive, too, was happy. Though in her late thirties, she had no fears of spinsterhood because she had been assiduously courted for fifteen years by Charlie Hudson from the Darrowby fish shop and though Charlie was not a tempestuous suitor there was nothing flighty about him and he was confidently expected to pop the question over the next ten years or so.

Mr Pickersgill offered me another buttered scone and when I declined he cleared his throat a few times as though trying to find words. 'Mr Herriot,' he said at last, 'I don't like to tell nobody his job, but we've tried all your remedies for them masticks and we've still got trouble. Now when I studied under Professor Malleson I noted down a lot of good cures and I'd like to try this 'un. Have a look at it.'

He put his hand in his hip pocket and produced a yellowed slip of paper almost falling apart at the folds. 'It's an udder salve. Maybe if we gave the bags a good rub with it it'd do t'trick.'

I read the prescription in the fine copperplate writing. Camphor, eucalyptus, zinc oxide – a long list of the old familiar names. I couldn't help feeling a kind of affection for them but it was tempered by a growing disillusion. I was about to say that I didn't think rubbing anything on the udder would make the slightest difference when the farmer groaned loudly.

The action of reaching into his hip pocket had brought on a twinge of his lumbago and he sat very upright, grimacing with pain.

'This bloody old back of mine! By gaw, it does give me some stick, and doctor can't do nowt about it. I've had enough pills to make me rattle but ah get no relief.'

I'm not brilliant but I do get the odd blinding flash and I had one now.

'Mr Pickersgill,' I said solemnly, 'you've suffered from that lumbago ever since I've known you and I've just thought of something. I believe I know how to cure it.'

The farmer's eyes widened and he stared at me with a childlike trust in which there was no trace of scepticism. This could be expected, because just as people place more reliance on the words of knacker men and meal travellers than their vets' when their animals are concerned it was natural that they would believe the vet rather than their doctor with their own ailments.

'You know how to put me right?' he said faintly.

'I think so, and it has nothing to do with medicine. You'll have to stop milking.'

'Stop milking! What the 'ell . . .?'

'Of course. Don't you see, it's sitting crouched on that little stool night and morning every day of the week that's doing it. You're a big chap and you've got to bend to get down there – I'm sure it's bad for you.'

Mr Pickersgill gazed into space as though he had seen a vision. 'You really think . . .'

'Yes, I do. You ought to give it a try, anyway. Olive can do the milking. She's always saying she ought to do it all.'

'That's right, Dad,' Olive chimed in. 'I like milking, you know I do, and it's time you gave it up – you've done it ever since you were a lad.'

'Dang it, young man, I believe you're right! I'll pack it in, now – I've made my decision!' Mr Pickersgill threw up his fine head, looked imperiously around him and crashed his fist on the table as though he had just concluded a merger between two oil companies.

I stood up, 'Fine, fine. I'll take this prescription with me and make up the udder salve. It'll be ready for you tonight and I should start using it immediately.'

It was about a month later that I saw Mr Pickersgill. He was on a bicycle, pedalling majestically across the market place and he dismounted when he saw me.

'Now then, Mr Herriot,' he said, puffing slightly. 'I'm glad I've met you. I've been meaning to come and tell you that we don't have no flakes in the milk now. Ever since we started with t'salve they began to disappear and milk's as clear as it can be now.'

'Oh, great. And how's your lumbago?'

'Well I'll tell you, you've really capped it and I'm grateful. Ah've never milked since that day and I hardly get a twinge now.' He paused and smiled indulgently. 'You gave me some good advice for me back, but we had to go back to awd Professor Malleson to cure them masticks, didn't we?'

My next encounter with Mr Pickersgill was on the telephone.

'I'm speaking from the cossack,' he said in a subdued shout.

'From the what?'

'The cossack, the telephone cossack in t'village.'

'Yes, indeed,' I said, 'and what can I do for you?'

'I want you to come out as soon as possible, to treat a calf for semolina.'

'I beg your pardon?'

'I 'ave a calf with semolina.'

'Semolina?'

'Aye, that's right. A feller was on about it on t'wireless the other morning.'

'Oh! Ah yes, I see.' I too had heard a bit of the farming talk on Salmonella infection in calves. 'What makes you think you've got this trouble?'

'Well it's just like that feller said. Me calf's bleeding from the rectrum.'

'From the ...? Yes, yes, of course. Well I'd better have a look at him – I won't be long.'

The calf was pretty ill when I saw him and he did have rectal bleeding, but it wasn't like Salmonella.

'There's no diarrhoea, you see, Mr Pickersgill,' I said. 'In fact, he seems to be constipated. This is almost pure blood coming away from him. And he hasn't got a very high temperature.'

The farmer seemed a little disappointed. 'Dang, I thowt it was just same as that feller was talking about. He said you could send samples off to the labrador.'

'Eh? To the what?'

'The investigation labrador – you know.'

'Oh yes, quite, but I don't think the lab would be of any help in this case.'

'Aye well, what's wrong with him, then? Is something the matter with his rectrum?'

'No, no,' I said. 'But there seems to be some obstruction high up his bowel which is causing this haemorrhage.' I looked at the little animal standing motionless with his back up. He was totally preoccupied with some internal discomfort and now and then he strained and grunted softly.

And of course I should have known straight away – it was so obvious. But I suppose we all have blind spells when we can't see what is pushed in front of our eyes, and for a few days I played around with that calf in a haze of ignorance, giving it this and that medicine which I'd rather not talk about.

But I was lucky. He recovered in spite of my treatment. It wasn't until Mr Pickersgill showed me the little roll of necrotic tissue which the calf had passed that the thing dawned on me.

I turned, shame-faced, to the farmer. 'This is a bit of dead bowel all telescoped together – an intussusception. It's usually a fatal condition but fortunately in this case the obstruction has sloughed away and your calf should be all right now.'

'What was it you called it?'

'An intussusception.'

Mr Pickersgill's lips moved tentatively and for a moment I thought he was going to have a shot at it. But he apparently decided against it. 'Oh,' he said. 'That's what it was, was it?'

'Yes, and it's difficult to say just what caused it.'

The farmer sniffed. 'I'll bet I know what was behind it. I always said this one 'ud be a weakly calf. When he was born he bled a lot from his biblical cord.'

Mr Pickersgill hadn't finished with me yet. It was only a week later that I heard him on the phone again.

'Get out here, quick. There's one of me pigs going bezique.'

'Bezique?' With an effort I put away from me a mental picture of two porkers facing each other over a green baize table. 'I'm afraid I don't quite...'

'Aye, ah gave him a dose of worm medicine and he started jumpin' about and rollin' on his back. I tell you he's going proper bezique.'

'Ah! Yes, yes I see, right. I'll be with you in a few minutes.'

The pig had quietened down a bit when I arrived but was still in considerable pain, getting up, lying down, trotting in spurts round the pen. I gave him half a grain of morphine hydrochloride as a sedative and within a few minutes he began to relax and finally curled up in the straw.

'Looks as though he's going to be all right,' I said. 'But what's this worm medicine you gave him?'

Mr Pickersgill produced the bottle sheepishly.

'Bloke was coming round sellin' them. Said it would shift any worms you cared to name.'

'It nearly shifted your pig, didn't it?' I sniffed at the mixture. 'And no wonder. It smells almost like pure turpentine.'

'Turpentine! Well by gaw is that all it is? And bloke said it was summat new. Charged me an absorbent price for it, too.'

I gave him back the bottle. 'Well never mind, I don't think there's any harm done, but I think the dustbin's the best place for that.'

As I was getting into my car I looked up at the farmer. 'You must be about sick of the sight of me. First the mastitis, then the calf and now your pig. You've had a bad run.'

Mr Pickersgill squared his shoulders and gazed at me with massive composure. Again I was conscious of the sheer presence of the man.

'Young feller,' he said. 'That don't bother me. Where there's stock there's trouble and ah know from experience that trouble allus comes in cycloncs.'

Beggar your Neighbour

John Lucas

For what do we live, but to make sport for our neighbours,
and laugh at them in our turn

Jane Austen

There is a popular impression – fostered, I'm sorry to say, by nursery catalogues, gardening periodicals, glossy magazines and Sunday newspaper correspondents – that the ideal for which we should all strive, reaching upwards with our muddy, chlorophyll-stained palms, is that other Eden where peace reigns eternally. Where borders show bank after bank of prize blooms whose colours intermingle in gorgeous masses and every petal is kissed with dew. Where lawns are cropped to bowling-green velvet and trees decorously incline their branches before a zephyr flirting from the west, and the sun smiles down on all with warm approval.

Now, this spurious world of the chocolate box is quite unattainable. In real life we can see that gardening and gardens are anything but perfect. In fact, it's all pretty sinful, really. An internecine struggle. Total war. A fight to the death between bird and grub, mower and grass-blade, spade and soil – and neighbour and neighbour. Science and Nature can offer some help, but against your neighbour you're absolutely on your own. It's tough hand-to-hand stuff, and may the best man – you, naturally – win.

In those private twilight moments between consciousness and sleep you can tell yourself you have the best-stocked, tidiest, most fascinating garden in Christendom. Then a few minutes later your subconscious will cook up a dream stating in several succinct images what you really fear – that your neighbour has an even better one. The turf in the next-door garden, says the voice of turncoat Truth, is always greener.

So what can you do about that heap of mouldering vegetation outside your picture window that you hopefully call a garden? In the first place, play it cool. Adopt the tactics of a prosecuting counsel faced with witnesses for a defendant with a cast-iron case. Make your neighbour begin to doubt himself, to come to realize himself for the bumbling fool you yearn for him to be.

Nothing so crude as a frontal attack like shouting rude words through the trellis. Take time to discover his vulnerable spots, then in goes the rapier, or pruning knife, figuratively speaking, right between his *Potentilla fruticosa* and his *Cistus crispus*. It is not enough to have a better garden, or even to want a better one, than the man next door. He must feel he has the worst.

One weapon close to hand is Age. When you see your neighbour preparing for a morning's mowing, brightly offer to do it for him. If you're older than he is, he'll take it that he appears inadequate. If you're younger, he'll feel older than ever. If you're about the same age – well, it's quite obvious who's wearing better.

Sex is another factor worth exploiting. Offer help in the presence of his wife, and you score double marks. Treble if there's a sister or two about, and a special bonus in the case of a daughter. Your neighbour's female relatives can be excellent, though unwitting, allies for you if you strike your blows within their hearing. No man likes to be demeaned before his family – it saps more of his confidence than ever. But don't overdo it. Women are capricious creatures, and unless you steer a careful course they will spring to his defence at your expense, leaving *you* smarting.

Now a simple border manoeuvre.

The chances are he doesn't know Latin – or if he learnt it he's forgotten it. Couple this with the fact that birds have a liking for pecking plant labels out of the ground. Give the birds a hand. Every night, hop over that gap in the fence that you and he (poor unsuspecting fool) have left in the interests of *entente cordiale* and remove one or two labels. In a few days he'll realize he's got a collection of plants without a name among them.

Your own plot, of course, resembles a Latin textbook, a source of much comment among your friends, who won't be slow to detect that anonymous, *uninformed* look about your neighbour's garden. If you don't know the names of your plants, then use your imagination, man! I have a considerable show, for example, of *Petrushka appassionata cadenza*, and a worthy group of *Bananianthus skinniosus* set off by a flourish of *Byzantium cavalleria rusticana*.

The fact that you are locked in combat with your neighbour in a horticultural, sporting sense – in the way that two athletes wish each other would drop dead as they approach the tape – is no reason to feel unfriendly towards him. No indeed, the friendlier you are, the bigger the chance of his playing into your hands.

Invite him round one Sunday morning for a glass of lager, and as you comment on the serenity of the summer scene, edge him towards your newly set-up row of a dozen flower-pots, all tagged but apparently offering no sign of life. When he inquires what they contain tell him you are nurturing seeds of an extremely rare (and of course costly) form of Icelandic sunflower which takes seven years to germinate. The truth, that the pots are quite empty but for the soil, will be quite safe. If your war of nerves succeeds, he'll be out of his house well before the seven years are up.

Seize every opportunity for conversation, but don't be openly disparaging. Blatant criticism will brand you as a churl – and fail.

Be subtle. If you find him planting tulip bulbs in long neat rows, praise them. But make approving comments, too, on similar ones planted in long neat rows in the local park – 'where,' tell him, 'formal planting is, of course, appropriate. I prefer the *in*formal approach myself. Makes a garden more natural, don't you think, with colour, as it should be, in smudges or drifts?'

The point should get home that, compared with yours, his garden is doomed to have that deadly institutional pallor about it. Nature with the town hall look, toeing the party line. Yours will have the pleasing stamp of Nature running free, held in check only by the gentlest discipline.

And here's a useful unnerving feint. Spend some time contemplating a patch of soil close to the dividing fence while he is busy on his side. Put in some tape-measure work, steering the conversation round to the poplar you want to plant there. Express some anxiety about the tree's tendency to dry out soil and cause settlement to buildings. Then stroll thoughtfully back indoors.

A few weeks later, plant your tree. It'll be months before he realizes it isn't a poplar at all but a quite innocuous rowan – though not without a haul of sleepless nights in your favour.

Always useful is a tactic in which you become the injured party at your neighbour's inept hands. If you see him spraying his roses with insecticide one evening when the wind's blowing slightly your way, go out and admire his blooms. In the middle of telling him they're the most delicate specimens you've ever seen, suddenly clap a hand over your eyes muttering 'sprays . . . danger to birds . . . human beings . . . needless suffering,' and grope your manifestly painful way indoors with a moan.

When your neighbour calls in to ask after your welfare, remember to wear dark glasses. Assure him your eyes seem fine, thanks, and you trust – no, you're pretty certain – that with luck and skilful surgery there will be no permanent damage.

Only an insensitive man will fail to lose face and wonder, Is Gardening Really Worth it?, when human safety becomes subordinated to the perversions of commercial science and a few old roses. And only one with the hide of an ox will fail to uproot the lot in remorse. Another round to you.

Close observation of your neighbour's activities will suggest numerous strategems. If his wife mentions to your wife that he intends to erect a greenhouse in a sun-drenched spot, get in first with a large tool-shed that will cast a long shadow, then invite him in to admire it.

Refer to his *London Pride*, but your *Saxifraga umbrosa*.

Talk of his *greenfly*, but your *aphides*.

His *lean-to*, but your *conservatory*.

Get your wife to take him a cup of tea just as he reaches the trickiest point of a rose-grafting.

At Christmas give him a book with a title like *Gardening for Beginners* or *Garden Know-how for Novices*.

You can carry Nature's ruthless fight into your neighbour's territory in a thousand ways. In a couple of seasons he'll be at worst reduced to employing outside help; at best, broken down. In the space of only five years, two of my neighbours have moved away and a third called me in to give advice.

I count all these as undoubted victories, but having a forgiving nature I've made a special point of remaining on excellent terms with each of my adversaries. This is the supreme test. We gardeners must keep a sense of proportion above all. The garden is the last place on God's earth – is it not? – to allow oneself to be seized and twisted by distrust, jealousy or rancour.

The Hitch Hiker's Guide to the Galaxy

Douglas Adams

The Hitch Hiker's Guide to the Galaxy *is a wholly remarkable book. It has been compiled and recompiled many times over many years and under many different editorships. It contains contributions from countless numbers of travellers and researchers.*

The introduction begins like this:

'Space,' *it says,* 'is big. Really big. You just won't believe how vastly hugely mindbogglingly big it is. I mean you may think it's a long way down the road to the chemist, but that's just peanuts to space. Listen ...' *and so on.*

(After a while the style settles down a bit and it begins to tell you things you really need to know, like the fact that the fabulously beautiful planet Bethselamin is now so worried about the cumulative erosion by ten billion visiting tourists a year that any net imbalance between the amount you eat and the amount you excrete whilst on the planet is surgically removed from your bodyweight when you leave: so every time you go to the lavatory there it is vitally important to get a receipt.)

To be fair though, when confronted by the sheer enormity of the distances between the stars, better minds than the one responsible for the Guide's *introduction have faltered. Some invite you to consider for a moment a peanut in Reading and a small walnut in Johannesburg, and other such dizzying concepts.*

The simple truth is that interstellar distances will not fit into the human imagination.

Even light, which travels so fast that it takes most races thousands of years to realize that it travels at all, takes time to journey between the stars. It takes eight minutes to journey from the star Sol to the place where the Earth used to be, and four years more to arrive at Sol's nearest stellar neighbour, Alpha Proxima.

For light to reach the other side of the Galaxy, for it to reach Damogran for instance, takes rather longer: five hundred thousand years.

The record for hitch hiking this distance is just under five years, but you don't get to see much on the way.

The Hitch Hiker's Guide to the Galaxy *says that if you hold a lungful of air you can survive in the total vacuum of space for about thirty seconds. However it does go on to say that what with space being the mind boggling size it is the chances of getting picked up by another ship within those thirty seconds are two to the power of two hundred and sixty-seven thousand seven hundred and nine to one against.*

By a totally staggering coincidence that is also the telephone number of an Islington flat where Arthur once went to a very good party and met a very nice girl whom he totally failed to get off with – she went off with a gatecrasher.

Though the planet Earth, the Islington flat and the telephone have all now been demolished, it is comforting to reflect that they are all in some small way commemorated by the fact that twenty-nine seconds later Ford and Arthur were rescued.

A computer chattered to itself in alarm as it noticed an airlock open and close itself for no apparent reason.

This was because Reason was in fact out to lunch.

A hole had just appeared in the Galaxy. It was exactly a nothingth of a second long, a nothingth of an inch wide, and quite a lot of millions of light years from end to end.

As it closed up lots of paper hats and party balloons fell out of it and drifted off through the universe. A team of seven three-foot-high market analysts fell out of it and died, partly of asphyxiation, partly of surprise.

Two hundred and thirty-nine thousand lightly fried eggs fell out of it too, materializing in a large wobbly heap on the famine-struck land of Poghril in the Pansel system.

The whole Poghril tribe had died out from famine except for one last man who died of cholesterol poisoning some weeks later.

The nothingth of a second for which the hole existed reverberated backwards and forwards through time in a most improbable fashion. Somewhere in the deeply remote past it seriously traumatized a small random group of atoms drifting through the empty sterility of space and made them cling together in the most extraordinarily unlikely patterns. These patterns quickly learnt to copy themselves (this was part of what was so extraordinary about the patterns) and went on to cause massive trouble on every planet they drifted on to. That was how life began in the Universe.

Five wild Event Maelstroms swirled in vicious storms of unreason and spewed up a pavement.

On the pavement lay Ford Prefect and Arthur Dent gulping like half-spent fish.

'There you are,' gasped Ford, scrabbling for a fingerhold on the pavement as it raced through the Third Reach of the Unknown, 'I told you I'd think of something.'

'Oh sure,' said Arthur, 'sure.'

'Bright idea of mine,' said Ford, 'to find a passing spaceship and get rescued by it.'

The real universe arched sickeningly away beneath them. Various pretend ones flitted silently by, like mountain goats. Primal light exploded, splattering space-time as with gobbets of junket. Time blossomed, matter shrank away. The highest prime number coalesced quietly in a corner and hid itself away for ever.

'Oh come off it,' said Arthur, 'the chances against it were astronomical.'

'Don't knock it, it worked,' said Ford.

'What sort of ship are we in?' asked Arthur as the pit of eternity yawned beneath them.

'I don't know,' said Ford, 'I haven't opened my eyes yet.'

'No, nor have I,' said Arthur.

The Universe jumped, froze, quivered and splayed out in several unexpected directions.

Arthur and Ford opened their eyes and looked about in considerable surprise.

'Good God,' said Arthur, 'it looks just like the sea front at Southend.'

'Hell, I'm relieved to hear you say that,' said Ford.

'Why?'

'Because I thought I must be going mad.'

'Perhaps you are. Perhaps you only thought I said it.'

Ford thought about this.

'Well, did you say it or didn't you?' he asked.

'I think so,' said Arthur.

'Well, perhaps we're both going mad.'

'Yes,' said Arthur, 'we'd be mad, all things considered, to think this was Southend.'

'Well, do you think this is Southend?'

'Oh yes.'

'So do I.'

'Therefore we must be mad.'

'Nice day for it.'

'Yes,' said a passing maniac.

'Who was that?' asked Arthur.

'Who – the man with five heads and the elderberry bush full of kippers?'
'Yes.'
'I don't know. Just someone.'
'Ah.'

They both sat on the pavement and watched with a certain unease as huge children bounced heavily along the sand and wild horses thundered through the sky taking fresh supplies of reinforced railings to the Uncertain Areas.

'You know,' said Arthur with a slight cough, 'if this is Southend, there's something very odd about it...'

'You mean the way the sea stays steady as a rock and the buildings keep washing up and down?' said Ford. 'Yes I thought that was odd too. In fact,' he continued as with a huge bang Southend split itself into six equal segments which danced and span giddily round each other in lewd and licentious formations, 'there is something altogether very strange going on.'

Wild yowling noises of pipes and strings seared through the wind, hot doughnuts popped out of the road for ten pence each, horrid fish stormed out of the sky and Arthur and Ford decided to make a run for it.

They plunged through heavy walls of sound, mountains of archaic thought, valleys of mood music, bad shoe sessions and footling bats and suddenly heard a girl's voice.

It sounded quite a sensible voice, but it just said, 'Two to the power of one hundred thousand to one against and falling,' and that was all.

Ford skidded down a beam of light and span round trying to find a source for the voice but could see nothing he could seriously believe in.

'What was that voice?' shouted Arthur.

'I don't know,' yelled Ford, 'I don't know. It sounded like a measurement of probability.'

'Probability? What do you mean?'

'Probability. You know, like two to one, three to one, five to four against. It said two to the power of one hundred thousand to one against. That's pretty improbable you know.'

A million-gallon vat of custard upended itself over them without warning.

'But what does it mean?' cried Arthur.

'What, the custard?'

'No, the measurement of improbability!'

'I don't know. I don't know at all. I think we're on some kind of spaceship.'

'I can only assume,' said Arthur, 'that this is not the first-class compartment.'

Bulges appeared in the fabric of space-time. Great ugly bulges.

'Haaaauuurrgghhh ...' said Arthur as he felt his body softening and bending in unusual directions. 'Southend seems to be melting away ... the stars are swirling ... a dustbowl ... my legs are drifting off into the sunset ... my left arm's come off too.' A frightening thought struck him: 'Hell,' he said, 'how am I going to operate my digital watch now?' He wound his eyes desperately around in Ford's direction.

'Ford,' he said, 'you're turning into a penguin. Stop it.'

Again came the voice.

'Two to the power of seventy-five thousand to one against and falling.'

Ford waddled around his pond in a furious circle.

'Hey, who are you?' he quacked. 'Where are you? What's going on and is there any way of stopping it?'

'Please relax,' said the voice pleasantly, like a stewardess in an airliner with only one wing and two engines, one of which is on fire, 'you are perfectly safe.'

'But that's not the point!' raged Ford. 'The point is that I am now a perfectly safe penguin, and my colleague here is rapidly running out of limbs!'

'It's alright, I've got them back now,' said Arthur.

'Two to the power of fifty thousand to one against and falling,' said the voice.

'Admittedly,' said Arthur, 'they're longer than I usually like them, but ...'

'Isn't there anything,' squawked Ford in avian fury, 'you feel you ought to be telling us?'

The voice cleared its throat. A giant *petit four* lolloped off into the distance.

'Welcome,' the voice said, 'to the Starship Heart of Gold.'

The voice continued.

'Please do not be alarmed,' it said, 'by anything you see or hear around you. You are bound to feel some initial ill effects as you have been rescued from certain death at an improbability level of two to the power of two hundred and seventy-six thousand to one against – possibly much higher. We are now cruising at a level of two to the power of twenty-five thousand to one against and falling, and we will be restoring normality just as soon as we are sure what is normal anyway. Thank you. Two to the power of twenty thousand to one against and falling.'

The voice cut out.

Ford and Arthur were in a small luminous pink cubicle.

Ford was wildly excited.

'Arthur!' he said, 'this is fantastic! We've been picked up by a ship powered by the Infinite Improbability Drive! This is incredible! I heard rumours about it before! They were all officially denied, but they must have done it! They've built the Improbability Drive! Arthur, this is ... Arthur? What's happening?'

Arthur had jammed himself against the door to the cubicle, trying to hold it closed, but it was ill fitting. Tiny furry little hands were squeezing themselves through the cracks, their fingers were inkstained; tiny voices chattered insanely.

Arthur looked up.

'Ford!' he said, 'there's an infinite number of monkeys outside who want to talk to us about this script for *Hamlet* they've worked out.'

The Infinite Improbability Drive is a wonderful new method of crossing vast interstellar distances in a mere nothingth of a second, without all that tedious mucking about in hyperspace.

It was discovered by a lucky chance, and then developed into a governable form of propulsion by the Galactic Government's research team on Damogran.

This, briefly, is the story of its discovery.

The principle of generating small amounts of *finite* improbability by simply hooking the logic circuits of a Bambleweeny 57 Sub-Meson Brain to an atomic vector plotter suspended in a strong Brownian Motion producer (say a nice cup of tea) were of course well understood – and such generators were often used to break the ice at parties by making all the molecules in the hostess's undergarments leap simultaneously one foot to the left, in accordance with the Theory of Indeterminacy.

Many respectable physicists said that they weren't going to stand for this – partly because it was a debasement of science, but mostly because they didn't get invited to those sort of parties.

Another thing they couldn't stand was the perpetual failure they encountered in trying to construct a machine which could generate the *infinite* improbability field needed to flip a spaceship across the mind-paralysing distances between the furthest stars, and in the end they grumpily announced that such a machine was virtually impossible.

Then, one day, a student who had been left to sweep up the lab after a particularly unsuccessful party found himself reasoning this way:

If, he thought to himself, such a machine is a *virtual* impossibility, then it must logically be a *finite* improbability. So all I have to do in order to make one is to work out exactly how improbable it is, feed that figure into the finite improbability generator, give it a fresh cup of really hot tea ... and turn it on!

He did this, and was rather startled to discover that he had managed to create the long sought after golden Infinite Improbability generator out of thin air.

It startled him even more when just after he was awarded the Galactic Institute's Prize for Extreme Cleverness he got lynched by a rampaging mob of respectable physicists who had finally realized that the one thing they really couldn't stand was a smartass.

Good Neighbours

Richard Gordon

Peregrine was my visitor from London. He is a smart fellow, with square glasses, a moustache wilting like a bar of chocolate in the sun, corduroy shoes and leather trousers, a pad in Chelsea and a job in public relations. He chaffed me on my possession of a watch and a calendar.

'Surely, me old darling,' Peregrine said, in that voice weary from continual subjection to the daily hectic whirl of the London Underground. 'You don't need such implements, not in *your* life. It makes not the slightest difference down here what hour or month it is. And it must be bleeding difficult to tell, anyway.'

I explained to my sharp urban friend, that was precisely why I required such *aides-memoire* to the passage of time. 'You city folk are obsessed with hours and minutes,' I chided him, kindly but assertively. 'Here in the suburbs, we can sit back on our patios and observe the sun's daily picket across the sky. And we appreciate each solar march from dawn to nightfall as part of his glorious, multi-hued procession from each year's frost-bitten, dusky start to its end under similar conditions.'

'Suppose the bleeding sun isn't shining, then?' he demanded, with that sourness which lies upon city dwellers like the mould on the overlooked Czechoslovakian gherkins.

'For the eye, and for the ear, of those among us who have sat at Mother Nature's dame school,' I reproved him gently, 'the season of the year and time of day is apparent from our immediate surroundings. Just as you sophisticated people discover them from the changing displays in Harrods windows or the Post Office speaking clock.'

I leant back in my gaily coloured deckchair, observing contentedly the sparrows disporting in the bird-bath against the lawn, under the well-creosoted trellis with the ramblers. Butch, our miniature poodle, lay newly clipped at my feet. Above my head spread the striped beach umbrella we had brought back from Fuengirola, stuck in its flowerpot of gravel. It was a glorious summer evening, the sun still high over the conical yew, the patio glowing in its nook beside the car port. We were sipping our gin-and-Slimlines, while the wife in the kitchen was preparing our dinner and listening to the Archers.

In a patient voice, I painted for Peregrine the subtle shading of the seasons in suburbia.

We know that spring has come, when the Atcos start chattering merrily to one another and the Tarpens screech happily in the hedgerows. The scritch-scritch of the hoe rises from the rose arbours, the milkman whistles as he clinks down his morning bottles, and we locate again the tennis markers on the lawn by jabbing all round with the hand-fork. The joyful vernal festival is upon us, of turning off the central heating and resetting the boiler time-switch for hot water only. In the lengthening evening sun, suburban men gossip over their fences, as for generation upon generation, about the impossibility of meeting the rate demands.

In summer, the tennis players perform their ritual dances, uttering their wild orgasmic cries. The dawn chorus of sparrows now rouses us, even before the lively hoots of the earliest electric train. From the sward comes the tangy fragrance of hormonal weedkillers, and in the evening the gentle rain droppeth from the Green Queen. When dusk begins to edge on midnight, the television screens shine with faint, bluish flicker to each other through the open picture windows, like mating glow-worms.

Come autumn, our village lies under a pall of smoke. How delightful are the passive pleasures of pyromania! We lean on our rubber rakes, in our wartime duffle coats, in our wellies patched by the children's puncture outfits, placidly watching the combustion of leaves ignited by yesterday's *Telegraph*. As we contemplate the billowy column, rising straight into the darkening teatime air like some released but benevolent genie, perhaps we give a thought to the ultimate incineration which awaits us all over at Beckenham Crematorium.

We squirt aerosols on the final marauding wasps, we gather in the plastic trug our last maggot-laden apples, we scrape a summer's cuttings from the Flymo and make chutney from the immutably green tomatoes. The early frosts rime the decorative ironwork and even glaze the bird-bath. They also sear enough vegetation to reveal the featherboarding which we meant to repair in the spring, and which still suggests a set of bad teeth.

Approaching winter chivvies the busy husbandman. Dahlias once blackened must be lifted, and laid carefully in Sainsbury's cardboard boxes next to the deep freeze in the garage. Beds must be replanted with shrubs and roses from the garden centre. The tennis-netting is taken down, the car Bluecoled and garaged securely for the night.

When the cold frames have been finally frost-proofed, when the dog's tartan coat has been looked out from the loft and examined for moth-holes, when the electric blanket has been plugged-in with the Teasmade, and when the sodium lamps' amber gleam cheers the homecoming traveller through the chilly haze, then we can stretch our slippered toes towards the smokeless Gloco and relax in our cardi with our Cadbury's drinking chocolate over the winter schedules on the telly.

Soon we know that Christmas is coming, because of the drunks in the pubs.

As I finished my recital of the suburbanite's calendar, Peregrine took a drag at his fragrant Gauloise and tipped up his drained glass for the fourth occasion, in the hope of being offered another gin-and-Slimline.

For a moment he was silent. 'Man, you know how it all sounds? Like Hollywood in the 1920s,' he said, not entirely seriously. 'Or maybe the Roman Empire, just between the lovely decline and the fall.'

'Admittedly, the pastoral changes with our seasons may be simple,' I retaliated quite sharply from my deckchair. 'But they are only adjustments made to Nature, expressing an ecology which is infinitely complex.'

'You're joking?'

'Let me describe to you a typical day in Suburbia.'

He made no reply, just crushed out his Gauloise in the souvenir ashtray from Rimini and tipped his empty glass rapidly twice. I proceeded.

I depicted each village morning, beginning with a reveille of burglar alarms, sleepily triggered by inhabitants blearily groping for the newspapers on the mat. At seven, the Post Office sends a man round to rev up a pop-popping two-stroke under the bedroom windows, to wake up the remaining sluggards. The first hour of the day tightly compresses the most violent activity. Dogs and cats are let out and in. The bathroom is occupied and reoccupied with the split-second timing of a Feydeau farce. Traffic bulletins must be absorbed from the transistor while the attention is simultaneously engaged in eating or shaving or reading the newspaper or shouting at the children, on some mornings all four together. The whole house is vibrant with the flush of toilets.

The hour ends in a sudden and amazing climax. All the males hurriedly flee. They leave the women with Tony Blackburn and utterly unprotected. This regular daily abandonment finds no parallel in any anthropological study known to the world. The males' only safeguard is a makeshift chastity belt of prying, under-school-age children.

Predators move in swiftly. Milkmen, deliverymen, dustmen to redistribute the household rubbish along the front path. Repairmen, whose numbers equal the square of the number of labour-saving gadgets inside (*The Law of Dynamic Obsolescence*). Men with tatty vans, selling eggs and manure guaranteed fresh from the farm. Men with a load of tar left over from the last job, eager to tarmac the drive cheap. Pollsters and Jehovah's Witnesses. Men giving good prices for old silver. And window cleaners, all with the blood of George Formby flowing in their veins.

Among these predators appears from time to time the local medicine man. He enjoys a different and enviable status.

The medicine man's holy aura, his fearsome power, his essentiality in ill-health, his necessity in even the simplest activities and plans of suburban life, afford him the unquestioning reverence and even abasement of his flock. The medicine man can enter any house he wishes, without even setting a definite time in advance. The woman can be entirely alone, in bed, stark naked. The medicine man simply rings the doorbell and goes upstairs to the bedroom.

Such is the awesomeness of the medicine man that the husband readily accepts this conduct. He may even suggest it. He would not generally do the same with, for instance, an insurance broker who was a fellow-member of the golf club.

The medicine man carries his bag of charms, strange and frightening designs in metal, glass and plastic. He will display some of his charms in the bedroom, but never all of them at once. The case contains also his *ju-ju*, which he always uses while weaving his spells.

The ju-ju closely resembles a water-diviner's cleft stick, and is employed for the same purpose. The medicine man wears it round his neck. Though the ju-ju is primarily to detect the evil in his suppliants, the medicine man affords it a secondary role in the performance of ritualistic, and sometimes threatening, gestures towards them.

His mystique and frightening potency are enough in themselves to reduce his votaries to dumb intimidation or terror. He has no necessity to perform ritual dances or intone chants in the course of his duties. But his magic spells are pronounced in tones of considerable and sometimes crushing solemnity.

The indispensable item of the medicine man's equipment is his mask. It carries an expression of amiable, bland impassiveness, resembling the smiling Buddhas of the Ming period during the sixteenth century. The mask is to shield his inner feelings. They can only be speculated upon by the women when the medicine man lays hands – without encouragement, or even much invitation – upon the most intimate portions of their bodies. The husband does not object to this, and it is thought that the woman does not, either.

Still wearing his mask, playing with his ju-ju, the medicine man hears all the deepest, and often the otherwise unuttered, confidences of the village. He is the only suburban man, apart from her husband, with whom a suburban woman can freely, unguiltily and conveniently share her innermost secrets. And often the husband does not get to know the half of it.

The medicine man is careful never to form an attachment to any particular woman in the village. Nor does he give her the remotest impression that such would be possible. 'Dodge the grab when they try to hold your hand,' a seasoned medicine man of the suburbs told me. 'I advise them all to join the Weight Watchers. It seems to turn them off.'

Persistence with this cautiously distant, but doubtless infuriating, attitude allows the medicine man to enjoy the intimacy of all the available women in the village.

I had reached no further with this account of a single, and to myself fascinating, day in the life of our village, when my lady wife appeared smiling on the patio for her customary Campari, announcing that dinner was shortly to be served. We had sacrificed a chicken to the stranger, in the way of the simple natives in Dahomey (Geoffrey Gorer, *Africa Dances*). As we entered our dining-room with the green flock wallpaper and bracket lights, I was pleased to notice that the wife had served with it, in deference to Peregrine's sophistication, frozen runner beans instead of her usual peas. The repast opened with freshly thawed prawns in Heinz salad cream and afters was ices.

My house is among the oldest in BR1 2AX. It is of russet Edwardian brick, tile-hung and shingle-roofed, its chimneys as graceful as a pianist's fingers pointing smokeless to the sky, built amid a nest of scaffold-poles in sand-tubs by ragged trousered philanthropists. The dormer window of my attic workroom views like a watchtower the gardens and glades, the shrubberies and copses (subject to tree-preservation orders), the rooftops and green-houses, the barbecues and climbing-frames, the eternal, measured flashing of the traffic lights and the twinkling direction-indicators which comprise our busy village. Its sounds have grown as familiar to me as the beat of the sea to a fisherman. Even with the windows firmly shut, I hear the rattle of the electric trains like hastening steel skeletons, the strident wail of police-car and fire-engine, the summer transistor warbling its tuneless note, the competitive snarl of young men's motor-bikes, and the lively chatter of schoolchildren, playing their boisterous little sexy games and lighting their fags once out of school.

I have seen twenty-one years of our country's history reflected in the usually expressionless face of BR1 2AX. After the servants had departed, and before the electronically programmed wash had arrived, houses living in companionship to mine honeycombed themselves into awkward little flats. In the property boom of the 1960s, much Edwardian brickwork was demolished, house and garden was replaced with a new town of Chartreuse-coloured roofs and white plastic clapboard.

The fences were down, front lawn was confluent with front lawn. The abodes stood as close as volumes on a shelf, conversation in any lounge becoming confusingly mingled with that in the next (*The Ayckbourn Effect*). Neighbourliness was brought to the village at last, by the property developers. But your true-bred suburban man is a Conservative fellow, suspicious of new-fangled inventions, and the neighbourliness has been used as little as the pre-installed bathroom ultraviolet sun lamp or the heatless imitation coal fire.

Now there is a property slump again. Times resemble that winter when I first viewed the residence, tramping up a frosted drive to discover a tangled garden and that someone had pinched the lead from the roof. Estate agents' boards once more droop and rot over the fences, as forlorn as ensigns from the taffrails of laid-up ships. BR1 2AX may be on its way to a ghost village, dilapidated and unmown, populated by a few hammered stockbrokers, bankrupt company directors and underwriters for whom the Lutine Bell has tolled.

So bleak an end recently decided us to move. I wrote for particulars of houses in the near-by villages of TN9 and TN13, even as far afield as RU8. Only one residence appealed to me. Its attractive features included charming L-shaped oak-panelled hall, sun-trap patio, double garaging, mature garden, sep. WC and spacious receps. The price was exactly what we could afford. I discovered that I had picked up the estate agent's description of my own house. We bought it.

We shall never get to Montego Bay. I can make myself as happy in suburbia as Robinson Crusoe on his desert island, because I have a suburban mind. This is cause for neither shame nor denial. The commuter-computed suburbs of London run from Broadstairs to Bath, which is convenient for Bristol, and from Worthing to Leamington Spa on the edge of Birmingham. The residents of both Philadelphia and Baltimore live in the suburbs of both New York and Washington. Legislators commute as easily from Canberra to Sydney as from Ottawa to Montreal. The European Economic Community had to be formed because Brussels lies in the suburbs of all the principal towns of North Europe.

Millions of Americans have been uprooted from their homes to live in Zip Code, a place akin to Dodge City. French peasants have been forced into *Boîtes*, which are nightclubs. Rugged Australians from the outback are penned like their own sheep into Boxes, and South Africans scattered across the veldt even done up into numbered Bags.

The world's suburbs extend unbroken from Funabashi north of Tokyo to Sea Point near Cape Town, from St Kilda south of Melbourne to Whytecliff outside Vancouver, via Bogorodskoye on the outskirts of Moscow. We are all suburbanites now. Even from Cap Ferrat, you can get a bus equally easily to Nice or Monte Carlo.

The Other Half

Richard Ingrams & John Wells

In his highly confidential correspondence to a golfing friend, Bill, the fictional Mr Thatcher zooms in on the situation in Guadaloupe.

Dear Bill,

Thanks a bunch for your p.c. from Guadaloupe. I say, what a remarkably fine pair! The lady in question, though somewhat duskier of countenance, put me very much in mind of the barmaid at the Goat & Compasses at Sandwich in the old days. Vera, I think her name was, but I expect she's gone to the broker's yard long since, poor old thing. Luckily M. was late coming down that morning, so I was able to slip it into my dressing-gown pocket without the usual acrimony.

I imagine word has reached you of our little Dieppe raid. As you know, the Major had been on at me for some time to join him and Picarda on a day off the leash, the plan being for a trip across the Channel on the ferry, a slap-up beano at one of those big French watering-holes – five courses and fifty-seven varieties of booze, followed by a bracing eighteen holes at the nearby links run by a very decent expatriate accountant chum of Picarda's. After which, tinctures were envisaged prior to a real God Almighty blowout at a four-star establishment where they cook everything in alcohol, ending up with a tour of the waterfront nightspots, casino etc, and back home on the dawn hovercraft. Not a bad itinerary, I think you'll agree, Bill, and my only slight qualm was that your absence in tropical zones would mean that you could only be with us in spirit. Many a slip, however, twixt cup and lip, best laid plans etc.

M. had taken three days off at some damnfool health hydro at Virginia Water – a total waste of money if you ask me but Fatty Soames said he shed three stones there in a week and Saatchis have been leaning on her to do something about her chins – so the coast was clear. I drove the Humber down to Folkestone, taking on board the Major and little Picarda at the Flag & Anchor, and after a bracing snort or twain contre le mal de mer we drove the old bus onto the Sealink Ferry. Usual rather tripperish crowd on board, but we managed to commandeer a quiet corner of the bar on B Deck, and we were soon putting the world to rights with the help of an impressive army of miniatures.

At some point – I can't remember when, but we were certainly well out to sea – we found ourselves joined by a rather crusty old bugger from Roehampton who claimed he had been at school with me, though I couldn't for the life of me put a name to him. I find it pretty hard to put a name to anyone, quite honestly Bill, nowadays. Do you find that, as you get older? Eric, the priggish little twerp, says it's the drink but according to our GP, whose name funnily enough I can't remember either, about three billion brain cells burn off every year in any normal person after the age of nineteen. Anyway, this cove Mackevoy, or it may have been Patterson, had some kind of log stove business near Wokingham that was making a fortune, and he and Picarda immediately got on like a house on fire.

Time flew by and before we knew it the ship lurched violently to one side as all the ghastly trippers rushed to the rail to catch their first glimpse of La Belle France. We old codgers had seen it all before and decided to stay below. I thought something was up from the tone of the voices upstairs. The ship seemed to be stationary for rather a long time, and various incomprehensible announcements were made over the tannoy. Eventually the Major suggested we pop up on deck for a shufty.

I had always been under the impression, Bill, that one of the few things to be said in favour of our Gallic neighbours across the water was that they kept the lower orders in their place. From time to time the workers get a bit restless during the hot weather and start winkling out the cobblestones with a view to using them as offensive weapons, whereupon the Riot Police know exactly what to do and do it pretty damn quick. None of that Blair Peach nonsense over there. Well, all I can say is that that appears to be a thing of the past.

From where we stood on the deck you could quite clearly see the quayside awash with tiny black figures in berets and three days' growth of beard, behaving like bloody hooligans and not a gendarme in sight. As I said to old whatever his name was, the log-burner wallah, Grunwick all over again. Banners waving about, chanting of idiotic slogans in their incomprehensible lingo, and meanwhile progress of SS *Sibelius* effectively blocked by a barrage of little bateaux roped together, and weighed down to the gunwhales with more gesticulating Frogs, all yelling the odds about the price of Golden Delicious, or something else dear to their hearts.

The Major, to do him credit, took in the situation at a glance. No time to be wasted. Up the little steps to the bridge and a sharp word with Captain Olafsson, a shifty cove with a beard who looked to be the worse for drink, telling him to do his duty as a Norwegian and go full steam ahead through the fishing boats and get us to the restaurant before our table was given away to the natives. All to no avail, Bill. Grin grin from Olafsson, 'of course, gentlemen', next thing we know four burly matelots appear from nowhere and usher us below with no great ceremony. Another half hour elapses, a bit of parley-voo through the megaphone, one or two of the more spirited trippers lob the odd beer bottle at the Frog, fire is returned with airgun pellets and the Captain does a smart about-turn to Folkestone. The Major, who by now is in a very nasty mood – the bar unaccountably having run dry – insists once ashore on buttonholing a bloke in the ticket office and asks for our money back. Thingummybob, the log-burner, does his best to restrain him before the police arrive, and we spend a very miserable evening in a horrible little pub down by the docks with a very loud jukebox, being sneered at by a gang of punks on their way to set fire to the pier.

I tell you, Bill, that's the last time I have any truck with Abroad. Sticky said it was just as bad going by air. He and Polly had to spend four hours sitting on the runway at Benidorm in a temperature of 106 degrees, screaming babies being sick all over them, and all because a couple of Spanish oiks with table tennis bats wanted a longer teabreak. I told M. when she got back, from her hydro, looking pretty tetchy I must say, that this old country of ours may be a bugger's muddle but at least you can speak the language. Do tell, Bill, how did you manage in Martinique?

Yours agog,

DENIS

Pig-Hoo-o-o-o-ey!

P. G. Wodehouse

Thanks to the publicity given to the matter by *The Bridgnorth, Shifnal, and Albrighton Argus* (with which is incorporated *The Wheat-Growers' Intelligence and Stock Breeders' Gazetteer*), the whole world today knows that the silver medal in the Fat Pigs class at the eighty-seventh annual Shropshire Agricultural Show was won by the Earl of Emsworth's black Berkshire sow, Empress of Blandings.

Very few people, however, are aware how near that splendid animal came to missing the coveted honour.

Now it can be told.

This brief chapter of Secret History may be said to have begun on the night of the eighteenth of July, when George Cyril Wellbeloved (twenty-nine), pig-man in the employ of Lord Emsworth, was arrested by Police-Constable Evans of Market Blandings for being drunk and disorderly in the tap-room of the Goat and Feathers. On July the nineteenth, after first offering to apologize, then explaining that it had been his birthday, and finally attempting to prove an alibi, George Cyril was very properly jugged for fourteen days without the option of a fine.

On July the twentieth, Empress of Blandings, always hitherto a hearty and even a boisterous feeder, for the first time on record declined all nourishment. And on the morning of July the twenty-first, the veterinary surgeon called in to diagnose and deal with this strange asceticism, was compelled to confess to Lord Emsworth that the thing was beyond his professional skill.

Let us just see, before proceeding, that we have got these dates correct:

July 18. – Birthday Orgy of Cyril Wellbeloved.
July 19. – Incarceration of Ditto.
July 20. – Pig Lays off the Vitamins.
July 21. – Veterinary Surgeon Baffled.
Right.

The effect of the veterinary surgeon's announcement on Lord Emsworth was overwhelming. As a rule, the wear and tear of our complex modern life left this vague and amiable peer unscathed. So long as he had sunshine, regular meals, and complete freedom from the society of his younger son Frederick, he was placidly happy. But there were chinks in his armour, and one of these had been pierced this morning. Dazed by the news he stood at the window of the great library of Blandings Castle, looking out with unseeing eyes.

As he stood there, the door opened. Lord Emsworth turned; and having blinked once or twice, as was his habit when confronted suddenly with anything, recognized in the handsome and imperious looking woman who had entered, his sister, Lady Constance Keeble. Her demeanour, like his own, betrayed the deepest agitation.

'Clarence,' she cried, 'an awful thing has happened.'

Lord Emsworth nodded dully. 'I know. He's just told me.'

'What! Has he been here?'

'Only this moment left.'

'Why did you let him go? You must have known I would want to see him.'

'What good would that have done?'

'I could at least have assured him of my sympathy,' said Lady Constance stiffly.

'Yes, I suppose you could,' said Lord Emsworth, having considered the point. 'Not that he deserves any sympathy. The man's an ass.'

'Nothing of the kind. A most intelligent young man, as young men go.'

'Young? Would you call him young? Fifty, I should have said, if a day.'

'Are you out of your senses? Heacham fifty?'

'Not Heacham. Smithers.'

As frequently happened to her in conversation with her brother, Lady Constance experienced a swimming sensation.

'Will you kindly tell me, Clarence, in a few simple words, what you imagine we are talking about?'

'I'm talking about Smithers. Empress of Blandings is refusing her food, and Smithers says he can't do anything about it. And he calls himself a vet!'

'Then you haven't heard? Clarence, a dreadful thing has happened. Angela has broken off her engagement to Heacham.'

'And the Agricultural Show on Wednesday week!'

'What on earth has that got to do with it?' demanded Lady Constance, feeling a recurrence of the swimming sensation.

'What has it got to do with it?' said Lord Emsworth warmly. 'My champion sow, with less than ten days to prepare herself for a most searching examination in competition with all the finest pigs in the county, starts refusing her food—'

'Will you stop maundering on about your insufferable pig and give your attention to something that really matters? I tell you that Angela – your niece Angela – has broken off her engagement to Lord Heacham and expresses her intention of marrying that hopeless ne'er-do-well, James Belford.'

'The son of old Belford, the parson?'

'Yes.'

'She can't. He's in America.'

'He is not in America. He is in London.'

'No,' said Lord Emsworth, shaking his head sagely. 'You're wrong. I remember meeting his father two years ago out on the road by Meeker's twenty-acre field, and he distinctly told me the boy was sailing for America next day. He must be there by this time.'

'Can't you understand? He's come back.'

'Oh? Come back? I see. Come *back*?'

'You know there was once a silly sentimental sort of affair between him and Angela; but a year after he left she became engaged to Heacham and I thought the whole thing was over and done with. And now it seems she met this young man Belford when she was in London last week, and it has started all over again. She tells me she has written to Heacham and broken the engagement.'

There was a silence. Brother and sister remained for a space plunged in thought. Lord Emsworth was the first to speak.

'We've tried acorns,' he said. 'We've tried skim milk. And we've tried potato-peel. But, no, she won't touch them.'

Conscious of two eyes raising blisters on his sensitive skin, he came to himself with a start.

'Absurd! Ridiculous! Preposterous!' he said, hurriedly. 'Breaking the engagement? Pooh! Tush! What nonsense! I'll have a word with that young man. If he thinks he can go about the place playing fast and loose with my niece and jilting her without so much as a –'

'Clarence!'

Lord Emsworth blinked. Something appeared to be wrong, but he could not imagine what. It seemed to him that in his last speech he had struck just the right note – strong, forceful, dignified.

'Eh?'

'It is Angela who has broken the engagement.'

'Oh, Angela?'

'She is infatuated with this man Belford. And the point is, what are we to do about it?'

Lord Emsworth reflected.

'Take a strong line,' he said firmly. 'Stand no nonsense. Don't send 'em a wedding-present.'

There is no doubt that, given time, Lady Constance would have found and uttered some adequately corrosive comment on this imbecile suggestion; but even as she was swelling preparatory to giving tongue, the door opened and a girl came in.

She was a pretty girl, with fair hair and blue eyes which in their softer moments probably reminded all sorts of people of twin lagoons slumbering beneath a southern sky. This, however, was not one of those moments. To Lord Emsworth, as they met his, they looked like something out of an oxy-acetylene blow-pipe; and, as far as he was capable of being disturbed by anything that was not his younger son Frederick, he was disturbed. Angela, it seemed to him, was upset about something; and he was sorry. He liked Angela.

To ease a tense situation, he said:

'Angela, my dear, do you know anything about pigs?'

The girl laughed. One of those sharp, bitter laughs which are so unpleasant just after breakfast.

'Yes, I do. You're one.'

'Me?'

'Yes, you. Aunt Constance says that, if I marry Jimmy, you won't let me have my money.'

'Money? Money?' Lord Emsworth was mildly puzzled. 'What money? You never lent me any money.'

Lady Constance's feelings found vent in a sound like an overheated radiator.

'I believe this absent-mindedness of yours is nothing but a ridiculous pose, Clarence. You know perfectly well that when poor Jane died she left you Angela's trustee.'

'And I can't touch my money without your consent till I'm twenty-five.'

'Well, how old are you?'

'Twenty-one.'

'Then what are you worrying about?' asked Lord Emsworth, surprised. 'No need to worry about it for another four years. God bless my soul, the money is quite safe. It is in excellent securities.'

Angela stamped her foot. An unladylike action, but how much better than kicking an uncle with it, as her lower nature prompted.

'I have told Angela,' explained Lady Constance, 'that, while we naturally cannot force her to marry Lord Heacham, we can at least keep her money from being squandered by this wastrel on whom she proposes to throw herself away.'

'He isn't a wastrel. He's got quite enough money to marry me on, but he wants some capital to buy a partnership in a –'

'He is a wastrel. Wasn't he sent abroad because –'

'That was two years ago. And since then –'

'My dear Angela, you may argue until –'

'I'm not arguing. I'm simply saying that I'm going to marry Jimmy, if we both have to starve in the gutter.'

'What gutter?' asked his lordship, wrenching his errant mind away from thoughts of acorns.

'Any gutter.'

'Now, please listen to me, Angela.'

It seemed to Lord Emsworth that there was a frightful amount of conversation going on. He had the sensation of having become a mere bit of flotsam upon a tossing sea of female voices. Both his sister and his niece appeared to have much to say, and they were saying it simultaneously and *fortissimo*. He looked wistfully at the door.

It was smoothly done. A twist of the handle, and he was beyond those voices where there was peace. Galloping gaily down the stairs, he charged out into the sunshine.

His gaiety was not long-lived. Free at last to concentrate itself on the really serious issues of life, his mind grew sombre and grim. Once more there descended upon him the cloud which had been oppressing his soul before all this Heacham-Angela-Belford business began. Each step that took him nearer to the sty where the ailing Empress resided seemed a heavier step than the last. He reached the sty; and, draping himself over the rails, peered moodily at the vast expanse of pig within.

For, even though she had been doing a bit of dieting of late, Empress of Blandings was far from being an ill-nourished animal. She resembled a captive balloon with ears and a tail, and was as nearly circular as a pig can be without bursting. Nevertheless, Lord Emsworth, as he regarded her, mourned and would not be comforted. A few more square meals under her belt, and no pig in all Shropshire could have held its head up in the Empress's presence. And now, just for lack of those few meals, the supreme animal would probably be relegated to the mean obscurity of an 'Honourably Mentioned'. It was bitter, bitter.

He became aware that somebody was speaking to him; and, turning, perceived a solemn young man in riding breeches.

'I say,' said the young man.

Lord Emsworth, though he would have preferred solitude, was relieved to find that the intruder was at least one of his own sex. Women are apt to stray off into side-issues, but men are practical and can be relied on to stick to the fundamentals. Besides, young Heacham probably kept pigs himself and might have a useful hint or two up his sleeve.

'I say, I've just ridden over to see if there was anything I could do about this fearful business.'

'Uncommonly kind and thoughtful of you, my dear fellow,' said Lord Emsworth, touched. 'I fear things look very black.'

'It's an absolute mystery to me.'

'To me, too.'

'I mean to say, she was all right last week.'

'She was all right as late as the day before yesterday.'

'Seemed quite cheery and chirpy and all that.'

'Entirely so.'

'And then this happens – out of a blue sky, as you might say.'

'Exactly. It is insoluble. We have done everything possible to tempt her appetite.'

'Her appetite? Is Angela ill?'

'Angela? No, I fancy not. She seemed perfectly well a few minutes ago.'

'You've seen her this morning, then? Did she say anything about this fearful business?'

'No. She was speaking about some money.'

'It's all so dashed unexpected.'

'Like a bolt from the blue,' agreed Lord Emsworth. 'Such a thing has never happened before. I fear the worst. According to the Wolff-Lehmann feeding standards, a pig, if in health, should consume daily nourishment amounting to fifty-seven thousand eight hundred calories, these to consist of proteins four pounds five ounces, carbohydrates twenty-five pounds –'

'What has that got to do with Angela?'

'Angela?'

'I came to find out why Angela has broken off our engagement.'

Lord Emsworth marshalled his thoughts. He had a misty idea that he had heard something mentioned about that. It came back to him.

'Ah, yes, of course. She has broken off the engagement, hasn't she? I believe it is because she is in love with someone else. Yes, now that I recollect, that was distinctly stated. The whole thing comes back to me quite clearly. Angela has decided to marry someone else. I knew there was some satisfactory explanation. Tell me, my dear fellow, what are your views on linseed meal?'

'What do you mean, linseed meal?'

'Why, linseed meal,' said Lord Emsworth, not being able to find a better definition. 'As a food for pigs.'

'Oh, curse all pigs!'

'What!' There was a sort of astounded horror in Lord Emsworth's voice. He had never been particularly fond of young Heacham, for he was not a man who took much to his juniors, but he had not supposed him capable of anarchistic sentiments like this. 'What did you say?'

'I said, "Curse all pigs!" You keep talking about pigs. I'm not interested in pigs. I don't want to discuss pigs. Blast and damn every pig in existence!'

Lord Emsworth watched him, as he strode away, with an emotion that was partly indignation and partly relief – indignation that a landowner and a fellow son of Shropshire could have brought himself to utter such words, and relief that one capable of such utterance was not going to marry into his family. He had always in his woollen-headed way been very fond of his niece Angela, and it was nice to think that the child had such solid good sense and so much cool discernment. Many girls of her age would have been carried away by the glamour of young Heacham's position and wealth; but she, divining with an intuition beyond her years that he was unsound on the subject of pigs, had drawn back while there was still time and refused to marry him.

A pleasant glow suffused Lord Emsworth's bosom, to be frozen out a few moments later as he perceived his sister Constance bearing down upon him. Lady Constance was a beautiful woman, but there were times when the charm of her face was marred by a rather curious expression; and from nursery days onward his lordship had learned that this expression meant trouble. She was wearing it now.

'Clarence,' she said, 'I have had enough of this nonsense of Angela and young Belford. The thing cannot be allowed to go drifting on. You must catch the two o'clock train to London.'

'What! Why?'

'You must see this man Belford and tell him that, if Angela insists on marrying him, she will not have a penny for four years. I shall be greatly surprised if that piece of information does not put an end to the whole business.'

Lord Emsworth scratched meditatively at the Empress's tank-like back. A mutinous expression was on his mild face.

'Don't see why she shouldn't marry the fellow,' he mumbled.

'Marry James Belford?'

'I don't see why not. Seems fond of him and all that.'

'You never have had a grain of sense in your head, Clarence. Angela is going to marry Heacham.'

'Can't stand that man. All wrong about pigs.'

'Clarence, I don't wish to have any more discussion and argument. You will go to London on the two o'clock train. You will see Mr Belford. And you will tell him about Angela's money. Is that quite clear?'

'Oh, all right,' said his lordship moodily. 'All right, all right.'

The emotions of the Earl of Emsworth, as he sat next day facing his luncheon-guest, James Bartholomew Belford, across a table in the main dining-room of the Senior Conservative Club, were not of the liveliest and most agreeable. It was bad enough to be in London at all on such a day of golden sunshine. To be charged, while there, with the task of blighting the romance of two young people for whom he entertained a warm regard was unpleasant to a degree.

For, now that he had given the matter thought, Lord Emsworth recalled that he had always liked this boy Belford. A pleasant lad, with, he remembered now, a healthy fondness for that rural existence which so appealed to himself. By no means the sort of fellow who, in the very presence and hearing of Empress of Blandings, would have spoken disparagingly and with oaths of pigs as a class. It occurred to Lord Emsworth, as it has occurred to so many people, that the distribution of money in this world is all wrong. Why should a man like pig-despising Heacham have a rent roll that ran into the tens of thousands, while this very deserving youngster had nothing?

These thoughts not only saddened Lord Emsworth – they embarrassed him. He hated unpleasantness, and it was suddenly borne in upon him that, after he had broken the news that Angela's bit of capital was locked up and not likely to get loose, conversation with his young friend during the remainder of lunch would tend to be somewhat difficult.

He made up his mind to postpone the revelation. During the meal, he decided, he would chat pleasantly of this and that; and then later, while bidding his guest good-bye, he would spring the thing on him suddenly and dive back into the recesses of the club.

Considerably cheered at having solved a delicate problem with such adroitness, he started to prattle.

'The gardens at Blandings,' he said, 'are looking particularly attractive this summer. My head-gardener, Angus McAllister, is a man with whom I do not always find myself seeing eye to eye, notably in the matter of hollyhocks, on which I consider his views subversive to a degree; but there is no denying that he understands roses. The rose garden –'

'How well I remember that rose garden,' said James Belford, sighing slightly and helping himself to brussels sprouts. 'It was there that Angela and I used to meet on summer mornings.'

Lord Emsworth blinked. This was not an encouraging start, but the Emsworths were a fighting clan. He had another try.

'I have seldom seen such a blaze of colour as was to be witnessed there during the month of June. Both McAllister and I adopted a very strong policy with the slugs and plant lice, with the result that the place was a mass of flourishing Damasks and Ayrshires and –'

'Properly to appreciate roses,' said James Belford, 'you want to see them as a setting for a girl like Angela. With her fair hair gleaming against the green leaves she makes a rose garden seem a veritable Paradise.'

'No doubt,' said Lord Emsworth. 'No doubt. I am glad you liked my rose garden. At Blandings, of course, we have the natural advantage of loamy soil, rich in plant food and humus; but, as I often say to McAllister, and on this point we have never had the slightest disagreement, loamy soil by itself is not enough. You must have manure. If every autumn a liberal mulch of stable manure is spread upon the beds and the coarser parts removed in the spring before the annual forking –'

'Angela tells me,' said James Belford, 'that you have forbidden our marriage.'

Lord Emsworth choked dismally over his chicken. Directness of this kind, he told himself with a pang of self-pity, was the sort of thing young Englishmen picked up in America. Diplomatic circumlocution flourished only in a more leisurely civilization, and in those energetic and forceful surroundings you learned to Talk Quick and Do It Now, and all sorts of uncomfortable things.

'Er – well, yes, now you mention it, I believe some informal decision of that nature was arrived at. You see, my dear fellow, my sister Constance feels rather strongly–'

'I understand. I suppose she thinks I'm a sort of prodigal.'

'No, no, my dear fellow. She never said that. Wastrel was the term she employed.'

'Well, perhaps I did start out in business on those lines. But you can take it from me that when you find yourself employed on a farm in Nebraska belonging to an applejack-nourished patriarch with strong views on work and a good vocabulary, you soon develop a certain liveliness.'

'Are you employed on a farm?'

'I was employed on a farm.'

'Pigs?' said Lord Emsworth in a low, eager voice.

'Among other things.'

Lord Emsworth gulped. His fingers clutched at the table-cloth.

'Then perhaps, my dear fellow, you can give me some advice. For the last two days my prize sow, Empress of Blandings, has declined all nourishment. And the Agricultural Show is on Wednesday week. I am distracted with anxiety.'

James Belford frowned thoughtfully.

'What does your pig-man say about it?'

'My pig-man was sent to prison two days ago. Two days!' For the first time the significance of the coincidence struck him. 'You don't think that can have anything to do with the animal's loss of appetite?'

'Certainly. I imagine she is missing him and pining away because he isn't there.'

Lord Emsworth was surprised. He had only a distant acquaintance with George Cyril Wellbeloved, but from what he had seen of him he had not credited him with this fatal allure.

'She probably misses his afternoon call.'

Again his lordship found himself perplexed. He had had no notion that pigs were such sticklers for the formalities of social life.

'His call?'

'He must have had some special call that he used when he wanted her to come to dinner. One of the first things you learn on a farm is hog-calling. Pigs are temperamental. Omit to call them, and they'll starve rather than put on the nose-bag. Call them right, and they will follow you to the ends of the earth with their mouths watering.'

'God bless my soul! Fancy that.'

'A fact, I assure you. These calls vary in different parts of America. In Wisconsin, for example, the words "Poig, Poig, Poig" bring home – in both the literal and the figurative sense – the bacon. In Illinois, I believe they call "Burp, Burp, Burp," while in Iowa the phrase "Kus, Kus, Kus" is preferred. Proceeding to Minnesota, we find "Peega, Peega, Peega" or alternatively, "Oink, Oink, Oink," whereas in Milwaukee, so largely inhabited by those of German descent, you will hear the good old Teuton "Komm Schweine, Komm Schweine." Oh, yes, there are all sorts of pig-calls, from the Massachusetts "Phew, Phew, Phew" to the "Loo-ey, Loo-ey, Loo-ey" of Ohio, not counting various local devices such as beating on tin cans with axes or rattling pebbles in a suit-case. I knew a man out in Nebraska who used to call his pigs by tapping on the edge of the trough with his wooden leg.'

'Did he, indeed?'

'But a most unfortunate thing happened. One evening, hearing a woodpecker at the top of a tree, they started shinning up it; and when the man came out he found them all lying there in a circle with their necks broken.'

'This is no time for joking,' said Lord Emsworth, pained.

'I'm not joking. Solid fact. Ask anybody out there.'

Lord Emsworth placed a hand to his throbbing forehead.

'But if there is this wide variety, we have no means of knowing which call Wellbeloved...'

'Ah,' said James Belford, 'but wait. I haven't told you all. There is a master-word.'

'A what?'

'Most people don't know it, but I had it straight from the lips of Fred Patzel, the hog-calling champion of the Western States. What a man! I've known him to bring pork chops leaping from their plates. He informed me that, no matter whether an animal has been trained to answer to the Illinois "Burp" or the Minnesota "Oink", it will always give immediate service in response to this magic combination of syllables. It is to the pig world what the Masonic grip is to the human. "Oink" in Illinois or "Burp" in Minnesota, and the animal merely raises its eyebrows and stares coldly. But go to either State and call "Pig-hoo-oo-ey!" . . .'

The expression on Lord Emsworth's face was that of a drowning man who sees a lifeline.

'Is that the master-word of which you spoke?'

'That's it.'

'Pig –?'

'– hoo-oo-ey.'

'Pig-hoo-o-ey?'

'You haven't got it right. The first syllable should be short and staccato, the second long and rising into a falsetto, high but true.'

'Pig-hoo-o-o-ey.'

'Pig-hoo-o-o-ey.'

'Pig-hoo-o-o-ey!' yelled Lord Emsworth, flinging his head back and giving tongue in a high, penetrating tenor which caused ninety-three Senior Conservatives, lunching in the vicinity, to congeal into living statues of alarm and disapproval.

'More body to the "hoo,"' advised James Belford.

'Pig-hoo-o-o-o-ey!'

The Senior Conservative Club is one of the few places in London where lunchers are not accustomed to getting music with their meals. White-whiskered financiers gazed bleakly at bald-headed politicians, as if asking silently what was to be done about this. Bald-headed politicians stared back at white-whiskered financiers, replying in the language of the eye that they did not know. The general sentiment prevailing was a vague determination to write to the Committee about it.

'Pig-hoo-o-o-o-ey!' carolled Lord Emsworth. And, as he did so his eye fell on the clock over the mantelpiece. Its hands pointed to twenty minutes to two.

He started convulsively. The best train in the day for Market Blandings was the one which left Paddington station at two sharp. After that there was nothing till the five-five.

He was not a man who often thought; but, when he did, to think was with him to act. A moment later he was scudding over the carpet, making for the door that led to the broad staircase.

Throughout the room which he had left, the decision to write in strong terms to the Committee was now universal; but from the mind, such as it was, of Lord Emsworth the past, with the single exception of the word 'Pig-hoo-o-o-o-ey!' had been completely blotted.

Whispering the magic syllables, he sped to the cloakroom and retrieved his hat. Murmuring them over and over again, he sprang into a cab. He was still repeating them as the train moved out of the station; and he would doubtless have gone on repeating them all the way to Market Blandings, had he not, as was his invariable practice when travelling by rail, fallen asleep after the first ten minutes of the journey.

The stopping of the train at Swindon Junction woke him with a start. He sat up, wondering, after his usual fashion on these occasions, who and where he was. Memory returned to him, but a memory that was, alas, incomplete. He remembered his name. He remembered that he was on his way home from a visit to London. But what it was that you said to a pig when inviting it to drop in for a bite of dinner he had completely forgotten.

It was the opinion of Lady Constance Keeble, expressed verbally during dinner in the brief intervals when they were alone, and by means of silent telepathy when Beach, the butler, was adding his dignified presence to the proceedings, that her brother Clarence, in his expedition to London to put matters plainly to James Belford, had made an outstanding idiot of himself.

There had been no need whatever to invite the man Belford to lunch; but, having invited him to lunch, to leave him sitting, without having clearly stated that Angela would have no money for four years, was the act of a congenital imbecile. Lady Constance had been aware ever since their childhood days that her brother had about as much sense as a—

Here Beach entered, superintending the bringing-in of the savoury, and she had been obliged to suspend her remarks.

This sort of conversation is never agreeable to a sensitive man, and his lordship had removed himself from the danger zone as soon as he could manage it. He was now seated in the library, sipping port and straining a brain which Nature had never intended for hard exercise in an effort to bring back that word of magic of which his unfortunate habit of sleeping in trains had robbed him.

'Pig—'

He could remember as far as that; but of what avail was a single syllable? Besides, weak as his memory was, he could recall that the whole gist or nub of the thing lay in the syllable that followed. The 'pig' was a mere preliminary.

Lord Emsworth finished his port and got up. He felt restless, stifled. The summer night seemed to call to him like some silver-voiced swineherd calling to his pig. Possibly, he thought, a breath of fresh air might stimulate his brain-cells. He wandered downstairs; and, having dug a shocking old slouch hat out of the cupboard where he hid it to keep his sister Constance from impounding and burning it, he strode heavily out into the garden.

He was pottering aimlessly to and fro in the parts adjacent to the rear of the castle when there appeared in his path a slender female form. He recognized it without pleasure. Any unbiased judge would have said that his niece Angela, standing there in the soft pale light, looked like some dainty spirit of the Moon. Lord Emsworth was not an unbiased judge. To him Angela merely looked like Trouble. The march of civilization has given the modern girl a vocabulary and an ability to use it which her grandmother never had. Lord Emsworth would not have minded meeting Angela's grandmother a bit.

'Is that you, my dear?' he said nervously.

'Yes.'

'I didn't see you at dinner.'

'I didn't want any dinner. The food would have choked me. I can't eat.'

'It's precisely the same with my pig,' said his lordship. 'Young Belford tells me—'

Into Angela's queenly disdain there flashed a sudden animation.

'Have you seen Jimmy? What did he say?'

'That's just what I can't remember. It began with the word "Pig"—'

'But after he had finished talking about you, I mean. Didn't he say anything about coming down here?'

'Not that I remember.'

'I expect you weren't listening. You've got a very annoying habit, Uncle Clarence,' said Angela maternally, 'of switching your mind off and just going blah when people are talking to you. It gets you very much disliked on all sides. Didn't Jimmy say anything about me?'

'I fancy so. Yes, I am nearly sure he did.'

'Well, what?'

'I cannot remember.'

There was a sharp clicking noise in the darkness. It was caused by Angela's upper front teeth meeting her lower front teeth; and was followed by a sort of wordless exclamation. It seemed only too plain that the love and respect which a niece should have for an uncle were in the present instance at a very low ebb.

'I wish you wouldn't do that,' said Lord Emsworth plaintively.

'Do what?'

'Make clicking noises at me.'

'I will make clicking noises at you. You know perfectly well, Uncle Clarence, that you are behaving like a bohunkus.'

'A what?'

'A bohunkus,' explained his niece coldly, 'is a very inferior sort of worm. Not the kind of worm that you see on lawns, which you can respect, but a really degraded species.'

'I wish you would go in, my dear,' said Lord Emsworth. 'The night air may give you a chill.'

'I won't go in. I came out here to look at the moon and think of Jimmy. What are you doing out here, if it comes to that?'

'I came here to think. I am greatly exercised about my pig, Empress of Blandings. For two days she has refused her food, and young Belford says she will not eat until she hears the proper call or cry. He very kindly taught it to me, but unfortunately I have forgotten it.'

'I wonder you had the nerve to ask Jimmy to teach you pig-calls, considering the way you're treating him.'

'But –'

'Like a leper, or something. And all I can say is that, if you remember this call of his, and it makes the Empress eat, you ought to be ashamed of yourself if you still refuse to let me marry him.'

'My dear,' said Lord Emsworth earnestly, 'if through young Belford's instrumentality Empress of Blandings is induced to take nourishment once more, there is nothing I will refuse him – nothing.'

'Honour bright?'

'I give you my solemn word.'

'You won't let Aunt Constance bully you out of it?'

Lord Emsworth drew himself up.

'Certainly not,' he said proudly. 'I am always ready to listen to your Aunt Constance's views, but there are certain matters where I claim the right to act according to my own judgement.' He paused and stood musing. 'It began with the word "Pig" –'

From somewhere near at hand music made itself heard. The servants' hall, its day's labours ended, was refreshing itself with the housekeeper's gramophone. To Lord Emsworth the strains were merely an additional annoyance. He was not fond of music. It reminded him of his younger son Frederick, a flat but persevering songster both in and out of the bath.

'Yes. I can distinctly recall as much as that. Pig – Pig –'

'WHO –'

Lord Emsworth leaped in the air. It was as if an electric shock had been applied to his person.

'WHO stole my heart away?' howled the gramophone. 'Who –'

The peace of the summer night was shattered by a triumphant shout.

'Pig-HOO-o-o-o-ey!'

A window opened. A large, bald head appeared. A dignified voice spoke.

'Who is there? Who is making that noise?'

'Beach!' cried Lord Emsworth. 'Come out here at once.'

'Very good, your lordship.'

And presently the beautiful night was made still more lovely by the added attraction of the butler's presence.

'Beach, listen to this.'

'Very good, your lordship.'

'Pig-hoo-o-o-o-ey!'

'Very good, your lordship.'

'Now you do it.'

'I, your lordship?'

'Yes. It's a way you call pigs.'

'I do not call pigs, your lordship,' said the butler coldly.

'What do you want Beach to do it for?' asked Angela.

'Two heads are better than one. If we both learn it, it will not matter should I forget it again.'

'By Jove, yes! Come on, Beach. Push it over the thorax,' urged the girl eagerly. 'You don't know it, but this is a matter of life and death. At-a-boy, Beach! Inflate the lungs and go to it.'

It had been the butler's intention, prefacing his remarks with the statement that he had been in service at the castle for eighteen years, to explain frigidly to Lord Emsworth that it was not his place to stand in the moonlight practising pig-calls. If, he would have gone on to add, his lordship saw the matter from a different angle, then it was his, Beach's, painful duty to tender his resignation, to become effective one month from that day.

But the intervention of Angela made this impossible to a man of chivalry and heart. A paternal fondness for the girl, dating from the days when he had stooped to enacting – and very convincingly, too, for his was a figure that lent itself to the impersonation – the *role* of a hippopotamus for her childish amusement, checked the words he would have uttered. She was looking at him with bright eyes, and even the rendering of pig-noises seemed a small sacrifice to make for her sake.

'Very good, your lordship,' he said in a low voice, his face pale and set in the moonlight. 'I shall endeavour to give satisfaction. I would merely advance the suggestion, your lordship, that we move a few steps farther away from the vicinity of the servants' hall. If I were to be overheard by any of the lower domestics, it would weaken my position as a disciplinary force.'

'What chumps we are!' cried Angela, inspired. 'The place to do it is outside the Empress's sty. Then, if it works, we'll see it working.'

Lord Emsworth found this a little abstruse, but after a moment he got it.

'Angela,' he said, 'you are a very intelligent girl. Where you get your brains from, I don't know. Not from my side of the family.'

The bijou residence of the Empress of Blandings looked very snug and attractive in the moonlight. But beneath even the beautiful things of life there is always an underlying sadness. This was supplied in the present instance by a long, low trough, only too plainly full to the brim of succulent mash and acorns. The fast, obviously, was still in progress.

The sty stood some considerable distance from the castle walls, so that there had been ample opportunity for Lord Emsworth to rehearse his little company during the journey. By the time they had ranged themselves against the rails, his two assistant were letter-perfect.

'Now,' said his lordship.

There floated out upon the summer night a strange composite sound that sent the birds roosting in the trees above shooting off their perches like rockets. Angela's clear soprano rang out like the voice of the village blacksmith's daughter. Lord Emsworth contributed a reedy tenor. And the bass notes of Beach probably did more to startle the birds than any other one item in the programme.

They paused and listened. Inside the Empress's boudoir there sounded the movement of a heavy body. There was an inquiring grunt. The next moment the sacking that covered the doorway was pushed aside, and the noble animal emerged.

'Now!' said Lord Emsworth again.

Once more that musical cry shattered the silence of the night. But it brought no responsive movement from Empress of Blandings. She stood there motionless, her nose elevated, her ears hanging down, her eyes everywhere but on the trough where, by rights, she should now have been digging in and getting hers. A chill disappointment crept over Lord

Emsworth, to be succeeded by a gust of petulant anger.

'I might have known it,' he said bitterly. 'That young scoundrel was deceiving me. He was playing a joke on me.'

'He wasn't,' cried Angela indignantly. 'Was he, Beach?'

'Not knowing the circumstances, Miss, I cannot venture an opinion.'

'Well, why has it no effect, then?' demanded Lord Emsworth.

'You can't expect it to work right away. We've got her stirred up, haven't we? She's thinking it over, isn't she? Once more will do the trick. Ready, Beach?'

'Quite ready, Miss.'

'Then when I say three. And this time, Uncle Clarence, do please for goodness' sake not yowl like you did before. It was enough to put any pig off. Let it come out quite easily and gracefully. Now, then. One, two – three!'

The echoes died away. And as they did so a voice spoke.

'Community singing?'

'Jimmy!' cried Angela, whisking round.

'Hullo, Angela. Hullo, Lord Emsworth. Hullo, Beach.'

'Good evening, sir. Happy to see you once more.'

'Thanks. I'm spending a few days at the Vicarage with my father. I got down here by the five-five.'

Lord Emsworth cut peevishly in upon these civilities.

'Young man,' he said, 'what do you mean by telling me that my pig would respond to that cry? It does nothing of the kind.'

'You can't have done it right.'

'I did it precisely as you instructed me. I have had, moreover, the assistance of Beach here and my niece Angela –'

'Let's hear a sample.'

Lord Emsworth cleared his throat. 'Pig-hoo-o-o-o-ey!'

James Belford shook his head.

'Nothing like it,' he said. 'You want to begin the "Hoo" in a low minor of two quarter notes in four-four time. From this build gradually to a higher note, until at last the voice is soaring in full crescendo, reaching F sharp on the natural scale and dwelling for two retarded half-notes, then breaking into a shower of accidental grace-notes.'

'God bless my soul!' said Lord Emsworth, appalled. 'I shall never be able to do it.'

'Jimmy will do it for you,' said Angela. 'Now that he's engaged to me, he'll be one of the family and always popping about here. He can do it every day till the show is over.'

James Belford nodded.

'I think that would be the wisest plan. It is doubtful if an amateur could ever produce real results. You need a voice that has been trained on the open prairie and that has gathered richness and strength from competing with tornadoes. You need a manly, wind-scorched voice with a suggestion in it of the crackling of corn husks and the whisper of evening breezes in the fodder. Like this!'

Resting his hands on the rail before him, James Belford swelled before their eyes like a young balloon. The muscles on his cheek-bones stood out, his forehead became corrugated, his ears seemed to shimmer. Then at the very height of the tension, he let it go like, as the poet beautifully puts it, the sound of a great Amen.

'Pig-HOOOOO-OOO-OOO-O-O-ey!'

They looked at him, awed. Slowly, fading off across hill and dale, the vast bellow died away. And suddenly, as it died, another, softer sound succeeded it. A sort of gulpy, gurgly, plobby, squishy, woffle-some sound, like a thousand eager men drinking soup in a foreign restaurant. And, as he heard it, Lord Emsworth uttered a cry of rapture.

The Empress was feeding.

The Seventh Pullet

Saki (H. H. Munro)

'It's not the daily grind that I complain of,' said Blenkinthrope resentfully; 'it's the dull grey sameness of my life outside of office hours. Nothing of interest comes my way, nothing remarkable or out of the common. Even the little things that I do try to find some interest in don't seem to interest other people. Things in my garden, for instance.'

'The potato that weighed just over two pounds,' said his friend Gorworth.

'Did I tell you about that?' said Blenkinthrope; 'I was telling the others in the train this morning. I forgot if I'd told you.'

'To be exact you told me that it weighed just under two pounds, but I took into account the fact that abnormal vegetables and freshwater fish have an after-life, in which growth is not arrested.'

'You're just like the others,' said Blenkinthrope sadly, 'you only make fun of it.'

'The fault is with the potato, not with us,' said Gorworth; 'we are not in the least interested in it because it is not in the least interesting. The men you go up in the train with every day are just in the same case as yourself; their lives are commonplace and not very interesting to themselves, and they certainly are not going to wax enthusiastic over the commonplace events in other men's lives. Tell them something startling, dramatic, piquant, that has happened to yourself or to someone in your family, and you will capture their interest at once. They will talk about you with a certain personal pride to all their acquaintances. "Man I know intimately, fellow called Blenkinthrope, lives down my way, had two of his fingers clawed clean off by a lobster he was carrying home to supper. Doctor says entire hand may have come off." Now that is conversation of a very high order. But imagine walking into a tennis club with the remark: "I know a man who has grown a potato weighing two and a quarter pounds." '

'But hang it all, my dear fellow,' said Blenkinthrope impatiently, 'haven't

I just told you that nothing of a remarkable nature ever happens to me?'

'Invent something,' said Gorworth. Since winning a prize for excellence in Scriptural knowledge at a preparatory school he had felt licensed to be a little more unscrupulous than the circle he moved in. Much might surely be excused to one who in early life could give a list of seventeen trees mentioned in the Old Testament.

'What sort of thing?' asked Blenkinthrope, somewhat snappishly.

'A snake got into your hen-run yesterday morning and killed six out of seven pullets, first mesmerizing them with its eyes and then biting them as they stood helpless. The seventh pullet was one of that French sort, with feathers all over its eyes, so it escaped the mesmeric snare, and just flew at what it could see of the snake and pecked it to pieces.'

'Thank you,' said Blenkinthrope stiffly; 'it's a very clever invention. If such a thing had really happened in my poultry-run I admit I should have been proud and interested to tell people about it. But I'd rather stick to fact, even if it is plain fact.' All the same his mind dwelt wistfully on the story of the Seventh Pullet. He could picture himself telling it in the train amid the absorbed interest of his fellow passengers. Unconsciously all sorts of little details and improvements began to suggest themselves.

Wistfulness was still his dominant mood when he took his seat in the railway carriage the next morning. Opposite him sat Stevenham, who had attained to a recognized brevet of importance through the fact of an uncle having dropped dead in the act of voting at a Parliamentary election. That had happened three years ago, but Stevenham was still deferred to on all questions of home and foreign politics.

'Hullo, how's the giant mushroom, or whatever is was?' was all the notice Blenkinthrope got from his fellow travellers.

Young Duckby, whom he mildly disliked, speedily monopolized the general attention by an account of a domestic bereavement.

'Had four young pigeons carried off last night by a whacking big rat. Oh, a monster he must have been; you could tell by the size of the hole he made breaking into the loft.'

No moderate-sized rat ever seemed to carry out any predatory operations in these regions; they were all enormous in their enormity.

'Pretty hard lines that,' continued Duckby, seeing that he had secured the attention and respect of the company; 'four squeakers carried off at one swoop. You'd find it rather hard to match that in the way of unlooked-for bad luck.'

'I had six pullets out of a pen of seven killed by a snake yesterday afternoon,' said Blenkinthrope, in a voice which he hardly recognized as his own.

'By a snake?' came in excited chorus.

'It fascinated them with its deadly, glittering eyes, one after the other, and struck them down while they stood helpless. A bedridden neighbour, who wasn't able to call for assistance, witnessed it all from her bedroom window.'

'Well, I never!' broke in the chorus, with variations.

'The interesting part of it is about the seventh pullet, the one that didn't get killed,' resumed Blenkinthrope, slowly lighting a cigarette. His diffidence had left him, and he was beginning to realize how safe and easy depravity can seem once one has the courage to begin. 'The six dead birds were Minorcas; the seventh was a Houdan with a mop of feathers all over its eyes. It could hardly see the snake at all, so of course it wasn't mesmerized like the others. It just could see something wriggling on the ground, and went for it and pecked it to death.'

'Well, I'm blessed!' exclaimed the chorus.

In the course of the next few days Blenkinthrope discovered how little the loss of one's self-respect affects one when one has gained the esteem of the world. His story found its way into one of the poultry papers, and was copied thence into a daily news-sheet as a matter of general interest. A lady wrote from the North of Scotland recounting a similar episode which she had witnessed as occurring between a stoat and a blind grouse. Somehow a lie seems so much less reprehensible when one can call it a lee.

For a while the adapter of the Seventh Pullet story enjoyed to the full his altered standing as a person of consequence, one who had had some share in the strange events of his times. Then he was thrust once again into the cold grey background by the sudden blossoming into importance of Smith-Paddon, a daily fellow-traveller, whose little girl had been knocked down and nearly hurt by a car belonging to a musical-comedy actress. The actress was not in the car at the time, but she was in numerous photographs which appeared in the illustrated papers of Zoto Dobreen inquiring after the well-being of Maisie, daughter of Edmund Smith-Paddon, Esq. With this new human interest to absorb them the travelling companions were almost rude when Blenkinthrope tried to explain his contrivance for keeping vipers and peregrine falcons out of his chicken-run.

Gorworth, to whom he unburdened himself in private, gave him the same counsel as theretofore.

'Invent something.'

'Yes, but what?'

The ready affirmative coupled with the question betrayed a significant shifting of the ethical standpoint.

It was a few days later that Blenkinthrope revealed a chapter of family history to the customary gathering in the railway carriage.

'Curious thing happened to my aunt, the one who lives in Paris,' he began. He had several aunts, but they were all geographically distributed over Greater London.

'She was sitting on a seat in the Bois the other afternoon, after lunching at the Roumanian Legation.'

Whatever the story gained in picturesqueness for the dragging-in of diplomatic 'atmosphere,' it ceased from that moment to command any acceptance as a record of current events. Gorworth had warned his neophyte that this would be the case, but the traditional enthusiasm of the neophyte had triumphed over discretion.

'She was feeling rather drowsy, the effect probably of the champagne, which she's not in the habit of taking in the middle of the day.'

A subdued murmur of admiration went round the company. Blenkinthrope's aunts were not used to taking champagne in the middle of the year, regarding it exclusively as a Christmas and New Year accessory.

'Presently a rather portly gentleman passed by her seat and paused an instant to light a cigar. At that moment a youngish man came up behind him, drew the blade from a swordstick, and stabbed him half a dozen times through and through. "Scoundrel," he cried to his victim, "you do not know me. My name is Henri Leturc." The elder man wiped away some of the blood that was spattering his clothes, turned to his assailant, and said: "And since when has an attempted assassination been considered an introduction?" Then he finished lighting his cigar and walked away. My aunt had intended screaming for the police, but seeing the indifference with which the principal in the affair treated the matter she felt that it would be an impertinence on her part to interfere. Of course I need hardly say she put the whole thing down to the effects of a warm, drowsy afternoon and the Legation champagne. Now comes the astonishing part of my story. A fortnight later a bank manager was stabbed to death with a swordstick in that very part of the Bois. His assassin was the son of a charwoman formerly working at the bank, who had been dismissed from her job by the manager on account of chronic intemperance. His name was Henri Leturc.'

From that moment Blenkinthrope was tacitly accepted as the Munchausen of the party. No effort was spared to draw him out from day to day in the exercise of testing their powers of credulity, and Blenkinthrope, in the false security of an assured and receptive audience, waxed industrious and ingenious in supplying the demand for marvels. Duckby's satirical story of a tame otter that had a tank in the garden to swim in, and whined restlessly whenever the water-rate was overdue, was scarcely an unfair parody of some of Blenkinthrope's wilder efforts. And then one day came Nemesis.

Returning to his villa one evening Blenkinthrope found his wife sitting in front of a pack of cards, which she was scrutinizing with unusual concentration.

'The same old patience-game?' he asked carelessly.

'No, dear; this is the Death's Head patience, the most difficult of them all. I've never got it to work out, and somehow I should be rather frightened if I did. Mother only got it out once in her life; she was afraid of it, too. Her great-aunt had done it once and fallen dead from excitement the next moment, and mother always had a feeling that she would die if she ever got it out. She died the same night that she did it. She was in bad health at the time, certainly, but it was a strange coincidence.'

'Don't do it if it frightens you,' was Blenkinthrope's practical comment as he left the room. A few minutes later his wife called to him.

'John, it gave me such a turn, I nearly got it out. Only the five of diamonds held me up at the end. I really thought I'd done it.'

'Why, you can do it,' said Blenkinthrope, who had come back to the room; 'if you shift the eight of clubs on to that open nine the five can be moved on to the six.'

His wife made the suggested move with hasty, trembling fingers, and piled the outstanding cards on to their respective packs. Then she followed the example of her mother and great-grand-aunt.

Blenkinthrope had been genuinely fond of his wife, but in the midst of his bereavement one dominant thought obtruded itself. Something sensational and real had at last come into his life; no longer was it a grey, colourless record. The headlines which might appropriately describe his domestic tragedy kept shaping themselves in his brain. 'Inherited presentiment comes true.' 'The Death's Head patience: Card-game that justified its sinister name in three generations.' He wrote out a full story of the fatal occurrence for the *Essex Vedette*, the editor of which was a friend of his, and to another friend he gave a condensed account, to be taken up to the office of one of the halfpenny dailies. But in both cases his reputation as a romancer stood fatally in the way of the fulfilment of his ambitions. 'Not the right thing to be Munchausening in a time of sorrow,' agreed his friends among themselves, and a brief note of regret at the 'sudden death of the wife of our respected neighbour, Mr John Blenkinthrope, from heart failure,' appearing in the news column of the local paper was the forlorn outcome of his visions of widespread publicity.

Blenkinthrope shrank from the society of his erstwhile travelling companions and took to travelling townwards by an earlier train. He sometimes tries to enlist the sympathy and attention of a chance acquaintance in details of the whistling prowess of his best canary or the dimensions of his largest beetroot; he scarcely recognizes himself as the man who was once spoken about and pointed out as the owner of the Seventh Pullet.

The Lady at Sport and Play

Douglas Sutherland

English Ladies are not the helpless silly-little-me types who sit around, fluttering their eyelashes in the hope that some big, strong, and hopefully, handsome male will rush to their rescue.

Quite the contrary. English Ladies as a class are almost indecently energetic and competent. As the men are settling down for a quiet siesta after a good luncheon, it is always some Amazon who burst into the room crying: 'Who's for tennis?', or, no matter what the weather, gird themselves in an assortment of deerstalker hats, anoraks and wellies and drag everyone off on a five mile trek.

The result is that most Ladies, as the years advance, develop complexions of deep-sea fishermen, with a taste for the bottle.

The trouble, so far as men are concerned, is that ladies generally are frightfully *good at things*, and particularly at those things in which males take pride in excelling. Television viewers are inured to seeing ladies take the top honours, not only in the jumping arena but also in those fearsome cross-country events which require the maximum of stamina, whilst their prowess in the hunting field, even in the days when they were handicapped by having to ride side-saddle, is legendary.

If it stopped there, it might be acceptable to the chauvinistic male on the grounds that most young ladies spend their formative years almost entirely with, and in love with, horses but, unfortunately, this is far from being the case.

Ladies excel in such supposedly exclusively male sports as shooting, in spite of the fact that they generally shoot with a lighter gun than their male counterparts. This infuriates some husbands to such an extent that they try to bar their wives from their shooting parties, on the grounds that someone has to see to the supervision of the luncheon arrangements.

I can well remember a crisis in my own family when, after an all-male shooting party, the bag was laid out at the front door for inspection. It so happened that it had been a poor day, which led my mother to make some rather indiscreet remarks about the skill of the participants. 'Let me show you how it is done,' she said, picking up a child's Diana air rifle which happened to be at hand. Putting it to her shoulder, she aimed at a bat fluttering high above her head in the gathering dusk, whilst the men smirked behind their hands. A moment later there was a scarcely audible 'phut' and the unfortunate pipistrelle collapsed in mid-flight.

It was the signal for the men to beat an undignified retreat to the gun room, where they stayed for a long time, fresh supplies of whisky being rushed in at regular intervals.

Fishing is another gentlemanly sport at which ladies have an aggravating habit of returning with the largest catches. The Queen Mother has a deservedly high reputation as a salmon fisherperson. Indeed, not only was the record for the heaviest salmon ever caught held by a lady friend of my family for many years but, when it was beaten, it was beaten by another lady. On the other hand, one cannot deny that there is an argument that ladies are born lucky. I can recollect one long cold day fishing for salmon on the Tay, both from the bank and a boat, which threatened to prove a blank, when at the last minute a large fish rose clean out of the water and landed back in the bottom of the boat – which was, of course, occupied by a lady!

Many and various are the excuses made by men for not playing mixed games with ladies. At tennis, for example, 'Much more fun for you girls to make up a four amongst yourselves. Make it less one-sided, you know.' Or, at croquet, 'Don't play with the ladies. Awful cheats, you know.'

There are certain games, however, where women are at a distinct disadvantage, not, let it be said, for lack of skill, but for inbuilt feminine characteristics. A typical example is bridge, where all but the most dedicated of women players cannot resist retailing the latest piece of gossip at great length in the middle of the bidding, which tends to destroy concentration, whilst at poker they have an aggravating habit of suddenly remarking, 'Does a flush beat a full house?', which has the effect of making her male opponents tear their hair with exasperation.

Machinery:

Another ladylike characteristic is a determination not to demonstrate their skill on any matter which they do not consider to fall within their proper province. Although they are adept at mending a complicated piece of machinery, like their electric sewing machine – and, indeed, would be horrified if any male member of the family were to lay a hand on it – they regard the motor car as an exclusively male preserve. Nevertheless, if put to it, they could show a much greater skill in, say, adjusting the points than their gentlemanly husbands who, as I have already remarked in my book on the habits of the English Gentleman, have absolutely no knowledge of what goes on under the bonnet.

(Incidentally, when discussing this curious reluctance of ladies to have anything to do with motor cars with a lady friend, she said: 'Stuff and nonsense! Whenever anything goes wrong with any of our family cars, we send for my grandmother!' This, I feel, must be the exception which proves the rule.)

This is not to say that ladies do not have an affection for their own cars, which they identify with even to the extent of always referring to it as 'she' and having a pet name for it, like a dog. They are, however, maddening as drivers, as any male waiting patiently for a lady driver to vacate a parking space will confirm. By the time she has taken her seat behind the wheel, touched up her make-up in the driving mirror, seen that her hat is set at the correct angle, and made a lengthy search in her handbag for the car keys, the man waiting for her to move out will either have burst a blood vessel or given the whole thing up as a bad job.

Whilst many ladies driving on their own can exhibit an expertness comparable with any man, if she is accompanied by a lady passenger, her driving is unpredictable to a point of being quite ridiculous. Whilst incessant chatter is quite harmless over the tea table, it can prove lethal when behind the wheel in heavy traffic.

Sometimes one feels that the determination of ladies is, to put it mildly, to be eccentric when it comes to motor cars. I will just quote one example which goes to show that I am not biased in this matter.

A middle-aged lady, who had recently learned to drive, conscientiously followed what she had been taught that, in starting her car when cold, she should pull out the choke. This she conscientiously did, and then would hang her handbag on it and motor around all day, with a cloud of blue smoke pouring out of her exhaust. This is why second-hand cars advertised as 'carefully driven by one lady owner' should be regarded with some suspicion.

Clubs:

In the last century ladies' clubs proliferated. The one difference between ladies' clubs and gentlemen's was that *no* gentlemen's club admitted ladies but *all* ladies' clubs admitted gentlemen. At some ladies' clubs even heavy gambling took place although most of them were innocent social meeting places. The last of the great ladies' clubs was the Ladies Curzon Club where before they were driven out by the gambling craze Dame Edith Sitwell used to entertain her friends daily to tea. Now the genteel clatter of tea cups has given way to the raucous cries of croupiers.

The English Lady and her Wedding

Douglas Sutherland

The English Lady, like her male counterpart, can be relied upon to preserve a stiff upper lip at all times of crisis, like having the elastic of her knickers snap in Fortnum & Mason's or being bucked off her hunter into the village duckpond.

The only exception to her determined composure is at the mention of weddings. Then her eyes go all misty, she clutches her bosom and the famous stiff upper lip trembles visibly for, to the Lady, as indeed to all females, romance is the very stuff of life. In this matter Kipling wrote truly when he said:

> 'The Colonel's Lady
> And Judy O'Grady
> Are sisters under the skin'.

Of course, it is a prerequisite to this reaction that the wedding should be a 'suitable' one. Should her daughter's inamorata not come up to mother's expectation, it is quite a different matter. Her back stiffens, her mouth snaps shut like stars on a very frosty night indeed. A Lady whose daughter has become involved with someone with an unacceptable track record will refer to it as an 'infatuation'. Only if the prospective bridegroom comes up to snuff in all respects does she refer to it as love.

Assuming, however, that the match is approved, both mother and daughter, from the moment the announcement appears in *The Times*, enter into some sort of trance from which they only finally emerge when the bridal car sweeps away from the reception down the gravelled drive, with both of them in floods of tears. The husband, whose only role for months has been to supply a steady stream of cheques, will certainly not be in tears but almost equally certainly drunk.

The bridegroom-to-be has virtually nothing to do with the whole business. He is expected to call regularly, in case there are some orders he has to be given and to have his nomination of best man and ushers approved. In recognition of the monk-like conduct expected of him during the engagement period, he is permitted to get drunk with his closest friends on the night before the nuptials. His appearance the following day at St Margaret's, Westminster, with dark rings under his eyes, sheet-white face, and hands so shaky that he can scarcely get the wedding ring on the correct finger is charitably put down to deep emotion.

The attention to detail in the run-up period of a fashionable wedding is at least as great as one would expect of a General about to commit a whole army to battle. However friendly the bride's mother may have been with the bridegroom's parents, it all counts for nothing when the great operation gets under way. Indeed, they almost become the enemy, so desperate is she that any interference from them might mar her daughter's finest hour.

Whilst dress designers are driven frantic with orders and counter-orders about the getting together of the trousseau and sketches for the wedding dress are pored over and over again, there are a multitude of other matters of world-shaking importance which have to be personally attended to. Few mothers are content to hand over the catering entirely to one of the many highly qualified experts in the field, even the vicar is called in for a course of instruction on his duties, and a full scale rehearsal is carried out to make sure that everyone understands what is expected of them on the BIG DAY.

All this activity is, however, dwarfed when it comes to drawing up the invitation list. It is on this ground that pitched battles are generally fought and a lady's commmercial instincts blatantly revealed. She is torn between the need to ask the famous and titled, who are notoriously stingy in the presents they give but ensure a good showing in the Society magazines and the obvious advantages of asking the social climbing rich on the grounds that they can be relied upon to bear with them ostentatiously rich gifts. It is an opportunity, also, to pay off old scores by putting a blue pencil through the names of those who have for some reason offended in the past.

This latter practice can backfire. I recollect a lady of spirit who had been accorded the brush-off treatment and decided to get her own back. She wrote a polite refusal to the wedding to which she had not been asked on the grounds that she had a prior engagement and sent a richly wrapped parcel bearing the name of a top people's shop. When opened, it was found to contain a can of well-known deodorant.

On the great day itself ladies show a fierce determination that they shall reap every possible grain of credit from the occasion and take the greatest pride in everything going off without a hitch from the splendour of the flowers in the Church to the choice of hymns. It is, after all, their finest hour.

At the same time, it is to completely disregard the torment to which the guests are subjected.

It is bad enough that the men should be required to squeeze themselves into morning coats which no longer accommodate their expanding corporations or, alternatively, have been put to the considerable expense of hiring suitable attire from Moss Bros. Worse still is the dreadful ritual of the Reception.

No hostess in her right mind would insist under normal circumstances that her guests should be required to consume rich fruit cake accompanied by champagne, however excellent, at three o'clock in the afternoon. It is this appalling practice which leads many people to believe that champagne 'does not agree' with them. There is also the vulgar practice of displaying all the wedding gifts, so that the guests can sneer at the humbler offerings and criticize the over-expensive. And then, of course, to turn the final twist to the rack, there are the speeches. Speeches are a comparatively modern addition to the trials of attending a wedding. At the turn of the century before toasts were drunk speeches, especially long ones, were regarded as in bad taste. Whoever set about altering this admirable practice has much to answer for.

The only person who comes out of the whole business at all well is the bride's father who, if he is a wise man, will have a carefully concealed store of whisky with which he can anaesthetize himself and his intimate friends.

Weddings, popularly supposed to be the happiest day in a girl's life, in fact show off the English Lady at her worst.

The Agony of Captain Grimes

Evelyn Waugh

Two days later Beste-Chetwynde and Paul were in the organ-loft of the Llanabba Parish Church.

'I don't think I played that terribly well, do you, sir?'

'No.'

'Shall I stop for a bit?'

'I wish you would.'

'Tangent's foot has swollen up and turned black,' said Beste-Chetwynde with relish.

'Poor little brute!' said Paul.

'I had a letter from my mamma this morning,' Beste-Chetwynde went on. 'There's a message for you in it. Shall I read you what she says?'

He took out a letter written on the thickest possible paper. 'The first part is all about racing and a row she's had with Chokey. Apparently he doesn't like the way she's rebuilt our house in the country. I think it was time she dropped that man, don't you?'

'What does she say about me?' asked Paul.

'She says: "*By the way, dear boy, I must tell you that the spelling in your last letter has been just too shattering for words. You know how terribly anxious I am for you to get on and go to Oxford, and everything, and I have been thinking, don't you think it might be a good thing if we were to have a tutor next holidays? Would you think it too boring? Some one young who would fit in. I thought, would that good-looking young master you said you liked care to come? How much ought I to pay him? I never know these things. I don't mean the drunk one, tho' he was sweet too.*" I think that must be you, don't you?' said Beste-Chetwynde; 'it can hardly be Captain Grimes.'

'Well, I must think that over,' said Paul. 'It sounds rather a good idea.'

'Well, yes,' said Beste-Chetwynde doubtfully, 'it might be all right, only there mustn't be too much of the schoolmaster about it. That man Prendergast beat me the other evening.'

'And there'll be no organ lessons, either,' said Paul.

Grimes did not receive the news as enthusiastically as Paul had hoped; he was sitting over the Common Room fire despondently biting his nails.

'Good, old boy! That's splendid,' he said abstractedly. 'I'm glad; I am really.'

'Well, you don't sound exactly gay.'

'No, I'm not. Fact is, I'm in the soup again.'

'Badly?'

'Up to the neck.'

'My dear chap, I *am* sorry. What are you going to do about it?'

'I've done the only thing: I've announced my engagement.'

'That'll please Flossie.'

'Oh, yes, she's as pleased as hell about it, damn her nasty little eyes.'

'What did the old man say?'

'Baffled him a bit, old boy. He's just thinking things out at the moment. Well, I expect everything'll be all right.'

'I don't see why it shouldn't be.'

'Well, there *is* a reason. I don't think I told you before, but fact is, I'm married already.'

That evening Paul received a summons from the Doctor. He wore a double-breasted dinner-jacket, which he smoothed uneasily over his hips at Paul's approach. He looked worried and old.

'Pennyfeather,' he said, 'I have this morning received a severe shock, two shocks in fact. The first was disagreeable, but not wholly unexpected. Your colleague, Captain Grimes, has been convicted before me, on evidence that leaves no possibility of his innocence, of a crime – I might almost call it a course of action – which I can neither understand nor excuse. I daresay I need not particularize. However, that is all a minor question. I have quite frequently met with similar cases during a long experience in our profession. But what has disturbed and grieved me more than I can moderately express is the information that he is engaged to be married to my elder daughter. That, Pennyfeather, I had not expected. In the circumstances it seemed a humiliation I might reasonably have been spared. I tell you all this, Pennyfeather, because in our brief acquaintance I have learned to trust and respect you.'

The Doctor sighed, drew from his pocket a handkerchief of *crêpe de chine*, blew his nose with every accent of emotion, and resumed:

'He is *not* the son-in-law I should readily have chosen. I could have forgiven him his wooden leg, his slavish poverty, his moral turpitude, and his abominable features; I could even have forgiven him his incredible vocabulary, if only he had been a gentleman. I hope you do not think me a snob. You may have discerned in me a certain prejudice against the lower orders. It is quite true. I *do* feel deeply on the subject. You see, I married one of them. But that, unfortunately, is neither here nor there. What I really wished to say to you was this: I have spoken to the unhappy young woman my daughter, and find that she has no particular inclination towards Grimes. Indeed, I do not think that any daughter of mine could fall as low as that. But she is, for some reason, uncontrollably eager to be married to somebody fairly soon. Now, I should be quite prepared to offer a partnership in Llanabba to a son-in-law of whom I approved. The income of the school is normally not less than three thousand a year – that is with the help of dear Diana's housekeeping – and my junior partner would start at an income of a thousand, and of course succeed to a larger share upon my death. It is a prospect that many young men would find inviting. And I was wondering, Pennyfeather, whether by any chance, looking at the matter from a business-like point of view, without prejudice, you understand, fair and square, taking things as they are for what they are worth, facing facts, whether possibly *you* ... I wonder if I make myself plain?'

'No,' said Paul. 'No, sir, I'm afraid it would be impossible. I hope I don't appear rude – no, really I'm afraid ...'

'That's all right, my dear boy. Not another word! I quite understand. I was afraid that would be your answer. Well, it must be Grimes, then. I don't think it would be any use approaching Mr Prendergast.' ·

'It was very kind of you to suggest it, sir.'

'Not at all, not at all. The wedding shall take place a week today. You might tell Grimes that if you see him. I don't want to have more to do with him than I can help. I wonder whether it would be a good thing to give a small party?' For a moment a light sprang up in Dr Fagan's eyes and then died out. 'No, no, there will be no party. The sports were not encouraging. Poor little Lord Tangent is still laid up, I hear.'

Paul returned to the Common Room with the Doctor's message.

'Hell!' said Grimes. 'I still hoped it might fall through.'

'What d'you want for a wedding present?' Paul asked.

Grimes brightened. 'What about that binge you promised me and Prendy?'

'All right!' said Paul. 'We'll have it tomorrow.'

*　　*　　*

The Hotel Metropole, Cympryddyg, is by far the grandest hotel in the north of Wales. It is situated on a high and healthy eminence overlooking the strip of water that railway companies have gallantly compared to the Bay of Naples. It was built in the ample days preceding the war, with a lavish expenditure on looking-glass and marble. Today it shows signs of wear, for it has never been quite as popular as its pioneers hoped. There are cracks in the cement on the main terrace, the winter garden is draughty, and one comes disconcertingly upon derelict bathchairs in the Moorish Court. Besides this, none of the fountains ever play, the string band that used to perform nightly in the ballroom has given place to a very expensive wireless set which one of the waiters knows how to operate, there is never any notepaper in the writing-room, and the sheets are not long enough for the beds. Philbrick pointed out these defects to Paul as he sat with Grimes and Mr Prendergast drinking cocktails in the Palm Court before dinner.

'And it isn't as though it was really cheap,' he said. Philbrick had become quite genial during the last few days. 'Still, one can't expect much in Wales, and it is something. I can't live without some kind of luxury for long. I'm not staying this evening, or I'd ask you fellows to dine with me.'

'Philbrick, old boy,' said Grimes, 'me and my pals here have been wanting a word with you for some time. How about those yarns you spun about your being a shipowner and a novelist and a burglar?'

'Since you mention it,' said Philbrick with dignity, 'they were untrue. One day you shall know my full story. It is stranger than any fiction. Meanwhile I have to be back at the Castle. Good night.'

'He certainly seems quite a swell here,' said Grimes as they watched him disappear into the night escorted with every obsequy by the manager and the head-waiter. 'I daresay he *could* tell a story if he wanted to.'

'I believe it's their keys,' said Mr Prendergast suddenly. It was the first time that he had spoken. For twenty minutes he had been sitting very upright in his gilt chair and very alert, his eyes unusually bright, darting this way and that in his eagerness to miss nothing of the gay scene about him.

'What's their keys, Prendy?'

'Why, the things they get given at the counter. I thought for a long time it was money.'

'Is that what's been worrying you? Bless your heart, I thought it was the young lady in the office you were after.'

'Oh, Grimes!' said Mr Prendergast, and he blushed warmly and gave a little giggle.

Paul led his guests into the dining-room.

'I haven't taught French for nothing all these years,' said Grimes, studying the menu. 'I'll start with some jolly old *huîtres*.'

Mr Prendergast ate a grape-fruit with some difficulty. 'What a big orange!' he said when he had finished it. 'They do things on the large scale here.'

The soup came in little aluminium bowls. 'What price the ancestral silver?' said Grimes. The Manchester merchants on the spree who sat all round them began to look a little askance at Paul's table.

'Someone's doing himself well on bubbly,' said Grimes as a waiter advanced staggering under the weight of an ice-pail from which emerged a Jeroboam of champagne. 'Good egg! It's coming to us.'

'With Sir Solomon Philbrick's compliments to Captain Grimes and congratulations on his approaching marriage, sir.'

Grimes took the waiter by the sleeve. 'See here, old boy, this Sir Solomon Philbrick – know him well?'

'He's here quite frequently, sir.'

'Spends a lot of money, eh?'

'He doesn't entertain at all, but he always has the best of everything himself, sir.'

'Does he pay his bill?'

'I really couldn't say, I'm afraid, sir. Would you be requiring anything else?'

'All right, old boy! Don't get stuffy. Only he's a pal of mine, see?'

'Really, Grimes,' said Mr Prendergast, 'I am afraid you made him quite annoyed with your questions, and that stout man over there is staring at us in the most marked way.'

'I've got a toast to propose. Prendy, fill up your glass. Here's to Trumpington, whoever he is, who gave us the money for this binge!'

'And here's to Philbrick,' said Paul, 'whoever *he* is!'

'And here's to Miss Fagan,' said Mr Prendergast, 'with our warmest hopes for her future happiness!'

'Amen,' said Grimes.

After the soup the worst sort of sole. Mr Prendergast made a little joke about soles and souls. Clearly the dinner-party was being a great success.

'You know,' said Grimes, 'look at it how you will, marriage is rather a grim thought.'

'The three reasons for it given in the Prayer-book have always seemed to me quite inadequate,' agreed Mr Prendergast. 'I have never had the smallest difficulty about the avoidance of fornication, and the other two advantages seem to me nothing short of disastrous.'

'My first marriage,' said Grimes, 'didn't make much odds either way. It was in Ireland. I was tight at the time, and so was everyone else. God knows what became of Mrs Grimes. It seems to me, though, that with Flossie I'm in for a pretty solemn solemnization. It's not what I should have chosen for myself, not by a long chalk. Still, as things are, I suppose it's the best thing that could have happened. I think I've about run through the schoolmastering profession. I don't mind telling you I might have found it pretty hard to get another job. There are limits. Now I'm set up for life, and no more worry about testimonials. That's something. In fact, that's all there is to be said. But there have been moments in the last twenty-four hours, I don't mind telling you, when I've gone cold all over at the thought of what I was in for.'

'I don't want to say anything discouraging,' said Mr Prendergast, 'but I've known Flossie for nearly ten years now, and –'

'There isn't anything you can tell me about Flossie that I don't know already. I almost wish it was Dingy. I suppose it's too late now to change. Oh dear!' said Grimes despondently, gazing into his glass. 'Oh, Lord! oh, Lord! That I should come to this!'

'Cheer up, Grimes. It isn't like you to be as depressed as this,' said Paul.

'Old friends,' said Grimes – and his voice was charged with emotion – 'you see a man standing face to face with retribution. Respect him even if you cannot understand. Those that live by the flesh shall perish by the flesh. I am a very sinful man, and I am past my first youth. Who shall pity me in that dark declivity to which my steps inevitably seem to tend? I have boasted in my youth and held my head high and gone on my way careless of consequence, but ever behind me, unseen, stood stark Justice with his two-edged sword.'

More food was brought then. Mr Prendergast ate with a hearty appetite.

'Oh, why did nobody warn me?' cried Grimes in his agony. 'I should have been told. They should have told me in so many words. They should have warned me about Flossie, not about the fires of hell. I've risked them, and I don't mind risking them again, but they should have told me about marriage. They should have told me that at the end of that gay journey and flower-strewn path were the hideous lights of home and the voices of children. I should have been warned of the great lavender-scented bed that was laid out for me, of the wistaria at the windows, of all the intimacy and confidence of family life. But I daresay I shouldn't have listened. Our life is lived between two homes. We emerge for a little into the light, and then the front door closes. The chintz curtains shut out the sun, and the hearth glows with the fire of home, while upstairs, above our heads, are enacted again the awful accidents of adolescence. There's a home and family waiting for every one of us. We can't escape, try how we may. It's the seed of life we carry about with us like our skeletons, each one of us unconsciously pregnant with desirable villa residences. There's no escape. As individuals we simply do not exist. We are just potential home-builders, beavers, and ants. How do we come into being? What is birth?'

'I've often wondered,' said Mr Prendergast.

'What is this impulse of two people to build their beastly home? It's you and me, unborn, asserting our presence. All we are is a manifestation of the impulse of family life, and if by chance we have escaped the itch ourselves, Nature forces it upon us another way. Flossie's got that itch enough for two. I just haven't. I'm one of the blind alleys off the main road of procreation, but it doesn't matter. Nature always wins. Oh, Lord! oh, Lord! Why didn't I die in that first awful home? Why did I ever hope I could escape?'

Captain Grimes continued his lament for some time in deep bitterness of heart. Presently he became silent and stared at his glass.

'I wonder,' said Mr Prendergast, 'I wonder whether I could have just a little more of this very excellent pheasant?'

'Anyway,' said Grimes, 'there shan't be any children; I'll see to that.'

'It has always been a mystery to me why people marry,' said Mr Prendergast. 'I can't see the smallest reason for it. Quite happy, normal people. Now I can understand it in Grimes' case. He has everything to gain by the arrangement, but what does Flossie expect to gain? And yet she seems more enthusiastic about it than Grimes. It has been the tragedy of my life that whenever I start thinking about any quite simple subject I invariably feel myself confronted by some flat contradiction of this sort. Have you ever thought about marriage – in the abstract, I mean, of course?'

'Not very much, I'm afraid.'

'I don't believe,' said Mr Prendergast, 'that people would ever fall in love or want to be married if they hadn't been told about it. It's like abroad: no one would want to go there if they hadn't been told it existed. Don't you agree?'

'I don't think you can be quite right,' said Paul; 'you see, animals fall in love quite a lot, don't they?'

'Do they?' said Mr Prendergast. 'I didn't know that. What an extraordinary thing! But then I had an aunt whose cat used to put its paw up to its mouth when it yawned. It's wonderful what animals can be taught. There is a sea-lion at the circus, I saw in the paper, who juggles with an umbrella and two oranges.'

'I know what I'll do,' said Grimes. 'I'll get a motor bicycle.'

This seemed to cheer him up a little. He took another glass of wine and smiled wanly. 'I'm afraid I've not been following all you chaps have said. I was thinking. What were we talking about?'

'Prendy was telling me about a sea-lion who juggled with an umbrella and two oranges.'

'Why, that's nothing. I can juggle with a whacking great bottle and a lump of ice and two knives. Look!'

'Grimes, don't! Everyone is looking at you.'

The head-waiter came over to remonstrate. 'Please remember where you are, sir,' he said.

'I know where I am well enough,' said Grimes. 'I'm in the hotel my pal Sir Solomon Philbrick is talking of buying, and I tell you this, old boy: if he does, the first person to lose his job will be you. See?'

Nevertheless he stopped juggling, and Mr Prendergast ate two *pêches Melba* undisturbed.

'The black cloud has passed,' said Grimes. 'Grimes is now going to enjoy his evening.'

The Marx Brothers

S. J. Perelman

One October evening in the fall of 1931, a few minutes after the curtain had risen on the second act of *Animal Crackers*, a musical comedy starring the Four Marx Brothers, the occupant of the seat adjoining mine, a comely person with a mink coat folded on her lap, suddenly reached through it and twitched my sleeve. I was then, and still fatuously conceive myself to be, a hot-blooded young man; and if I did not respond immediately, there were several cogent reasons. To begin with, the occupant of the *other* seat adjoining mine, whom I had espoused a couple of years before, was holding hands with me, so that I had none left over to twitch back. Furthermore, the custodian of the lady in mink, I had observed during the entr'acte, was a chap with an undershot jaw and beefy neck, the kind of lout I knew would tolerate no poaching. More important than either consideration, however, was the fact that I was breathlessly and rapturously absorbed in Groucho's courtship onstage of the immortal Margaret Dumont, impersonating a dowager named Mrs Rittenhouse. It was at least five seconds accordingly, before I realized that my neighbor was extending a note and gesticulating toward an usher in the aisle to indicate its source. Straining to decipher the message in the half darkness, I grew almost dizzy with exultation. Mr Marx acknowledged the card I had sent in during the break to express my admiration, and requested me to call on him backstage after the show.

While our meeting was in no sense epochal, it did have an unpredictable consequence, and my forehead, to say nothing of my career, might have been far less wrinkled had I not paid this fortuitous homage. For the half-dozen years preceding, I had been a contributor, in the dual capacity of artist and writer, to *Judge* and *College Humour*. Both these magazines, during my undergraduate days at Brown University, had reprinted drawings I had done for the college periodical, and when faced with the choice of a livelihood, I turned naturally (if naïvely) to comic art. There were vicissitudes that seemed insurmountable at the time, but thanks to a stomach that shrank as they arose, I managed to weather them. About the end of 1928, my work was appearing in some profusion, and Horace Liveright, whose daring as a publisher verged on audacity, brought out a collection of it called *Dawn Ginsbergh's Revenge*. It was a curious little volume, bound in the horripilating green plush called 'flock' used to upholster railroad chairs, and as far as one could tell, it had only two distinctive aspects. The title page omitted any mention whatever of an author – I presumably was so overawed at the permanence I was achieving that I neglected to check this detail – and the dust jacket bore a blurb from, coincidentally, Groucho Marx. It read: 'From the moment I picked up your book until I laid it down, I was convulsed with laughter. Some day I intend reading it.'

To say, therefore, that I had set the Thames on fire by that fateful evening in 1931 would be hardly accurate. The brush and quill were yielding a pittance which I had persuaded the idealistic lady whose hand I held to share with me, and through some legerdemain we had managed to squeeze in two summers abroad on the cheap. But the magazines I worked for were feeling the Depression, and all of a sudden the barometer began to fall. I started receiving a trickle of letters from the bank that soon grew into a cascade. Perhaps, its officials hinted delicately, I would like to transfer to some bank that had facilities for handling smaller accounts. Maybe I didn't need a bank after all, they hazarded, but merely a mattress or a loose brick in the fire-place. A deep cleft, resembling the Rift Valley in East Africa, appeared between my eyebrows about the first of every month. Beyond rending my clothes or dropping an occasional reference to the poorhouse, though, I was careful to conceal my anxieties from my helpmate. Whether she suspected anything from the newspaper recipes I left around the kitchen, cheap but hearty agglomerations of macaroni and tuna fish, I cannot say. If she did, she gave no hint of it.

This was our approximate situation, then, at the moment the summons from Groucho arrived, and it was without any portent that the encounter would be fateful that I hastened backstage after the performance. Once, however, we had exchanged cordialities – a bit awkward for my wife since Groucho was clad only in his shorts – he breezily confessed to an ulterior purpose in his invitation. One of the networks had latterly been entreating the Marxes to appear in a radio series, and he wondered if I could be cozened into writing it. Flattering as I found his esteem, I was frankly overwhelmed.

'I – I wouldn't know how to begin,' I faltered. 'I've never worked on a radio script.'

'Neither has Will Johnstone,' admitted Groucho. 'He's the fellow we'd like you to collaborate with.' He went on to explain; Johnstone, like myself a comic artist and a staff member of the *Evening World*, was the author of 'I'll Say She Is,' a boisterous vaudeville sketch which the Marxes had amplified into their first Broadway success. 'Yes siree,' he concluded somberly. 'I can't imagine two people worse equipped for the job, but there's one thing in your favour. You're both such tyros you might just come up with something fresh.'

It was a dubious basis for any undertaking, and yet, as events proved, his words had a certain perverse logic. Johnstone turned out to be a jovial, exuberant chap in his late fifties, a raconteur with a fund of newspaper stories. We put in a couple of enjoyable sessions that got nowhere, except for a misty notion that the Marxes might be characterized as stowaways aboard an ocean liner. On the day designated to report our progress, the two of us met outside the Astor, resolved to confess our inadequacy and throw in the towel. Luncheon with the troupe was as disorganized as my colleague predicted it would be. Groucho expatiated at length on his stock-market losses, Chico kept jumping up to place telephone bets, and Harpo table-hopped all over the dining room, discomposing any attractive lady who gave him a second glance. Finally, the issue could be postponed no longer, and Johnstone, courageously assuming the burden, divulged the sum total of our conferences. To our stupefaction, it evoked hosannas.

'Listen,' said Groucho, after a whispered colloquy with his brothers. 'You fellows have stumbled on something big. This isn't any fly-by-night radio serial – it's our next picture!'

Primed for a totally opposite reaction, Johnstone and I surveyed him speechless; we had expected to be pistol-whipped and summarily flung into Times Square, and in our humility, thought he was being ironical. Within the next half hour, the brothers dispelled any doubt of their enthusiasm. Pinioning our arms, they hustled us across the street into the office of Jesse Lasky, the head of Paramount Pictures. There was a short, confused interval brim-full of references to astronomical sums of money, contracts, and transportation to the Coast, inexplicably for our wives as well. We were to entrain for Hollywood within the week, it was tempestuously agreed, to write the screenplay. The Marxes, scheduled to terminate their Broadway run in a fortnight, were off to London for an engagement at the Palladium, after which they would return to California to shoot our film. When Johnstone and I reeled out into what was now truly the Gay White Way, our faces had the ecstatic, incredulous look of prospectors who had just blundered across the Lost Dutchman Mine.

The delirium of leavetaking for California was, of course, punctuated by the usual untoward incidents that complicate life at such moments. My wife – deliberately, I felt at the time – slipped on an icy sidewalk and fractured her arm, and Johnstone, an undisguised foe of Prohibition, was suddenly disheartened by rumors that applejack was unprocurable in Los Angeles. Solutions materialized for both dilemmas; at the eleventh hour, my consort was able to board the Twentieth Century encased in a cast, and influential friends of Johnstone's mercifully supplied him with three stone crocks of his life-giving ichor. To further restrict our mobility, we took with us our pet of the moment, a large and aggressive schnauzer whose antipathy to trainmen and porters kept the compartment in an uproar. He was eventually exiled to the baggage car, where he ululated for three thousand miles and spread neurasthenia among the postal clerks. Much more awesome than any scenery we saw on the trip, it developed, was Johnstone's creative drive. In less than sixty-five hours, he dashed off fifteen or twenty strip cartoons for his paper, not to mention innumerable water-colors of the sunsets, mesas, and hogans en route. How his hand remained sufficiently steady, considering the roadbed of the Santa Fe and the contents of the three stone crocks, was a mystery. I sometimes lay awake in my berth for as long as two minutes pondering it.

Of all the world's storied thoroughfares, it must be confessed that none produces quite the effect of Hollywood Boulevard. I have been downcast in Piccadilly, chopfallen on the Champs Elysées, and *doloroso* on the Via Veneto, but the avenues themselves were blameless. Hollywood Boulevard, on the contrary, creates an instant and malign impression in the breast of the beholder. Viewed in full sunlight, its tawdriness is unspeakable; in the torrential downpour of the rainy season, as we first saw it, it inspired an anguish similar to that produced by the engravings of Piranesi. Our melancholy deepened when the mem and I took an exploratory walk around the hotel. As we sat in a Moorish confectionary patterned after the Alcázar, toying with viscid malted milks and listening to a funereal organ rendition of 'Moonlight in Kalua,' the same thought occurred to each of us, but she phrased it first.

'Listen,' she said. 'Do we really need the money this much?'

'That's cowardice,' I said, vainglorious because I had held my tongue.

'Why, we just got here – you can't judge a place so fast. Besides, it's raining. It's probably beautiful when the sun comes out.'

'It's no such thing,' she retorted. 'You're whistling in the dark, and you know it. It's the Atlantic City boardwalk – a hayseed's idea of the Big Apple. We've made a terrible mistake.'

'Oh, we have, have we?' I shouted. Two or three cadavers near us startled out of their torpor turned to survey me, but I didn't care. 'Well, you're certainly a comfort. Here we are in the mecca of show business, the paradise everyone dreams about, with one foot on the golden ladder –'

'Unscramble your metaphors,' she interrupted coldly. 'This town's already beginning to affect you.'

'Well, you don't have to sprinkle weed killer over our hopes the first day,' I said sulkily. 'You could fake a little optimism.'

'OK,' she said, assuming an insincere metallic smile. 'No more crabbing. Maybe it's that dismal hotel room of ours that got me down – let's go find a cheerful nest somewhere and start acting like forty-niners.'

The bivouac we ultimately settled into, a modest duplex in a bungalow court, had only one advantage – it was new. Otherwise, it was an unalloyed horror, from its overstuffed suite to its painted bedsteads, from its portable gas heaters to its garish dinette. Seated there of an evening over our avocado salads while the radio tinkled out commercials for high-colonics, crematoriums and sculptured broadlooms, one had the sense of living in a homemaker's magazine. After a few days, I could have sworn that our faces began to take on the hue of Kodachromes, and even the dog, an animal used to bizarre surroundings, developed a strange, off-register look, as if he were badly printed in overlapping colors. Our neighbors were the customary hodgepodge – studio technicians, old ladies studying Bahai, bit players, chippies, and all the mysterious lamisters who tenant the Los Angeles substratum. They rarely emerged from their burrows, but once in a while we could hear upraised voices extolling the virtues of various faith healers or laxatives. Country people in general display a preoccupation with their innards bordering on the religious, and in Los Angeles, a metropolis made up of innumerable Midwestern hamlets, it amounted to a fixation. Apart from dry cleaners, saddleries, and stores that eternalized baby shoes in bronze, almost every shop in the district was a health-food depot. I have no figures on the per-capita consumption, in Southern California during the early thirties, of soy bean, wheat germ, and blackstrap molasses, and I am thankful. It was frightening.

At the studio, where Johnstone and I were now daily applying ourselves to the script, another and equally fanciful atmosphere prevailed. The two of us were quartered in a ramshackle warren of tan stucco that housed thirty or forty other scribes. They were all in various stages of gestation, some spawning gangster epics and horse operas, others musical comedies, dramas, and farces. Few of them were writers in the traditional sense, but persuasive, voluble specialists adept in contriving trick plot situations. Many had worked before the advent of dialogue, in silent pictures; they viewed the playwrights, novelists, and newspapermen who were beginning to arrive from New York as usurpers, slick wordmongers threatening their livelihood, and rarely fraternized. My collaborator and I, however, had little time to promote social contacts, for a managerial eye was fixed on us to ensure that the script would be forthcoming on time. Herman Mankiewicz, our supervisor, was a large, Teutonic journalist and *The New Yorker*'s first dramatic critic. Though he was married into the Hollywood hierarchy, his fondness for cards and good living kept him in a state of perpetual peonage and had made him a sort of Johnsonian figure in the industry. Luckily, his duties as our overseer lay lightly on him. He stressed the fact that we were to proceed as fancy dictated, cynically adding that in any case, the Marxes would keelhaul us.

'They're mercurial, devious and ungrateful,' he said. 'I hate to depress you, but you'll rue the day you ever took the assignment. This is an ordeal by fire. Make sure you wear asbestos pants.'

Johnstone, whose earlier association with the brothers had left no scars, was inclined to scoff at these sentiments, but several weeks later, an incident occurred that unnerved us both. One morning, we were called to Mr Lasky's office and shown a cable from the Marxes in London. Stating their disenchantment with us in the most succinct terms, they recommended our instant dismissal and replacement by capable writers. Transfixed, we pointed out to Lasky that nobody thus far had seen a word we'd written. He nodded paternally.

'Don't be upset,' he advised, smiling. 'Actors, you know – they're all a little unstable. I've already replied. I told them to stick to their vaudeville and we'd worry about the movie end.'

Evidently the vaudeville was providing its quota of headaches, because rumors of a very cool reception in England soon drifted back to us. Music-hall audiences were not yet attuned to anarchic comedy, and they saluted the Marxes' whirlwind antics by jeering and pitching pennies onto the stage.

Insulated from their problems by a continent and an ocean, however, my collaborator and I continued to peg away at our script. We devised jokes and plot twists so hilarious that we could barely gasp them out to each other; we grovelled with laughter in our lazaret as we invented extravagant puns for Groucho, pantomimic flights and Italian malapropisms for his brothers. Zeppo, the youngest, was never a concern, since he was always cast as the juvenile love interest. His speeches were usually throwaways like 'Yes, Father' or song cues on the order of 'I think you have the loveliest blue eyes I've ever seen.'

Six weeks from the day we had begun work, we were notified that the deadline was looming. The troupe was back in the country and about to converge on Hollywood, and we were to read the screenplay to them, *viva voce*, the following Friday night at the Roosevelt Hotel. We put in some intensive burnishing, though, truth to tell, our handiwork already seemed to us to outshine the Kohinoor. To make it still more acceptable, we decided to salt our pages with as many technical movie phrases as we could, many of which we only half understood. We therefore went over the action line by line, panning, irising down, and dissolving, painstakingly sandwiched in Jackman and Dunning shots, and even, at one point, specified that the camera should vorkapich around the faces of the ballroom guests. Neither of us, of course, had the remotest notion of what this last meant, and it was years before I discovered that it derived from a special-effects genius named Slavko Vorkapich. I still have no idea, between ourselves, whether this technique could be applied with impunity to the human face.

At eight-thirty on the appointed evening, I met Johnstone in the suite reserved for our audition. The onus of reading aloud a 126-page script weighed heavily on both of us, so we flipped a coin and I, to my despair, was elected. Half an hour passed without any sign of the quartet, during which I twice urged my colleague to abandon the whole enterprise and leave by the fire escape, but his dentures were chattering so loudly that he did not hear me. Fifteen minutes later, the first auditors arrived – Papa Marx, the progenitor of the band, accompanied by a fellow pinochle player. Our whiplash, Mankiewicz, turned up next, in company with his brother Joseph, then a rising screenwriter at Paramount. They were followed by Zeppo and his wife, who brought along a stately brace of Afghans they had purchased in England. The dogs had eaten the upholstery of a Packard convertible that afternoon and were somewhat subdued in consequence, but they looked intimidating, and they took up a position near my feet that boded ill. Harpo now strolled in with a couple of blond civilians he had dined with, and close on his heels the Chico Marxes, leading a scrappy wirehaired terrier which immediately tangled with the Afghans. In the midst of the tohu-bohu, Groucho and his wife entered; I supposed that thirteen constituted a quorum and made as if to start, but was told to desist – other guests were due. These, it proved, were three gagmen the Marxes had picked up in transit, each of whom was to furnish japes tailored to their respective personalities. (Zeppo, as indicated earlier, could expect only leavings.) Behind the gagmen came *their* wives, sweethearts, and an unidentifiable rabble I took to be relatives, and last of all several cold-eyed vultures obviously dispatched by the studio. When I counted noses and paws before ringing up the curtain there were twenty-seven people and five dogs confronting me.

The very apogee of embarrassment, according to Madison Avenue, is to dream oneself in some stylish locale, say Carnegie Hall, clad in a bra other than Maidenform or a supporter not manufactured by Haines. Had I been wearing either or both that night, I could not have experienced worse panic as I stammered forth the setting of our opus. Destiny, whatever its intentions, had never supplied me with forensic gifts, and my only thespian flight theretofore had been a minor role in a high-school pageant based on Pocahontas. The incredible folly of my position, the temerity of a virgin scenarist hoping to beguile a hardened professional audience, suddenly overtook me. I became faint, and the roar of a mighty cataract like the Zambesi Falls sounded in my ears. Stricken, I turned to Johnstone for succor, but cataleptic fear had seized him too; his face, the color of an eggplant, was contorted in a ghastly, fixed smile like Bartholomew's Sholto's in *The Sign of the Four*, and I thought for one horrid moment he was defunct.

'Go ahead, man,' said a voice I distantly recognized as Groucho's. 'Get a move on. As the donkey said, we're all ears.'

Short of committing hara-kiri on the spot, there was nothing to do but comply, so, clearing my throat with a force that loosened the sidelights, I continued. I had not proceeded very far before I began to sense a distinct change in the mood of my listeners. At first it was pliant – indulgent, so to speak – and there was an occasional polite ripple. This soon ceased and they became watchful – not hostile as yet, but wary. It was as if they were girding themselves, flexing for trouble they knew was inevitable. Then, by slow degrees, an attitude of sullen resentment stole into their faces. They had been betrayed, lured away from their klabiatsch and easy chairs by a will-o'-the-wisp promise of entertainment, and they grew vengeful. *Some* of them got vengeful, that is; the majority got sleepy, for by then I had stopped inflecting my voice to distinguish one character from another and had settled into a monotonous lilt like a Hindu chanting the Bhagavad Gita. I spared them nothing – the individual shots, the technical jargon, our colorful descriptions of sets and characters. At times my voice faded away altogether and I whispered endless pages of dialogue to the unheeding air. All the while, Johnstone sat with his eyes fixed alternately on his palms and the ceiling, patently trying to dissociate himself from me. Not once did he or anyone else bid me take respite or a glass of water. The whole room – exclusive of those who were asleep, naturally – was watching a man hang himself with a typewriter ribbon, and not a finger was lifted to save him. When I finally croaked 'Fade Out' at the end of my ninety-minute unspectacular, there was no sound except the stertorous breathing of the dogs.

After an aeon, Chico stretched, revolved in his chair, and addressed Groucho. 'What do you think?' he growled.

With the deliberation of a diamond cutter, Groucho bit the end off his cigar, and applying a match, exhaled a jet of smoke. 'It stinks,' he said, and arose. 'Come on.' As he stalked toward the door, he was engulfed in a wedge of sycophants hissing agreement and post-mortems. In another few seconds, the only occupants of the suite were a pair of forlorn sourdoughs numbed by the realization that the Lost Dutchman Mine was actually fool's gold.

Such was my baptism into the picture business, the glamorous and devil-may-care world of illusion I had envied from childhood. I crept away that night to lick my wounds, convinced that this was Waterloo, that contumely and public disgrace would be our portion forever. Happily, I was wrong; in the scalding light of day, our critics capriciously reversed themselves and decided that traces of our handiwork could be salvaged. It took five months of drudgery and Homeric quarrels, ambuscades, and intrigues that would have shamed the Borgias, but it finally reached the cameras, and the end product was *Monkey Business*, a muscular hit. I read the New York reviews in the most ideal surroundings imaginable – a café terrace at Bandol on the Côte d'Azur, midway between Marseilles and Toulon. A soft inshore breeze stirred my wife's hair, a Chambéry *fraise* waited at my elbow, and the schnauzer snored contentedly at our feet. Far more blissful, though, was the certainty that there wasn't a frosted papaya or a sneak preview within a thousand miles. Even that prince of porcupines, Thoreau, couldn't have asked for more than that.

*   *   *

My own relationship with Groucho was, in a sense, a baffling one. I loved his lightning transitions of thought, his ability to detect pretentiousness and bombast, and his genius for disembowelling the spurious and hackneyed phrases that litter one's conversation. And I knew that he liked my work for the printed page, my preoccupation with clichés, baroque language, and the elegant variation. Nevertheless, I sensed as time went on that this aspect of my work disturbed him; he felt that some of the dialogue I wrote for him was 'too literary.' He feared that many of my allusions would be incomprehensible to the ordinary moviegoer, whom he regarded as a wholly cretinous specimen.

'What'll this mean to the barber in Peru?' he was wont to complain whenever he came across a particularly fanciful reference. The barber, in his mind, was a prototypical figure – not a South American, but a Midwestern square in Peru, Indiana, whose funny bone the Marxes sought to tickle. Groucho visualized him, exhausted from his day's work and attended by a wife and five children, staring vacuously at the screen and resenting japes he could not understand. I tried to convince Groucho that his comedy was unique, a kaleidoscope of parody, free association, and insult, but he brushed me aside. 'That's OK for the Round Table at the Algonquin,' he said impatiently. 'Jokes – that's what I need. Give me jokes.'

The producer charged with supervising *Horsefeathers*, as it happened, was the same awesome figure who had guided the destinies of *Monkey Business*, Herman Mankiewicz. The choice, I suspect, was a deliberate one on the part of Paramount's front office, for it needed a tough foreman to ride herd on our anarchical troupe. Mankiewicz, whose stormy Teutonic character and immoderate zest for the grape and gambling have since been well delineated in connection with the authorship of *Citizen Kane*, was a brilliant man, but if he had any lovable qualities, he did his best to conceal them. He had a tongue like a rasp, and his savage wit demolished anyone unlucky enough to incur his displeasure. I myself was the recipient on various occasions, but one, which Groucho delighted to recall many years later, deserves repetition.

On a very hot midday in July, it seemed, Mankiewicz betook himself to a celebrated restaurant in Hollywood named Eddie Brandstetter's, much frequented by gourmands, where he treated his palate to two whiskey sours and a Gargantuan lunch consisting of lentil soup with frankfurters, rinderbrust with spaetzle, red cabbage and roast potatoes, and noodle pudding, irrigating the mixture with three or four flagons of Pilsener. Then, eyeballs protruding, he lumbered painfully to his car and drove to his office at Paramount. Thrusting aside the handful of messages his secretary extended, he enjoined her not to admit any callers, however importunate, for the next couple of hours and retired into his private sanctum. With the Venetian blinds tightly drawn, he stretched out on a sofa, shielded his face with a copy of the *Hollywood Reporter*, and sank into a blissful snooze.

Barely ten minutes later, he was awakened by a timid, repeated knocking at the door. Mankiewicz's face, mottled with perspiration and mounting fury, swelled like a sunfish as he sat up, prepared to decapitate whoever had flouted his express orders.

'Who the hell is it?' he shouted. 'Come in, damn you!'

Two pale-faced young men, twitching with fright, entered haltingly. They were Arthur Sheekman, a gagman Groucho had imported to assist with his material, and myself, and luckless as always, I had been nominated to voice our petition.

'I – I'm sorry to intrude,' I began, 'but the fact is – the truth of the matter –'

'What the devil do you want?' Mankiewicz barked. 'Get the marbles out of your mouth!'

'Well, it's like this,' I squeaked, moistening my lips. 'In this sequence we're working on, we're kind of perplexed about the identity of the Marx Brothers – the psychology of the characters they're supposed to represent, so to speak. I mean, who are they? We – we wondered if you could analyze or define them for us.'

'Oh, you did, did you?' he grated. 'OK, I'll tell you in a word. One of them is a guinea, another a mute who picks up spit, and the third an old Hebe with a cigar. Is that all clear, Beaumont and Fletcher? Fine,' he concluded, forcing a poisonous smile. 'Now get back to your hutch, and at teatime I'll send over a lettuce leaf for the two of you to chew on. Beat it!'

Dr Gordon's Casebook

Richard Gordon

A chronicle of the life of an ordinary GP, *Dr Gordon's
Casebook* highlights the chaotic nature of his day...

21 JUNE

Midsummer. Slack surgeries. Lovely. Before noon, phone call from Mrs
Noakes, she utterly bedridden, could I please succour. Jump in car at once,
round to 'Shangri La', up fully carpeted stairs to bedroom overlooking pool.
'The doctor so soon?' Smiles invitingly, throws aside *Harpers and Queen*.
'Advantage of being a private patient, I suppose? I was telling my daily
woman only yesterday, *don't* dissipate your husband's wages on video and
Horizon Tours and microwave ovens, join BUPA, *much* more rewarding.'

I am all professional (remember Mrs Blessington). 'How long have you
been ill, Mrs Noakes?'

'I've been utterly prostrate all morning, do sit on the bed. These circular
ones are rather fun. Just had the place refitted – Hereward asked rather
grumpily why a bedroom had to match your lifestyle, when you were mostly
unconscious in it – but when one's trapped here helplessly as I am today, one
really appreciate one's Louis Quinze. Like the quilt? White goose down.'

'And what seems to be the trouble?' She in candy-striped trad nightshirt,
unbuttoned all down front.

'My usual *intolerable* headache got worse and worse. Hereward wondered
whether to stay at home, but of course I'd feel an utterly disloyal wife being
ill and impeding his career, so I said, off you go in the Jag, darling, I shall be
a martyr – ah, Ortrud. What a gorgeous display from Moyses Stevens,
Hereward must have got his secretary to order it just as soon as he reached
the office, how caring of him. Where was I, Doctor –? The damn phone never
stops ringing, hello?'

Delightful smile. 'Fiona! How sweet to call me. Yes, I am, I'm afraid. *The doctor is with me now.*' Hushed solemnity. 'I hope it isn't *too* serious, either, but one never knows, *of course* I remember poor Janet Morgan-Jones, nothing but a slight cough and a week later that utterly freezing afternoon at the crematorium, thank you *so* much.'

Replaced pink telephone (little knobs instead of dial). 'Dreadful bitch, she only rang hoping I was half dead – oh, Fiametta. What a lovely basket of fruit. Why, it's from my fellow bridge-players, how thoughtful, I suppose they've taken enough money off me in my time. Peach, Doctor?'

'These headaches – how long have you had them?'

'Sometimes I think I was *born* with one.' Phone. 'Excuse me again. Hello? Pamela! Fiona just phoned you? Yes, the sad news is true, I'm in bed under the doctor. So we'll have to postpone our lovely lunch today until I'm completely fit, won't we? I know I've been overdoing it for months, I'd love to go somewhere and lie as flat as a haddock in the sun, but Hereward's desperately busy, and of course a top executive's wife is simply part of his job these days, a constant stream of Americans and Japanese and Arabs to be lavishly entertained, as soon as Mohammedans glimpse a bottle of Cliquot, all thoughts of reaching the Seventh Heaven fly from their minds. Bye! That's a date I don't mind missing, at that place Sylph's in Templar Lane, wonderful for our figures, shredded lettuce, grated celeriac and carrot-juice, ugh. Have a chocolate, Doctor? They're *disastrous* for my weight, I know, but surely you can succumb to temptation when you're ill and feeling awful?'

'Indeed, Mrs Noakes, *most* of my patients are martyrs to self-indulgence,' I remarked austerely. 'And who can blame them? Flu is the housewife's winter holiday. After being taken for granted all year, nothing makes mother more lovingly appreciated than the family coming home from work and having to cook its own mince and potatoes. Illness is a chance for most people to feel important, for many their only one. Do you know, I've seen patients in hospital as proud of their diseases as old soldiers of their scars.'

'It's all right for some,' Mrs Noakes objected, 'like my daily woman's husband, drawing their sick pay and lying reading the *Sun* all day, but I've always a million things to do. You should see my diary, coffee mornings for cystic fibrosis, hairdresser, garden centre, Oxfam – oh dear!' she remembered. 'I must phone Naomi and cancel our shopping expedition, though they're always so embarrassing, she's dreadfully broke, poor thing, her husband's only in middle management, I end up with something cheap and shoddy which is pure waste as I can't possibly be seen in it, not with Hereward, anyway.'

'About the headache –'

'Absolutely *throbbing*, right above the eyes. Yes, Ortrud? Ah, the portable Sony, put it beside the Teasmade, we usually let the *au pairs* have it, but I'd be stretched out here utterly bored, and I should *die* if I didn't see what happens next in "Crossroads".'

'Any other symptoms, Mrs Noakes?'

'Doctor, I'm utterly *riddled* with them, sleeplessness, weariness, lassitude, complete loss of appetite – Ortrud, I'll just have an egg and milk beaten with brandy for lunch, I've got to keep my strength up, surely that's what Dr Gordon would advise?'

Ortrud retired to Nibelheim.

'Now she's gone, I can be utterly frank.' Mrs Noakes patted the bed beside her. 'Make yourself comfy with a pillow. Do you know what *I* think causes my headaches? My sex life with Hereward. I'll start right at the beginning, with my honeymoon – but I'm not the slightest feverish,' she objected.

'Thermometer under the tongue, please.' The doctor's oldest trick. 'It's a rather old-fashioned instrument, takes five minutes to work, ten if we want to be absolutely sure.'

Sat on bed and read *Vogue*.

'Thank you, Mrs Noakes.' Removed it. 'Perfectly normal. I'm sure that's a relief?'

'It's given me time to sort out exactly what I'm going to say –'

'And it's given *me* time to make a diagnosis,' I interrupted firmly. 'In 1901, Freud wrote *The Psychopathology of Everyday Life –*'

'*I* certainly have none of those awful complexes he described.'

'On the contrary, Mrs Noakes, every woman wears under her skirt a Freudian slip. The book was as popular with ordinary readers as with doctors, because people were fascinated by his idea that lots of highly irrational human behaviour was really highly rational. Getting on the wrong train and avoiding your creditors. Making a detour and missing an impudent beggar. Asking for the wrong number, of a girl you didn't dare to speak to – he was writing in the days before dialling and assertive sexual manners. Losing an umbrella, because you'd stolen it. Losing even your memory, to hide yourself like an ostrich in the desert. Ever suffered from amnesia, Mrs Noakes?'

'Well, if I had, it would be something I'd want to forget.'

'Do you know why you're spending today in bed?'

'Because of my headache.'

'No! You haven't got a headache. Or if you have, it's no worse than one you'd exorcise with an aspirin and then go off to Ascot or Henley. You're in bed because you don't want to consume raw veg with Pamela nor shop down-market with Naomi, you want to get your own back on the bridge club and savage the box of Suchard which has been the temptation of the Devil since your party, better still, to milk sympathy from your flinty-breathed friends, and better than that –' I paused. 'Have your husband tell you he loves you with flowers.'

She stared silently at the fitted dressing-table unit. At last I was getting on top of Mrs Noakes. Professionally, that is. I asked intensely, 'What are you missing this evening?'

'A lovely birthday party at the Hyde Park Hotel for the son of Hereward's chairman. Then we were all going on to see "The Sound of Music".'

'An unmarried son, I take it?'

'Yes.'

'Of course, Hereward will be present?'

'Yes.'

'Might I ask you something painful, Mrs Noakes?'

'Yes.'

'You'll be frank with me?'

'Yes.'

'This young man – what's his name –'

'Robin.'

'Have you been out with him?'

'Yes.'

'I mean, by yourselves.'

'Yes. When Hereward's in New York or somewhere, and I'm lonely.'

'Ha! Where do you go?'

'Generally, I've driven up to London and had lunch with him.'

'Ha, ha! You're fond of him?'

'Yes. I am. Very.'

'Ha, ha, *ha*! And he of you?'

'Extremely, by all evidence.'

'There we are! Diagnosis made. You don't want to be in the simultaneous company of Hereward and Robin. Mrs Noakes, you are suffering not from headaches, but feelings of guilt.'

'I don't see why.'

'It's very flattering for any woman to invoke the attention of a sexy young feller.'

'It is, Doctor, it is, but the chairman's son is only six.'

'Oh.'

She smiled. 'You're terribly sweet to take such trouble over my case, but you've got it wrong. My marriage, my social life, Hereward's job, they're the only things I've got to fuss over. If only I could have had a child....'

She held my hand. For once, I let her.

1 JULY

'The English winter – ending in July to recommence in August.' Byron got it right, at least until 8.30 am.

'Good morning, Mr Cowley. What a lovely day! Had your holiday yet?'

'No, Doctor, that's why I've come. You know how me and the wife are always careful over our health?'

'Of course. You wear crash helmets for your ride-on mower. Admirable.'

Mr Cowley, dark, neat, comfortable house overlooking Pilgrim's Way, runs office-supply business. Small, brown-haired wife subservient as a spaniel. Regular patient, in waiting-room plays musical chairs to avoid touch, breath, undefined miasmas from fellow-patients, gets on Mrs Shakepear's nerves. Gather from his wife that on return from surgery Mr Cowley immediately strips, has clothes laundered, takes bath, probably adds pint or two of Jeyes' Fluid. He would seem concerned about germs.

'Though of course, Doctor, this is the salubrious season –'

'Salubrious? You're joking. Haven't you thought about the perils of summer? Do you realize that wasps and bees claim five British lives a year? Which is more than you can accuse our atomic power-stations of, eh? Though I don't suppose there'd be much keenness for a demo round the hives. Ban the Bee and that sort of thing. You can be struck by lightning, nipped by adders, do a fry-up of toadstools, swig the weedkiller, spin off the rollercoaster, get beaten up by mods and rockers on the prom, not to mention every day drowning and falling off cliffs. It's happening all season. *Plus* tennis elbow, nettlerash, hay fever, poison ivy and midsummer madness.'

Overkill only way to treat his assumption whole world as dangerous as London 1664–5.

'But surely, Doctor,' Mr Cowley protested nervously, 'the lovely sunshine –'

'"The great bronze disc of church-emptying Apollo, hardener of heart and skin."' Arms flung wide, quoting Cyril Connolly, obese man of letters.

'Sunlight absolutely wrecks the epidermis, though I suppose it can hardly be accused of fossilizing the coronaries.'

'I'm with you there,' he said more cheerfully. 'I always baste the wife with Ambre Solaire, and fold a fruit-gum packet for my nose.'

'When were you conceived?'

Looking blank. 'Beg pardon, Doctor?'

'Some interesting research was done in America ten years ago. You'd imagine summer was Nature's smiling season for starting babies, wouldn't you? Dancing round the maypole, plenty of cover in the cornfields, it's traditional.' He nodded obediently. 'But no,' I corrected him. 'Love in the winter produces, the following autumn, one-third more offspring with high IQs than summer's passion fruits. People like Picasso and Mrs Thatcher, as opposed to Mozart and Mr Macmillan.'

'Perhaps that's because clever people don't watch so much telly during the winter nights?' he suggested (I thought rather brightly).

'A professor in Dublin said it was the thunderstorms.'

'I know they turn the milk, Doctor, we always pour ours away just in case, though the man from Unigate says we're daft.'

'Thunderstorms cause anxiety in newly pregnant women, which mental state affects the hormones circulating in her blood, which in turn get through to the baby and blunt the cutting-edge of its brain.'

'A bit far-fetched, isn't it?' Mr Cowley complained morosely. 'Why only thunderstorms? It's really worrying, these days, the number of things there are to make you anxious.'

'The Dublin professor went further. He reckoned *whole countries* became anxious.'

'How'd he know?' Mr Cowley demanded.

'Easy. You go by the suicide rate, car smashes, alcoholism and so on. I don't know exactly *why* they should be barometers of anxiety, but the professors do. Japan is the most anxious country, with Italy and France. *All have lots of thunderstorms.* The first ear-splitting crack, the Japanese start committing *hara-kiri,* the French grab the cognac, and the Italians continue driving as usual. We in Britain are terribly lucky, because we have only a few thunderstorms and a placid, easy-going temperament. In the Dublin professor's own country, I shouldn't imagine it ever thunders at all. Where are you going for your hols?'

'That's where I wanted your advice, Doctor,' he replied eagerly. 'Travelling's always a health hazard, I reckon, even stopping for a pork pie at a motorway caff, never know what it can give you.'

'How right you are,' I agreed heartily. 'Millions of air passengers buzzing round the world, more pestilential than rat fleas. Nowadays, you needn't go all that way to the White Man's Grave to catch horrible tropical diseases, you can suffer them in the convenience of your own bedroom. We doctors see malaria in Muswell Hill, Lassa fever in Lyme Regis, typhus in Taplow and sleeping sickness in Slough.'

'The wife and I know that foreigners have some funny health habits, of course. Just like their other ones. We'd certainly not care to bathe from their beaches –'

'You no longer swim in the Mediterranean. You go through the motions. Old medical joke.'

'So we thought we'd be safer on a cruise.'

'Are you mad? Shut yourself in a tin can wallowing in the hot sun, everyone blowing germs over each other from the range of a few inches? Thousands of miles from the nearest life-support system? I excluded the lifeboats, of course.'

'But every cruise liner carries a qualified doctor –'

'Don't talk to *me* about ship's doctors. Their surgical skills are limited to splicing the mainbrace. I ought to know, because I was one. Ships are terribly dangerous places, Mr Cowley, take it from me. I'd have put icebergs as the least of the *Titanic*'s troubles.'

'Well, if we do risk going abroad, on terra firma, as you might say, can you recommend a country which provides a proper doctor, should anything go wrong?'

'A country's medicine has its own style, like its music,' I said romantically. 'In France, they tend to give everything by suppository, even cough mixture. In Spain, the whole family comes into hospital with you. In Brazil, you have to bring your own sandwiches. In Italy, people pray over you a good deal. In Germany, they have means of making you better. In America, all regular credit cards are accepted. A lot of British patients today could go to India and Pakistan, fall ill, and still feel at home,' I pointed out hearteningly. 'Why not Japan? There's this new hotel in Osaka.'

'What's special about it?' he asked warily.

'It consists of 411 sleeping capsules, like a honeycomb. Burn a greenhouse fumigating cone, crawl inside, shut the lid, and you'll be free from infection for a fortnight. You can't even fall out of bed. Good morning.'

'Where are *you* going, Doctor?'

'Nowhere. In this job, you never really feel fit enough to face a holiday.'

8 JULY

This morning saw Mrs Charrington, headmistress of St Ursula's (fnd. 1920, 300 girls, boarding fees three thou. plus a year, bright blue uniform, summer straw hats, Oxbridge successes, tennis and netball, careers mistress, gravel soil). She large, pink, jolly, in sensible non-crush grey linen-suit, sensible 20-denier seal tights, sensible flat-heeled shoes, sensible brooch of Royal Navy Crest, and tiny red blisters all up her forearms.

Reassure her, 'It's a slight allergic rash, Mrs Charrington, there's a lot of it about this time of year.'

She affronted. 'But it's utterly amazing that I'm here at all, I always take such good care of my health, and of my girls' health at St Ursula's. I permit nothing in their school dinners grown with chemical fertilizers, what comes out of a factory is far less natural than what comes out of a horse, that's obvious.'

Mrs Charrington is a compost-grown-stone-ground-wholemeal-sunflower-oil nut.

'I always buy health foods, Doctor, at the Hygea Stores in Templar Lane, they're criminally pricey, but I'm sure *you'll* agree nothing's too much to pay for a *corpore sano*, even if a *mens sana* is utterly impossible to maintain these days. I've quite a reputation in the common room for my wholesome gourmet treats,' she revealed. 'You must come one evening for my sesame seed stew with mung beans, topped up with a dollop of halva on charcoal crackers.'

'I'll write you a prescription—'

'My husband George simply couldn't start the day without his muesli with tenderized prunes and a vegetable sausage – the poor man is an absolute martyr to the wind – and after my lunchtime slug of ginseng I can face the girls like a giant refreshed. I feed my husband on lots of living raw foods because he is, as you know, somewhat short and of thin physique, the fifth form scrawled some outrageously vulgar graffiti about him in the loo. I must confess, I visited the hakim's shop by the station – "hakim" means "wise one", you'd be called that in Bangladesh, Doctor – and bought George some powdered rhino horn, which is famous over two continents for putting lead in pencils, as they say, this is in the *strictest* confidence, if the fifth form got to hear I don't know *what* I'd find in the loo.'

'I'll give you an antihistamine drug –'

'As I'm being jolly frank, I can tell you there were evenings during our courtship when I insisted George had a dozen oysters.'

'And only ten of them worked, I suppose? Old joke.'

She frowned. 'I don't follow, Doctor? And I'm famous at St Ursula's for my sense of humour.'

'Try it on the fifth form,' I advised.

'There's a lot you doctors can learn, you know. George's poor back, doctors despaired of it, so he went to an osteopath, one crack and never a twinge since. My sister Pru had a lot of feminine trouble, the doctors were utterly hopeless, actually suggested a psychiatrist, quite insulting, my family are *perfectly* normal, she went to see a man in Pimlico who stuck foot-long needles all over her and cured her instantly. I remember he said that it let out her *qi*, the energy of life – I must say Pru has enough for a dozen, a dreadfully talkative woman – and that trouble was imbalance of her *yin* and *yang* which does sound rather like a team of Chinese acrobats. My other sister Crystal suffered from vertigo, she got converted to RC, so she made the pilgrimage to Lourdes, it was rather a disaster, she had a nasty attack in the sacred grotto and fell into the candles, they had to put her out by sluicing her with the holy water.'

'These tablets may cause sleepiness –'

'My brother Clarence suffered lassitude for years, quite baffled Harley Street, then he heard about radiesthesia, he sent them a few hairs to put in their black box and test for vibrations, they told him he'd got overstrain, though as a joke he'd sent hairs from the tail of his Labrador, he gave the dog some conditioning powders and from that day they both never looked back.'

'So be careful if you're driving –'

'Now I'm into, as the fifth form say, yoga, I stand George on his head every morning and do my *asanas*, which are yogic postures, on my study floor during bunbreak. I know you doctors don't approve of unorthodox medicine, no more than those dreadful trade unions their childish scabs and blacklegs, but *why* does it make the patients feel better?'

'A little of what you fancy does you good.'

'Heavens, is that the time?' She stared at her sensibly huge wristwatch. 'The lower sixth will become utterly Trotskyist if they're kept waiting. As I'm here, Doctor, I'd like a prescription for some aspirins – my garlic and seaweed pills don't seem to touch my headaches this term, it must be the stress of the O levels and A levels, I suffer *far* more than the girls – and some

Elastoplast dressings, they're so much handier than slippery elm for cuts and scalds, and half a dozen pairs of support tights. After all, we pay our taxes, and if we're never ill we must get something for our money. Have you any medical advice you'd particularly like me to follow?'

'Yes. Eat an apple a day.'

'Is that another joke? Perhaps I'd better have the fifth form explain it. Good morning, Doctor,' gathering up her prescriptions. 'I say, you've been jolly D to me, can't I do a favour for you? Come along to our end-of-term concert. Absolutely insist. The fifth form's doing "Hiawatha", though I don't think their heart's in it.'

The Identikit Soap Opera

Barry Took

I have, in fact, written what I consider the blueprint for the perfect British soap opera.

MEMO
To: The Managing Director. Rockall Television.
From: United Computer Script Writing Company Limited.
Subject: Proposed new twice-weekly tv serial.

Starting from your brief which indicated you wished to introduce a new serial of the type colloquially known as 'soap opera', we at United Computer Scripts have examined the existing products on the market, and have noted certain facts about current series of this type: 'Crossroads', 'Emmerdale Farm', and 'Coronation Street'. Our findings suggest that the cast should number 15.3 people. Of the sample tested week ending 5 February, 'Crossroads' had 20 people, 'Coronation Street' 17 people, and 'Emmerdale Farm' 8, thus the average is 15.3 and should contain as many variations of age and social class as possible.

The surnames should be of two syllables, e.g. Sugden, Odgen, Hunter, Parker, Potter, Bradshaw – Christian names too tend to be of two syllables, e.g. Annie, Elsie and Betty, but monosyllables seem to be preferred (e.g. Jim, Meg, Stan, Jill, etc.). We have also noted that the more successful series have a provincial background. We assume this to be because social changes in these areas are less rapid than in the capital, and in addition a provincial locale provides the possibility of aspiration, e.g. 'I'm chucking this and going to live in London.' (There is no recorded case of a participant in a series set in London saying 'I'm chucking this and going to live in Eccles.')

In search of the ideal soap opera, we at UCSW then began to consider possible locations in which to set our series. We discarded a lighthouse as being insufficiently flexible for long-running dramatic action. The light is either on or it's off and that's it. While it is possible for the 15-plus cast envisaged to be present in the lighthouse, they could only be there as survivors of a shipwreck, illegal immigrants, or squatters, none of which possibilities was felt to get the audience identification which is the core of a successful soap opera.

In considering other locations, we discarded a home for distressed gentlefolk, a prison, a labour exchange, and a battery chicken farm because of their lack of immediate identification for a mass audience. Some branch of the Armed Forces was considered, but it was felt to be adequately covered, some might say more than adequately, in other series (e.g. 'Sailor', 'Warship', 'Dad's Army', 'Get Some in') as indeed are the activities of the police who appear, on superficial examination, to be under contract to the BBC.

After much discussion, the UCSW team came up with the following suggestions which I append for your approval.

Title: T'Corner Shop
The story concerns the day to day adventures of the owners and customers of a typical corner grocery shop situated on the outskirts of a small farming community near Walsall.

The Principal Characters

Maggie Oakroyd Mid-fifties, the owner of the shop. On the surface a termagant, but underneath she has a heart of gold, always ready to help pensioners and the unemployed. In spite of that she has no time for social security scroungers. She likes young people 'so long as they've got clean hair' but has no time for football hooligans or socialists who she thinks should be locked up. She is married to –

Jeb Oakroyd Maggie's second husband. (Her first met a tragic end when he fell into a grain silo on their honeymoon in 1947.) Jeb is a simple, no-nonsense, please-yourself, call-a-spade-a-spade chap, happier in his pigeon loft than in t'shop. Believes all blackies should be sent home except the local cricket team's opening bat and leg spin bowler, who is –

Amin Patel   Softly spoken and mild mannered (except on cricket field) an ex-Ugandan Asian who works in a nearby dye works as well as driving the shop's delivery van. He's saving up to open a Tandoori takeaway in the village. Goes to night school to improve his English, but still uses amusing antique anglicisms, such as 'well bowled, old sport', 'wizard prang', 'can I do you now, sir', and 'how's your belly off for spots'. He is emotionally attached to –

Fanny Beaver   The village good-time girl. An intensely beautiful, wayward and magnetic titian-haired creature of 55 who has kept her wonderful figure, thanks to a foundation garment apparently made by the British Steel Corporation. (NB This may seem incongruous, but our researches reveal that most soap operas have this type of sex goddess in their cast.)

Early in the series, we meet:
Jim Beaver   Fanny's illegimate son (his father was a US serviceman stationed in the area) on leave from the Royal Navy and thinking of joining the local constabulary when his service is completed and thus replacing:
Old Fred   The village policeman. Dull but reliable.

Then there's:
Old Bert   A wise old farmhand. Reliable but dull.
Old Sid   A stupid old farmhand. The butt of –
Old Ted   Landlord of the Goat And Trouserpress, the local pub. His speciality is keeping real ale for passing journalists and drinking bottled Double Diamond himself. Often to be seen in the snug of the Goat And Trouserpress is:
Lady Vicuna Stavely, JP   The Lady of the Manor, who finds a strange affinity with Maggie Oakroyd, though they are from different ends of the social scale. Lady Vicuna spends most of her time worrying about the madcap antics of:
The Hon. Peter Staveley   Her ne'er do well son. (Hobbies: hang gliding, stock car racing, and flower arrangement.) Whenever the Hon. Peter

gets in a scrape (e.g. found intoxicated in a transvestite club in Newton-le-Willows) he is invariably saved from public disgrace by:

Ramsbottom The Staveleys' unflappable chauffeur, whose suave exterior hides the fact that he's an ex-convict and the real father of:

Nyrere Thicket A young village girl whose ambition is to emigrate to Australia and make a new life for herself. Her secret shame is known only to:

Sylvia Anthrax The district nurse, who knows everyone's private affairs but keeps them to herself until she can contain herself no longer and unburdens herself to:

James Ferret A vet who is secretly a best-selling novelist writing under the pseudonym of Stanley McMurtry, and using the village folk as his models.

That completes the list of the requisite 15 characters; the .3 is taken care of by the fact that Nyrere Thicket is three months pregnant. By whom, we shall discover as the series progresses.

The stories for 'T'Shop' should be in line with the other main contenders in the field and be simple, uncomplicated and easily extendable. We fed all our information into the computer and append the following print-out:

'During a village cricket match a loose ball bowled by Amin Patel is struck for six by the Hon. Peter Staveley who has turned out for the Visitors as they've arrived a man short. The ball crashes through the window of the snug at the Goat And Trouserpress spattering Old Bert, Old Sid, Old Ted, Fanny Beaver, and Lady Vicuna with broken glass. Some moments later, Fanny complains of severe abdominal pains. Has she ingested broken glass in the meat pie she was eating at the time of the cricket-ball incident?

'Nurse Anthrax is on a case at an outlying farm, so James Ferret, the vet (who's been fielding at long leg) is summoned. Unused to human ailments, he is nonplussed, but the indefatigable Maggie Oakroyd suggests an X-ray. They carry the comatose figure of Fanny to the Staveley Rolls Royce, and the suave Ramsbottom whisks the party to Ferret's surgery.

'On arrival they surprise Nyrere and Jim Beaver in a hot embrace behind the sterilizer. They explain that they were sheltering from a sudden summer storm and had removed their clothes to dry them. It's clear from James Ferret's reaction that beneath his calm exterior, the vet is a seething mass of twisted desire – but for which of the lovers? Meanwhile, the seething mass of Fanny Beaver is X-rayed and found to have swallowed not broken glass but a two-inch hoop ear-ring of the type only sold in t'corner shop. Clearly, there was a foreign body in the meat pie. Is Maggie Oakroyd guilty of negligence under the Shops and Catering (Processed Meat Amendment) Act of 1912? Was it an act of sabotage designed to discredit Maggie and close t'shop?

'James Ferret remembers Amin Patel and the Hon. Peter Staveley in deep and furtive conversation before the match. Was Amin's long hop and the Hon. Peter's mighty six pure chance? What were Nyrere and Jim really doing in Ferret's surgery? Before the various cross-currents of doubt and suspicion are resolved, it's learned that Jeb Oakroyd has inadvertently fallen down a flooded mineshaft. Can he be rescued before the gritty waters engulf him? Maggie enlists the help of the local WI who form a human chain and . . .'

We regret to inform you that at this point the computer exploded. Pending the arrival of new parts, we beg to conclude our submission.

Donald G. Panderbody
for United Computer Scripts Limited

The Good Life

John Esmonde & Bob Larbey

Tom Good and his wife, Barbara, have decided to drop out
of the rat race. Tom has left his job at JJM, a big
advertising agency, and he and Barbara have decided to
become self-sufficient in Surbiton. To many of their neighbours they are laughable, but to the trendy well-heeled
couple living next door – Jerry Leadbetter and his snooty
wife, Margo – they are simply insane.

A little miracle had happened in the front garden – the Goods' first pea had
poked its head above ground and Tom and Barbara were taking a
photograph for posterity. Barbara was already posed, kneeling by the tiny
shoot and pointing. Tom fiddled with the camera, which he had placed on an
upturned bucket. 'Ready?' he said at last.

'Have been for ten minutes.'

Tom edged closer, holding the lead and plunger.

'Go!' he shouted, then pressed the plunger and rushed to pose with
Barbara.

At this moment, Jerry came back from his Saturday stroll to the end of the
Avenue and arrived just in time to see the tableau. He had long since
accepted Tom and Barbara's weird life-style and its attendant eccentricities.
Had they been tightrope walking on their clothes-line he would not have
been surprised. He considered them dispassionately.

'You look like two figures on an Egyptian frieze.'

Tom 'shushed' him through his frozen smile. 'Say "Isis",' he ordered
Barbara like a ventriloquist.

They 'Isised' together, but the delayed action mechanism of the camera
seemed particularly delayed.

'Isis,' repeated Tom.

'Chocolates,' added Barbara. 'Cigarettes.'

Jerry amusedly contributed to the ventriloquial act.

'Gottle of geer! Gottle of geer!'

Tom broke from the tableau.

'Well don't just laugh,' he ordered Jerry, 'make yourself useful and take it for us.'

This did not seem too much like hard work, so Jerry came into the garden and picked up the camera.

Tom resumed the pose with Barbara. Jerry focused but then lowered the camera.

'Just a minute,' he asked, 'what exactly are you pointing at?'

Tom looked exasperated.

'Just the miracle of new life, that's all.'

'What, a bit of grass?'

Tom pushed Jerry's probing suede boot away. 'Bit of grass indeed!' he said, outraged. 'That, mate, is our first pea! The first, I might add, of several hundredweight.'

Jerry, being Jerry, was not impressed. 'Most people grow begonias,' he said.

Tom sneered. 'We are not most people.'

'True,' said Jerry who was nothing if not logical. He put the camera to his eye again.

'Right – say, "pea"!'

Tom and Barbara obeyed and Jerry took the photograph.

'Ta,' said Tom. 'Come and have a look around the back, Jerry. Everything's coming up.'

'Well it would if you planted it,' answered Jerry being logical again.

'Yes,' Tom persisted, 'but it's coming up! Lettuces, beetroot, broad beans.'

Jerry shook off the arm at his elbow. 'Oh no,' he said warily. 'You're not getting me round there again. Last time I ended up mucking out your rotten chickens. I'm going home to a boring, civilized Martini and a decadent sprawl in my armchair. Bye!'

'Sybarite!' shouted Tom at Jerry's retreating figure.

'Peasants!' Jerry called back good-naturedly.

Tom turned back to Barbara, who was now sitting on the upturned bucket.

'Nice bloke, old Jerry.'

Barbara nodded. 'Actually, I wouldn't mind a sit-down myself.'

'Uh-uh,' Tom forbade. 'Not till we finish the old Ho Chi Minh Trail.'

Tom started hoeing enthusiastically, chanting 'Ho! Ho! Ho Chi Minh!'

Barbara sighed, stood up and followed suit, but without the same drive.

From the road came the multi-syllabic but quite unintelligible cry of a rag-and-bone man asking for any old lumber.

'Round here?' Tom smiled. 'You'll be lucky.'

The horse and cart continued along the Avenue. Tom looked idly at it, then suddenly looked fired.

'It's one of those!' he shouted and ran after the cart excitedly.

Barbara watched, bemused, then had a nasty suspicion as she saw what was on the back of the cart – a large old iron kitchen-range, the worse for wear and heavily rusted.

Apart from being heavily rusted, the range was also simply heavy, and dragging it round the back and into the kitchen had almost brought Tom, Barbara and the rag-and-bone man to their knees. With a final heave, they settled it in the old open fire-place. The rag-and-bone man was the first to get his breath.

'Cor! Another couple of steps with that and we'd have both had a Julius.'

Tom nodded in agreement, then realized he didn't understand.

'Julius?' he queried.

'Yeah. Cockney rhyming slang of old London. Julius Caesar – Calpurnia – Hernia.'

Tom shook his head. 'I've never heard that one before.'

The rag-and-bone man sat himself down, obviously fancying a rest and a chat at the same time.

'You interested in all that, are you then,' he asked Tom – 'the old London patois?'

Tom wasn't actually, but felt he should be polite to a fellow range-shover.

'Well – fairly. I understand it originated with the old cut-purses and such-like. They used it as a sort of secret language so that the law wouldn't know what they were talking about.'

'Yes,' yawned Barbara. 'I read that somewhere.'

The rag-and-bone man shook his head.

'No – that is a common ricket. Rhyming slang was actually invented by a bloke who could never remember the right names for things – so he made them up. Tommy Lang his name was. See? Tommy Lang – Slang.'

'You mean he couldn't even remember his own name?' queried Barbara suspiciously.

'Yeah. That's how bad it was.' The rag-and-bone man pushed on. 'My name is Sam, right? Do you know what he used to call me? Bacon and ham – Sam. Get it?'

All this was ringing less and less true to Tom and Barbara, but Sam obviously believed in blanket-bombing. He chuckled fondly.

'Yeah. Very famous he was, old Tommy Lang. I remember seeing him at the Great Exhibition at the Crystal Palace. Had a little stall, he did. You bunged him a tanner, give him a word and wallop! He'd give you the rhyming slang!'

This was too much.

'The Great Exhibition at the Crystal Palace was in 1851,' Tom said flatly.

Barbara joined in. 'That would make you a hundred and something!'

'Did I say 1851?' Sam wriggled, 'No, I meant *1951* – The Festival of Britain.'

Tom wanted to get on.

'Well,' he said, 'I went to The Festival of Britain umpteen times and Tommy Lang was conspicuous by his absence.'

Knowing he was losing ground rapidly, Sam decided to quit and stood up.

'Yeah – well – anyway,' he pointed at the flue pipe, 'you've got your tubing, lady.'

'My didgereedoo,' volunteered Barbara.

Sam looked puzzled.

'Eh?'

It was Barbara's turn to bluff.

'My didgereedoo – flue.'

Sam laughed uneasily. 'Oh yeah – that old one.' He decided on a change to a safer subject. 'I couldn't help noticing your garden, like, as we came round. Different, ain't it?'

'Aren't you going to ask why?' said Tom, knowing the answer.

'Well it was on the old bacon – bacon rind – mind,' answered Sam.

'You've heard of self-sufficiency?'

'Yeah.'

'Well I'm self and she's sufficiency.'

Sam didn't know whether to be shocked or impressed, but did ask the obvious question.

'What round here? Why ain't you got a farm then?'

Barbara stood up. 'Because we like living here,' she snapped uncharacteristically, 'and sooner or later someone is going to come up with a more original question!'

Sam looked a little guilty as Barbara walked out. 'Whoops,' he said. 'Dropped a coat have I?'

'Dropped a what?' asked Tom, a little testy himself now.

'A coat – coat hanger – clanger.'

'You've been dropping them since you came through that door! Cockney rhyming slang of old London! You're making it up as you go along!'

Sam shuffled, then smiled.

'Yeah, well there is a reason for that.'

'What?'

'I'm a fake. Only round a toffee-nose district like this it goes down well, see – a bit of the old Costermonger rubbish. They think, "Hello – one of our old traditions that hasn't died." Puts them in a good mood, see? Good for business. And talking of business ...' Sam pointed at the range. 'Cough, cough!'

Tom took the hint, liking the real Sam better than the fake one. He handed over an electric hair-dryer and a toaster.

'That's what we agreed wasn't it?'

Sam nodded. ''Course, this is the old barter system coming back, isn't it? All part of your health and efficiency.'

The invented slang was a joke now.

'Self-sufficiency – yes,' worked out Tom.

Sam looked out of the back door. 'Talking of which, you want to watch them birds. They're pecking your shoots to smithereens.'

'Oh blimey!' Tom ran to the door and clapped his hands. 'I'll have to do something about that – have to get a birdscarer. Either that or sellotape their beaks together.'

Sam prepared to leave. 'I'll keep my eyes open on the round for you,' he offered, 'I come across some strange things in my business.'

'Like us?'

'Yes. See you then, squire.'

'See you then, squire,' replied Tom.

He closed the back door behind Sam, smiling at his receding shouts to the birds of 'Go on – flit off, you feathered gits!' and then went in search of Barbara.

Barbara was curled up on the couch in the Big Room, asleep, as Tom came in.

He shook her gently. 'Want to buy a battleship?'

'Oh don't!'

'Something the matter?'

Barbara sat up. 'I'm just whacked, that's all.'

'Yes, I know,' said Tom. 'It's working a thirty-six-hour day that does it.' There was concern in his voice now. 'It's not getting too much for you is it?'

Recognizing the worry in his tone, Barbara rallied.

'Too much? I might tell you they turn out a pretty gritty sort of chap at Roedean.'

'You didn't go to Roedean.'

'Neither did you.'

Losing the point cheered Tom. He took Barbara's hand.

'Come and have a look at the range.'

In the kitchen they looked at the range, Barbara somewhat mystified but Tom proudly.

'We're dead lucky,' he pronounced. 'There aren't many of these about, you know.'

He kicked the door, which spoiled the weight of his words by falling off.

Barbara smiled mischievously. 'You keep kicking it like that and there'll be one less.'

'Yes, but do you *like* it?'

'Yes. I've always wanted a couple of tons of rusty old iron in the kitchen. What's it for?'

'What's it for?' asked Tom in amazement. 'It's a range. You range on it – with it – ranging things.'

This sort of technical expertise did not impress Barbara.

'Tom,' she said, 'I know what it is, but we've got a perfectly good cooker.'

'True. But it won't be much good in a couple of weeks when we have the electricity cut off, will it?'

Barbara took the point and looked more closely at the rust-covered range.

'Clever. I suppose I could learn to cook on it. This must be the oven.'

She peered in and looked disgusted. Tom had a look too.

'Oh that's all right,' he said lightly, 'it's only a bit of Victorian dripping.'

Barbara was still poking around at the range.

'Including the Victorian dripping, how much did we pay for this?'

'Your hair-dryer and the toaster.'

'Thanks very much.'

'No electricity,' Tom pointed out. 'No, if you want to dry your hair in future, just stick it in there. And as for toast – this is *the* way to make toast.'

'Will you be swapping your electric razor for something?' inquired Barbara innocently.

'Yes, I expect so. Why?'

'Well this thing's so versatile, I want to know how you're going to shave with it.'

Tom pinched her bottom. 'Come on clever-cuts, let's get the rust off.'

Barbara spread newspapers on the floor as Tom got a couple of stiff brushes and joined her.

'Can you see this, all black-leaded?' he asked.

Barbara made the first sweep with her brush, producing a cloud of rust. 'Not at the moment, no,' she coughed.

Tom went to the back door. 'Strewth! Let's get some air in here.' He opened the door and was immediately distracted.

'They're back! Get off!' he shouted, 'I won't tell you again. Clear off!'

'Pan's People after you again?'

Tom brooded, missing her dig at his fantasy harem.

'It's those birds after our seedlings.'

'Oh no,' Barbara was concerned now, 'we broke our backs putting those in.'

'Right. I'll have to think of something to frighten them off.' He had an instant inspiration. 'Of course! The old Chinese idea!'

'Kung-Fu?'

Again Tom missed the joke, and headed determinedly for the garden.

'Yes, that's it! Just carry on.'

Barbara looked at the rusty heap in front of her.

'Gosh, thanks, Tom,' she said to herself.

An hour later, Tom stood in the garden looking proudly at a Heath Robinson contraption he had fashioned with a selection of old tins and bottles suspended on strings.

'Well what do you think?' he demanded of Geraldine the goat.

Geraldine chewed impassively.

'You're just jealous because you didn't think of it.'

Tom turned and called towards the house. 'Barbara! Come and see! Barbara!'

Barbara came out from the kitchen, rusty and somewhat dishevelled.

Tom pointed proudly at his tins and bottles. 'Tah-rah! One Chinese bird-scarer!' He demonstrated by rattling the contraption with his hand. 'Windee blow. Tinee rattle. Birdee scared. Confucius!'

Barbara looked unimpressed. 'You must be.'

'What?'

'Confucius. What happens when the wind doesn't blow?'

There was a long silence as Tom looked at Barbara, looked at the bird-scarer and then back at Barbara.

'I thought you were getting the rust off that range?' he said aggressively.

Barbara pulled a face and went back indoors. Tom looked accusingly at Geraldine.

'You and your stupid ideas!'

The man from the G.P.O. was disconnecting the telephone in the Big Room as Tom, seated at the bureau, worked on an idea for the Bird-Scarer Mark II.

'Tom, what *are* you doing in there?' called Barbara from the kitchen, and had Tom been less preoccupied, he would have noticed the edge in her voice.

'Research!' he called back.

Wanting a sounding-board for his latest idea, Tom turned to the Engineer.

'Look, perhaps you can help.'

The Engineer stood up with the telephone in his hand, a thin, lugubrious man.

'I'll do what I can,' he said doubtfully.

'Right.' Tom was in his stride now. 'You're a bird – right?'

The Engineer made the necessary mental adjustment and nodded.

'Now you,' Tom went on, 'are in my garden.'

'Am I sitting down or walking about?'

Tom wasn't after this much detail. 'It doesn't matter – either. Now, unbeknown to you, I have rigged a series of trip-wires.'

The Engineer nodded and edged away a little bit.

Tom came to the point. 'You hit one of the trip-wires, which sets off a record of Count Basie at full blast. Would you be frightened?'

The Engineer considered. 'No,' he stated, 'I *like* Count Basie.'

'Look,' said Tom impatiently, 'remember you are a bird!'

'So what? Why should a bird be frightened by Count Basie?'

It seemed to make sense and Tom went off the idea.

'No, you're quite right,' he said, sitting again. 'It's all too complicated anyway. Let's get back to basics. Answer me this simple question. What is the best way to scare birds?'

The Engineer mulled over the problem for a moment, and then delivered his answer.

'Flashing on the Common, I suppose.'

Tom stared for a moment, then indicated the telephone.

'Have you finished?'

'Yes,' said the Engineer, wondering why his help was no longer required. He left the room with Tom as the doorbell rang.

Tom opened the front door to admit Margo, who carried a plastic bag.

'Hello Tom. It's Margo,' she announced unnecessarily.

Tom studied her closely. 'Yes, it's you all right.' He called towards the kitchen. 'Barbara!'

'Just a minute!' Barbara called back.

Meanwhile Margo was looking at the G.P.O. Engineer as though he were a bailiff.

'G.P.O. I see,' she said significantly.

He, silly fool, decided to try a little joke.

'Me lady? No. I'm an eccentric millionaire. I carry the phone round with me because I get so many calls.'

Margo froze the smile on his face by simply saying 'Goodbye' – two syllables which, from her mouth, sounded like a total rejection of his sense of humour, not to say personality.

As Tom led Margo into the Big Room, she was already looking meaningfully at the bare telephone table.

'I see you've had to let the phone go. Are things *that* bad, Tom?'

'No. It just wasn't an essential,' he tried to explain.

'Not essential? Say I wanted to phone you up?'

Tom looked very serious. 'Damn! I hadn't thought of that!'

'No,' Margo smiled forgivingly.

'I suppose,' said Tom, 'you'll just have to walk all the way round from next door and speak to us in person.'

Margo returned to safer ground – social niceties.

'Tom, would you please tell Barbara that it's Margo?'

Barbara came in from the kitchen at this moment, rustier than ever. Tom went over to her.

'Barbara,' he said, pointing out Margo, 'that's Margo over there.'

'Hello Margo.' Barbara wiped her face with the back of her hand, leaving a rust-trail behind. Margo looked at Barbara as though she were a war refugee.

'Barbara! What *have* you been doing to yourself?'

'It's rust. I've been suffering from it for years.'

Margo laughed because she had an inkling that this must be a joke, and waited for a proper explanation. None came.

'Well,' said Margo, 'let me show you what I've got.'

She produced a dress from the bag – a full-skirted evening gown in very bright colours.

'Oh that's nice.' Barbara thought she should say this.

'That's what I thought when I bought it,' agreed Margo, 'but I'm afraid it was a terrible mistake.'

'A jolly expensive one,' said Barbara who, woman-like, had noticed the maker's name. Margo waved the minor details like the price aside.

'That's not important. The point is, Barbara, that I got it home, put it on and I said, I said to myself, "Margo, that simply looks cheap and nasty." So I wondered if you'd like it.'

Barbara shook her head. 'Margo, you are the mistress of the unfortunate phrase.'

'Oh, I'm sorry,' Margo floundered, 'I didn't mean ... I simply thought of you because, well, I'd have only thrown it away and I know how difficult things are. I mean, I saw the telephone being taken away.'

'That's all right,' said Barbara straight-faced, 'I haven't worn the telephone for years.'

'Don't be defensive, Barbara. You know what I mean.'

'Margo. No thank you!'

'I should have it,' interposed Tom from the bureau.

Barbara was getting angry. 'Tom, I am not wearing hand-me-downs!'

Margo picked up the dress with her patient resignation face on.

'So be it,' she said, 'I feel totally humiliated, Barbara, if that was your objective, thank you very much. Nevertheless' – pointed, this bit – '*I* know my manners and I will say this. You are still always welcome to drop in on Jerry and me whenever you feel like it, you know that.'

Barbara sighed at the bruised blossom act. 'All right, Margo. Thanks.'

Unusually, Tom got up to usher Margo to the front door.

'I'll see you out, Margo.'

'Thank you very much, Tom,' said Margo, pleased, if surprised, at his politeness to her.

As he opened the front door, Tom whispered, 'Margo, give *me* the dress.'
'Yes,' she nodded sagely, 'that's probably the best way to do it.'
She handed Tom the dress and then, as an afterthought, the plastic bag.
'Have the bag as well.'
'Golly, thanks,' answered Tom as Margo left, just beginning to wonder whether there had been a note of sarcasm in his voice.
As Tom turned in from the door, Barbara was waiting.
'I thought so. I told you, Tom. I don't want hand-me-downs!'
'It's not for you. It's for me.'
Tom headed for the garden, leaving Barbara to briefly consider tranvestitism and then reject it.

Margo was at peace with the world, wearing her immaculate 'gardening set' and spraying greenfly whilst singing 'This is My Lovely Day.' Then she looked over the fence and stopped in mid-trill. There was now a scarecrow in Tom's garden and the scarecrow was wearing the dress she had given to Tom. Seeing Tom coming out of his chicken-run, Margo marched towards the fence.
'Tom! Tom!'
Tom stopped. 'Hello Margo. Fancy a fresh egg for your tea?'
'Don't try to butter me up with eggs, Tom. I want an explanation!' She pointed at the scarecrow.
'It's a scarecrow,' he said.
'I know what it is! I want to know why you are trying to humiliate me in front of the whole neighbourhood!'
'I'm not. I'm utilizing something you didn't want.'
'Oh yes! And thereby telling the world and his wife that Margo Leadbetter's clothes are only fit for scarecrows!'
Tom looked round for the world and his wife, but could only see the goat.
'Look,' he reasoned, 'where are all these people and how do they know it's your dress when you've never worn it?'
'*I* know,' stated Margo, 'and that's enough, thank you very much. Well, I certainly shan't get a wink of sleep tonight, knowing that I am being abused in your garden.'
Tom leered. 'If you were being abused in my garden, you wouldn't get a wink of sleep, would you?'

Margo, as intended, winced at the implication, but pressed on. 'Tom, either you take my dress down or I shall call the Police!' She thought quickly, anticipating his reply, 'And I am aware that didn't come out right but you know what I mean!'

'Oh all right.'

Margo did not want to make her victory too crushing. 'I'm sorry, I had to bludgeon you, Tom,' she began, 'but...'

Tom pointed at the scarecrow.

'Don't kid yourself,' he said. 'I've just realized that your rotten dress doesn't scare birds.'

Several pigeons sitting on the scarecrow proved his point for him.

If there ever had been a thrill for Barbara in de-rusting a stove, it had quite worn off. She laboured on, rustier and more dishevelled than ever.

Tom came in from the garden with Margo's dress, his cheerful self.

'No go. The birds love this dress. I wonder if Francis of Assisi wore something like that.'

'Are you going to give me a hand now, Tom?' Barbara asked as patiently as she could.

'Sorry love. Bit busy.' He didn't help by pointing at the stove. 'You missed a bit.'

'Thank you,' she gritted.

By now, Tom had armed himself with a pair of scissors and an old cereal packet. Whistling tunelessly, he began cutting.

Barbara looked up. 'Is that you being busy then?'

'Oh yes,' Tom answered, missing the edge in her voice. 'See, a few dozen cardboard shapes like hawks suspended over the garden, right? They cast their shadows and it is a well-known fact that the shadow of a predatory bird scares the living daylights out of all the little also-rans. I should have thought of this before.'

'I wish you had.' Barbara's temper was rising. Tom continued cutting happily. 'Great this, isn't it? I mean, everything in our kind of life now is a challenge. None of that boring, repetitive bit.'

Barbara's lips tightened as she brushed boringly and repetitively away.

'I mean,' Tom philosophized on, 'the human animal wasn't meant to be a robot.'

Barbara pushed up her reading glasses she wore for protection against the rust, revealing a racing-driver's mask.

'Not meant to be, no,' she agreed.

'All right, we don't get much leisure time these days, but who needs it?' Again Tom missed the look Barbara gave him. 'Take Margo and Jerry at this minute. They're probably lounging about in their Swedish armchairs, drinking Martinis and vegetating in front of their colour telly. I ask you, who'd swap for that?'

Barbara flung down her brush and stood up.

'I bloody would!' she shouted.

'Something wrong?' asked Tom stupidly.

'Yes, there is something wrong! I'm sick of the sight of that ... that thing! I'm tired. I'm filthy! I feel about 120 and I must look 180!'

Tom threw fat on the fire. 'Why didn't you say, love?'

'I thought you might have noticed!'

'Oh come on. We've never gone in for that guessing-games rubbish.'

Rust cascaded off Barbara as she stamped in frustration. 'You don't have to guess! Just look at me!'

Tom did.

'O.K.,' he agreed. 'You're filthy. So what?'

She saw the sense in this. 'All right. It's not so much being filthy. What really gets me is you chirruping away about how lovely it all is!'

'But it is.' Tom was sure of this.

'Not today! Don't you understand? Not today!'

For a moment Tom thought he understood all and patted his wife's shoulder.

'I'm sorry love, of course. I don't keep track of dates these days.'

Barbara looked homicidal. 'Oh God, it's not that! I actually mean what I've just been talking about.'

'Very well,' Tom said, slightly martyred, 'I'm not sure I like the term "chirruping" but if you mean this life makes me happy, yes it does and I thought it made you happy.'

'Not today! I was happy yesterday. I shall probably be happy tomorrow, but not today!'

Tom would not let go. 'But surely there's a joy in everything we do now!'

'What, scraping half a ton of rust off that thing?' snapped Barbara, pointing a trembling finger at the range.

'Well there is for me,' said Tom staunchly. 'Even the really grotty jobs seem enjoyable.'

'Like digging up the tree-stump?' Barbara reminded.

This gave Tom pause. 'Well – yes. I'm not saying it was easy. But,' he added quickly, 'there was a joy in it – albeit a savage, primeval joy.'

'You lying hound!' choked Barbara. 'You chucked the pick-axe at the goat!'

'That was just a mood,' he explained.

'What do you think I'm in?' Barbara almost bounced with rage. 'And if you ask me now, this minute, now, today, if I'd sooner be sitting in an armchair with a drink than kneeling on the floor getting rusty, the answer is "Yes I would" – and what's more, I'm bloody well going to!'

Barbara stormed out of the room. Tom puzzled for a moment and then, not being able to reach any conclusion, went back to cutting out shapes and whistling tunelessly.

All was not exactly sweetness and light next door, either. Margo was looking daggers at Jerry who had turned away, overtly to get a drink.

'I know you're sniggering, Jerry,' she accused. 'It's no good trying to camouflage it because I can see your shoulders shaking!'

Jerry turned.

'Well it does have its funny side doesn't it? You pay fifty guineas for a dress and it ends up on Tom's scarecrow!'

'*I* didn't pay fifty guineas for it. I charged it to your account.'

Jerry choked on his drink as the whole thing suddenly became very unfunny.

'You did what?'

'I charged it to your account.' Margo looked defiantly at him. 'Well don't look at me like that, Jerry. I shouldn't have needed to if you weren't so penny-pinching with my dress allowance.'

This was patently unfair, as Margo hardly ever seemed to wear the same dress twice.

'Penny-pinching?' Jerry protested. 'I could run a third car on your dress allowance – a big one!'

But Margo was in overdrive again.

'As it is, I have to scour Bond Street for basically shoddy goods which are only really fit for scarecrows anyway.'

'Yes, but fifty pounds,' Jerry did a rough computation. 'Good Lord, Barbara would buy three dresses for that money.'

'Yes.' Nobody but Margo could give the word such undertones.

'What do you mean, "yes"?' mimicked Jerry.

'I mean that the homespun suits Barbara.'

Jerry considered the way Barbara filled her clothes and, foolishly, let it show.

'I always think she looks rather cute, actually.'

'I see!' Margo's mouth tightened. 'So you are married to a frump!'

'Now how on earth did you work that one out?'

'You used the word, Jerry!'

'The word "frump" did not pass my lips,' he outraged.

'It didn't need to. It was written all over your face!'

The only reasoned argument Jerry could think of was to point at his face as though indicating spots and intone, 'Frump! Frump! Frump! Frump!'

The doorbell signalled the end of the first round.

'Door please, Jerry!' snapped Margo.

Jerry thought about pouring his drink over her head, but went to answer the door instead.

Margo just had time to fit her cigarette into her 'social' cigarette-holder before Jerry came back with the caller.

'It's that cute little girl from next door,' he announced, only too well aware that the 'cute little girl' looked an absolute mess.

Margo greeted Barbara with delighted compassion.

'Barbara!'

'You said drop in, so I did,' said Barbara, already wishing she'd bathed and changed first. Things did not improve as she sat down, crossed her legs and revealed a hole in her tights – a rust-coloured knee peeping through.

Jerry and Margo's eyes were riveted, but Margo quickly dissociated herself from such bad manners.

'Don't embarrass Barbara, Jerry,' she reproved, 'it's just a hole in her tights.'

Barbara re-crossed her legs quickly – a waste of time because the hole in the other knee was even bigger.

'Never mind the tights. I was just looking at her legs,' said Sir Jerry gallantly.

The grateful smile Barbara gave him was cancelled by Margo's petulance.

'Well of course,' she said, 'when you're having to look at a frump all day . . .'

'Oh for Heaven's sake, Margo!'

'Look,' said Barbara, sensing an atmosphere, 'have I come at a bad time?'

'Of course not, dear.' Margo spoke as though Jerry were a small child.

'Jerry was simply determined to start a silly argument.'

'Silly is the *mot juste*.' Jerry turned to Barbara to change the subject. 'Well, I must say you're looking very ... very.'

He could not find the word but Barbara could.

'Horrible. I'm sorry, I shouldn't have come in here in this state.'

'Heavens above, dear. We're old friends. What does it matter?' Margo said, then took the gilt off the gingerbread by slipping a magazine under Barbara's bottom.

This made Barbara feel *really* dirty and again Jerry came to the rescue.

'Drink, Barbara. Have a drink.'

'Yes. Two dry martinis, please.'

As Jerry mixed the drinks, Margo again looked at Barbara.

'Barbara, what *have* you been doing? You look worse than you did this morning.'

Barbara explained. 'Well, we got this old range, you see – what with the electricity going off soon – and I've been trying to get the rust off it all day.'

'Just you?' asked Jerry – disapproval in his voice. 'What about Tom?'

'Oh he's been trying to invent the ultimate deterrent in bird-scarers.'

'Well, the less said about that episode the better, thank you very much,' said Margo, remembering the scarecrow.

Jerry handed Barbara two drinks.

'Jerry,' Margo looked pained, 'we *do* have larger glasses.'

'She wanted two drinks.'

'Damn right! Cheers!' Barbara emphasized the point by downing one immediately.

Margo's female antennae picked up a signal.

'Something wrong *chez toi*?' she inquired over-solicitously.

Barbara's denial carried little conviction.

'*You* wouldn't have had a silly argument, would you?'

Barbara tried again. 'No – no – well not really ... well ...' She gave in. 'Well yes, we did have a bit of an argument actually.'

'What about?' asked Margo, leaning forward so as not to miss a thing.

'Well, I'd been stuck on that blasted range all day and there comes a point when rust ceases to be a novelty. In the end I suppose it just corroded my sense of humour.' Barbara regretted saying this immediately as Tom emerged as the villain of the piece.

'I'm not surprised,' said Margo who willingly cast Tom as the villain of any piece. 'That's hardly a woman's work, is it?'

'Quite,' agreed Jerry.

Margo applauded sarcastically. 'Oh, three cheers. Jerry actually agrees with Margo!'

'I agree with you in this instance because you're right. We do share some opinions, you know.'

Margo only admitted to being in the wrong about twice a year and this was one of those times. 'I'm sorry, Jerry,' she said meekly.

'That's all right.' Jerry returned to Barbara. 'He'll have you yoked to a plough next. He's just an armchair revolutionary, old Tom. You're the one who has to man the barricades – or "woman" the barricades in your case.'

'No, just a minute,' said Barbara for the Defence. But the Leadbetters united were difficult to stop.

'Let me see your hands,' Margo ordered.

Involuntarily, Barbara held out her hands. Margo looked at them and tutted.

'I'm sorry to say this, Barbara, but they are the hands of a navvy. I rest my case.'

Barbara tried again. 'No, you've got it all wrong. You're making Tom sound like The Squaw Man. He does his share – more than his share.'

'I've always admired your loyalty,' said Margo, getting up.

Jerry took over. 'When was the last time Tom suggested you have a lie-in?'

'This morning, as a matter of fact,' Barbara defended. 'I didn't get up till half past six.'

Jerry looked appalled.

'Good God, you could join the Army and do that!'

Margo returned to the attack, armed with a carpet-sweeper which she used to pick up some of Barbara's rust fall-out.

'No, I'm sorry Barbara. Tom has turned you into a drudge and if you allow it to continue, I can see you becoming one of those wrinkled old crones that one sees in Europe.'

'You've missed a bit,' Barbara smiled sweetly. Margo smiled over-sweetly back, executed a quick stroke with the cleaner and went to put it away.

'I wouldn't have put it quite as subtly as that,' Jerry said, 'but let's face it, marriage must have a fair division of labour.'

'Like ours,' agreed Margo.

Jerry considered for a moment. 'Well no – not exactly like ours. I was thinking of more 50–50.'

Margo froze in her tracks and turned on Jerry.

'Meaning what, Jerry?'

'Well. Not 80–20.'

She was not having this. 'Jerry, I would hardly call keeping this entire house in immaculate condition a mere twenty per cent!'

'You don't,' Jerry pointed out. 'Mrs Pearson comes in five times a week.'

'There is the garden.'

'I know. *Mr* Pearson comes in three times a week.'

'I pick and arrange all my own flowers, Jerry.'

'I bet you wouldn't do that if the Pearsons had a daughter who did flower-arranging!'

Having lost the battle, Margo decided to win the war. 'Jerry I don't know what has prompted this poisonous outburst, but so long as we are dragging skeletons from under the bed –'

'Oh get your metaphors right,' Jerry crowed, 'skeletons come out of the cupboards!'

'Well, thank you very much for correcting me in front of company! I really must apologize for Jerry, Barbara. I can only think –'

Margo stopped short. The only sign that Barbara had been there were some specks of rust in the armchair.

'Well,' said Margo, misconstruing Barbara's departure, 'the manners of some people!'

Tom did not notice Barbara as she came quietly into the Big Room. He stood on a chair, trying to suspend one of his paper hawks from the light. It dangled, looking less like a hawk than a bit of cereal packet, then detached itself from the string and fluttered to the floor.

He saw Barbara as he got down from the chair and also saw the love in her eyes.

Tom kissed her and the Goods, being the Goods, knew *their* row was dead and gone.

'Cup of coffee?' he asked.

'Lovely.'

Tom took her hand and led her towards the kitchen. 'Come on. I've got something to show you.'

Barbara's rusty little face lit up as they came into the kitchen. The last of the rust had gone from the range. It was newly black-leaded, wood crackled cosily in its belly and a kettle boiled on the hob.

'I like that,' she said simply. 'I like that very much.'

'That's the tree-stump in there. We can get chilblains together in front of that.'

'That will be nice.'

Barbara sat down, kicked off her shoes and wriggled her toes.

'Oh yes, coffee,' said Tom, then delivered a brief, quite unnecessary little lecture. 'Now I want you to remember this, Barbara. When you take anything off the range, always use a kitchen glove. Thermal conduction of metals, you see.'

He demonstrated with the kettle and Barbara nodded seriously, loving him when he was pedantic. Then she settled, luxuriating in the glow from the range, as Tom took the kettle to the table behind her. He poured hot water into the cups which already had coffee in them, then put the kettle down as he added milk and sugar. They needed topping up and Tom, unthinking, went to pick up the kettle without using the oven glove. Barbara sat contentedly, missing the silent, agonized fandango being performed behind her.

Tom came to sit beside her in front of the range, handing her a cup of coffee.

'How are Jerry and Margo?' he asked through his pain.

'Heading for separate bedrooms when I left.'

'Yes, of course, it's Saturday – it's their row night.'

Barbara giggled. 'I'm glad we don't have rows.'

'Yes – waste of time, aren't they?'

Further complacency was interrupted by someone knocking at the back door.

'Oh blimey,' Barbara said, 'I hope they haven't come here for the second round.'

Tom went to open the door. 'Don't worry. I'll tell them we've got fowl-pest.'

'Evening, Squire!' The caller was Sam, but a very different Sam, wearing a suit which even Jerry might have coveted, and carrying a small holdall.

'Hello Sam,' Tom said with some surprise. 'Come in.'

Sam did so, noticing the angry red burn on Tom's hand.

'Nasty burn you've got there.'

'No,' Tom hastened to add, 'it's a bruise. Not a burn. A bruise.'

Barbara shot Tom a suspicious look, but Sam's attention had been caught by the gleaming range, and he cut short his greeting to Barbara.

'Well look at that! Who put the work in on that?'

Tom and Barbara pointed at each other.

'He did!'

'She did!'

They smiled secretively as Sam admired the stove.

'Well, if I'd known it was going to come up like that, I'd have knocked you for your vacuum cleaner as well,' he declared.

It occurred to Barbara that Sam's visit seemed to have no obvious reason, so she asked. 'Well, Sam – not that you're not welcome round the old cat and mouse...'

Sam looked blank. 'Eh?'

'Cockney rhyming slang of old London,' she reminded gently. 'Cat and mouse – house.'

Sam laughed good-naturedly. '*Touché!*'

'But why are you round here?' Barbara went on.

'Oh yeah – of course,' Sam remembered. 'I said I'd try to pick up a bird-scarer for you – and I've got one.'

Sam opened the holdall and produced a small black kitten.

'There you are,' he said, handing it to Barbara, 'Shere Khan.'

Barbara cuddled the kitten. 'Oh Sam – he's beautiful!'

'That's brilliant,' said Tom, with some experience of trying to invent bird-scarers. 'How much do we owe you, Sam?'

'To anyone else in the Avenue, an electric tooth-brush. To you – nothing.'

'Thank you, Sam. Cup of coffee?' asked Barbara.

Sam looked at his watch. 'No thanks. I'd better be going.'

'You're looking very sharp tonight,' observed Tom. 'Got a date?'

'No, I'm going to my Evening Classes.'

'What are you taking – "O" Level Totting?'

'No. Spanish. Well I've got a villa out there. Thought I might as well learn the language. *Buenas noches, muchachos!*'

Tom and Barbara loved this.

'*Adios!*'

'*Auf wiedersehen!*'

Sam went off to broaden his horizons as Barbara cuddled the kitten.

'Oh Tom, isn't he lovely?'

'Now, now! None of that lap-dog business.'

'He's a cat,' Barbara pointed out.

'None of this lap-cat business then. That is a working animal.'

Barbara gave the kitten to Tom, reassuring it. 'Don't worry, Rover. His bark is worse than his bite.'

If it were possible to give a small kitten a man-to-man look, Tom did it.

'Now listen,' he instructed, 'if you want the old saucer of milk, cod's head and tickle under the chin routine, you've got to graft, right? Now –' pointing to the back garden – 'out there – birds. You scare birds. Got it? Charge!'

Tom headed the kitten out of the back door.

'He's a bit small,' remonstrated Barbara.

'Well, they're not vultures out there, are they?'

'Not so far, no.'

They settled comfortably in front of the range again. All seemed right with the world.

'That's another problem solved,' Barbara said contentedly.

'Providing that Shere Khan does chase birds.'

'True.'

A little silence, then the sound of frantic clucking from the garden proved that Shere Khan did chase birds – the wrong sort – chickens!

Oxford as I See It

Stephen Leacock

My private station being that of a university professor, I was naturally deeply interested in the system of education in England. I was therefore led to make a special visit to Oxford and to submit the place to a searching scrutiny. Arriving one afternoon at four o'clock, I stayed at the Mitre Hotel and did not leave until eleven o'clock next morning. The whole of this time, except for one hour spent in addressing the undergraduates, was devoted to a close and eager study of the great university. When I add to this that I had already visited Oxford in 1907 and spent a Sunday at All Souls with Colonel L. S. Amery, it will be seen at once that my views on Oxford are based upon observations extending over fourteen years.

At any rate, I can at least claim that my acquaintance with the British university is just as good a basis for reflection and judgement as that of the numerous English critics who come to our side of the water. I have known a famous English author arrive at Harvard University in the morning, have lunch with President Lowell, and then write a whole chapter on the excellence of higher education in America. I have known another one come to Harvard, have lunch with President Lowell, and do an entire book on the decline of serious study in America. Or take the case of my own university. I remember Mr Rudyard Kipling coming to McGill and saying in his address to the undergraduates at 2.30 pm, 'You have here a great institution.' But how could he have gathered this information? As far as I knew, he spent the entire morning with Sir Andrew Macphail in his house beside the campus, smoking cigarettes. When I add that he distinctly refused to visit the Palaeontologic Museum, that he saw nothing of our new hydraulic apparatus, or of our classes in Domestic Science, his judgement that we had here a great institution seems a little bit superficial. I can only put beside it, to redeem it in some measure, the hasty and ill-formed judgement expressed by Lord Milner, 'McGill is a noble university'; and the rash and indiscreet expression of the Prince of Wales, when we gave him an LLD degree, 'McGill has a glorious future.'

To my mind these unthinking judgements about our great college do harm, and I determined, therefore, that anything that I said about Oxford should be the result of the actual observation and real study based upon a *bona fide* residence in the Mitre Hotel.

On the strength of this basis of experience I am prepared to make the following positive and emphatic statements. Oxford is a notable university. It has a great past. It is at present the greatest university in the world; and it is quite possible that it has a great future. Oxford trains scholars of the real type better than any other place in the world. Its methods are antiquated. It despises science. Its lectures are rotten. It has professors who never teach and students who never learn. It has no order, no arrangement, no system. Its curriculum is unintelligible. It has no president. It has no state legislature to tell it how to teach, and yet – it gets there. Whether we like it or not, Oxford gives something to its students, a life and a mode of thought which in America as yet we can emulate but not equal.

If anybody doubts this let him go and take a room at the Mitre Hotel (ten and six for a wainscoted bedroom, period of Charles I) and study the place for himself.

These singular results achieved at Oxford are all the more surprising when one considers the distressing conditions under which the students work. The lack of an adequate building fund compels them to go on working in the same old buildings which they have had for centuries. The buildings at Brasenose had not been renewed since the year 1525. In New College and Magdalen the students are still housed in the old buildings erected in the sixteenth century. At Christ Church I was shown a kitchen which had been built at the expense of Cardinal Wolsey in 1527. Incredible though it may seem, they have no other place to cook in than this and are compelled to use it today. On the day when I saw this kitchen, four cooks were busy roasting an ox whole for the students' lunch: this, at least, is what I presumed they were doing from the size of the fire-place used; but it may not have been an ox, perhaps it was a cow. On a huge table, twelve feet by six and made of slabs of wood five inches thick, two other cooks were rolling out a game pie. I estimated it as measuring three feet across. In this rude way, unchanged since the time of Henry VIII, the unhappy Oxford students are fed. I could not help contrasting it with the cosy little boarding houses on Cottage Grove Avenue where I used to eat when I was a student at Chicago, or the charming little basement dining-rooms of the students' boarding-houses in Toronto. But then, of course, Henry VIII never lived in Toronto.

The same lack of a building fund necessitates the Oxford students living in the identical old boarding-houses they had in the sixteenth and seventeenth centuries. Technically they are called 'quadrangles,' 'closes,' and 'rooms'; but I am so broken in to the usage of my student days that I can't help calling them boarding-houses. In many of these the old stairway has been worn down by the feet of ten generations of students; the windows have little latticed panes; there are old names carved here and there upon the stone, and a thick growth of ivy covers the walls. The boarding-house at St John's dates from 1509, the one at Christ Church from the same period. A few hundred thousand pounds would suffice to replace these old buildings with neat steel and brick structures like the normal school at Schenectady, NY, or the Peel Street High School at Montreal. But nothing is done. A movement was, indeed, attempted last autumn towards removing the ivy from the walls, but the result was unsatisfactory and they are putting it back. Anyone could have told them beforehand that the mere removal of the ivy would not brighten Oxford up, unless at the same time one cleared the stones of the old inscriptions, put in steel fire-escapes, and, in fact, brought the boarding-houses up to date.

But Henry VIII being dead, nothing was done. Yet, in spite of its dilapidated buildings and its lack of fire-escapes, ventilation, sanitation, and up-to-date kitchen facilities, I persist in my assertion that I believe that Oxford, in its way, is the greatest university in the world. I am aware that this is an extreme statement and needs explanation. Oxford is much smaller in numbers, for example, than the State University of Minnesota, and is much poorer. It has, or had till yesterday, fewer students than the University of Toronto. To mention Oxford beside the 26,000 students of Columbia University sounds ridiculous. In point of money, the $39,000,000 endowment of the University of Chicago, the $35,000,000 of Columbia, and the $43,000,000 of Harvard seem to leave Oxford nowhere. Yet the peculiar thing is that it is not nowhere. By some queer process of its own it seems to get there every time. It was therefore of the very greatest interest to me, as a profound scholar, to try to investigate just how this peculiar excellence of Oxford arises.

It has hardly been due to anything in the curriculum or programme of studies. Indeed, to anyone accustomed to the best models of a university curriculum as it flourishes in the United States and Canada, the programme of studies is frankly quite laughable. There is less Applied Science in the place than would be found with us in a theological college. Hardly a single professor at Oxford would recognize a dynamo if he met it in broad daylight. The Oxford student learns nothing of chemistry, physics, heat, plumbing, electric wiring, gasfitting, or the use of a blow-torch. Any American college student can run a motor-car, take a gasoline engine to pieces, fix a washer on a kitchen tap, mend a broken electric bell, and give an expert opinion on what has gone wrong with the furnace. It is these things, indeed, which stamp him as a college man and occasion a very pardonable pride in the minds of his parents. But in all these things the Oxford student is the merest amateur.

This is bad enough. But, after all, one might say, this is only the mechanical side of education. True; but one searches in vain in the Oxford curriculum for any adequate recognition of the higher and more cultured studies. Strange though it seems to us on this side of the Atlantic, there are no courses at Oxford in Housekeeping, or in Salesmanship, or in Advertising, or on Comparative Religion, or on the influence of the press. There are no lectures whatever on Human Behaviour, on Altruism, on Egotism, or on the Play of Wild Animals. Apparently, the Oxford student does not learn these things. This cuts him off from a great deal of the larger culture of our side of the Atlantic. 'What are you studying this year?' I once asked a fourth-year student at one of our great colleges. 'I am electing Salesmanship and Religion,' he answered. Here was a young man whose training was destined inevitably to turn him into a moral business man: either that or nothing. At Oxford, Salesmanship is not taught, and Religion takes the feeble form of the New Testament. The more one looks at these things the more amazing it becomes that Oxford can produce any results at all.

The effect of the comparison is heightened by the peculiar position occupied at Oxford by the professor's lectures. In the colleges of Canada and the United States the lectures are supposed to be a really necessary and useful part of the student's training. Again and again I have heard the graduates of my own college assert that they had got as much, or nearly as much, out of the lectures at the college as out of athletics or the Greek Letter Society or the Banjo and Mandolin Club. In short, with us the lectures form a real part of the college life. At Oxford it is not so. The lectures, I understand, are given and may even be taken. But they are quite worthless and are not supposed to have anything much to do with the development of the student's mind. 'The lectures here,' said a Canadian student to me, 'are punk.' I appealed to another student to know if this was so. 'I don't know whether I'd call them exactly punk,' he answered, 'but they're certainly rotten.' Other judgements were that the lectures were of no importance; that nobody took them; that they don't matter; that you can take them if you like; that they do you no harm.

It appears, further, that the professors themselves are not keen on their lectures. If the lectures are called for they give them; if not, the professor's feelings are not hurt. He merely waits and rests his brain until in some later year the students call for his lectures. There are men at Oxford who have rested their brains this way for over thirty years: the accumulated brain power thus dammed up is said to be colossal.

I understand that the key to this mystery is found in the operations of the person called the tutor. It is from him, or rather with him, that the students learn all that they know: one and all are agreed on that. Yet it is a little odd to know just how he does it. 'We go over to his rooms,' said one student, 'and he just lights a pipe and talks to us.' 'We sit round with him,' said another, 'and he simply smokes and goes over our exercises with us.' From this and other evidence I gather that what an Oxford tutor does is to get a little group of students together and smoke at them. Men who have been systematically smoked at for four years turn into ripe scholars. If anybody doubts this, let him go to Oxford and he can see the thing actually in operation. A well-smoked man speaks and writes English with a grace that can be acquired in no other way.

In what was said above, I seem to have been directing criticism against the Oxford professors as such; but I have no intention of doing so. For the Oxford professor and his whole manner of being I have nothing but a profound respect. There is, indeed, the greatest difference between the modern up-to-date American idea of a professor and the English type. But even with us in older days, in the bygone time when such people as Henry Wadsworth Longfellow were professors, one found the English idea: a professor was supposed to be a venerable kind of person, with snow-white whiskers reaching to his stomach. He was expected to moon around the campus oblivious of the world around him. If you nodded to him he failed to see you. Of money he knew nothing; of business, far less. He was, as his trustees were proud to say of him, 'a child.'

On the other hand, he contained within him a reservoir of learning of such depth as to be practically bottomless. None of this learning was supposed to be of any material or commercial benefit to anybody. Its use was in saving the soul and enlarging the mind.

At the head of such a group of professors was one whose beard was even whiter and longer, whose absence of mind was even still greater, and whose knowledge of money, business, and practical affairs was below zero. Him they made the president.

All this is changed in America. A university professor is now a busy, hustling person, approximating as closely to a business man as he can do it. It is on the business man that he models himself. He has a little place that he calls his 'office,' with a typewriter machine and a stenographer. Here he sits and dictates letters, beginning after the best business models, 'In *re* yours of the eighth ult, would say, etc. etc.' He writes these letter to students, to his fellow-professors, to the president – indeed, to any people who will let him write to them. The number of letters that he writes each month is duly counted and set to his credit. If he writes enough he will get a reputation as an 'executive,' and big things may happen to him. He may even be asked to step out of the college and take a post as an 'executive' in a soap company or an advertising firm. The man, in short, is a 'hustler,' an 'advertiser' whose highest aim is to be a 'live-wire.' If he is not, he will presently be dismissed, or, to use the business term, be 'let go,' by a board of trustees who are themselves hustlers and live-wires. As to the professor's soul, he no longer needs to think of it, as it has been handed over along with all the others to a Board of Censors.

The American professor deals with his students according to his lights. It is his business to chase them along over a prescribed ground at a prescribed pace like a flock of sheep. They all go humping together over the hurdles with the professor chasing them with a set of 'tests' and 'recitations,' 'marks' and 'attendances,' the whole apparatus obviously copied from the time-clock of the business man's factory. This process is what is called 'showing results.' The pace set is necessarily that of the slowest, and thus results in what I have heard Mr Edward Beatty describe as the 'convoy system of education.'

In my own opinion, reached after fifty-two years of profound reflection, this system contains in itself the seeds of destruction. It puts a premium on dullness and a penalty on genius. It circumscribes that attitude of mind which is the real spirit of learning. If we persist in it we shall presently find that true learning will fly away from our universities and will take rest wherever some individual and inquiring mind can mark out its path for itself.

Now, the principal reason why I am led to admire Oxford is that the place is little touched as yet by the measuring of 'results' and by this passion for visible and provable 'efficiency.' The whole system at Oxford is such as to put a premium on genius and to let mediocrity and dullness go their way. On the dull student Oxford, after a proper lapse of time, confers a degree which means nothing more than that he lived and breathed at Oxford and kept out of jail. This for many students is as much as society can expect. But for the gifted student Oxford offers great opportunities. There is no question of his hanging back till the last sheep has jumped over the fence. He need wait for no one. He may move forward as fast as he likes, following the bent of his genius. If he has in him any ability beyond that of the common herd, his tutor, interested in his studies, will smoke at him until he kindles him into a flame. For the tutor's soul is not harassed by herding dull students, with dismissal hanging by a thread over his head in the class-room. The American professor has no time to be interested in a clever student. He has time to be interested in his 'department,' his letter-writing, his executive work, and his organizing ability and his hope of promotion to a soap factory. But with that his mind is exhausted. The student of genius merely means to him a student who gives no trouble, who passes all his 'tests,' and is present at all his 'recitations.' Such a student also, if he can be trained to be a hustler and an advertiser, will undoubtedly 'make good.' But beyond that the professor does not think of him. The everlasting principle of equality has inserted itself in a place where it has no right to be, and where inequality is the breath of life.

American or Canadian college trustees would be horrified at the notion of professors who apparently do no work, give few or no lectures, and draw their pay merely for existing. Yet these are really the only kind of professors worth having – I mean, men who can be trusted with a vague general mission in life, with a salary guaranteed at least till their death, and a sphere of duties entrusted solely to their own conscience and the promptings of their own desires. Such men are rare, but a single one of them, when found, is worth ten 'executives' and a dozen 'organizers.'

The excellence of Oxford, then, as I see it, lies in the peculiar vagueness of the organization of its work. It starts from the assumption that the professor is a really learned man whose sole interest lies in his own sphere; and that a student, or at least the only student with whom the university cares to reckon seriously, is a young man who desires to know. This is an ancient mediaeval attitude long since buried in more up-to-date places under successive strata of compulsory education, state teaching, the democratization of knowledge and the substitution of the shadow for the substance, and the casket for the gem. No doubt, in newer places, the thing has got to be so. Higher education in America flourishes chiefly as a qualification for entrance into a money-making profession, and not as a thing in itself. But in Oxford one can still see the surviving outline of a nobler type of structure and a higher inspiration.

I do not mean to say, however, that my judgement of Oxford is one undiluted stream of praise. In one respect at least I think that Oxford has fallen away from the high ideals of the Middle Ages. I refer to the fact that it admits women students to its studies. In the Middle Ages women were regarded with a peculiar chivalry long since lost. It was taken for granted that their brains were too delicately poised to allow them to learn anything. It was presumed that their minds were so exquisitely hung that intellectual effort might disturb them. The present age has gone to the other extreme; and this is seen nowhere more than in the crowding of women into colleges originally designed for men. Oxford, I regret to find, has not stood out against this change.

To a profound scholar like myself the presence of these young women, many of them most attractive, flittering up and down the streets of Oxford in their caps and gowns is very distressing.

Who is to blame for this and how they first got in I do not know. But I understand that they first of all built a private college of their own close to Oxford, and then edged themselves in foot by foot. If this is so, they only followed up the precedent of the recognized method in use in America. When an American college is established, the women go and build a college of their own overlooking the grounds. Then they put on becoming caps and gowns and stand and look over the fence at the college athletics. The male undergraduates, who were originally and by nature a hardy lot, were not easily disturbed. But inevitably some of the senior trustees fell in love with the first-year girls and became convinced that co-education was a noble cause. American statistics show that between 1880 and 1900 the number of trustees and senior professors who married girl undergraduates, or who wanted to do so, reached a percentage of – I forget the exact percentage; it was either a hundred or a little over.

I don't know just what happened at Oxford, but presumably something of the sort took place. In any case, the women are now all over the place. They attend the college lectures, they row in a boat, and they perambulate the High Street. They are even offering a serious competition against the men. Last year they carried off the ping-pong championship and took the chancellor's prize for needlework, while in music, cooking, and millinery the men are said to be nowhere.

There is no doubt that, unless Oxford puts the women out while there is yet time, they will overrun the whole university. What this means to the progress of learning few can tell, and those who know are afraid to say.

Cambridge University, I am glad to see, still sets its face sternly against this innovation. I am reluctant to count any superiority in the University of Cambridge. Having twice visited Oxford, having made the place a subject of profound study for many hours at a time, having twice addressed its undergraduates, and having stayed at the Mitre Hotel, I consider myself an Oxford man. But I must admit that Cambridge has chosen the wiser part.

Last autumn, while I was in London on my voyage of discovery, a vote was taken at Cambridge to see if the women who have already a private college close by should be admitted to the university. They were triumphantly shut out; and, as a fit and proper sign of enthusiasm, the undergraduates went over in a body and knocked down the gates of the women's college. I know that it is a terrible thing to say that anyone approved of this. All the London papers came out with headings that read, ARE OUR UNDERGRADUATES TURNING INTO BABOONS? and so on. The *Manchester Guardian* bordered its pages in black, and even the *Morning Post* was afraid to take bold ground in the matter. But I do know, also, that there was a great deal of secret chuckling and jubilation in the London clubs. Nothing was expressed openly. The men of England have been too terrorized by the women for that. But in safe corners of the club, out of ear-shot of the waiters and away from casual strangers, little groups of elderly men chuckled quietly together. 'Knocked down their gates, eh?' said the wicked old men to one another, and then whispered guiltily behind an uplifted hand, 'Serve 'em right.' Nobody dared to say anything outside. If they had, someone would have got up and asked a question in the House of Commons. When this is done all England falls flat upon its face.

But, for my part, when I heard of the Cambridge vote I felt as Lord Chatham did when he said in parliament, 'Sir, I rejoice that America has resisted.' For I have long harboured views of my own upon the higher education of women. In these days, however, it requires no little hardihood to utter a single word of criticism against it. It is like throwing half a brick through the glass roof of a conservatory. It is bound to make trouble. Let me hasten, therefore, to say that I believe most heartily in the higher education of women; in fact, the higher the better. The only question to my mind is: What is 'high education,' and how do you get it? With which goes the secondary inquiry: What is a woman, and is she just the same as a man? I know that it sounds a terrible thing to say in these days, but I don't believe she is.

Let me say, also, that when I speak of co-education I speak of what I know. I was co-educated myself some thirty-five years ago, at the very beginning of the thing. I learned my Greek alongside a bevy of beauty on the opposite benches that mashed up the irregular verbs for us very badly. Incidentally, those girls are all married long since, and all the Greek they know now you could put under a thimble. But of that presently.

I have had further experience as well. I spent three years in the graduate school of Chicago, where co-educational girls were as thick as autumn leaves – and some thicker. And as college professor at McGill University, in Montreal, I have taught mingled classes of men and women for twenty years.

On the basis of which experience I say with assurance that the thing is a mistake and has nothing to recommend it but its relative cheapness. Let me emphasize this last point and have done with it. Co-education is, of course, a great economy. To teach ten men and ten women in a single class of twenty costs only half as much as to teach two classes. Where economy must rule, then, the thing has got to be. But where the discussion turns not on what is cheapest, but on what is best, then the case is entirely different.

The fundamental trouble is that men and women are different creatures, with different minds and different aptitudes and different paths in life. There is no need to raise here the question of which is superior and which is inferior (though I think, the Lord help me, I know the answer to that too). The point lies in the fact that they are different.

But the mad passion for equality has masked this obvious fact. When women began to demand, quite rightly, a share in higher education, they took for granted that they wanted the same curriculum as the men. They never stopped to ask whether their aptitudes were not in various directions higher and better than those of the men, and whether it might not be better for their sex to cultivate the things which were best suited to their minds. Let me be more explicit. In all that goes with physical and mathematical science, women, on the average, are far below the standard of men. There are, of course, exceptions. But they prove nothing. It is no use to quote to me the case of some brilliant girl who stood first in physics at Cornell. That's nothing. There is an elephant in the zoo that can count up to ten; yet I refuse to reckon myself his inferior.

Tabulated results spread over years, and the actual experience of those who teach, show that in the whole domain of mathematics and physics

women are outclassed. At McGill the girls of our first year have wept over
their failures in elementary physics these twenty-five years. It is time that
someone dried their tears and took away the subject.

But, in any case, examination tests are never the whole story. To those
who know, a written examination is far from being a true criterion of
capacity. It demands too much of mere memory, imitativeness, and the
insidious willingness to absorb other people's ideas. Parrots and crows would
do admirably in examinations. Indeed, the colleges are full of them.

But take, on the other hand, all that goes with the aesthetic side of
education, with imaginative literature and the cult of beauty. Here women
are, or at least ought to be, the superiors of men. Women were in primitive
times the first story-tellers. They are still so at the cradle side. The original
college woman was the Witch, with her incantations and her prophecies and
the glow of her bright imagination, and if brutal men of duller brains had not
burned it out of her she would be incanting still. To my thinking, we need
more witches in the colleges and less physics.

I have seen such young witches myself – if I may keep the word: I like it –
in colleges such as Wellesley in Massachusetts and Bryn Mawr in
Pennsylvania, where there isn't a man allowed within a three-mile limit. To
my mind, they do infinitely better thus by themselves. They are freer, less
restrained. They discuss things openly in their classes; they lift up their
voices, and they speak; whereas a girl in such a place as McGill, with men all
about her, sits for four years as silent as a frog full of shot.

But there is a deeper trouble still. The careers of the men and women who
go to college together are necessarily different, and the preparation is all
aimed at the man's career. The men are going to be lawyers, doctors,
engineers, business men, and politicians. And the women are not.

There is no use pretending about it. It may sound an awful thing to say,
but the women are going to be married. That is, and always has been, their
career; and what is more, they know it; and even at college, while they are
studying algebra and political economy, they have their eye on it sideways all
the time. The plain fact is that, after a girl has spent four years of her time
and a great deal of her parents' money in equipping herself for a career that
she is never going to have, the wretched creature goes and gets married, and
in a few years has forgotten which is the hypotenuse of a right-angled
triangle, and she doesn't care. She has much better things to think of.

At this point someone will shriek: 'But surely, even for marriage, isn't it
right that a girl should have a college education?' To which I hasten to

answer: most assuredly. I freely admit that a girl who knows algebra, or once knew it, is a far more charming companion and a nobler wife and mother than a girl who doesn't know x from y. But the point is this: Does the higher education that fits a man to be a lawyer also fit a person to be a wife and mother? Or, in other words, is a lawyer a wife and mother? I say he is not. Granted that a girl is to spend four years in time and four thousand dollars in money in going to college, why train her for a career that she is never going to adopt? Why not give her an education that will have a meaning and a harmony with the real life that she is to follow?

For example, suppose that during her four years every girl lucky enough to get a higher education spent at least six months of it in the training and discipline of a hospital as a nurse. There is more education and character making in that than in a whole bucketful of algebra.

But no, the woman insists on snatching her share of an education designed by Erasmus or William of Wykeham or William of Occam for the creation of scholars and lawyers; and when later on in her home there is a sudden sickness or accident, and the life or death of those nearest to her hangs upon skill and knowledge and a trained fortitude in emergency, she must needs send in all haste for a hired woman to fill the place that she herself has never learned to occupy.

But I am not here trying to elaborate a whole curriculum. I am only trying to indicate that higher education for the man is one thing, for the woman another. Nor do I deny the fact that women have got to earn their living. Their higher education must enable them to do that. They cannot all marry on their graduation day. But that is no great matter. No scheme of education that anyone is likely to devise will fail in this respect.

The positions that they hold as teachers or civil servants they would fill all the better if their education were fitted to their wants.

Some few, a small minority, really and truly 'have a career' – husbandless and childless – in which the sacrifice is great and the honour to them, perhaps, all the higher. And others, no doubt, dream of a career in which a husband and a group of blossoming children are carried as an appendage to a busy life at the bar or on the platform. But all such are the mere minority, so small as to make no difference to the general argument.

But there – I have written quite enough to make plenty of trouble except, perhaps, at Cambridge University. So I return with relief to my general study of Oxford.

Viewing the situation as a whole, I am led, then, to the conclusion that

there must be something in the life of Oxford itself that makes for higher
learning. Smoked at by his tutor, fed in Henry VIII's kitchen, and sleeping
in a tangle of ivy, the student evidently gets something not easily obtained in
America. And the more I reflect on the matter the more I am convinced that
it is the sleeping in the ivy that does it. How different it is from student life as
I remember it!

When I was a student at the University of Toronto thirty years ago I lived,
from start to finish, in seventeen different boarding-houses. As far as I am
aware, these houses have not, or not yet, been marked with tablets. But they
are still to be found in the vicinity of McCaul and Darcy and St Patrick
Streets. Anyone who doubts the truth of what I have to say may go and look
at them.

I was not alone in the nomadic life that I led. There were hundreds of us
drifting about in this fashion from one melancholy habitation to another. We
lived, as a rule, two or three in a house, sometimes alone. We dined in the
basement. We always had beef, done up in some way after it was dead, and
there were always soda biscuits on the table. They used to have a brand of
soda biscuits in those days in the Toronto boarding-houses that I have not
seen since. They were better than dog biscuits, but with not so much snap.
My contemporaries will all remember them. A great many of the leading
barristers and professional men of Toronto were fed on them.

In the life we led we had practically no opportunities for association on a
large scale, no common rooms, no reading rooms, nothing. We never saw the
magazines – personally I didn't even know the names of them. The only
interchange of ideas we ever got was by going to the Caer Howell Hotel on
University Avenue and interchanging them there.

I mention these melancholy details not for their own sake, but merely to
emphasize the point that when I speak of students' dormitories, and the
larger life which they offer, I speak of what I know.

If we had had at Toronto, when I was a student, the kind of living-in
system and common rooms that they have at Oxford, I don't think I would
ever have graduated. I'd have been there still. The trouble is that the
universities on our continent are only just waking up to the idea of what a
university should mean. They were, very largely, instituted and organized
with the idea that a university was a place where young men were sent to
absorb the contents of books and to listen to lectures in the class-rooms. The
student was pictured as a pallid creature, burning what was called the
'midnight oil,' his wan face bent over his desk. If you wanted to do something

for him, you gave him a book; if you wanted to do something really large on his behalf, you gave him a whole basketful of them. If you wanted to go still further and be a benefactor to the college at large, you endowed a competitive scholarship and set two or more pallid students working themselves to death to get it.

The real thing for the student is the life and environment that surrounds him. All that he really learns he learns, in a sense, by the active operation of his own intellect and not as the passive recipient of lectures. And for this active operation what he really needs most is the continued and intimate contact with his fellows. Students must live together and eat together, talk and smoke together. Experience shows that that is how their minds really grow. And they must live together in a rational and comfortable way. They must eat in a big dining-room or hall, with oak beams across the ceiling, and the stained glass in the windows, and with a shield or tablet here or there upon the wall, to remind them between times of the men who went before them and left a name worthy of the memory of the college. If a student is to get from his college what it ought to give him, rooms in college, with the life in common that they bring, are his absolute right. A university that fails to give it to him is cheating him.

If I were founding a university – and I say it with all the seriousness of which I am capable – I would found first a smoking room; then when I had a little more money in hand I would build rooms; then after that, or more probably with it, a decent reading room and a library. After that, if I still had money over that I couldn't use, I would hire a professor and get some textbooks.

This chapter has sounded in the most part like a continuous eulogy of Oxford with but little in favour of our American colleges. I turn therefore with pleasure to the more congenial task of showing what is wrong with Oxford and with the English university system generally, and the aspect in which our American universities far excel the British.

The point is that Henry VIII is dead. The English are so proud of what Henry VIII and the benefactors of earlier centuries did for their universities that they forget the present. There is little or nothing in England to compare with the magnificent generosity of individuals, provinces, and states which is building up the colleges of the United States and Canada. There used to be. But by some strange confusion of thought the English people admire the noble gifts of Cardinal Wolsey and Henry VIII and Queen Margaret, and do not realize that the Carnegies and Rockefellers and the William Macdonalds are the Cardinal Wolseys of today. The University of Chicago was founded upon oil. McGill University rests largely on a basis of tobacco. In America the world of commerce and business levies on itself a noble tribute in favour of the higher learning. In England, with a few conspicuous exceptions, such as that at Bristol, there is little of the sort. The feudal families are content with what their remote ancestors have done: they do not try to emulate it in any great degree.

In the long run this must count. Of all the various reforms that are talked of at Oxford, and of all the imitations of American methods that are suggested, the only one worth while, to my thinking, is to capture a few millionaires, give them honorary degrees at a million pounds sterling apiece, and tell them to imagine that they are Henry VIII. I give Oxford warning that if this is not done the place will not last another two centuries.

Old Junk and New Money

Stephen Leacock

A LITTLE STUDY IN THE LATEST ANTIQUES

I went the other day into the beautiful home of my two good friends, the Hespeler-Hyphen-Joneses, and I paused a moment, as my eye fell on the tall clock that stood in the hall.

'Ah,' said Hespeler-Hyphen-Jones, 'I see you are looking at the clock – a beautiful thing, isn't it, a genuine antique?'

'Does it go?' I asked.

'Good gracious, no!' exclaimed my two friends. 'But isn't it a beautiful thing!'

'Did it ever go?'

'I doubt it,' said Hespeler-Hyphen-Jones. 'The works, of course, are by Salvolatile – one of the really *great* clockmakers, you know. But I don't know whether the works ever went. That, I believe, is one way in which you can always tell a Salvolatile. If it's a genuine Salvolatile, it won't go.'

'In any case,' I said, 'it has no hands.'

'Oh dear, no,' said Mrs Jones. 'It never had, as far as we know. We picked it up in such a queer little shop in Amalfi and the man assured us that it never had had any hands. He guaranteed it. That's one of the things, you know, that you can tell by. Charles and I were terribly keen about clocks at about that time and really studied them, and the books all agreed that no genuine Salvolatile has any hands.'

'And was the side broken too, when you got it?' I asked.

'Ah, no,' said my friend. 'We had that done by an expert in New York after we got back. Isn't it exquisitely done? You see, he has made the break to look exactly as if someone had rolled the clock over and stamped on it. Every genuine Salvolatile is said to have been stamped upon like that.

'Of course our break is only imitation, but it's extremely well done, isn't it? We go to Ferrugi's, that little place on Fourth Avenue, you know, for everything that we want broken. They have a splendid man there. He can break anything.'

'Really!' I said.

'Yes, and the day when we wanted the clock done Charles and I went down to see him do it. It was really quite wonderful, wasn't it, Charles?'

'Yes, indeed. The man laid the clock on the floor and turned it on its side and then stood looking at it intently, and walking round and round it and murmuring in Italian as if he were swearing at it. Then he jumped in the air and came down on it with both feet.'

'Did he?' I asked.

'Yes, and with such wonderful accuracy. Our friend Mr Appin-Hyphen-Smith – the great expert, you know – was looking at our clock last week and he said it was marvellous, hardly to be distinguished from a genuine *fractura*.'

'But he did say, didn't he, dear,' said Mrs Jones, 'that the better way is to throw a clock out of a fourth-storey window? You see, that was the height of the Italian houses in the thirteenth century – is it the thirteenth century I mean, Charles?'

'Yes,' said Charles.

'Do you know, the other day I made the silliest mistake about a spoon. I thought it was a twelfth-century spoon and said so and in reality it was only eleven and a half. Wasn't it, Charles?'

'Yes,' said Charles.

'But do come into the drawing-room and have some tea. And, by the way, since you are interested in antiques, do look please at my teapot.'

'It looks an excellent teapot,' I said, feeling it with my hand, 'and it must have been very expensive, wasn't it?'

'Oh, not *that* one,' interposed Mr Hespeler-Hyphen-Jones. 'That is nothing. We got that here in New York at Hoffany's – to make tea in. It *is* made of solid silver, of course, and all that, but even Hoffany's admitted that it was made in America and was probably not more than a year or so old and had never been used by anybody else. In fact, they couldn't guarantee it in any way.'

'Oh, I see,' I said.

'But let me pour you out tea from it and then do look at the perfect darling beside it. Oh, don't touch it please, it won't stand up.'

'Won't stand up?' I said.

'No,' said Hespeler-Hyphen-Jones, 'that's one of the tests. We know from that that it is a genuine Swaatsmaacher. None of them stand up.'

'Where did you buy it,' I asked, 'here?'

'Oh, heavens, no, you couldn't buy a thing like that here! As a matter of fact, we picked it up in a little gin shop in Obehellandam in Holland. Do you know Obehellandam?'

'I don't,' I said.

'It's just the dearest little place, nothing but little, wee, smelly shops filled with most delightful things – all antique, everything broken. They guarantee that there is nothing in the shop that wasn't smashed at least a hundred years ago.'

'You don't use the teapot to make tea,' I said.

'Oh, no,' said Mrs Hespeler-Hyphen-Jones as she handed me a cup of tea from the New York teapot. 'I don't think you could. It leaks.'

'That again is a thing,' said her husband, 'that the experts always look for in a Swaatsmaacher. If it doesn't leak, it's probably just a faked-up thing not twenty years old.'

'Is it silver?' I asked.

'Ah, no. That's another test,' said Mrs Jones. 'The real Swaatsmaachers were always made of pewter bound with barrel iron off the gin barrels. They try to imitate it now by using silver, but they can't get it.'

'No, the silver won't take the tarnish,' interjected her husband. 'You see, it's the same way with ever so many of the old things. They rust and rot in a way that you simply cannot imitate. I have an old drinking horn that I'll show you presently – ninth century, isn't it, dear? – that is all coated inside with the most beautiful green slime, absolutely impossible to reproduce.'

'Is it?' I said.

'Yes, I took it to Squeeziou's, the Italian place in London – they are the great experts on horns, you know; they can tell exactly the century and the breed of cow – and they told me that they had tried in vain to reproduce that peculiar and beautiful rot. One of their head men said that he thought that this horn had probably been taken from a dead cow that had been buried for fifty years. That's what gives it its value, you know.'

'You didn't buy it in London, did you?' I asked.

'Oh, no,' answered Hespeler-Hyphen-Jones. 'London is perfectly impossible – just as hopeless as New York. You can't buy anything real there at all.'

'Then where do you get all your things?' I asked, as I looked around at the collection of junk in the room.

'Oh, we pick them up here and there,' said Mrs Jones. 'Just in any out-of-the-way corners. That little stool we found at the back of a cow stable in Loch

Aberlocherty. They were actually using it for milking. And the two others –
aren't they beautiful? though really it's quite wrong to have two chairs alike
in the same room – came from the back of a tiny little whisky shop in Galway.
Such a delight of an old Irishman sold them to us and he admitted he himself
had no idea how old they were. They might, he said, be fifteenth century, or
they might not.

'But, oh, Charles,' my hostess interrupted herself to say, 'I've just had a
letter from Jane (Jane is my sister, you know) that is terribly exciting. She's
found a table at a tiny place in Brittany that she thinks would exactly do in
our card room. She says that it is utterly unlike anything else in the room and
has quite obviously no connection with cards. But let me read what she says
– let me see, yes, here's where it begins:

'"... a perfectly sweet little table. It probably had four legs originally and
even now has two which, I am told, is a great find, as most people have to be
content with one. The man explained that it could either be leaned up
against the wall or else suspended from the ceiling on a silver chain. One of
the boards of the top is gone, but I am told that that is of no consequence, as
all the best specimens of Brittany tables have at least one board out."

'Doesn't that sound fascinating, Charles? Do send Jane a cable at once not
to miss it.'

And when I took my leave a little later, I realized once and for all that the
antique business is not for me.

How to Borrow Money

Stephen Leacock

THE PROCESS IS QUITE EASY, PROVIDED YOU BORROW ENOUGH

Have you ever, my dear readers, had occasion to borrow money? Have you ever borrowed ten dollars under a rigorous promise of your word of honour as a Christian to pay it back on your next salary day? Have you ever borrowed as much as a million at a time?

If you have done these things, you cannot have failed to notice how much easier it is to borrow ten thousand dollars than ten, how much easier still to borrow a hundred thousand, and that when you come at last to raising an international loan of a hundred million the thing loses all difficulty.

Here below are the little things that take place on the occasion of an ascending series of loans.

Tableau No. 1

The scene in which Hardup Jones borrows ten dollars till the first of next month from his friend, Canny Smith

'Say, look here, old man, I was wondering whether perhaps you wouldn't mind letting me have ten dollars till the end of the month—'

'Ten dollars!!'

'Oh, I could give it back all right, for dead sure, just the minute I get my salary.'

'Ten dollars!!!'

'You see, I've got into an awful tangle – I owe seven and a half on my board, and she said yesterday she'd have to have it. I couldn't pay my laundry last week, so he said he wouldn't leave it, and I got this cursed suit on the instalment plan and they said they'd seize my trunk, and—'

'Say, but God darn it, I lent you five dollars, don't you remember, last November, and you swore you'd pay it back on the first and I never got it till away after New Year's—'

'I know, I know. But this is absolutely sure. So help me, I'll pay it right on the first, the minute I get my cheque.'

'Yes, but you won't—'

'No, I swear I will—'

And after about half an hour of expostulations and protests of this sort, having pledged his soul, his body, and his honour, the borrower at last gets his ten dollars.

Tableau No. II

The scene in which Mr McDuff of the McDuff Hardware Store in Central City (pop. 3,862) borrows $1,000 from the local bank

The second degree in borrowing is represented by this scene in which Mr John McDuff, of McDuff Bros. Hardware Store (Everything in Hardware), calls on the local bank manager with a view to getting $1,000 to carry the business forward for one month till the farmers' spring payments begin to come in.

Mr McDuff is told by one of the (two) juniors in the bank to wait – the manager is engaged for the moment.

The manager in reality is in his inner office, sorting out trout flies. But he knows what McDuff wants and he means to make him wait for it and suffer for it.

When at last McDuff gets in, the manager is very cold and formal.

'Sit down, Mr McDuff,' he says.

When they go fishing together, the manager always calls McDuff 'John.' But this is different. McDuff is here to borrow money. And borrowing money in Central City is a criminal act.

'I came in about that loan,' says McDuff.

The manager looks into a ledger.

'You're overdrawn $17.00 right now,' he says.

'I know, but I'll be getting my accounts in any time after the first.'

Then follows a string of severe questions. What are McDuff's daily receipts? What is his overhead? What is his underfoot? Is he a church-goer? Does he believe in a future life?

And at last even when the manager finally consents to lend the thousand dollars (he always meant to do it), he begins tagging on conditions:

'You'll have to get your partner to sign.'

'All right.'

'And you'd better get your wife to sign.'

'All right.'

'And your mother, she might as well sign too–'

There are more signatures on a county bank note for one month than on a Locarno treaty.

And at last McDuff, of Everything in Hardware, having pledged his receipts, his premises, his credit, his honour, his wife, and his mother – gets away with the thousand dollars.

Tableau No. III

How Mr P. Q. Pingpoint, of the great financial House of Pingpoint, Pingpong and Company, New York and London, borrows a million dollars before lunch

Here the scene is laid in a fitting setting. Mr Pingpoint is shown into the sumptuous head office of the president of the First National Bank.

'Ah, good morning,' says the president as he rises to greet Mr Pingpoint, 'I was expecting you. Our general manager told me that you were going to be good enough to call in. Won't you take this larger chair – you'll find it easier?'

'Ah, thank you. You're very comfortable here.'

'Yes, we rather think this is a pleasant room. And our board room, we think, is even better. Won't you let me show you our board room?'

'Oh, thanks, I'm afraid I hardly have the time. I just came in for a minute to complete our loan of a million dollars.'

'Yes, our executive vice-president said that you are good enough to come to us. It is very kind of you, I'm sure.'

'Oh, not at all.'

'And you are quite sure that a million is all you care to take? We shall be delighted, you know, if you will take a million and a half.'

'Oh, scarcely. A million, I think, will be ample just now; we can come back, of course, if we want more.'

'Oh, certainly, certainly.'

'And do you want us to give any security, or anything of that sort?'

'Oh no, quite unnecessary.'

'And is there anything you want me to sign while I am here?'

'Oh no, nothing, the clerks will attend to all that.'

'Well, thanks, then, I needn't keep you any longer.'

'But won't you let me drive you up-town? My car is just outside. Or, better still, if you are free, won't you come and eat some lunch with me at the club?'

'Well, thanks, yes, you're really extremely kind.'

And with this, quite painlessly and easily, the million dollars has changed hands.

But even that is not the last degree. Eclipsing that sort of thing, both in ease and in splendour, is the international loan, as seen in –

Tableau No. IV

The scenes which accompany the flotation of an Anglo-French loan, in the American market, of a hundred million dollars, by the Right Hon. Samuel Rothstein of England and the Vicomte Baton Rouge de Chauve Souris of France

This occurrence is best followed as it appears in its triumphant progress in the American press.

NEW YORK, *Friday*. – An enthusiastic reception was given yesterday to the Right Hon. Mr Samuel Rothstein, of the British Cabinet, and to the Vicomte de Chauve Souris, French plenipotentiary, on their landing from the Stacquitania. It is understood that they will borrow $100,000,000. The distinguished visitors expect to stay only a few days.

NEW YORK, *Saturday*. – An elaborate reception was given last evening in the home of Mrs Bildermont to the Right Hon. Samuel Rothstein and the Baron de Chauve Souris. It is understood that they are borrowing a hundred million dollars.

NEW YORK, *Monday*. – The Baron de Chauve Souris and the Right Hon. Samuel Rothstein were notable figures in the Fifth Avenue church parade yesterday. It is understood that they will borrow a hundred million dollars.

NEW YORK, *Tuesday*. – The Baron de Chauve Souris and the Right Hon. Samuel Rothstein attended a baseball game at the Polo Grounds. It is understood that they will borrow a hundred million dollars.

NEW YORK, *Wednesday*. – At a ball given by Mr and Mrs Ashcoop-Vandermore for the distinguished English and French plenipotentiaries, Mr Samuel Rothstein and the Baron de Chauve Souris, it was definitely stated that the loan which they are financing will be limited to a hundred million dollars.

NEW YORK (WALL STREET), *Thursday*. – The loan of $100,000,000 was subscribed this morning at eleven o'clock in five minutes. The Right Hon.

Mr Rothstein and the Baron Baton Rouge de Chauve Souris left America at twelve noon, taking the money with them. Both plenipotentiaries expressed their delight with America.

'It is,' said the Baron – 'how do you call it? – a cinch.'

EPILOGUE

And yet, six months later, what had happened? Who paid and who didn't?

Hardup Jones paid $5.40 within a month, $3.00 the next month and the remaining $1.60 two weeks later.

McDuff Bros. met their note and went fishing with the manager like old friends.

The Pingpoint Syndicate blew up and failed for ten million dollars.

And the international loan got mixed up with a lot of others, was funded, equated, spread out over fifty years, capitalized, funded again – in short, it passed beyond all recognition.

And, the moral is, when you borrow, borrow a whole lot.

When I first met Dr Hickey

E. E. Somerville & Martin Ross

There was a wonderful chandelier in the hotel dining-room. Fine bronze it was made of, with mermaids, and Tritons, and dolphins flourishing their tails up towards the dingy ceiling-paper, and beaked galleys, on whose prows sat six small lamps, with white china receptacles for paraffin, and smoky brown chimneys. Gone were the brave days when each prow had borne a galaxy of tall wax candles; the chandelier might consider itself lucky in that it had even the paraffin lamps to justify its existence, and that it still hung from a ceiling, instead of sharing the last resting-place of its twin brother, in the bed of the tidal river under the hotel windows.

James, the hotel waiter, knew the family history of the chandelier, as he knew that of most people and things in the county. I commented upon it to a young gentleman with a pointed beard, who sat next to me at dinner, and said that it looked to me like Renaissance. The young gentleman suggested, alternatively, that it looked more like bronze. I did not dispute the point, but I think he found the subject precarious, as he turned to the young lady on his left, and I heard him embark upon a new theme.

'I was half dead with the toothache all day,' he observed.

The young lady replied sympathetically that toothache was a fright.

'Well, indeed, that's true,' said James, smoothly entering the conversation from behind my chair. 'I got my own share of it. Sure there was one time I used to be roaring like a banshee all night with it.'

'Were you so?' said the gentleman, with a wink at me. 'That must have been a long time ago, James.'

'Well, indeed, it is too, Doctor,' replied James meditatively, 'going on forty years, I dare say. I went to Dublin, and I went to a great dentist that was in it that time, and he pulled all the teeth I had, and he gave me a new set entirely.'

'Oh, my!' said the young lady, 'that must have been very expensive.'

'It was so,' said James, not without pride. 'Twenty pounds I gave him.'

'That was awful,' said the young lady, feelingly; 'it was well to be you that had it to spend.'

'Well, it wasn't all out so bad,' said James; 'sure I only wore them a few times – I wouldn't be bothered with them, and a doctor that was a friend of mine gave me ten pounds for them.'

'I suppose they were a fit for a patient of his?' said the Doctor.

'They were a bad fit for me, anyway,' returned James, glancing over his shoulder at the clattering operations of his two female subordinates, with the eye of the sergeant-major – the eye that always contains a grievance. 'I was a footman with the old Lord Garretmore that time. Sure that was where the chandelier came from. A grand house it was, too – big slabs of marble on the tables, and gold legs under them, and ye'd bog to the knees in the carpets. Well, it was the first night after me getting the teeth, there was a gentleman stayed for dinner, and he was to go away by the night train. Forty horses were in the stables, and there wasn't one but was out at grass, and I had to go out beating the bushes for an old mare that was round the house always, herself and her foal, to put her under the side car. 'Prua! Prua!' says I, calling the mare in the dark, and with that the teeth lepped out of my mouth, with respects to you!'

'Oh fie!' said the mother of the young lady.

'What did you do then, James?' inquired the Doctor.

'I took the white tie off me, and I tied it to the bush that was next me, for a token, and 'twas that way I got them again the next morning, thanks be to God.'

Having concluded his story, James started on a perfunctory tour of the table with the wine card. He stopped to pull the turf fire together, and, with a furtive eye at the glass over the chimney-piece, he rearranged the long lock of hair that draped his bald pate. It was dyed of that peculiar shade of chestnut that disdains subterfuge, and the fact and its suggestions were distressing where an old servant was concerned; so also was the manner in which he hobbled on his heels.

'His walk's full of corns,' said the young Doctor, eyeing him not without sympathy. 'He's a great old character. I believe they keep him here to talk to the tourists.'

It is a melancholy fact that in Ireland, in these later days, 'characters' have become aware of their positions, and palpably live up to their reputation. But James was in a class of his own.

I said didactically, even combatively, that 'characters' were free and easy,
but that James was easy without being free.

'I'll bet he's not easy in his feet, anyhow!' said the Doctor brutally. 'Have
you any more soup there, James?'

The mother of the young lady, who had hitherto preserved a silence,
broken only by the audible assimilation of her soup, here laid down her
spoon and said in cryptic disparagement:

'Tin!'

'Well, I'd say it was the best we had yet,' said the Doctor. 'I'd undertake to
pull a puppy through distemper with it.'

'That's the soup she has always for th' assizes,' said James. 'Grand soup it
is, and I declare to ye, she makes it out of egg shells and every old rubbish!'

The young lady's mother emitted a short laugh, but her empty soup-plate
told heavily against her.

The meal wore slowly on. A sea fish, of a genus unknown to me, and
amazingly endowed with bones, was consumed in distracted silence.

'I hear you have a fish shop opened in Ballinager, Mrs M'Evoy,' remarked
the Doctor, taking his last fish bone out of action with professional
adroitness, and addressing the mother of the young lady. 'That's very up-to-
date. There wasn't one I met from Ballinager but was bragging of it.'

'It was the Hoolahanes that had it,' said Mrs M'Evoy. 'It's closed.'

'Oh dear, why so?' said the Doctor. 'Why did they do that, I wonder?'

'They said that morning, noon, and night people were bothering them for
fish,' returned Mrs M'Evoy, to whom this triumph of the artistic temperament presented no exceptional feature.

'Unless it might be on a fast day, I'd never ask to taste a bit of fish,'
remarked James, giving a helping hand to the conversation. 'There was a
man I knew from this place got his death in Liverpool from a bit of fish. It
stuck to the upper gum. "Bill," says he to the one that was with him, "so help
me God," says he, "I'm dyin'," says he; and sure that's how he met his
death! It was in some grand hotel he was, and he was too shy to give the puff
to send out the bit.'

'I'd like to send that to the "B.M.J.",' said the Doctor gravely. 'Maybe
you could give me the man's name, James?'

'There was them that could swear to it,' said James, depositing a syphon
on the table in a determined manner, 'but they were before your day, Doctor
Hickey.'

'How young is!' said Miss M'Evoy archly. 'Don't be flattering im, James.'

'Indeed I'll not flatter him,' returned James, 'there's plenty doing that.'

It was at about this point that a dish containing three roast ducks was placed in front of me. Circumstances had decreed that I sat at the end of the table; it was my task to deal with the ducks, and during the breathless and steamy struggle that ensued, I passed out of the conversation, which, indeed, had resolved itself into a more personal affair between Dr Hickey and Miss M'Evoy.

It was somewhere in the reposeful period that came with the cheese that Dr Hickey ordered a bottle of port, of which he very handsomely invited the ladies and me to partake. He leaned back in his chair.

'Was this in the cellar the time of the flood?' he said, putting down his glass. 'I don't mean Noah's flood, James; you mightn't remember that; but the time the river came up in the town here.'

'If it was Noah's flood itself,' said James, instantly accepting combat, 'it couldn't get into *our* cellars. But, faith, it was up in this room you're sitting in, and I had to get up on the table from it, and it ruz to the table, and I had to hang out of the chandelier, and a boat came into the room then and took me out. Sure that was the time that the porpoise came up the river, with the dint of the flood, and she was in it for a week, in front of the hotel.'

'In compliment to the visitors, I suppose?' said the Doctor. 'And what happened to her, James?'

'She was in it till a whale came up the river,' replied James, with the simplicity of Holy Writ, 'and b'Jove he banished her!'

'It's a wonder you'd let him treat a lady that way, James,' said Dr Hickey.

It was still twilight when we left the dining-room, and strayed to the open hall door, and out into the September evening. In the east a rose-pink moon was rising in lavender haze, and a faint wind blew from it; the subtle east wind of September, warmed by its journey across the cornfields, turf-scented by the bogs. There was a narrow garden between the hotel and the river, a place where were new and already-neglected flower-beds, and paths heavy with coarse river gravel, and grass that had been cut, not too recently, with a scythe. A thatched summer-house completed the spasmodic effort of the hotel to rise to smartness. The West of Ireland cannot be smart, nor should any right-minded person desire that it should be so.

Dr Hickey and I sat and smoked on the parapet wall above the river, while the slated and whitewashed town darkened into mystery. Little lights came slowly out, and behind the town the grey shape of Dreelish mountain lowered in uncompromising abruptness, a brooding presence, felt rather than seen.

In the summer-house James was lighting a Chinese lantern, of a somewhat crumpled and rheumatic outline.

'Well, now, that's a great notion!' said Dr Hickey, with the lethargic and pessimistic humour of his type. 'That'll be in the prospectus – "hotel grounds illuminated every night". I wonder did they buy that at the Jumble Sale after the Fancy Fair in the Town Hall?'

We sat there, and the moon and the round red Chinese lantern looked at each other across the evening, and had a certain resemblance, and I reflected on the fact that an Irishman is always the critic in the stalls, and is also, in spirit, behind the scenes.

'Look at James now,' said the Doctor. 'He's inviting the ladies out to have coffee in the summer-house. That's very fashionable. I suppose we should go there too.'

We sat with Mrs and Miss M'Evoy in the summer-house, and drank something that was unearthly black in the red light, and was singularly unsuggestive of coffee. The seats were what is known as 'rustic', and had aggressive knobs in unexpected places; the floor held the invincible dampness of the West, yet the situation was not disagreeable. At the other side of the river men were sitting on a wall, and talking, quietly, inexhaustibly; now and then a shout of laughter broke from one of them, like a flame from a smouldering fire.

'These lads are waiting to go back on the night mail,' said the Doctor; 'you wouldn't think they're up since maybe three this morning to come in to the fair.'

Here a railway whistle made a thin bar of sound somewhere out under the low moon, that had now lifted herself clear of the haze. A voice called from the hillside:

'Hora-thu! Tommeen! Let yee be coming on!'

The men tumbled on to the road, and hurried, heavy-footed, in the direction of the station.

'Sure, they've half an hour yet, the creatures,' said Mrs M'Evoy.

'They have, and maybe an hour before they have the pigs shunted,' said James, re-entering with a plate of biscuits, adorned with pink and white sugar.

'Ah! what signifies half an hour here or there on this line!' said Dr Hickey. 'I'm told there was a lady travelling on it last week, and she had a canary in a cage, and the canary got loose and flew out of the window, and by George, the lady pulled the communication cord, and stopped the train!'

'Well, now, she showed her sense,' said Mrs M'Evoy, with an utterance slightly muffled in pink biscuit.

'She and the guard went then trying to catch the canary,' continued Dr Hickey, 'and he'd sit till they'd get near him, and then he'd fly on another piece. Everyone that was in the train was hanging out of it, and betting on it, from one carriage to another, and some would back the lady and some would back the bird, and everyone telling them what to do.'

'It's a pity *you* weren't in it,' said Miss M'Evoy, 'they'd have been all right then.'

'It was that bare bit of bog near Bohirmeen,' pursued Dr Hickey, without a stagger, 'not a tree in it. 'If he have a fly left in him at all,' says a chap out of a Third Smoker, 'ye'll get him in Mike Doogan's bush.' That was the only bush in the country.'

' 'Twas true for him,' said James.

'Well, they got him in the bush,' proceeded Dr Hickey, 'singing away for himself; but they had some trouble crossing the drains. I'm told the guard said the lady lepped like a horse!'

'You had it right, all to the singing,' commented Mrs M'Evoy, advancing as it were to the footlights. 'I have the little bird upstairs this minute, and she never sang a note yet!'

Mrs M'Evoy here permitted herself to subside into fat and deep-seated chuckles, and Miss M'Evoy, James, and I gave way suitably to our feelings.

'Well, now, I thought it was a nice idea, the canary to be singing,' said Dr Hickey, emerging from the situation as from a football scrimmage in which he had retained possession of the ball. 'The next time I tell the story I'll leave that out, and I can say that the lady that lepped like a horse was Mrs M'Evoy. They'll believe me then.'

'Why wouldn't you say the canary was an eagle?' said Miss M'Evoy. 'There used to be plenty eagles in these mountains back here.'

'Well, indeed, I might too,' said Dr Hickey. 'I remember it was somewhere in these parts that an uncle of mine was staying one time, and a man came to the hotel with an eagle to sell to the tourists. My uncle was like Mrs M'Evoy here, he was very fond of birds; and the man said the eagle'd be a lovely pet. Whatever way it was, he bought it.' He paused to light a cigarette, and James pretended to collect the coffee cups.

'He gave the eagle to the Boots to mind for him,' resumed the Doctor, 'and the Boots put it into an empty bedroom. It wasn't more than seven o'clock next morning when my uncle was wakened up, and the waiter came in.

'There's a man in the kitchen, your honour,' says he, 'and he has a great fighting aigle, and he says he'll fight your honour's aigle in the passage.' They had a grand fight between the two o' them in the spare room, and in the end my uncle's eagle went up the chimney, and the man's eagle went out through the glass in the window. My uncle had a nice bill to pay for all that was broken in the room, and in the end he gave the eagle to the Zoo.'

'Faith, he did not!' shouted James suddenly. 'He left him stuck in the chimbley! And sure it was I that got him out, and meself that sold him to a gentleman that was going to Ameriky. Sure, I was the waiter!'

Dr Hickey threw himself back in his rustic chair.

'Holy smoke! This is no place for me,' he said; 'every story I have is true in spite of me.'

Soon afterwards the ladies went to bed, and Dr Hickey and I smoked on for a time. He explained to me that he was here as 'locum' for a friend of his; it wasn't much of a catch, but he was only just after passing for his Medical, and you'd nearly go as locum for a tinker's dog after you had three years' grinding in Dublin put in. This was a Godforsaken sort of a hole, not a hound within fifty miles, nor anyone that would know a hound if they saw one, but the fishing was middling good. From this point the conversation flowed smoothly into channels of sport, and the dual goals of Dr Hickey's ambition were divulged to me.

'There was a chap I was at school with – Knox his name was – that has a little pack of foxhounds down in the South, and he's as good as promised me I'm to whip-in to him if I can get the Skebawn Dispensary that's vacant now, and I might have as good a chance of it as another.'

My own ambitions were also, at the moment, dual, being matrimonial, with a Resident Magistracy attached, but I did not feel it necessary to reveal them. I mentioned that I was having a day's fishing here on my way to Donegal to shoot grouse, but did not add that Philippa, to whom I was newly engaged, was implicated in the grouse party, still less that it was my intention to meet her the next afternoon at Carrow Cross Junction, an hour away, and proceed with her to the home of her uncle, an hour or so further on.

'You might have three hours, or maybe four, to wait at Carrow Cross,' said Dr Hickey, as if tracking my thought; 'why wouldn't you drive out to the Sports at Carrow Bay? It's only four miles, and there's a regatta there tomorrow, and when the tide goes out they have races on the sands. I believe there's a trotting-match too, and an exhibition of crochet.'

It did not seem to me that I wanted to go to Carrow Bay, but it was not necessary to say so.

Trucks at the station were banging into their neighbours, with much comment from the engine; I thought of Tommeen and his comrades, up since 3 a.m., and still waiting to get home, and it suggested the privileges of those who could go to bed.

It was over a whisky and soda in the heavily reminiscent atmosphere of the smoking-room that Dr Hickey told me he was going to take the ladies to the Sports, and mentioned that there would be a train at eleven, and a spare seat on the car from Carrow Cross. It required no special effort to see the position that I was to occupy in relation to Mrs M'Evoy; I followed the diplomatic method of my country; I looked sympathetic, and knew certainly that I should not be there.

I leaned out of my window that night, to look at the river, with the moon on it, hustling over the shallows, and thought of the porpoise, who had been so unchivalrously banished by the whale. I also wondered when the English post got in. I was presently aware of a head projecting from a window just below, and a female voice said, as if in continuance of a conversation:

'We should coax James for the cold duck to take with us.'

'That's a good idea,' replied the rotund voice of Mrs M'Evoy; 'we'll get nothing out there that a Christian could eat, and there might be that gentleman too.' (That gentleman closed one eye.) 'Come in now, Ally! There's an east wind coming in that would perish the crows.'

The guillotine slam of the sash followed. The river warbled and washed through the stillness; its current was not colder, more clear, than 'that gentleman's' resolve that he would not grace the luncheon party at Carrow Bay Sports.

I breakfasted late and in solitude, ministered to by one of the female underlings of James; the voice of James himself, I heard distinctly, in war and slaughtering, somewhere behind the scenes. The letter that I wanted had not failed me, and I smoked a very honeyed cigarette over it in the garden afterwards. A glimpse of Dr Hickey at the hotel door in a palpably new tie, and of Mrs and Miss M'Evoy in splendour in the hall, broke into my peace. I quietly but unhesitatingly got over the wall of the garden, and withdrew by way of the river bank.

When the eleven o'clock train had left I returned to the halcyon stillness of the hotel; my own train left at one-thirty; it was a time favourable, and almost attractive, for letter writing. As I wrote, I heard the voice of James demanding in thunder where was Festus O'Flaherty, and why hadn't he the chickens plucked. A small female voice replied that the Doctor and the ladies had left their lunch after them, and that Festus had run up to the station to try would he overtake them with it, and the thrain was gone.

'And if it was themselves they left after them,' retorted James, still in thunder, 'what was that to him?'

To this conclusion no answer was attempted; I bestowed upon Mrs M'Evoy some transient compassion, and she and her company departed, hull down, below the horizon of my thoughts.

A few hours afterwards, I trod the solitudes of Carrow Cross Junction, and saw the train that had brought me there bend like a caterpillar round a spur of hill, and disappear. When I looked round again the little bookstall was shuttered up, and the bookstall lady was vanishing down a flight of steps; the porter had entrenched himself in the goods store; the stationmaster was withdrawn from human ken with the completeness only achievable by his kind. I was suspended in space for three hours, and the indifference of my fellow-creatures was unconcealed. A long walk to nowhere and back again was the obvious resource of the destitute.

The town of Carrow Cross lay in a hollow below the station, with the blue turf smoke stagnant above its muddle of slate and thatched roofs; I skirted it, and struck out into the country. I did not find it attractive. Potato fields in September are not looking their best; there were no trees, and loose, crooked walls overran the landscape. The peak of Dreelish mountain was visible, but the dingy green country rose high between me and it, like the cope on the neck of a priest. I walked for an hour; I sat on a wall and read Philippa's letter again, and found, with a shock, that I had only one cigarette left. A fatuous fear of missing the train turned me back in the direction of the station, slightly hungry, and profoundly bored. I came into the town by a convent, and saw the nuns walking flowingly in twos, under chestnut trees; asceticism in its most pictorial aspect, with the orange leaves and the blue September haze, and the black robes and white headgear. I wondered how they managed to go on walking neatly to nowhere and back again with such purpose, and if they felt as jaded as I, and as little enlivened by the environs of Carrow Cross.

The town was an unprepossessing affair of two or three streets, whitewash and thatch squeezed between green and gold pubs, like old country-women among fashionable daughters. Everything was closed; as I looked along the empty street an outside car drawn by a dun pony turned into it at high speed, the pony forging with a double click-clack. As the car swung towards me someone flourished a stick, someone else a red parasol.

'We got a bit tired waiting for the sports,' Dr Hickey said as he assisted Mrs M'Evoy to alight at a house labelled Lynch's Railway Hotel, in royal blue; 'it seemed that the tide wasn't going out as fast as the Committee expected. It might be another hour or more before the racecourse would be above water, and we thought we might as well come on here and get something to eat at the hotel.'

'It has the appearance of being closed,' said Mrs M'Evoy, in a voice thinned by famine.

'That might be a fashion it has in the afternoon, when themselves does be at their dinner,' said the car-driver.

The front door was certainly closed, and there was neither knocker nor bell, nothing but a large well-thumbed keyhole. Dr Hickey hammered with his stick; nothing happened.

'They're gone to the races so,' said the car-driver.

In the silence that followed it seemed that I could hear the flagging beat of Mrs M'Evoy's heart.

'Wait awhile,' said Dr Hickey, 'the window isn't bolted.'

The sill was no more than two feet from the ground, the sash yielded to pressure and went up; Dr Hickey dived in, and we presently heard him assail the front door from inside.

It was locked, and its key had apparently gone to the races. I followed Dr Hickey by way of the window, so did Miss M'Evoy; we pooled our forces, and drew her mamma after us through the opening of two foot by three, steadily, as the great god Pan drew the pith from the reed.

We found ourselves in a small sitting-room, almost filled by a table; there was a mature smell of cabbage, but there was nothing else to suggest the presence of food. We proceeded to the nether regions, which were like a chapter in a modern realistic novel, and found a sickly kitchen fire, the horrid remains of the Lynch family breakfast, an empty larder, and some of the home attire of the race-goers, lying, as the tree lies, where it fell.

'There's a sort of a butcher in the town,' said Dr Hickey, when the search-parties had converged on each other, empty-handed, 'maybe we could cook something –'

'If it was even a bit of salt pork –' said Mrs M'Evoy, seizing the poker and attacking the sleepy fire.

'Let you get some water, and I'll wash the plates,' said Miss M'Evoy to Dr Hickey.

I looked at my watch, saw that I had still an hour and a half to play with, and departed to look for the butcher.

Neither by sign-board nor by shop front did the Carrow Cross butcher reveal himself. I was finally investigating a side street, where the houses were one-storied, and thatched, and wholly unpromising, when a heavy running step, that might have been a horse's, thundered behind me, and a cumbrous pale woman, with the face of a fugitive, plunged past me, and burst in at a cottage door like a mighty blast of wind. A little girl, in tears, thudded barefooted after her. The big woman turned in the doorway, and shrieked at me:

'Thim's madmen, from th'Asylum! Come inside from them, for God's sake!'

I looked behind me up the street, and saw a small, decorous party of men, flanked by a couple of stalwart keepers in uniform. One of the men, a white-faced being in seedy black, headed them, playing an imaginary fiddle on his left arm, and smiling secretly to himself. Whether the lady had invited me to her house as a protector, or as a refugee, I did not know: she herself had vanished, but through the still open door I saw, miraculously, a fragment or two of meat, hanging in the interior. I had apparently chanced upon the home of the Carrow Cross butcher.

A greasy counter and a chopping-block put the matter beyond doubt; I beat upon an inner door; a wail of terror responded, and then a muffled voice:

'Come in under the bed to me, Chrissie, before they ketch ye!'

There was nothing for it but to take from a hook a grey and white fragment that looked like bacon, place half a crown on the counter, and depart swiftly.

'I gave a few of the Asylum patients leave to go to the Sports,' said Dr Hickey, a little later, when we were seated between the large bare table and the wall of the little sitting-room, with slices of fried pork weltering on our plates. 'I saw the fellow waltzing down the street. Ah! he's fairly harmless, and they've a couple o' keepers with them anyway.'

'The only pity was that you left the half-crown,' said Mrs M'Evoy; 'a shilling was too much for it.'

Mrs M'Evoy was considerably flushed, and had an effective black smear on her forehead, but her voice had recovered its timbre. There was a tin of biscuits on the table, there was a war-worn brown teapot, and some bottles of porter; it was now four hours since I had eaten anything; in spite of the cold and clear resolve of the night before, I was feeding, grossly yet enjoyably, with Dr Hickey and his friends.

'This is a Temperance Hotel for the past year,' remarked Dr Hickey, delicately knocking off the head of a porter bottle with the sitting-room poker. 'That's why it was upstairs I found the porter. I suppose they took the corkscrew to the Sports with them.'

'How did they lose the licence at all?' said Mrs M'Evoy; 'I thought there wasn't a house in Carrow Cross but had one.'

'It was taken from them over some little mistake about selling potheen,' replied Dr Hickey, courteously applying the broken neck of the bottle to Mrs M'Evoy's tumbler. 'The police came to search the house, and old Lynch, that was in bed upstairs, heard them, and threw a two-gallon jar of potheen out of the top back window, to break it. The unlucky thing was that there was a goose in the yard, and it was on the goose it fell.'

'The creature!' said Miss M'Evoy, 'was she killed?'

'Killed to the bone, as they say,' replied the Doctor; 'but the trouble was, that on account of falling on the goose the jar wasn't broken, so the bobbies got the potheen.'

'Supposing they summons you now for the porter!' said Mrs M'Evoy, facetiously, casting her eye through the open window into the bare sunshiny street.

'They'll have summonses enough at Carrow Bay to keep them out of mischief,' returned Dr Hickey. 'It's a pity now, Major, you didn't patronize the Sports. They might have put you on judging the cakes with Mrs M'Evoy.'

'Why then, the one they put on with me was the man they had judging the vegetables,' said Mrs M'Evoy, after a comfortable pull at the contraband porter. 'That's a fine weighty cake,' says me lad, weighing a sponge-cake on his hand. 'We'll give that one the prize.'

'I wish you brought it here with you,' said her daughter, 'as weighty as it was.'

'They put me judging the row-boats,' said Dr Hickey, 'but after the third race I had to give up, and put five stitches in one of the men that was in the mark-boat.'

I said that the mark-boat ought to have been a fairly safe place.

'Safe!' said Dr Hickey. 'It was the hottest corner in the course. I thought they were sunk twice, but they might have been all right if they hadn't out-oars and joined in the race on the second round. They got in first, as it happened, and it was in the course of the protest that I had to put in the stitches. It was a good day's sport, as far as it went.'

'Ah, there's no life in a regatta without a band,' said Miss M'Evoy languidly, with her elbows on the table and her cup in her hand. 'Now Ringsend Regatta's sweet!'

'I'm afraid Miss M'Evoy didn't enjoy herself today,' said Dr Hickey. 'Of course she's used to so much attention in Dublin –'

'It's kind of you to say that,' said Miss M'Evoy; 'I'm sure you're quite an authority on Dublin young ladies.'

'Is it me?' said Dr Hickey; 'I'd be afraid to say Boo to a goose. But I've a brother that could tell you all about them. He's not as shy as I am.'

'He must be a great help and comfort to you,' returned Miss M'Evoy.

'He's very romantic,' said Dr Hickey, 'and poetical. He was greatly struck with two young ladies he met at the Ringsend Regatta last month. He mistook their address, someway, and when he couldn't find them, what did he do but put a poem in the papers – the Agony Column, y'know –'

'We'd like to hear that,' said Mrs M'Evoy, putting her knife into the salt with unhurried dexterity.

'I forget it all, only the last verse,' said Dr Hickey, 'it went this way:

> You are indeed a charming creature,
> Perfect alike in form and feature,
> I love you and none other.
> Oh, Letitia – Here's your Mother!'

As Dr Hickey, his eyes modestly on his plate, concluded the ode, I certainly intercepted a peculiar glance between the ladies.

'I call that very impident,' said Mrs M'Evoy, winking at me.

'It was worth paying a good deal to put that in print!' commented Miss M'Evoy unkindly. 'But that was a lovely regatta,' she continued, 'and the music and the fireworks were grand, but the society's very mixed. Do you remember, M'ma, what happened to Mary and me that evening, the time we missed you in the dark?'

'Indeed'n I do,' said Mrs M'Evoy, her eyes still communing with her daughter's, 'and I remember telling you it was the last evening I'd let you out of my sight.'

'It was a gentleman that picked up my umbrella,' began Miss M'Evoy artlessly.

Dr Hickey dropped his knife on the floor, and took some time to pick it up.

'And he passed the remark to me that it was a nice evening,' went on Miss M'Evoy. '"It is," said I. Now, M'ma, why wouldn't I give him a civil answer?'

'That's according to taste,' said Mrs M'Evoy.

'Well indeed I didn't fancy his looks at all. It was pitch dark only for the fireworks, but I thought he had a nasty kind of a foreign look, and a little pointed beard on him too. If you saw the roll of his eye when the green fire fell out of the rockets you'd think of Mephistopheles –'

'There's no doubt Mephistopheles was one of Shakespeare's grandest creations,' said Dr Hickey hurriedly. His eyes besought my aid. It struck me that this literary digression was an attempt to change the conversation.

Miss M'Evoy resumed her narrative.

'"That's a pretty flower you have in your button-hole," said he. "It is," said I.'

'You didn't tell him a great deal he didn't know,' said her mother.

'"Maybe you might give it to me?" said he. "Maybe I might not!" said I. "And where do you live?" said he. "Percy Place," says Mary, before you could wink. Anyone would have to believe her. "Upon my soul," said he, "I'll have the pleasure of calling upon you. Might I ask what your name is?" "O'Rooney," says Mary, "and this is my cousin Miss Letitia Gollagher." Well, when Mary said "Gollagher", I *burst*!'

Miss M'Evoy here put down her cup, and to some slight extent repeated the operation.

'I suppose the foreign gentleman told you his own name then?' said Dr Hickey, whose complexion had warmed up remarkably.

'He did not,' said Miss M'Evoy; 'but perhaps that was because he wasn't asked, and it was then M'ma came up. I can tell you he didn't wait to be introduced!'

'I have a sister-in-law living in Percy Place,' said Mrs M'Evoy, passing her handkerchief over her brow, and addressing no one in particular, 'and it was some day last month she was telling me of a young man that was knocking at all the doors down the street, and she thought he was a collector of some sort. He came to her house too, and he told the girl he was looking for some ladies of the name of Gollagher or O'Rooney.'

She paused, and regarded Dr Hickey.

'I wonder did he find them?' asked Dr Hickey, who was obviously being forced on to the ropes.

'I thought *you* might be able to tell us that!' said Mrs M'Evoy, delivering her knock-out blow with the suddenness that belongs to the highest walks of the art.

Miss M'Evoy, with equal suddenness, uttered a long and strident yell, and lay back in her place, grasping my arm as she did so, in what I am convinced was wholly unconscious sympathy. She and I were side by side, facing the window, and through the window, which, as I have mentioned, was wide open, I was aware of a new element in the situation.

It was a figure in blue in the street outside; a soft and familiar blue, and it bore a parasol of the same colour. The figure was at a standstill; and very blue, the burning blue of tropical heavens, were the eyes that met mine beneath the canopy of the parasol. Even before my own had time to blink I foreknew that never, in time or in eternity, should I be able to make Philippa accept thoroughly my explanation.

Philippa's explanation was extremely brief, and was addressed rather to the empty street of Carrow Cross than to me, as I crawled by her side. There had been, she said, half an hour to wait, and as I was not at the station – the blue eyes met mine for a steely moment – she had gone for a little walk. She had met some horrid drunken men, and turned into another street to avoid them, and then –

A brimming silence followed. We turned up the road that led to the station.

'There are those men again!' exclaimed Philippa, coming a little nearer to me.

In front of us, deviously ascending the long slope, was the Asylum party; the keepers, exceedingly drunk, being assisted to the station by the lunatics.

Weekends

Andrew McCall

'The ideal guest shows his virtues in many subtle ways, but
one of his salient qualities is that he is unpresuming.'
– Millicent Fenwick, *Vogue's Book of Etiquette*, 1948

The Potters

Friday:

When Allan had told Judith about running into Jan Mallory at a party in London, she had been delighted. She had been pleased, too, that Allan, thinking Jan was looking rather low, had invited her and her husband (a man called Potter, who had not been at the party) for the weekend of the 3rd. The only slight problem was that the Potters would have to put up with Uncle Simon and Aunt Isobel at Sunday lunch: the date of this annual event had been fixed months ago, not only with the Uncle and Aunt, but with the vicar of a nearby village, who was one of the very few of her old friends whom Aunt Isobel still chose to recognize. But Jan had always been such a sweet-natured girl. And it was only one lunch. It must be twelve years now since the Mallorys had gone off to live in Italy, and Jan, who must have been about seventeen at the time, had disappeared from their lives.

Warned now by the shrill yapping of Mr Wilson that the Potters had arrived, Judith stuck the last stem of honeysuckle into the vase on what was to be the Potters' dressing table, and went over to the window. On the gravel below, a glistening green Volvo estate car scrunched to a halt. From Mr Wilson, a magnificent show of ferocity: yap, yap, yap, yap. But then, as a door was pushed cautiously open, out leapt a labrador puppy – and there was poor old Mr Wilson flat on his back, his teeth bared in an ingratiating, lop-sided grin. The truth was out: Mr Wilson had bark but no bite. The puppy pranced about him in an ecstasy, bobbing down on his forelegs, sniffing at him, then tearing off again in another wild circle.

'Hm,' thought Judith, cupping a hand over the tortoiseshell butterfly which was flapping against the window pane, anxious to escape into the garden outside. A couple of weeks ago, Jan had telephoned to ask if it would be all right to bring their two children? Of course it would, Judith had said. Their own, who were away at school, were much older anyway. There was plenty of room. She just hoped they wouldn't be too bored. But nobody had said anything about a dog.

From the same door as the puppy there now emerged Jan, from the driver's side her husband, pulling off a pair of backless motoring gloves, and from behind a girl of about four and a boy of about seven. The girl had a gun in her hand.

'Magnus, stop it. Magnus, come here. Heel, Magnus,' Jan shouted at the uncomprehending puppy.

Judith pushed up the window, released the butterfly.

'It's all right,' she called out. 'Mr Wilson's quite used to it. I'll be down in a second.'

As she was crossing the hall, a chubby paw smashed through one the panes of the inner hall door, the upper half of which was a window. Having brushed aside the splintered glass with her foot, Judith opened the door and in shot Mr Wilson, who made a bolt for the kitchen, pursued by the puppy, spattering blood as he went.

'Oh, I'm so sorry,' Jan said, seeing the trail of bloodstains on the stone floor. 'And the window too. How awful.'

'Don't worry,' Judith told her, instantly recognizing what Allan had meant about her looking 'rather low'. From a plump, jolly teenager ('so outgoing for an only child,' people has always said), she seemed to have shrunk into one of those prematurely-aged, harassed housewives, whose glamorous friend is always telling her, on television, how to get her wash whiter, how to knock up a mouth-watering meal in three minutes flat, how to float through her day on a bubble of energy (out of a bottle: the product).

'I brought this,' Jan said. 'It isn't much. But I thought it might help.'

Judith found herself holding a casserole dish. She must have looked surprised.

'It's a rabbit stew.'

'Oh – how delicious.' Allan hated rabbit. Perhaps she could pretend it was chicken? Or decant it and keep it until after they were gone?

'And this is Tony,' Jan said, still looking flustered, as her husband came in with their suitcases. 'Oh, it *is* good to see you. Are you sure I couldn't get a cloth?'

'No, no, please don't bother. It's nothing.'

Judith slid the casserole on to the hall table, offered her hand to Tony.

'Nice place you've got,' said Tony, putting down the suitcases. 'Really, can't you stop him doing that?' He made a lunge behind Jan's back and pushed forward a thin, obviously very nervous little boy.

'Say hello, Ben,' said Jan coaxingly. 'This is Judith. An old friend of mine.'

The boy held out his hand, kept his eyes firmly on the ground.

'Come on now,' said Tony. 'Say hello properly.'

The hello was barely audible.

Tony patted the boy on the shoulder. 'Not like that. Say "Hello, Judith" – and how kind it is of her to ask you.'

'Hello, Ben,' Judith said quickly, taking the boy's hand. 'It's so nice of you to come.' But it was too late. The tears were already in his eyes and now he started to howl.

'Jesus!' said Tony.

'I'm so sorry,' said Jan, bending down to put her arms round the boy. 'I'm afraid he's a bit shy.'

'And whose fault is that?' said Tony. 'Mary, where are you? This is Judith, who's asked you to stay.'

'Hello, Judith,' said Mary and took careful aim at a point somewhere between Judith's eyes. There was a pop as the cork flew out of the gun on the end of its string.

'Got you,' said Mary. 'But you needn't lie down this time. Because I want you to show me where I'm going to sleep.'

'Oh dear,' said Jan. 'I'm afraid she's like that. I'm so terribly sorry.'

'There seems to have been a muddle,' said Allan, in bed. He had got down from London about an hour after the Potters' arrival, to find Tony sitting at his desk in the study, with his briefcase open in front of him, on the telephone.

'A muddle?'

'As if they'd been swopped over. The girl's more like a boy. And the boy's more like a girl.'

'Odd, isn't it? Poor Jan. She looks so crushed.'

'If only she'd stop apologizing all the time.'

'I know. He's not much of a help, is he? With anything. Always getting at that wretched little boy. And at Jan.'

'What was all that fuss about not eating pork? He hasn't changed his name from Potstein, has he?'

Judith laughed.

'No. And he's not a Muslim either. At least not altogether. But it does have to do with spending so much time in the Gulf. He thinks pork's unclean. Full of tapeworms. And you should see the things she's brought down for those children to eat. The kitchen's stuffed with yoghurt and wheatgerm and all sorts of health food.'

'No wonder the boy looks so pasty.'

'But not the girl, you have to admit. In any case, she nearly drove Mrs Clarke mad. I told her we had plenty of eggs and fish fingers and things, and that Mrs C. would be perfectly happy to make the children whatever supper they liked. But no, she didn't want to be "any trouble", she'd do it herself. And of course was a terrible nuisance. Kept chattering and asking where things were and generally getting under Mrs Clarke's feet. That's why dinner was so late.'

'Well, I hope Mrs C. doesn't give in her notice. The pork was particularly good, tapeworms or no.'

'What exactly does he do, did you gather?'

'Seems to sell valves and drilling equipment. He was quite interesting about the differences between the various Gulf States – even if he does think he's the greatest living authority on the Middle East. But I could have done without all that stuff about the wickedness of sending your children to private schools.'

'He did rather overdo it, didn't he?'

'Bloody rude – and, apart from anything else, I should have thought it was just what that boy needed.'

'Pretty offensive all round. What was all that telephoning about? He just marched into the study and got on with it.'

'Business. And I bet he's the sort who doesn't offer to pay for it. Where's that dog of theirs sleeping?'

'With them. Jan thought it would be best in a strange house. She'll get up and let it out, if it needs to be.'

'That's something, I suppose.'

'She was awfully upset about it breaking the window. Do you want me to have a word with her about the telephone?'

'Oh no, for Christ's sake don't. Let him make as many calls as he likes – anything rather than give her something else to apologize about.'

Saturday:

'I do hope you won't mind,' Jan asked Judith, looking more than usually apprehensive. 'It's an extraordinary coincidence really. I mean Tony had no idea he lived down here, this man he used to know in Qatar. He was in the tobacconist's with his wife. Tony's – I mean *we've* asked them for a drink. Before lunch.'

'Oh ... er – how nice,' said Judith. 'What time?'

'Pretty soon, I should think,' Tony told her. 'I said why didn't they come straight along here when they'd finished their shopping? They know the village. Once they're here, it's not difficult to find the house, is it?'

'No,' said Judith. 'I'd better tell Allan.'

Allen, watched by Mr Wilson and Magnus, the puppy, was marking out the tennis court.

'What a nerve,' he said.

'Well, I suppose it might have been worse. I wouldn't have put it past him to ask a whole lot of people to lunch.'

'Perhaps he has? Look out – here he comes.'

'Attractive garden you've got here,' said Tony. 'Wouldn't mind something like it myself. If I had the time of course. But then I expect you have gardeners?'

'Not really,' Allan told him. 'Mrs Clarke's (that's the cook's) sons help with the heavy stuff. Luckily the younger one's a bit of a mechanic. And for the time being, at any rate, he's crazy about the mowing machine.'

'How convenient,' said Tony. 'And I suppose they help with that too?' He removed his pipe from his teeth, pointed it in the direction of the swimming pool.

'As a matter of fact, yes, he does.'

'And they use it,' put in Judith, fairly certain that she had caught the drift of what Tony was thinking, 'whenever they like.'

There was a sound of tyres on gravel, and Mr Wilson and Magnus were off in full cry through the orchard, up towards the house.

Tony stuck his pipe back into his mouth.

'How very neatly you seem to have got everything worked out,' he said.

Judith saw the look that came over Allan's face and intervened. 'That must be your friends,' she said. 'We'd better go on up.'

'Yes, you do that,' said Allan. 'I'll be with you in a minute. I'll just finish this.'

* * *

Not content with giving his friends (a retired major and his wife) drinks, Tony also insisted on taking them on a conducted tour of the house (pointing out furniture and pictures – 'they're particularly proud of this one' and 'naturally they inherited most of it' Judith overheard him saying), the stableyard, the garden and pool. They had been back in the drawing room about twenty minutes, were on their third gin and tonic, when the gong rang for lunch and the Major's wife sprang up from her seat.

'Great Scott,' she said, looking at her watch. 'It's half past one, Jimbo. Time we were making tracks.'

The Major consulted his own time piece, a fob-watch.

'One twenty-eight,' he said. 'To be precise. But you're right, of course. Mustn't outstay our welcome, what?'

'Oh, you haven't done that,' Judith told him. 'Really you haven't. It's just that we're rather in the cook's hands. She doesn't like to be kept waiting.'

'I should think not,' said the Major emphatically, knocking back the last of his 'G and T'. 'Ready then, wife?'

'Pretty ship-shape, eh, Jim?' said Tony, as they all went outside to say goodbye. 'I'm glad to have got you all together.'

'A marvellous surprise,' said Mrs Major. She took a card from her bag, gave it to Judith. 'Our vital statistics. I hope you'll drop in if you're passing. It's not that I don't have plenty to do of course, but sometimes I get quite lonely when Jimbo's away on his travels.'

'I daresay,' said Tony at lunch, 'you thought Jim Ibsell a pretty good bore?'

'Oh no,' said Judith. 'I wouldn't say that.'

'Well, I have to tell you,' Tony continued, ignoring her not altogether convincing protest, 'that he probably knows more about the North Yemeni ascetics than anybody. No Oxford or Cambridge or anything like that.' (Allan had been at Cambridge; somehow it had come up the night before.) 'Completely self-taught. He's made them his life's work.'

'How interesting,' said Allan encouragingly. Much better to listen to whatever Tony was obviously determined to tell them about the North Yemeni ascetics than to be drawn into another argument about education or something like that. Just so long as lunch would soon be over. The children were eating with them and, although Ben was satisfactorily silent, the sight of Mary shovelling lumps of food into her gravy-smeared face was not an appealing one. ('Oh dear,' Jan said, doing her best to retrieve a potato which was being battered to a pulp on the table. 'I'm so sorry. I should have brought her high-chair. *Please*, Mary, stop that. Try to eat properly. Look – like Ben.' 'Because I like it this way,' said Mary, plopping another potato on to the table, preparatory to taking her spoon to it. 'And anyway Ben's wet. Ask Tony – he's always saying how wet he is.')

'Well he's gone to bed,' Allan said, coming into his and Judith's bedroom with what was left of his whisky. 'And taken that bloody dog with him. I must say, it might have picked another rug to chew a great hole in.'

'Unfortunate,' Judith agreed. 'She was dreadfully upset though. She wanted to give us some money but I told her not to be silly. You don't think that man in World's End...'

'A hole that size?'

'No, I suppose not. Why were you so long?'

'He had a call to make.'

'At this time of night?'

'To Singapore. Lucky we won that tenner off them at croquet.'

'That was odd, I thought. I mean his wanting to play for money. It didn't seem to fit.'

'Probably because he was sure he was going to win. He tried hard enough anyway. And bloody rude, I thought, to make all that fuss about having to play what *he* calls the "proper rules".'

'Didn't like losing it, did he? At one point it looked as if he was going to smash his mallet over poor Jan's head.'

'Contemptible. If he had done, I'd have smashed mine over his head. And broken that bloody pipe of his for good measure.'

'Allan!'

'It's the way he makes me feel. Why can't he let us answer the telephone in our own house? And how dare he go into the kitchen and give orders to Mrs Clarke?'

'Perhaps I shouldn't have told you about that?' Judith said. 'But at least Mrs C. seems to have simmered down. I don't think there will be any trouble.'

Sunday:

'What's that hanging out of the window?' Aunt Isobel asked querulously, hobbling along on the arm of Rogers, their chauffeur, while Judith followed behind with Uncle Simon.

'A bedcover,' Judith told her. 'It's the Potters', who are staying. Their dog had an accident in the night.'

'Dogs in bedrooms?'

'A puppy. It's all right now though. She's washed it out, she says. She must have put it there to dry.'

'Boarding house,' said Aunt Isobel. 'Potter, did you say? Do I know them?'

'You used to see her here years ago. As a child. Jan, you remember? The daughter of the Mallorys, who used to live in the Old Rectory.'

'Never heard of them.'

There was little point, Judith knew from experience, in pressing such matters. 'Yesterday was too cold,' she said instead, 'but it's such a marvellous day today, they're all down by the tennis court. The children are swimming and Allan's made some Pimms. Or would you rather be inside?'

'Certainly not. Simon's got his hat. And I want to see the garden. We spend far too much time inside as it is.'

In the orchard they came across Mr Wilson, stretched out, panting, in the shadow of a pile of scythed grass. Having been taken thus by surprise, he decided it was too late to bark and heaved himself over on to his back, rolling his eyes at them.

'That the one?' Aunt Isobel asked, stopping to peer at him.

'No. That's Mr Wilson. Our dog.'

'I thought you said he was dead.'

'No. Not yet. He is eleven though.'

'What?' said Uncle Simon, who refused to wear a hearing aid.

'The dog,' said Aunt Isobel. 'It's not dead after all.'

'Of course it's not,' said Uncle Simon. 'I just saw it move.'

Allan and Tony were playing tennis, watched by the Vicar and Jan, who was cuddling Ben in her arms. Mary was splashing about in the pool.

'She doesn't remember you,' Judith warned Jan, before she introduced them. 'I'll just get a couple more chairs. But is Ben all right? He's shivering all over.'

'I'm afraid Tony got rather angry with him,' Jan explained. 'The thing is he's been trying to teach him to swim for ages and he just doesn't seem to be able to learn. Mary can of course, like a fish. But I think Ben's frightened of the water. Anyhow, he started to cry, so Tony threw him in.'

'How monstrous of him.'

'Well yes, I know, it was rather awful of him. I'm so sorry, Judith.'

'My dear girl,' Judith was surprised to hear herself say (it was not a phrase she was conscious of ever having used before). 'What on earth have *you* got to be sorry about? Now come on, come and help me get some chairs, won't you, Ben, while Jan does the drinks?'

Reluctantly, the boy gave her his hand and they went over to the pool shed to bring a chair each.

'Out,' shouted Allan. 'Thirty-all.'

'Are you sure?'

'It was fifteen-thirty, wasn't it?'

'I mean about it being out.'

'Pretty sure, yes.'

'It didn't look out from here.'

'Well, if you don't think so. . .'

'On the line, I'd have said.'

'Okay then, we'd better have it again.'

Allan served. An ace.

'Sun in my eyes,' said Tony, who went on to lose the game. As he and Allan were changing ends, he said he thought he'd like to have a go with another racket.

'You could try that one there,' Allan told him. 'Or you can have mine if you like? But quite honestly I think the one you've got is probably the best.'

'Couldn't be much worse anyway,' said Tony, ignoring Allan's offer of his own racket, but exchanging his for the one that had been lying under the net-winder. The thing was, of course, he was used to playing on hard courts. He hadn't played on grass for years now, he said.

'That man's losing,' said Aunt Isobel, pointing a trembling finger at Tony. 'And with very bad grace. Rotten sport.'

Tony whistled to himself, pretending not to have heard her.

'What's that?' said Uncle Simon.

'That man,' said Aunt Isobel. 'Palmer? Potts? A rotten sport.'

'Not a cloud in the sky,' said the Vicar. 'That rare thing nowadays, a real summer's day.'

Perhaps, Judith suggested, Aunt Isobel would like to see round the rest of the garden. And the Vicar too? It was at its best at the moment.

'Indeed I would,' said Aunt Isobel. 'Rogers can stay here and keep an eye on Simon.'

The tour of the garden must have taken about half an hour, with Aunt Isobel moving very slowly, exclaiming about this and that, one constantly-twitching arm hooked through Judith's and the other through the Vicar's. 'I was always a spring pruner myself,' she was saying, as they came round a clump of shrubs, back to the pool end of the tennis court. 'Good heavens, Judith!'

Allan told Judith later that Tony, having lost the last point of the match, had flung down his racket in disgust. What he 'could do with' was a swim. To Allan's astonishment – or was he so astonished? – he had started to strip off, there and then, on the court.

What now confronted Aunt Isobel, the Vicar and Judith was the sight of Tony stepping out of a pair of sweaty Y-fronts, which, as he straightened (it seemed defiantly) up, he kicked to one side, before diving into the pool.

'What's happened to Roger then?' Tony asked, looking round the dining room table.

'Rogers,' Aunt Isobel corrected him. 'No doubt he's having his lunch.'

'Not with us?'

Aunt Isobel looked at him in blank amazement.

'He's our chauffeur,' she said.

'Oh, I *see*,' said Tony, with a heavy sarcasm that was quite lost on Aunt Isobel. 'That explains everything.'

'Perhaps you'd like me to cut up your meat for you?' Jan said kindly, noticing how difficult Aunt Isobel's shakes made it for her to eat.

('Oh God, I should have told her,' thought Judith.)

'Certainly not,' said Aunt Isobel. 'I'm not absolutely gaga, you know. And it doesn't help at all to shout at Simon, either,' she told Tony, who had been doing just that.

'Delicious,' said the Vicar tactfully. 'I always say your Mrs Clarke makes quite the best Yorkshire pudding.'

'Do you?' said Tony. 'Tell me, Vicar, how many people did you have in your church this morning?' And from that moment on nobody had any chance but to listen in silence, as Tony explained in detail to the Vicar how Christianity – and the Church of England, in particular – had got things wrong, whereas Mohammedanism, on the other hand, was getting so much right. Only once did he interrupt himself, and this was when Uncle Simon farted. 'And since when has a fart been funny?' he asked abruptly, rounding on Ben, who had been reduced to uncontrollable giggles. 'If you're going to behave like a snickering schoolgirl, get out. Go on, get out.'

Although Judith had made it as plain as she could that Sunday night was

Mrs Clarke's night off and that their guests usually left on Sunday afternoon (the latter was not, in fact, strictly true), Tony had made it still more clear that it would suit him best to leave after supper, when there would be less traffic and the children could sleep in the car. They could have Jan's rabbit stew, couldn't they?

So, after tea and Uncle Simon and Aunt Isobel's departure, they had sat down again in the drawing room and Allan and Judith had pretended to be absorbed in the Sunday papers. Ben and Mary, meanwhile, had been taken upstairs to the old nursery, to play with the few remaining toys that had not already been broken by other visiting children. When, at last, it was time to heat up the inescapable rabbit (Judith had thought it best to warn Allan about this: in case he should say something about it that might hurt Jan's feelings), Jan had insisted on going with her into the kitchen, where, in her eagerness to be helpful, she had been nothing but a nuisance. Then, somehow, the six of them had got through their shares of peculiarly tasteless rabbit (with lentils), had eaten raspberries from the garden with cream and some Stilton: and it was time for the Potters to leave.

When Mary said she would like to come again, both Allan and Judith affected not to have heard her.

'Ah well,' said Tony, his pipe firmly between his teeth. 'Expect we'll see you in London, eh?'

'It was wonderful,' said Jan. 'I can't thank you enough. I'm just so sorry about the rug ... and the window...'

'Never mind,' Judith told her firmly. The list could have been a long one. 'These accidents do happen.'

Tony was revving the engine.

'You're so sweet, so understanding,' murmured Jan, obeying his summons.

'Like hell I am,' said Judith, as she and Allan stood side by side, waving at the tail lights of the car. 'If she only knew how close I came to screaming at her this evening. I mean, how can she be so hopeless? Why doesn't she stand up for herself? Ever?'

'Do you think,' Allan wondered, 'they did anything about Mrs C.? If not, you know, we'd better.'

'I certainly didn't see him give her anything,' Judith said. 'But perhaps he left something in the room. I'll go and look. Also check that they didn't leave anything.'

Allan had gone back into the dining room for a last glass of port, was coming out again with it, when he heard a yell from Judith.

'What on earth was that?' he shouted up the stairs.

'Needless to say, they've left nothing,' Judith shouted back at him. 'But Mr Wilson – you filthy dog.' (Dull thump of flesh on fur. 'Filthy! He's just peed all over the bed. Where that brute of theirs left *his* tip for Mrs C.'

At that moment the telephone rang.

'I'll get it,' Allan said, and went into the study.

'Will Mr Tony Potter,' a female voice asked him, 'take a collect call from Caracas?'

'No,' said Allan. 'He will not.' And banged down the receiver.

Office Life

Keith Waterhouse

Clement Gryce, in the throes of redundancy, lands himself a
job in the Stationery Services department of British Albion.
Employed as a clerk he begins the endless round of
acquaintanceship with his colleagues, Seeds, Pam Fawce
(Miss Divorce), Mrs Rashman, Copeland, the Penney
twins, Ardagh, Mr Hakim and Beazley.

Staff canteen, it emerged, would have been rather a derogatory misnomer. It
was a staff restaurant more like, housed in the protruding bit on stilts which
Gryce had taken for the executive suite. It even had a restaurant-sounding
name: the Buttery. It reminded Gryce of all the hotel private-function rooms,
most of them called the Churchill Suite, where his various billets had held
their Christmas lunches.

Seemingly the Buttery was a fairly recent addendum to the main building,
costed originally at £120,000 but in the end devouring the best part of a
quarter of a million, thanks mainly to an architectural cock-up which had
rendered it inaccessible except via the fire-escape. The restaurant was
circular and it was supposed to revolve to catch the sun, but when the
supposition had been put to the test it had done one three-quarter turn and
then jammed, leaving the dining area in semi-darkness until four o'clock
each afternoon, Greenwich mean time.

'If you like salady things, cold roast beef, ham and egg pie, the Salad Bowl
isn't half bad,' advised Seeds as they travelled up the stainless steel escalator
from the first floor. To get to the first floor they had had to take the lift from
the seventh floor to the second, then walk down the stairs. Or they could
have gone to the ground floor and walked up. The lift was no longer
programmed to stop at the first floor – a throwback to an electricity economy
campaign during some long-forgotten fuel crisis. The Buttery was at third

floor level, but it could not be reached from the second floor because of an obstruction caused by the plant that was supposed to work the revolving mechanism, nor from the third floor itself because of a ventilation shaft that had been installed to deal with excessive condensation in the kitchens. These difficulties had been surmounted by a considerable engineering feat involving re-siting the fire escape and routing a covered escalator up the outer wall of the main building and into the Buttery. It was the only spiral escalator in Europe and, according to Seeds, had cost more than the original estimate for the entire restaurant annexe.

'But be warned against the Dish of the Day, probably some veal concoction. Sad to say our chef's imagination stretches farther than his capabilities.'

It was very kind of Seeds to invite Gryce to lunch, or he supposed more accurately to accompany him to lunch, by way, it was to be presumed, of showing him the ropes. It would be embarrassing if it turned out to be an invitation in the literal sense. He would have to reciprocate tomorrow and that might commit them to an arrangement that neither would relish. Buying tea or coffee turn and turn about was one thing, but having to stand each other lunch would put a strain on what ought to be an easy-going acquaintanceship.

The Buttery was full, for all that lunch hours at British Albion were staggered and there were in effect three sittings. Peering into the Arctic gloom induced by the faulty revolving machinery, Gryce was able to recognize several faces from Stationery Supplies: but not, to his disappointment, Miss Divorce, not Mrs Rashman who would be keeping that appointment in the wine bar, and not Copeland. The managers had their own restaurant on the twelfth floor called the Cockpit.

In the centre of the room was a buffet arrangement featuring the salady things recommended by Seeds. If you wanted the unrecommended veal concoction, or any other hot dish, you joined the queue at a cafeteria-looking counter.

'If you'd like to dive in, I'll see if I can grab a table,' said Seeds obligingly. Gryce attached himself to the throng of mainly women, he supposed they were all slimming, who were helping themselves at the Salad Bowl. He had garnished his plate with some potato salad and one or two radishes cut in the shape of tulips when he saw Miss Divorce, or Mrs Fawce as he had better start calling her, stepping off the escalator which after its convolutions fetched up a few feet from the Salad Bowl.

Hovering between the cold roast beef and the ham and egg pie, Gryce decided to hold his horses until Mrs Fawce, undoubtedly a salady things person, was on hand to advise him on the best choice. She would then, if there was a God in heaven, join him and Seeds for lunch as if it were the most natural thing in the world.

Not a salady things person after all. To his surprise Mrs Fawce was aiming towards the hot meals counter. Well, then: she probably took her main nourishment at lunch-time and made do with a light snack in the evening. With no substantial dinner to prepare, that might give her the leisure for a glass or two of wine on the way home.

They would have to be discreet, though. It only needed Mrs Rashman to stumble across them one evening and it would be all round the office.

Carrying his plate of potato salad and radishes, to which he had added a portion of sliced tomato while contemplating the next move, Gryce crossed to the hot meals counter, acquired a tray, and by sliding it along the rail affair and nudging Mrs Fawce gently in the buttocks with it, managed to draw attention to himself.

The smile was encouraging enough.

'We didn't meet properly. Pamela Fawce. Pam, to most people.'

'Clement Gryce. Abbreviated alas to Clem, which makes me sound like a former Prime Minister.' He wondered if he reminded her of, strangely enough, the late Hugh Gaitskell.

After establishing that he was finding his way around all right and agreeing that one's first few days in a new billet were always strange, by which time they were at the head of the queue, Pam Fawce ordered herself shepherds pie and then raised a query about his plate of salad.

'Couldn't you face the cold beef, then?'

'It wasn't that, it looked delicious. But then I was enticed over here by the tempting aroma of shepherds pie.'

'Make that two,' said Pam Fawce to one of the serving women. There were five of them, all coloured, plus another two on duty at the Salad Bowl with no clear function, since it was a serve-yourself affair. Then there were at least three women clearing the tables, and a fourth in charge of a slowly perambulating trolley dispensing coffee to those who required it. No shortage of staff in this establishment.

'The only thing is,' continued Pam Fawce, still on the plate of salad question, 'I'm *not sure* how she's going to charge you for it. You see normally you'd either have a complete salad, roast beef, something like that, *or* whatever you want from the hot counter. Then she tears off the ticket for what you've had and you pay on your way out.'

'Oh dear. Tears off what ticket?'

'You haven't been given one of these? Typical.'

Gryce now saw that Mrs Fawce – Pam – was clutching what looked like a wartime ration book. The pages were perforated into squares, each square being some such annotation as 'Main Dish', 'Dish of Day', 'Cheese & Biscuits', 'Salad Bowl' and so on. Some squares, another ration book touch, carried the words 'Not For Use'. He also saw that the woman he had taken to be a cashier at the end of the counter was not a cashier at all, but merely a functionary whose duty was to tear off the relevant coupons. Presumably there would be someone in the vicinity of the Salad Bowl performing the same task, while the woman who pushed round the percolator-trolley would be empowered to remove the coupon marked 'Coffee/Beverage'. You then, he imagined, would present your book at that booth affair by the escalators, where they would take possession of the uppermost page and work out the damage according to how many coupons had been detached. All the surrendered coupons would be collated and sorted, and they would have to correspond in value to the cash received. It seemed an unnecessarily cumbersome system.

Gryce seemed to have two problems: the presence on his tray of an incomplete salad in addition to his shepherds pie, and the absence of a pad of meal vouchers as he supposed they were called. No harm could come of placing himself thoroughly in the hands of Pam Fawce. Not only would she sort out his difficulties, but her doing so would forge a positive link between them. It would be a talking point for many an evening in the wine bar. 'What are you smiling at?' he would ask – 'I was remembering your look of absolute desperation when it suddenly dawned on you that you'd strayed into the Buttery without your meal vouchers.'

Pam commenced negotiations with the ticket-collecting woman, who quickly assessed the situation as outside her brief and pressed a bell-push to summon someone in authority. Standing to one side with his simulated mahogany tray, Gryce noted that Seeds had commandeered a vacant table and, with outstretched arms, was cradling two chairs in the expectation of Gryce and Pam relieving him so that he could come up for his own meal. He seemed to be growing impatient but there was nothing Gryce could do about that. He could hardly leave Pam to handle the situation on her own, since his plate of salad and rapidly cooling shepherds pie were evidence in the case, and besides, he wouldn't want to risk her wandering off and joining Grant-Peignton, Beazley and Co. at another table.

A senior-looking woman, wearing a suit in contrast to the lilac smocks of the serving staff, appeared on the scene and listened to Pam's explanations. After briefly examining Gryce she ruled that in the unusual circumstances, and on this occasion only, the potato salad and accompanying radishes and sliced tomato would be classed as vegetables, for which there was no extra charge, but that his shepherds pie would have to be accounted for by a Main Dish ticket from Pam's own book.

This suited Gryce admirably. It would mean that he owed Pam a lunch. That was an altogether different ball game from owing Seeds a lunch. He thanked the heavens above that the Buttery had been full, so that Seeds had opted to wait for a free table instead of accompanying him to the counter and having to assume responsibility for his food.

'Typical,' said Pam again as they joined Seeds and took up the seats he had been reserving, one on either side of him. '*Not only* have they not given him his SSTs *or* told him where to get them, the poor man didn't even know anything about them!'

SSTs, then, not meal vouchers. 'Supplementary Subsistence Tickets,' Pam explained. More jargon to remember. There was so much to learn in this place, it was like one's first day at school all over again.

'Typical,' agreed Seeds, adding '*Coh!*' as he rose and headed for the Salad Bowl. It could either have been an exclamation of disgust or his means of expressing laughter, on the lines of Gryce's own '*Sha!*' and that Personnel fellow's, Lucas's, '*Shock!*' Time would tell, when they had exchanged an office joke or two.

It came as a surprise to Gryce that Seeds hadn't said 'Let the dog see the rabbit' when he went up for his lunch.

This left him without anything to say to Pam by way of small talk. If Seeds had said 'Let the dog see the rabbit' he could have riposted '– or the ham-and-egg pie, as the case may be' and taken it from there. They could have talked about the food.

But Gryce need not have worried about keeping up a conversation. The theme of the SSTs, and the breakdown in communications that had led to the hold-up at the hot meals counter, kept Pam in full flow. It seemed there was a guideline leaflet, listing all the hundred and one things a new employee ought to know, that should rightly have been placed in Gryce's hands by Lucas of Personnel. But it was likely that the leaflet had been withdrawn for emendations and additions, as happened from time to time. In that event it fell to Grant-Peignton, who as Copeland's number two was responsible for departmental welfare, to show him the ropes, tell him where the first-aid room was for instance, and *particularly* clue him up on the Supplementary Subsistence Tickets.

They were called supplementary, Gryce was intrigued to learn, because they were originally an optional alternative to the conventional luncheon vouchers which could be used in any café or cheap restaurant. But that particular choice was being phased out because the Buttery, which was heavily subsidized, had been losing too much money. Under the old system you had signed for your supplementary tickets or luncheon vouchers up in the Welfare Office on a certain day of the month according to where your surname initial fell in the alphabet. But Pam believed that the Buttery's own administration office, she thought it was on the tenth or twelfth floor, was taking over the chore of issuing SSTs. She would have to find out soon enough on her own account, since she had only a four or five days' supply left. If Gryce liked she could let him know what the new arrangement was.

Gryce could think of nothing he would like more. There was a lot more to learn about the SSTs and the time passed very amiably, with no awkward pauses, before Seeds returned to the table with a plate piled high with tongue and cold chicken.

'One thing worth bearing in mind,' said Seeds, picking up the conversational thread from Pam, 'is that when your surrender a Main Meal ticket you're laying yourself open to paying nearly half as much again as if you'd surrendered a Salad Bowl ticket. Even though the portions are smaller.'

'Which reminds me,' said Pam. 'One shepherds pie. If you've got twenty-four pec handy?'

'Twenty-four pee? Is that all?'

'That's assuming you'll want coffee. The Main Meal's only twenty pee. Don't forget we're subsidized.'

'And your shepherds pie's subsidizing my tongue and cold chicken into the bargain,' said Seeds. 'This little lot came to only fifteen pee.'

Gryce's gratified surprise at the cost of the meal, dirt cheap he called it, had the edge taken off it somewhat by Pam's obvious, though quite understandable, keenness to keep the books straight. It meant he wouldn't owe her a lunch after all. But a thought struck him as he put down his knife and fork and meticulously counted out some coins, despite her protest that it would do later.

'But what about the Main Meal ticket you gave up for my lunch? Doesn't that throw you out?

'Oh, you can owe me that.' So the door was still open. He would be able to say, 'Methinks I'm indebted to you for a Main Meal, or more precisely an SST for same,' and she would have to accompany him to the Buttery. That was assuming the tickets were not valid unless detached by an authorized person, as was probably the case.

'Don't forget,' said Seeds, 'that when you apply for your SSTs, you'll want them back-dated as from today. Otherwise when you refund Pam's ticket you'll find yourself one short at the end of the issuing period, and you'll be wondering where it's got to.'

'That way madness lies,' agreed Gryce.

He liked all this talk about SSTs very much indeed. It reminded him of his Air Force days when there had often been similar detailed discussion of late-meal chitties, issuable to those who had been on guard duty.

The conversation became general, within the parameters of office affairs as they applied to the newcomer. Seeds confirmed what Pam had said about the guidelines leaflet being withdrawn for emendations and additions, but the pair of them, speaking in turn, were able to reconstruct its contents as they could best remember them. Gryce learned about the late arrivals book that was kept by the three one-armed commissionaires, the drill for collecting his salary on the first Thursday of each month, the holiday roster, the concession whereby he could take up to six separate (but not consecutive) days' compassionate leave a year without producing documentation; and much else. The compassionate leave concession, unheard of in any of his previous billets, interested him a lot. He could see the time coming when he and Pam would scoot off to Brighton for the day, catching the nine-something down and the four-something back. What his wife didn't know about she wouldn't grieve over.

'Any social activities at all?' he asked as Seeds waved his arm ineffectually to summon the coffee trolley. Gryce and Pam had elected not to have a pudding, but Seeds, not having selected his main course from the hot meals counter where the puddings were in evidence, had left the question open. Gryce had hoped to snatch another moment or two alone with Pam by mentioning that the chilled rhubarb fool looked well worth queuing for, but Seeds, beyond murmuring, 'Rhubarb fool, shall I or shan't I?' had taken no action in the matter. Pam might at least have encouraged him by urging, 'Go on, be a devil.' A pity, when they were getting on so famously.

'Depends entirely what you mean by social activities. *Coh!*' So it was a laugh after all. 'The principal recreation at this establishment is to be observed by feasting one's eyes on the next table.'

As directed, Gryce switched his glance discreetly. A middle-aged man and a middle-aged woman, their food untouched, were deep in an important-seeming discussion. From the woman's miserable expression and the man's haggard one, Gryce deduced a long-running affair that was going sour. That was where a casual glass of wine could lead you if you weren't too careful.

'Love's young dream,' said Pam softly.

'The long-suffering Cargill from Salary Accounts,' murmured Seeds. 'The lady, on the other hand, is definitely not Mrs Cargill, much though her ambitions might lie in that direction.'

'A certain obstacle in the shape of the present Mrs Cargill?' sniggered Gryce. It was good to be privy to office gossip so soon.

'The very substantial shape, from all I gather. Mark you, we can offer you rather more shall we say above-board examples of true love running smooth.'

'Don't be bitchy!' Pam chided, enjoying herself.

'I was thinking of the widow Rashman and a certain gentleman. I gather a date has been set.'

'Twenty-fifth of this month,' Pam confirmed. And for Gryce's benefit: 'You know Mrs Rashman, at least you've met her. At long last she's marrying her admirer from Stationery Stores. Honestly, this place gets more like a matrimonial bureau every day!'

'Exactly the same in my last billet,' said Gryce. A wine-bar romance had blossomed, then: a happy contrast to the sad example at the next table. 'We had four, no five office weddings last year. All colleagues, or former colleagues.'

'And someone coming round with a collecting tin on each occasion,' Seeds said.

'Oh, every time!' He wondered if he'd be asked to poppy up for Mrs Rashman. It would be a cheek if he were. 'And if it wasn't weddings it was retirements, and if it wasn't retirements it was someone leaving.' Which reminded Gryce that Comform had been the first billet he'd left where there'd been no presentation ceremony. Hardly feasible, he supposed, considering it had been not so much a leave-taking as a mass exodus.

'That's one thing you're unlikely to be stung for here,' said Seeds. 'People leaving, that is. Once you've signed on with British Albion you're generally regarded as being here for life.'

'Mrs Rashman's leaving, for one,' said Pam – blurted, almost, and at once looked as if she wished she hadn't.

'Exception proves the rule,' responded Seeds quickly, and quietly. He and Pam exchanged a curious sort of glance. If the subject hadn't been so innocuous, Gryce would have thought he had detected a warning given, and a warning acknowledged. Perhaps there was some skeleton in the cupboard apropos Mrs Rashman and her admirer from Stationery Stores.

It certainly looked that way, for Seeds laboriously changed the subject.

'But you were asking about social activities. There's various clubs of one kind or another. Chess.'

Gryce confessed that he could not play chess and Seeds and Pam admitted that they couldn't either. There followed an over-animated discussion about their failure to understand the game and how, when playing with young nephews or nieces, they had been trounced.

'What else can we offer you?' mused Seeds, looking more relaxed now. 'Squash. Swimming. Tennis. We're affiliated to the City and Guilds Sports Centre out at Acton, so you can get free membership. Or so I'm reliably informed. My own sporting activities are limited to walking to Turnham Green tube station every day.'

'That makes two of us.' Forest Hill Southern Region station in Gryce's case, but Seeds would know what he meant. What a pleasant lunch hour it had turned out to be. The coffee had arrived at long last and the conversation was going with such a swing that there was no opportunity to remark even briefly on how passable it was.

'There's always the Albion Players,' said Pam, with what seemed like diffidence, although what she had to be diffident about Gryce could not guess.

She'd said something out of the ordinary, though, for the effect on Seeds was very odd. 'The membership's closed!' he retorted, as rudely as he dare allow himself in front of a guest. Again Gryce caught the warning glance, now tinged with anger; but this time it was not acknowledged, or anyway it was not conceded.

'I *know* the membership's closed, ducky, I *do happen* to be the membership secretary,' said Pam through bared teeth. 'But if we don't find out who's interested and who isn't, we'll never get new blood when we need it, will we?'

Evidence of a temper there, for future reference.

'If Albion Players implies amateur dramatics –' began Gryce in a throat-clearing voice, with the object of pouring oil on troubled waters. Some internecine warfare here, clearly: some committee squabble that had been left to smoulder by an unwise chairman.

To his surprise Seeds did not so much cut him short as simply talk through his attempted interjection, leaving him to tail off foolishly.

'You know the rules as well as I do, Pamela. *All* approaches are made *after* consultation with the full–'

'You can't tell me anything about the rules, Ron, I helped to frame them.'

'– with the full *committee*, Pamela. *After* consultation and not before.'

If Seeds could sail blithely on after an interruption, then so could Gryce.

'*If* we're discussing amateur dramatics, and I *could* just be allowed a word in edgeways–' This time he chose a joshing voice, and felt even more foolish than before, for he was ignored.

'I'm sorry, Ron, but there is such a thing as being constructive. If I'm not even allowed to sound someone out we might just as well shut up shop.'

'By all means sound him out. By all means sound him out. I'm only trying to remind you–'

'– that the membership is closed. I know that without you telling me. All I was going to say, if you'd let me, was he seems like a suitable candidate.'

'Oh, eminently. I don't doubt that at all. All other things being equal.'

Gryce thought seriously about taking offence at being discussed in his own presence like this. On the other hand, it wasn't as if he were hearing no good of himself: Pam had said that he seemed a suitable candidate for the Albion Players and Seeds had endorsed her approval, all other things being equal, by which he presumably meant when the membership list was open again. They both seemed to be making heavy weather of a trivial issue, but doubtless the protocol of the Albion Players was not trivial to them. Gryce was glad now that they had not allowed him to finish his sentence, which would have been to the effect that amateur dramatics were not in his line. If Pam thought he seemed a suitable candidate, it would be folly not to keep his options open.

He was searching for some innocuous way of insinuating a word to this effect when Pam lightly, and rather deliciously in his opinion, touched his sleeve.

'He must think we're terribly rude.'

'Don't mind me in the least,' said Gryce with hearty gallantry. He would forgive her for apologizing in the third person, it was only a mannerism. 'All I was going to say–'

'I'm afraid passions run high when it comes to the Albion Players,' said

Seeds, cutting in again. Gryce did hope this wasn't a habit of his: there were mannerisms and mannerisms. 'As you've probably gathered the bone of contention is that once people have joined they've joined, so we can't be too careful. Nothing personal.'

'Oh, no offence taken, rest assured. In any case I was just going to say that amateur dramatics aren't quite my cup of tea.' Although that wasn't what he had just been going to say at all, pride seemed to demand it. He could wait for some suitable moment to ask Pam why she'd thought him a suitable candidate, and then allow her to win him over.

'Then we've inflicted an argument on you over nothing,' said Seeds, the snappishness in his voice aimed at Pam.

Gryce was inclined to agree with him. They drank their coffee in silence. Gryce furtively glanced at his watch: it was ten minutes to two, so allowing three minutes to get back to their desks they had seven minutes to kill. Neither Pam nor Seeds struck him as keen types who would get back to work a second before they had to.

It would be a shame if a stimulating lunch should fizzle out in this way. Ingratiatingly he asked: 'What production are the Albion Players embarked on this year, as a matter of interest?'

'It hasn't been decided. *An Inspector Calls* if I have my way, which I probably won't,' said Pam sulkily. So that was one door closed.

Gryce essayed one or two complimentary remarks about the Buttery, its range of food, its cleanliness and the acceptability of its coffee as against the witches' brew served from the machine upstairs. These comments were well, but taciturnly, received. Talking of the Buttery reminded him of the two questions he had meant to ask Lucas of Personnel when he came for his interview. The first one, concerning the existence of a staff canteen, had been somewhat overtaken by events. But the other one, the one that had slipped completely from his mind until now, would seem to have some mileage in it.

'Tell me, what exactly is it we do here?'

Again Gryce caught that curious look from Seeds: but this time it was directed at him personally.

'Hasn't Copeland explained the vital role of Stationery Supplies? No, he wouldn't, knowing Copeland.'

Seeds launched on a description of the department's function which was a fair summary of what Gryce had already heard from Copeland. It took them very nicely to three minutes to two. As they rose he thought he might as well throw in the supplementary question he had been holding in reserve.

'Yes, I understand all that. What I meant was, what does the company do? What is British Albion in aid of?'

'Well may you ask,' said Pam. Another of what Gryce was beginning to think of as Seeds' famous glances was shot at her. There was no mistaking it. It said, quite plainly, *'Shut up!'*

To Gryce, Seeds said in an airy, casual tone that was clearly costing him some effort: 'What is it not in aid of, that's more the question? When you finally get your guidelines leaflet, if that happy day ever comes, you'll find a list of all the firms for which Perfidious Albion is the holding company. None of them household names, but we do have our fingers in a large number of pies.'

They had reached the cash-desk by the spiral escalator, where Pam went into a lengthy reprise of her earlier negotiations with the supervisor on the unorthodox use of her SSTs. As they waited behind her, Seeds added unnecessarily: 'Does that answer your question?'

Gryce confirmed that it did. He felt no curiosity at all about what British Albion did or didn't do. What did strike him as intriguing, though, was the way these two had been behaving, particularly Seeds.

The settling-in period was always enjoyable for Gryce. It was what he most looked forward to when changing billets.

He acquired his own beaker, a Silver Jubilee remnant which young Thelma found for him in a nearby Oxfam shop. He learned that as well as the paper towels and hot-air machine in the men's room, there was a further option in the way of personal hand towels which were changed each Wednesday. He would wait until he had his own desk before signing for a personal hand towel.

He got to know something about his colleagues and their little foibles. Grant-Peignton picked his nose with his little finger. Seeds jingled change. Beazley, Mrs Rashman and Pam took saccharins in their coffee. Ardagh often brushed back the lock of hair that, together with his small moustache, made him look like Hitler.

The work of the department, it came as no surprise to Gryce, could easily have been done by four people or two at a push. Most of it seemed to fall, and none too heavily, on the shoulders of Seeds, Beazley and Grant-Peignton, with Copeland supervising. The others, apart from an hour or so's chores which they spread out over the day, were left pretty well to their own devices.

They wrote letters and filled in crosswords. After lunch each day a small group composed of Pam, Ardagh and the Penney twins did the *Evening Standard* word game on a competitive basis, the loser to buy the next day's paper. The Penney twins were also the departmental representatives of the seventh floor football pools syndicate, another example of over-manning if you wanted Gryce's opinion, since the operation for the entire floor could easily have been handled by one person. The Penney twins collected the football pool money on Tuesday mornings. They took Gryce aside and explained that while it would not be fair on the others to ask him to join the syndicate in the middle of the season, an invitation would certainly be extended to him at the appropriate time. Gryce quite understood this.

On the Thursday, to Gryce's astonishment, the industrious Beazley sold him a raffle ticket for a small sum. This too was evidently a weekly event – 'Beazley's Benefit' Seeds called it as he shelled out his five pence, but from what Gryce gathered from Beazley's mumbled explanation it was in aid of a new gymnasium for a boys' club in which he was interested. Several of the staff had on occasion won prizes, so it was not money thrown into the wind.

On the Friday, a stir was caused by the fact of Mr Hakim arriving for work with two carrier bags laden with fancy boxes of chocolates, boiled sweets and after-dinner mints. For a few minutes the office took on the appearance of a street market as most of the staff, including even Copeland, clustered around Hakim's desk to collect their pre-paid orders. It seemed that Mr Hakim had a brother who was a wholesale confectioner, so that anything in that line could be got at a discount. It was as well to put your requirements in by Wednesday evening, with cash in advance to avoid misunderstandings.

So the week had a pleasing shape. Monday, so far as Gryce could judge, was a fairly dead day. On Tuesday, the Penney brothers collected for the pools syndicate which he would be joining in due course, presumably at the beginning of the Australian season. On Wednesday a woman came round with the replacement hand towels. Thursday was Beazley's Benefit day, with the potential excitement of someone holding a winning ticket from the previous week. On Friday there was the highlight of Mr Hakim's makeshift sweetstall. (Gryce would have to think seriously about that. Although he and his wife shared a sweet tooth – it was one of the few things they could be said to have in common – it could be something of an embarrassment to be trundling a two-pound box of liquorice allsorts about in the event that he established any pattern of meeting Pam for a glass of wine on Friday evenings. Probably because of the discount margin involved, Hakim did not seem to deal in smaller sizes.)

As if this calendar of events were not enough, there were other regular diversions such as the mirth which each afternoon greeted Ardagh's efforts in the word game contest: one gathered that spelling was not his strong subject; he had tried, for example, to extract the word 'grill' from 'girlishness' by spelling it with one l. That had led to some good-natured ribbing. After the word game, Pam took it upon herself each day to read out the *Evening Standard* horoscopes for those who were interested in such things – Mr Hakim (Sagittarius), the Penney twins (Leo), Mrs Rashman (Cancer) and herself (Aquarius). (She did not, to Gryce's disappointment even though he did not believe in astrology, ask him for his birthsign.) It could be said, all in all, that newspaper-reading was quite a feature of the office. Young Thelma was an avid follower of a strip cartoon in the *Daily Express* and she would regularly clomp up to one or other member of the staff and ask shyly if they had seen that day's instalment.

Gryce registered, without having any prurient interest in the matter, the times at which his colleagues went to the lavatory each morning, and the number of minutes spent where no man could reach them. The record, he thought initially, was held by Grant-Peignton who regularly at ten minutes to eleven disappeared for upwards of half an hour with a bundle of papers under his arm. Not until the Thursday, when Gryce himself had to answer a call of nature at about this time, did he discover that Grant-Peignton was in fact stationed at the photo-copying machine in Traffic Control next door, where he was running off some plans of a new greenhouse for which planning permission was needed. They had quite a chat about greenhouses and cold-frames, although Gryce was no authority on the subject. Contrary to his first impression Grant-Peignton seemed a nice chap, not stand-offish at all.

Another visitor to the photo-copying machine, which he could see was quite the little social centre – rather like the water-cooler one saw in old American films – was Beazley, who was copying some private documents, probably the minutes of his precious boys' club. They exchanged pleasantries about a threatened miners' strike, Beazley gruffly advising Gryce to stock up on coal or coke. Although Gryce had installed gas-fired central heating with the insurance money accruing from his mother's death some years ago, he was grateful to Beazley. He had been right in thinking that the brusque manner was a mask for shyness.

One way or another, Gryce had conversations with everyone in Stationery Supplies before his first week was out, including even young Thelma who could be quite a chatterbox when you drew her out. She was keen on amateur dramatics, having once played the third witch in a school production of *Macbeth*, and was anxious to join the Albion Players as soon as there was a vacancy.

Mrs Rashman, Gryce was to learn, spoke of little but groceries: the nuisance it was that a particular brand of water biscuit was no longer stocked by most supermarkets, or the fact that small tins of corned beef were expensive, taken weight for weight with similar products. Her impending marriage to her gentleman friend from Stationery Stores, being a private matter, was never touched on. Not that Gryce had much curiosity about it, beyond still wondering if anyone would have the nerve to sting him for a contribution to her leaving present. He made no effort to picture Mrs Rashman going through the rigmarole of courtship – kissing, sitting about in City churchyards and so on. Provided they did not run into one another in the wine bar where the liaison had sprouted, she had no interest for him outside the context of the office.

Her obsession with groceries was a case in point. He was intrigued by the sheer volume of produce she accumulated on her shopping expeditions each lunch hour but he never wondered what she did with it all when it left the office. Her red canvas shopping bag crammed with special offers had a form, an entity, while it was perched at the side of her desk during office hours; it dematerialized, so far as Gryce was concerned, when its owner walked out of the lift in the evening. Mrs Rashman bought cat food, so it followed that she must own a cat: but since she never mentioned it, the cat had no existence. There would have had to be a blueprint for a cat, in the shape of a daily report on its doings, to give it any dimension, and even then it would exist only as an anecdotal facet of Mrs Rashman's own personality.

It was the same with Beazley's boys' club and its proposed new gymnasium, and Mr Hakim's brother who was a wholesale confectioner. They might be figments of the imagination for all Gryce cared, dreamed up to explain Beazley's raffle and Hakim's cutprice market in chocolates and sweets. They did not exist, because Beazley and Hakim did not exist outside office hours. Neither did any of the others. Neither did Gryce himself, as he had long ago realized.

That he led any kind of life beyond the office he was fuzzily aware of, in a sleepwalking kind of way, only while he was leading it. He had found in all his previous billets that once he had hung up his mackintosh and got his feet firmly beneath his own desk, the outside world evaporated, like the waking

memory of a dream. That was already beginning to happen at British
Albion, even though the desk he occupied could not be called his own: it
belonged to Vaart who was on holiday, and he could picture Vaart, even
though he had never met him, more vividly than he could conjure up the face
of the ticket collector at London Bridge or his local newsagent or even his
own wife. Trying to remember what his wife looked life, he could only focus
on an image of the tennis player Billie Jean King, whom she resembled when
her hair was done in a certain way. All this was proof that he had found a
billet which suited him very well.

His wife had only once impinged on his consciousness during his first week
with British Albion, and even that intrusion had been to do with an office
matter. In his elation at having landed the job, he had forgotten, when
leaving the building after his interview with Lucas of Personnel, to hand over
the Part Two of his appointment card to the three one-armed commissionaires. On the Sunday evening before taking up his appointment, while
emptying the pockets of his business suit so that his wife could sponge and
press it, he had discovered the crumpled document and asked her to remind
him at all costs to take it with him. This, naturally, she failed to do, and he
had sailed off without it. Thinking the matter important, as it certainly was,
his wife had tried to ring him at the office. She had found that British Albion
was not on the telephone. At least, it was not in the book under B for British
or A for Albion, and directory enquiries could not help her.

She had mentioned this curious fact to Gryce on the Monday evening, and
he in turn mentioned it to Copeland on the Tuesday. The opportunity arose
when he handed over the long-lost Part Two: he had done this on the advice
of the three one-armed commissionaires who, after a long conference, had
refused to accept it on the grounds that its absence had already been
recorded in their occurrence book.

He found Copeland at his desk in his partitioned-off space by the filing
cabinets, where he was meticulously smoothing out a toffee wrapper. Unlike
the rest of the clientele of Mr Hakim's Friday morning market stall,
Copeland did not buy his sweets for home consumption. He kept a large
presentation tin of Sharpe's Toffee Assortment in a private drawer of one of
the filing cabinets, and dipped into it often. Combined with ill-fitting teeth,
his fondness for sucking toffees probably accounted for his occasional
obscurities of speech.

Copeland's cubby-hole had no door and Gryce didn't think that knocking
on the waist-high metal partition would be appropriate. He placed himself in

Copeland's line of vision and hung about until Copeland looked up and, with
an encouraging 'Mm!' cordially beckoned him in. To Gryce's relief he
showed little interest either in the Part Two or in Gryce's confused account of
his adventures with it. To his further relief, Copeland did however agree to
take possession of the wretched thing, and flung it into a filing tray.

Copeland seemed disposed towards conversation. He could not ask Gryce
to sit down, since his status as departmental head did not rate a chair for
visitors, but he did perform a vaguely agreeable hand-signal which Gryce
recognized as equivalent to the 'Stand easy' wave of his Air Force days.

'Dialect wine,' said Copeland, after Gryce had told him, in the form of a
little anecdote, about his wife having hell's own job in trying to find British
Albion's number.

Effectively forestalling any attempt by Gryce to have this cryptic remark
amplified, Copeland then rose abruptly, went to the filing cabinet that
housed his private drawer, and swallowing the toffee that was already in his
mouth extracted another one from a large tin bearing a picture of Windsor
Castle. This was done quite openly, apparently without it crossing Copeland's mind that he ought to offer one to Gryce; but when it came to
unwrapping the toffee and popping it into his mouth, some belated delicacy
of feeling impelled him to turn his back and hunch his shoulders as if
performing a minor private ablution.

At the conclusion of, to Gryce's mind, this farcical business, Copeland
returned to his desk with the toffee wrapper concealed in his hand,
insinuating it on top of the one that was already lying there in the clear hope
of Gryce not noticing that there were now two wrappers on the desk instead
of one. He then went on to smooth out the top wrapper as he had done the
one beneath it. It seemed quite important to him to prove to his satisfaction
that the two toffee-papers, when smoothed out, were exactly the same size,
and when next he spoke, to ask Gryce if he was finding his feet, it was in an
abstracted sort of voice.

The question had already been asked of Gryce by several of his colleagues
and he gave the same answer: that it was a little like finding one's way
around an ocean liner. He had never been on an ocean liner but the simile
seemed appropriate, bearing in mind the slightly nautical flavour of the
phrase about finding his feet that everyone used. Copeland confessed that
there were parts of the building he was himself still unfamiliar with, giving
the piles suppository in haystack tree as an instance. Gryce thought he must
mean the Files Depository in basement three. He said that he would have to

find Gryce something to do, and Gryce said that he looked forward to it. And then, reverting to the subject of telephones as abruptly as he had departed from it, Copeland repeated:

'Yes, dialect wine.'

If, as Gryce now guessed, he was saying 'direct lines', it didn't go very far towards explaining the mystery. Gryce supposed if his wife had used a bit of initiative, she could have got him on the phone by unearthing his letter of appointment and ringing the direct line number quoted on it – except, come to think of it, that it would have been the direct line to Lucas of Personnel, so it wouldn't have helped her much. But that didn't explain why a big commercial concern like perfidious Albion should choose to be ex-directory, and it didn't explain why the telephones on the seventh floor, direct line or not, never seemed to ring.

He was not going to raise these questions with a busy head of department, but Copeland, who was now engaged in folding down the four corners of his toffee-papers to form an octogram, evidently sensed his puzzlement. Carefully serrating one of the folds with a thumb-nail, Copeland explained:

'It saves clogging up the twitchboard with outside calls, so our masters the business efficiency wallahs assure us. Each department has its own dialect wine. So if your wife does want to reach you in an immersion, see, she can always get you at this number here.'

Copeland gestured, more of a flaccid gesture this time, in the direction of his own telephone. He had only slightly stressed 'immersion, see', but enough for Gryce to gather that he was saying 'emergency' and that outside calls were not encouraged. Sound policy. It would stop his wife, especially if she were never given Copeland's direct line number, from ringing up to ask if he was working late again.

'Of course,' added Copeland, 'there's nothing to prevent you from making your own cause outboard.' Calls outward, that would be. 'Just dial nine on your internal extension and that gives you an outside wine, provided you don't wish to ring Australia. But you can't get incoming calls.'

'Except presumably from other departments?' ventured Gryce, anxious to seem alert.

'Not encouraged,' said Copeland firmly. 'Verbal enquiries play the merry dickens with the cistern, such as it is. Our cistern is to get everything in writing. Memo in, memo out, that's the idea. Then we all know where we are.'

Sounds more like the civil service every day, thought Gryce. But that was how these big firms tended to conduct themselves these days. The business efficiency wallahs were the masters now, as Copeland had rightly said. Gryce wouldn't have been surprised to hear that they'd had one of those American whizz-kids in.

Since Copeland had the quizzical look of one expecting further questions, Gryce was emboldened to ask: 'But isn't it unusual for a firm this size to go ex-directory?'

'Furiously enough, it's more common than you'd think. It does make cents, when you look at it from the business standpoint. Nine out of ten calls are from established clients who know what dialect wine to ring and whom they want to speak to. Your unsolicited calls – salesmen, dissatisfied customers and other pains in the nether regions – are eliminated completely. It cuts down on use of executive time enormously.'

Oh yes, they'd had the American whizz-kids in all right, revamping the organization from top to bottom.

Gryce, who had been encouraged by the tone of the interview to lean familiarly against Copeland's desk, straightened up. Thinking that Copeland might want to go back to the theme of how difficult it was to find one's way around a new billet, and perhaps express the hope that he had at least managed to find out where to draw his pay cheque, he did not immediately leave.

He was surprised when all Copeland said was, 'Does that add to your pension?' Gryce, with an inane grinning nod, withdrew. Not until he was back at his desk did he work out that Copeland had asked, 'Does that answer your question?', just as Seeds had done when asked what British Albion was in aid of.

Recollections of Notable Cops
[1900–10]

(FROM *Newspaper Days*, 1942)

H. L. Mencken

Some time ago I read in a New York paper that fifty or sixty college graduates had been appointed to the metropolitan police force, and were being well spoken of by their superiors. The news astonished me, for in my reportorial days there was simply no such thing in America as a book-learned cop, though I knew a good many who were very smart. The force was then recruited, not from the groves of Academe, but from the ranks of working-men. The best police captain I ever knew in Baltimore was a meat-cutter by trade, and had lost one of his thumbs by a slip of his cleaver, and the next best was a former bartender. All the mounted cops were ex-hostlers passing as ex-cavalrymen, and all the harbor police had come up through the tugboat and garbage-scow branches of the merchant marine. It took a young reporter a little while to learn how to read and interpret the reports that cops turned in, for they were couched in a special kind of English, with a spelling peculiar to itself. If a member of what was then called 'the finest' had spelled *larceny* in any way save *larsensy*, or *arson* in any way save *arsony*, or *fracture* in any way save *fraxr*, there would have been a considerable lifting of eyebrows. I well recall the horror of the Baltimore cops when the first board to examine applicants for places on the force was set up. It was a harmless body headed by a political dentist, and the hardest question in its first examination paper was 'What is the plural of *ox?*,' but all the cops in town predicted that it would quickly contaminate their craft with a great horde of what they called 'professors,' and reduce it to the level of letter-carrying or school-teaching.

But, as I have noted, their innocence of *literae humaniores* was not necessarily a sign of stupidity, and from some of them, in fact, I learned the valuable lesson that sharp wits can lurk in unpolished skulls. I knew cops who were matches for the most learned and unscrupulous lawyers at the Baltimore bar, and others who had made monkeys of the oldest and crabbedest judges on the bench, and were generally respected for it. Moreover, I knew cops who were really first-rate policemen, and loved their trade as tenderly as so many art artists or movie actors. They were badly paid, but they carried on their dismal work with unflagging diligence, and loved a long, hard chase almost as much as they loved a quick, brisk clubbing. Their one salient failing, taking them as a class, was their belief that any person who had been arrested, even on mere suspicion, was unquestionably and *ipso facto* guilty. But that theory, though it occasionally colored their testimony in a garish manner, was grounded, after all, on nothing worse than professional pride and *esprit de corps*, and I am certainly not one to hoot at it, for my own belief in the mission of journalism has no better support than the same partiality, and all the logic I am aware of stands against it.

In those days that pestilence of Service which torments the American people today was just getting under way, and many of the multifarious duties now carried out by social workers, statisticians, truant officers, visiting nurses, psychologists, and the vast rabble of inspectors, smellers, spies and bogus experts of a hundred different faculties either fell to the police or were not discharged at all. An ordinary flatfoot in a quiet residential section had his hands full. In a single day he might have to put out a couple of kitchen fires, arrange for the removal of a dead mule, guard a poor epileptic having a fit on the sidewalk, catch a runaway horse, settle a combat with table knives between husband and wife, shoot a cat for killing pigeons, rescue a dog or a baby from a sewer, bawl out a white-wings for spilling garbage, keep order on the sidewalk at two or three funerals, and flog half a dozen bad boys for throwing horse-apples at a blind man. The cops downtown, especially along the wharves and in the red-light districts, had even more curious and complicated jobs, and some of them attained to a high degree of virtuosity.

As my memory gropes backward I think, for example, of a strange office that an old-time roundsman named Charlie had to undertake every Spring. It was to pick up enough skilled workmen to effect the annual redecoration and refurbishing of the Baltimore City Jail. Along about May 1 the warden would telephone to police headquarters that he needed, say, ten head of painters, five plumbers, two blacksmiths, a tile-setter, a roofer, a bricklayer, a carpenter and a locksmith, and it was Charlie's duty to go out and find them. So far as I can recall, he never failed, and usually he produced two or three times as many craftsmen of each category as were needed, so that the warden had some chance to pick out good ones. His plan was simply to make a tour of the saloons and stews in the Marsh Market section of Baltimore, and look over the drunks in congress assembled. He had a trained eye, and could detect a plumber or a painter through two weeks' accumulation of beard and dirt. As he gathered in his candidates, he searched them on the spot, rejecting those who had no union cards, for he was a firm believer in organized labor. Those who passed were put into storage at a police-station, and there kept (less the unfortunates who developed delirium tremens and had to be handed over to the resurrection-men) until the whole convoy was ready. The next morning Gene Grannan, the police magistrate, gave them two weeks each for vagrancy, loitering, trespass, committing a nuisance, or some other plausible misdemeanor, the warden had his staff of master-workmen, and the jail presently bloomed out in all its vernal finery.

Some of these toilers returned year after year, and in the end Charlie recognized so many that he could accumulate the better part of his convoy in half an hour. Once, I remember, he was stumped by a call for two electricians. In those remote days there were fewer men of that craft in practise than today, and only one could be found. When the warden put on the heat Charlie sent him a trolley-car motorman who had run away from his wife and was trying to be shanghaied for the Chesapeake oyster-fleet. This poor man, being grateful for his security in jail, made such eager use of his meagre electrical knowledge that the warden decided to keep him, and even requested that his sentence be extended. Unhappily, Gene Grannan was a pretty good amateur lawyer, and knew that such an extension would be illegal. When the warden of the House of Correction, which was on the farm twenty miles from Baltimore, heard how well this system was working, he put in a requisition for six experienced milkers and a choirleader, for he had a herd of cows and his colored prisoners loved to sing spirituals. Charlie found the choir-leader in no time, but he bucked at hunting for milkers, and got rid of the nuisance by sending the warden a squad of sailors who almost pulled the poor cows to pieces.

Gene had been made a magistrate as one of the first fruits of the rising reform movement in Baltimore, and was a man of the chastest integrity, but he knew too much about reformers to admire them, and lost no chance to afflict them. When, in 1900, or thereabout, a gang of snoopers began to tour the red-light districts, seeking to harass and alarm the poor working women there denizened, he instructed the gals to empty slops on them, and acquitted all who were brought in for doing it, usually on the ground that the complaining witnesses were disreputable persons, and could not be believed on oath. One day, sitting in his frowsy courtroom, I saw him gloat in a positively indecent manner when a Methodist clergyman was led out from the cells by Mike Hogan, the turnkey. This holy man, believing that the Jews, unless they consented to be baptized, would all go to Hell, had opened a mission in what was then still called the Ghetto, and sought to save them. The adults, of course, refused to have anything to do with him, but he managed, after a while, to lure a number of *kosher* small boys into his den, chiefly by showing them magic-lantern pictures of the Buffalo Bill country and the Holy Land. When their fathers heard of this there was naturally an uproar, for it was a mortal sin in those days for an orthodox Jew to enter a *Goy Shul*. The ritual for delousing offenders was an arduous one, and cost both time and money. So the Jews came clamoring to Grannan, and he spent a couple of hours trying to figure out some charge to lay against the evangelist. Finally, he ordered him brought in, and entered him on the books for 'annoying persons passing by and along a public highway, disorderly conduct, making loud and unseemly noises, and disturbing religious worship.' He had to be acquitted of course, but Gene scared him so badly with talk of the penitentiary that he shut down his mission forthwith, and left the Jews to their post-mortem sufferings.

Gene was a high favourite among us young reporters, for he was always good for copy, and did not hesitate to modify the course of justice in order to feed and edify us. One day an ancient German, obviously a highly respectable man, was brought in on the incredible charge of beating his wife. The testimony showed that they had been placidly married for more than 45 years, and seldom exchanged so much as a bitter word. But the night before, when the old man came home from the saloon where he played *Skat* every evening, the old woman accused him of having drunk more than his usual ration of eight beers, and in the course of the ensuing debate he gave her a gentle slap. Astounded, she let off an hysterical squawk, an officious neighbour rushed in, the cops came on his heels, and so the old man stood before the bar of justice, weeping copiously and with his wife weeping even more copiously beside him. Gene pondered the evidence with a frown on his face, and then announced his judgment. 'The crime you are accused of committing,' he said, 'is a foul and desperate one, and the laws of all civilized

countries prohibit it under heavy penalties. I could send you to prison for life,
I could order you to the whipping-post [it still exists in Maryland, and for
wife-beaters only], or I could sentence you to be hanged. [Here both parties
screamed.] But inasmuch as this is your first offence I will be lenient. You
will be taken hence to the House of Correction, and there confined for twenty
years. In addition, you are fined $10,000.' The old couple missed the fine, for
at mention of the House of Correction both fainted. When the cops revived
them, Gene told the prisoner that, on reflection, he had decided to strike out
the sentence, and bade him go and sin no more. Husband and wife rushed
out of the courtroom hand in hand, followed by a cop with the umbrella and
market-basket that the old woman had forgotten. A week or two later news
came in that she was ordering the old man about in a highly cavalier manner,
and had cut down his evenings of *Skat* to four a week.

The cops liked and admired Gene, and when he was in good form he
commonly had a gallery of them in his courtroom, guffawing at his whimsies.
But despite his popularity among them he did not pal with them, for he was
basically a very dignified, and even somewhat stiff fellow, and knew how to
call them down sharply when their testimony before him went too far beyond
the bounds of the probable. In those days, as in these, policemen led a social
life almost as inbred as that of the justices of the Supreme Court of the
United States, and outsiders were seldom admitted to their parties. But
reporters were exceptions, and I attended a number of cop soirées of great
elegance, with the tables piled mountain-high with all the delicacies of the
season, and a keg of beer every few feet. The graft of these worthy men, at
least in my time, was a great deal less than reformers alleged and the envious
common people believed. Most of them, in my judgment, were very honest
fellows, at least within the bounds of reason. Those who patrolled the fish-
markets naturally had plenty of fish to eat, and those who manned the police
boats in the harbor took a certain toll from the pungy captains who brought
up Baltimore's supplies of watermelons, cantaloups, vegetables, crabs and
oysters from the Eastern Shore of Maryland: indeed, this last impost
amounted to a kind of *octroi*, and at one time the harbor force accumulated so
much provender that they had to seize an empty warehouse on the
waterfront to store it. But the pungy captains gave up uncomplainingly, for
the pelagic cops protected them against the thieves and highjackers who
swarmed in the harbor, and also against the land police. I never heard of
cops getting anything that the donor was not quite willing and even eager to
give. Every Italian who ran a peanut stand knew that making them free of it

was good institutional promotion and the girls in the red-light districts liked
to crochet neckties, socks and pulse-warmers for them. It was not unheard of
for a cop to get mashed on such a girl, rescue her from her life of shame, and
set her up as a more or less honest woman. I knew of several cases in which
holy matrimony followed. But the more ambitious girls, of course, looked
higher, and some of them, in my time, made very good marriages. One
actually married a banker, and another died only a few years ago as the
faithful and much respected wife of a prominent physician. The cops always
laughed when reformers alleged that the wages of sin were death –
specifically, that women who sold their persons always ended in the gutter,
full of dope and despair. They knew that the overwhelming majority ended at
the altar of God, and that nearly all of them married better men than they
could have had any chance of meeting and roping if they had kept their
virtue.

One dismal New Year's day I saw a sergeant lose an excellent chance to
pocket $138.66 in cash money: I remember it brilliantly because I lost the
same chance at the same moment. There had been the usual epidemic of
suicides in the waterfront flop-houses, for the dawn of a new year turns the
thoughts of homeless men to peace beyond the dissecting-room, and I
accompanied the sergeant and a coroner on a tour of the fatal scenes. One of
the dead men was lying on the fifth floor of a decaying warehouse that had
been turned into ten-cent sleeping quarters, and we climbed up the long
stairs to inspect him. All the other bums had cleared out, and the hophead
clerk did not offer to go with us. We found the deceased stretched out in a
peaceful attitude, with the rope with which he had hanged himself still
around his neck. He had been cut down, but then abandoned.

The sergeant loosed the rope, and began a search of the dead man's
pockets, looking for means to identify him. He found nothing whatever
of that sort, but from a pants pocket he drew out a fat wad of bills, and
a hasty count showed that it contained $416. A situation worthy of Scribe,
or even Victor Hugo! Evidently the poor fellow was one of the Russell Sages
that are occasionally found among bums. His money, I suppose, had been
diminishing, and he had bumped himself off in fear that it would soon be all
gone. The sergeant looked at the coroner, the coroner looked at me, and I
looked at the sergeant. Then the sergeant wrapped up the money in a piece of
newspaper lying nearby, and handed it to the coroner. 'It goes,' he said
sadly, 'to the State of Maryland. The son-of-a-bitch died intestate, and with
no heirs.'

The next day I met the coroner, and found him in a low frame of mind. 'It was a sin and a shame,' he said 'to turn that money over to the State Treasury. What I could have done with $138.67! (I noticed he made a fair split, but collared one of the two odd cents.) Well, it's gone now – damn the luck! I never *did* trust that flatfoot.'

Are the Rich Happy?

Stephen Leacock

Let me admit at the outset that I write this essay without adequate material. I have never known, I have never seen, any rich people. Very often I have thought that I had found them. But it turned out that it was not so. They were not rich at all. They were quite poor. They were hard up. They were pushed for money. They didn't know where to turn for ten thousand dollars.

In all the cases that I have examined this same error has crept in. I had often imagined, from the fact of people keeping fifteen servants, that they were rich. I had supposed that because a woman rode down-town in a limousine to buy a fifty-dollar hat, she must be well-to-do. Not at all. All these people turn out on examination to be not rich. They are cramped. They say it themselves. Pinched, I think is the word they use. When I see a glittering group of eight people in a stage box at the opera, I know that they are all pinched. The fact that they ride home in a limousine has nothing to do with it.

A friend of mine who has ten thousand dollars a year told me the other day with a sigh that he found it quite impossible to keep up with the rich. On his income he couldn't do it. A family that I know who have twenty thousand a year have told me the same thing. They can't keep up with the rich. There is no use in trying. A man that I respect very much who has an income of fifty thousand dollars a year from his law practice has told me with the greatest frankness that he finds it absolutely impossible to keep up with the rich. He says it is better to face the brutal fact of being poor. He says he can only give me a plain meal, what he calls a home dinner – it takes three men and two women to serve it – and he begs me to put up with it.

As far as I remember, I have never met Mr Carnegie. But I know that if I did he would tell me that he found it quite impossible to keep up with Mr Rockefeller. No doubt Mr Rockefeller has the same feeling.

On the other hand there are and there must be rich people, somewhere. I

run across traces of them all the time. The janitor in the building where I
work has told me that he has a rich cousin in England who is in the South-
Western Railway and gets ten pounds a week. He says that the railway
wouldn't know what to do without him. In the same way the lady who
washes at my house has a rich uncle. He lives in Winnipeg and owns his own
house, clear, and has two girls at the high school.

But these are only reported cases of richness. I cannot vouch for them
myself.

When I speak therefore of rich people and discuss whether they are happy,
it is understood that I am merely drawing my conclusions from the people
whom I see and know.

My judgment is that the rich undergo cruel trials and bitter tragedies of
which the poor know nothing.

In the first place I find that the rich suffer perpetually from money
troubles. The poor sit snugly at home while sterling exchange falls ten points
in a day. Do they care? Not a bit. An adverse balance of trade washes over
the nation like a flood. Who have to mop it up? The rich. Call money rushes
up to a hundred per cent, and the poor can still sit and laugh at a ten cent
moving picture show and forget it.

But the rich are troubled by money all the time.

I know a man, for example – his name is Spugg – whose private bank
account was overdrawn last month twenty thousand dollars. He told me so at
dinner at his club, with apologies for feeling out of sorts. He said it was
bothering him. He said he thought it rather unfair of his bank to have called
his attention to it. I could sympathize, in a sort of way, with his feelings. My
own account was overdrawn twenty cents at the time. I knew that if the bank
began calling in overdrafts it might be my turn next. Spugg said he supposed
he'd have to telephone his secretary in the morning to sell some bonds and
cover it. It seemed an awful thing to have to do. Poor people are never driven
to this sort of thing. I have known cases of their having to sell a little
furniture, perhaps, but imagine having to sell the very bonds out of one's
desk. There's a bitterness about it that the poor can never know.

With this same man, Mr Spugg, I have often talked of the problem of
wealth. He is a self-made man and he has told me again and again that the
wealth he has accumulated is a mere burden to him. He says that he was
much happier when he had only the plain, simple things in life. Often as I sit
at dinner with him over a meal of nine courses, he tells me how much he
would prefer a plain bit of boiled pork with a little mashed turnip. He says

that if he had his way he would make his dinner out of a couple of sausages, fried with a bit of bread. I forget what it is that stands in his way. I have seen Spugg put aside his glass of champagne – or his glass after he had drunk his champagne – with an expression of something like contempt. He says that he remembers a running creek at the back of his father's farm where he used to lie at full length upon the grass and drink his fill. Champagne, he says, never tasted like that. I have suggested that he should lie on his stomach on the floor of the club and drink a saucerful of soda water. But he won't.

I know well that my friend Spugg would be glad to be rid of his wealth altogether, if such a thing were possible. Till I understood about these things, I always imagined that wealth could be given away. It appears that it cannot. It is a burden that one must carry. Wealth, if one has enough of it, becomes a form of social service. One regards it as a means of doing good to the world, of helping to brighten the lives of others – in a word, a solemn trust. Spugg has often talked with me so long and so late on this topic – the duty of brightening the lives of others – that the waiter who held blue flames for his cigarettes fell asleep against a door post, and the chauffeur outside froze to the seat of his motor.

Spugg's wealth, I say, he regards as a solemn trust. I have often asked him why he didn't give it, for example, to a college. But he tells me that unfortunately he is not a college man. I have called his attention to the need of further pensions for college professors; after all that Mr Carnegie and others have done, there are still thousands and thousands of old professors of thirty-five and even forty, working away day after day and getting nothing but what they earn themselves, and with no provision beyond the age of eighty-five. But Mr Spugg says that these men are the nation's heroes. Their work is its own reward.

But, after all, Mr Spugg's troubles – for he is a single man with no ties – are in a sense selfish. It is perhaps in the homes, or more properly in the residences, of the rich that the great silent tragedies are being enacted every day – tragedies of which the fortunate poor know and can know nothing.

I saw such a case only a few nights ago at the house of the Ashcroft-Fowlers, where I was dining. As we went in to dinner, Mrs Ashcroft-Fowler said in a quiet aside to her husband, 'Has Meadows spoken?' He shook his head rather gloomily and answered, 'No, he has said nothing yet.' I saw them exchange a glance of quiet sympathy and mutual help, like people in trouble, who love one another.

They were old friends and my heart beat for them. All through the dinner as Meadows – he was their butler – poured out the wine with each course, I could feel that some great trouble was impending over my friends.

After Mrs Ashcroft-Fowler had risen and left us, and we were alone over our port wine, I drew my chair near to Fowler's and I said, 'My dear Fowler, I'm an old friend and you'll excuse me if I seem to be taking a liberty. But I can see that you and your wife are in trouble.'

'Yes,' he said very sadly and quietly, 'we are.'

'Excuse me,' I said. 'Tell me – for it makes a thing easier if one talks about it – is it anything about Meadows?'

'Yes,' he said, 'it is about Meadows.'

There was a silence for a moment, but I knew already what Fowler was going to say. I could feel it coming.

'Meadows,' he said presently, constraining himself to speak with as little emotion as possible, 'is leaving us.'

'Poor old chap!' I said, taking his hand.

'It's hard, isn't it?' he said. 'Franklin left last winter – no fault of ours; we did everything we could – and now Meadows.'

There was almost a sob in his voice.

'He hasn't spoken definitely as yet,' Fowler went on, 'but we know there's hardly any chance of his staying.'

'Does he give any reason?' I asked.

'Nothing specific,' said Fowler. 'It's just a sheer case of incompatibility. Meadows doesn't like us.'

He put his hand over his face and was silent.

I left very quietly a little later, without going up to the drawing-room. A few days afterwards I heard that Meadows had gone. The Ashcroft-Fowlers, I am told, are giving up in despair. They are going to take a little suite of ten rooms and four baths in the Grand Palaver Hotel, and rough it there for the winter.

Yet one must not draw a picture of the rich in colours altogether gloomy. There are cases among them of genuine, light-hearted happiness.

I have observed that this is especially the case among those of the rich who have the good fortune to get ruined, absolutely and completely ruined. They may do this on the Stock Exchange or by banking or in a dozen other ways. The business side of getting ruined is not difficult.

Once the rich are ruined, they are, as far as my observation goes, all right. They can then have anything they want.

I saw this point illustrated again just recently. I was walking with a friend of mine and a motor passed bearing a neatly dressed young man, chatting gaily with a pretty woman. My friend raised his hat and gave it a jaunty and cheery swing in the air as if to wave goodwill and happiness.

'Poor old Edward Overjoy!' he said, as the motor moved out of sight.

'What's wrong with him?' I asked.

'Hadn't you heard?' said my friend. 'He's ruined – absolutely cleaned out – not a cent left.'

'Dear me!' I said. 'That's awfully hard. I suppose he'll have to sell that beautiful motor?'

My friend shook his head.

'Oh, no,' he said. 'He'll hardly do that. I don't think his wife would care to sell that.'

My friend was right. The Overjoys have not sold their motor. Neither have they sold their magnificent sandstone residence. They are too much attached to it, I believe, to sell it. Some people thought they would have given up their box at the opera. But it appears not. They are too musical to care to do that. Meantime it is a matter of general notoriety that the Overjoys are absolutely ruined; in fact, they haven't a single cent. You could buy Overjoy – so I am informed – for ten dollars.

But I observe that he still wears a seal-lined coat worth at least five hundred.

Preparing for the West

H. F. Ellis

I always think it best to prepare myself, so far as may be, for any new experience. Some people argue that the slate should be wiped clean, so that it is ready for new impressions instead of being cluttered up with preconceptions and so on. But I don't know. I have seen a good many clean slates in my time as a schoolmaster, and most of them were not notably quick at receiving impressions. I suppose I mean wax rather than slate, but the sense is clear enough. One can have an open mind without its being entirely empty, and I never dream of going to Switzerland or Scotland or anywhere a bit out of the way without looking up the heights of the mountains in advance and reading about William Tell and Bonnie Prince Charlie. The natives can pull your leg unmercifully, for one thing, unless you have a few facts to check them by. For another, people are not always as well-informed about their own country as you might expect. I remember, years ago, telling a French acquaintance at Poitiers that Edward the Black Prince routed sixty thousand Frenchmen near there in 1356, although outnumbered by five to one – a thing he might not have known to this day, if I had not taken the trouble to look it up beforehand. I certainly don't intend to travel up and down America in a state of open-mouthed astonishment at everything I see and hear.

Friends have been most helpful in suggesting useful books to give me a foretaste of the general tone, the *ethos*, of the place. I have dipped into novels by William Faulkner and Marquand, looked more briefly at the work of a man called Cozens who, one must hope, does not give a representative picture, and of course refreshed my memory of *Huckleberry Finn*. I have also read widely in a book called *Inside U.S.A.*, kindly lent me by the Headmaster, which confirmed my belief that there is much in American life that would scarcely do over here. The author, a Mr John Gunther, constantly asks 'Who runs Nebraska?' and such-like questions, leaving me a little bewildered. What on earth would one say if one were asked who runs Birmingham? Or

Yorkshire? Still, there is a mass of information which no doubt will come in handy as I travel about. I shall take it with me, I think, for reference – unless I find that the *World Almanack* for 1955, which I confiscated this morning from Wrigley, will do instead. What on earth the boy was doing with such a thing in his possession I am at a loss to understand. It has a distinct American bias, being published I see in New York, and gives, to take an example at random, the number of Hungarian-born whites in North Dakota in 1950, which you would never find in a truly 'world' almanack published, say, in London. In the ordinary way, when boys are caught playing with darts, transistor sets and so on during working hours, we masters return the confiscated article after a few hours or days, according to the seriousness of the offence, but I do not feel that Wrigley will have any right to complain if I retain this almanack a little longer. Does the boy think that Burgrove is going to enter for one of these deplorable school quizzes on television?

Gilbert wandered into my room while I was conning over my collection of books and agreed that they ought to make a pretty good general introduction to the American scene. 'For instance,' he said, flipping one or two of them open at random, 'if you happen to find yourself floating down the Mississippi on a raft, with a man like Willis Wayde aboard, it will be useful to know that Stewart Thompson, of Yale, threw the discus 162 feet 7½ inches at the 20th Annual Heptagonal Track and Field Championships, Cambridge, Mass., on May 15th, 1954.'

'Yes, yes,' I said. 'Put that Almanack down, there's a good chap. It isn't mine.'

' "Oshkosh is known for overalls, trucks, motors and luggage," ' he read, 'You'll knock the Yanks for six all right, when you pass that bit of information on. "Wisconsin has 10,000 miles of trout streams, 8,500 lakes with sturgeon, muskellunge, pike, bass, perch, smelts. Hunting – as you know, Mrs Mulheimer – includes deer, bear, red fox, raccoon ..." They're going to go crazy over your light conversation, A.J.'

'I have a lot to do, if you will forgive me, Gilbert,' I said, not being in the mood for this kind of foolery. Naturally I am not proposing to cram my mind with a mass of trivial detail, some of which may well be out of date, still less try to pass it on to our good friends on the other side. 'Yanks' indeed! That is just the kind of contemptuous attitude that I am determined not to adopt.

What is 'Sorghum,' one wonders? I see that 6,170,000 tons of it were produced for forage as recently as 1953, and another 5,906,000 for silage. Which remind me that I must be careful to get my billions right over there.

One does not want to be too easily impressed through forgetting to knock off the last three noughts.

I suppose, at my age, I ought to be able to take a trip to America in my stride, and so in a way I can. But I confess to a feeling of excitement and exhilaration such as has scarcely visited me since I was chosen to play for my School Hockey XI – and that was a great many years ago. Shall I see Niagara Falls? and the Grand Canyon? I know very little as yet about the actual programme. Apparently I am to meet a Mr Herbert S. Bulkin – 'make contact' is the phrase used, as though we were a couple of electric wires – on my arrival in New York, and he will tell me of the arrangements. So far as there are to be arrangements, that is. I am to be free to make my own plans for at least part of the time, mix with the people and so on. It is not as if I were going to Moscow, with a so-called 'escort' dogging my footsteps to make sure that I took no photographs in the poorer quarters. There are one or two places where I am expected to give talks, and of course I shall want to see something of the educational system over there. But apart from that I shall be a bit of a gipsy, I dare say. The open road, eh? One might even find oneself in Oshkosh one of these fine days. Who knows? It has an un-English ring, overalls or no overalls.

It is difficult, one way and another, to give as much attention as I should like to the humdrum work of the School.

At Sea

There are nineteen coat-hangers in my cabin. One realizes, of course, that life at sea is a very different kettle of fish from life on land, and on the second day out one has hardly had time to sit down and get one's sea-boots on as the saying goes. But even so! I doubt whether there were as many as nineteen in the whole of Burgrove, excluding the Matron's which I have naturally not counted. I have also got ten light-switches, apart altogether from the bathroom, which is full of towels – two bath towels and from four to eight face towels. It is difficult to be more precise, because whenever I damp one, or even disarrange it, the steward takes it away and brings two more. One dislikes causing trouble, but even when I pat my hands lightly against the inside of the towel without unfolding it, he notices, and takes it away. Rich people are used to this sort of thing, I dare say, but I would just as soon hold my hands out of the port-hole and let them dry in the breeze as make all this fuss and pother every time I wash. Actually, one is warned not to open the scuttle oneself but to send for the steward, so it would be cutting off his nose to spite his face really.

The steward came in as I was jotting down these first impressions of life at sea, so I showed him the coat-hangers and asked him what the idea was. He said the idea was to hang coats on them – not meaning to be impertinent, I think, for he is a civil and well-spoken fellow, but misunderstanding my drift.

'Exactly,' I said. 'But why nineteen?'

To my embarrassment he suspected a complaint and would have brought another half-dozen had I not stopped him in time. Apparently people do make complaints from time to time on these ships, ludicrous as the idea may seem to anyone accustomed to life on the pay of an assistant master.

'Surely,' I asked, to make my point clearer, 'people don't cross the Atlantic with nineteen coats? Not in this direction, anyway.'

He said I should be surprised what some people crossed the Atlantic with, and not quite knowing what he meant I left him and went up to the sun-deck, where I was handed a cup of broth. There seems no end to the luxury and thoughtfulness on these great ships.

After the broth, I went and looked at the Atlantic. It is surprisingly black near the ship when you look down, except where it is churned up and frothing and so on; but further off it is green – unless the sun is shining, in which case it is blue as at Broadstairs. I mention this because people who have never crossed the Atlantic may think they are missing something, whereas in fact it is much the same in the middle as it is at the edges, though deeper naturally. Still, one looks at it a good deal.

One of the funnels is full of old rope. I discovered this quite by chance while up on the top deck wondering whether Mrs Duval expected an apology.* A sailor opened a door in the side of one of these huge flues and disappeared from sight under my very eyes. Naturally I thought he had fallen down into whatever it is the funnel is connected to below, and was on the point of raising a cry of 'Man down the funnel!' or whatever was appropriate when he reappeared with a length of cable and a broom. I could hardly have been more astonished if I had seen the vicar back at home take a bottle of port out of one of the organ pipes.

I mentioned the incident to the purser, who took it very lightly. It was quite a normal thing, he said, to have a false funnel, and he explained that

*I have asked Mr Wentworth to explain this allusion, but he declines.

when this ship was built passengers thought a single funnel was a bit *infra dig*. 'Besides,' he said, 'she looks better with two.'

I must say I thought it sailing a bit close to the wind.

'Supposing they started doing the same sort of thing with railway engines?' I said. 'Or motor cars and so on?'

He said that cars no longer had funnels, a fact of which I did not need to be reminded. 'I am speaking generally,' I said. 'If I were to buy a six-cylinder car, I certainly should not expect to find that two of the cylinders were intended for the storage of bits of rag, spare nuts and bolts and so on. Is not the parallel disturbingly close?'

The purser said he thought not. No deception was intended. The ship was not at present in the market, but if at any time she was put up for sale he felt sure the Company would include 'one dummy funnel' in the specification. Meanwhile, 'it isn't as if we blew dummy smoke through it,' he added, with what seemed to me an odd confusion of thought.

I don't know what to think, I am sure. It would be a fine thing if half the lifeboats turned out to be made of cardboard and only put there because they made the passengers feel safer. I put this point to a man at my table called Rumbolt, who is quite an experienced traveller, and he said it was all over the ship that I was claiming a reduction for misrepresentation of funnels. 'You ought to come back on one of the *Queens*,' he said. 'They carry two captains.' I could make no sense of this remark. Surely he dosn't mean that one of *them* is a dummy?

I am tired of being told to 'wait until you see the New York skyline'. One has no option. If it was Americans who made the remark I could understand and sympathize; one naturally likes to make the best of one's own country in advance. But the worst offender is Rumbolt, who is as English as I am. He is simply being the patronizing 'old hand', and will no doubt take all the credit for the view when we *do* see it. Just because he has seen these skyscrapers before he seems to be under the impression that he put them up himself – just as Old Rawlinson used to say 'Why don't you go to my dear Provence next hols?' on the strength of ten days there, seven of which I know for a fact he spent in a hospital at Orange.

Somebody sighted a whale yesterday, but I was asleep.

Thick fog from the Nantucket Lightship onwards. So the New York skyline was neither more nor less impressive than a row of beans at midnight. I should have been sorry about this, but for Rumbolt. 'Never known such a thing in all my fifty-four crossings,' he said. 'You don't know what you're missing.'

'Is this your *fifty-fourth* crossing?' I asked in amazement.

'It is and all, boy,' he said.

'In that case,' I replied, with as much calmness as I could muster after being addressed in such a fashion, 'surely you must have started from the wrong side?'

'When I say "crossing",' he explained airily, 'I mean of course the double event – there and back, boy, there and back.'

Well! I am the last person to make a hasty or unkind judgement, but I am bound to say that had he been a member of my IIIA Mathematics set I should have told him that the only honourable thing to do when caught out in a lie is to own up. I hardly think he is the kind of person to be a successful 'unofficial ambassador' (which, in a sense, one is here) in a country where tact and a determination to treat people as equals are of such vital importance.

Perhaps fortunately, I was saved from the neccessity of replying by the intervention of an American who pointed out to me the Statue of Liberty, just discernible through the murk.

'Why, it's tiny!' I cried involuntarily, adding, in case he should think I was in any way belittling the famous symbol, 'Not that mere size is of any significance. We Englishmen have at least, in a thousand years of history, learnt *that*.'

'I certainly trust,' he said after a pause, 'that you will have a fruitful and interesting stay in my large young country, Mr Wentworth.' There is a grave courtesy about the best type of American that is altogether refreshing and delightful.

I cannot say the same for the Customs man, whose manner I thought decidedly offhand. I told him very politely that I had nothing of value in my luggage – unless, I added with a smile, some notes for a talk on education in England could be so described. He simply pointed to one of my bags and said 'That one!'

'I am British,' I said, speaking slowly and distinctly in case my unfamiliar accent had confused him. 'I have come here by invitation on an exchange basis arranged by – not a Fulbright exactly –'

'Open it up,' he said.

Well, really! Still, there was no help for it, and I was naturally put out when the fellow rummaged about among my shirts and so on, without a with-your-leave or by-your-leave, finally coming up with the bottle of fruit salts without which I never travel. 'What's this then?' he demanded.

I explained as best I could, without going into details which were none of his business, but even then he had to unscrew the top and taste the stuff on the tip of his finger, 'Fizzy', was all he said.

'It takes all salts to make a world,' I told him, thinking a bit of a joke would lighten things up a little. I might as well have been talking about the unitary method of my IIIA boys for all the interest he showed. So I said no more, even when he began to ram my personal possessions back into the case in the reverse order to that in which I had carefully packed them. One does *not* want one's pyjamas right at the bottom.

'Staying long?' he asked me eventually, with an attempt at friendliness, if such it was, that came a great deal too late to mollify me.

'It begins to look like it,' I said. I had him there, I think.

It was a disappointing start, though, after the fog and so on. As a matter of fact, the very first words addressed to me as I stepped off the gangway on to American soil were 'Put that pipe out, you!' Land of the free, eh?

Contacts

Herbert S. Bulkin is unfortunately away in Seattle, Washington – not of course the well-known Washington but the state which was originally named Columbia and was then changed to Washington because of the existence of the District of Columbia in which the other Washington lies. I suspect some muddle-headedness here, though I naturally have better manners than to say so until I get home. Washington, née Columbia, has thirteen community forests, according to the notes I made at Burgrove, which gives an idea of the scale one is up against here, despite the odd wording. At any rate, that is where Mr Bulkin has gone, leaving me high and dry for the moment but for a note which was very thoughtfully waiting for me at my hotel. This put me in touch with a Fergus Henson Junior, who turned out to be in hospital, but someone at his apartment, as they say, whose name I did not quite catch, was most helpful, and as a result of all this I had an interesting talk with a Mr Schnaffler, whom I met at a dinner party given by a Mrs Teeling. I do not know who Mrs Teeling is exactly, but I was taken there by somebody called Ted, who it turned out did not know Mrs Teeling either. This might have been rather awkward, but Ted said that George A. Mopus had fixed it up through a mutual friend and would introduce us all when we got there.

There was nobody at the party called Mopus actually, but Mrs Teeling was most gracious and invited me to spend a week with a Mr and Mrs Riggery of Colorado Springs any time I was over Denver way. American hospitality is quite overwhelming. One cannot help wondering what friends in England would think if Mr and Mrs George Mopus, to take a name at random, turned up for a weekend with them at my suggestion. Still, I suppose if everybody does it it comes to the same thing in the end.

This Mr Schnaffler took me aside when he heard that this was my first visit to the States and warned me very earnestly to remember that all his countrymen still had a great feeling of inferiority when talking to an Englishman. 'It's the background,' he explained. 'We haven't the built-in culture.' He said he really admired the way we English sprinkled our conversation with literary allusions and references and *bon mots*, just casually and not bothering, and went right along talking as though nothing had happened; whereas your American had to do his damnedest to drag up something suitable out of Donne or Congreve or Sterne to keep his end up. He quoted from Cowper and Crabbe and Gibbon and James Joyce to prove his point, and was halfway through a laughing admission about an acquaintance of his who thought the poet Rochester had a mad wife when Mrs Teeling came up to us and said that her other guests were dying to talk with the guest of honour.

'Guest of honour, Mrs Teeling?' I cried. 'I! I'm afraid I am only an unheard-of schoolmaster,' and I explained that in fact I was really looking for a Herbert S. Bulkin, who was in Seattle.

'Remember what I've told you,' Mr Schnaffler called out as I was led away, 'and you'll understand why we Americans are often a bit tongue-tied and awkward when you come over and see us.'

Somebody took my glass out of my hand as I was passing and substituted a full one, and on turning round to protest I found myself face to face with a tall lady in black who took hold of my tie and said 'British. You can't mistake it,' in a surprisingly deep voice. Meanwhile my hostess was saying to someone behind me, 'I want to have you meet Mr Wentworth, an unheard-of schoolmaster from England who has come over to look for a Herbert S. Bulkin in Seattle,' thus putting me in rather a predicament. I turned my head as far as it would go, in an effort to be polite, and became conscious of a man holding a bowl of white matter flecked with green at my elbow. 'Dip,' he commanded me. 'It has a nuance.'

'I cannot dip,' I said on the spur of the moment, gesturing with my two hands, both of which had now by some means became laden with glasses, 'and to beg I am ashamed.'

'They missed that one,' said the voice of Mr Schnaffler out of the press on my left. 'What did I tell you?'

'Upon my soul,' I burst out, scarcely knowing whether I was on my head or my heels, 'You really are a most extraordinary and likeable people!'

Everybody laughed, and presently I found myself sitting on the floor with quite a pretty young girl who said gravely, 'I heard you are looking for a Herbert S. Bulkin, Mr Wentworth?'

'Do you know him?' I asked.

'Never heard of the man,' she told me. 'I think you are wasting your time. There are better things to see in America than Herbert S. Bulkin, *whoever* he is.'

A mood almost of irresponsibility came over me and I told her that in the State of Washington, where Herbert Bulkin had gone, there were thirteen community forests and I hardly cared whether he got lost in all of them. 'It isn't as if I knew the man,' I said, 'except by name; and even that doesn't seem very likely to me.'

'Mr Wentworth's stopped looking for Herbert S. Bulkin,' the girl called out, and there was a general cheer. All in fun, of course. But it is a far cry from Burgrove School, eh?

There was food, I think, and later on Mr Schnaffler very kindly gave me the historical reasons for America's cultural backwardness, citing (if I remember right) George Fox's *Journal*, a number of Acts of Parliament, *The Federalist*, William James and the pragmatists, the Munroe Doctrine, Henry Cabot Lodge and Ernest Hemingway. 'But all this is familiar ground to you, Mr Wentworth,' he ended (we were in the kitchen at the time, I recall, pounding up ice). 'What I really wanted to ask you was what is the precise rating just now, over in your country, of James Gould Cozens and Wallace Stevens?'

'Well of course,' I said, with my mind in a whirl, 'it rather depends.'

A Mr Hackbut came up at this point with a cry of 'Aha! "The Thrilling regions of thick-ribbéd ice",' but I capped his quotation by remarking 'What we need is a sledded poleaxe on this, eh?'

'There you are, you see!' Mr Schnaffler said.

We all had some more Bourbon, and I remembered a thing of Dr

Johnson's which I forget. Altogether a most enjoyable evening. I have a note to ring up a Mrs Theodore Kramm of Los Angeles, though I am not sure what about. However, she will probably know.

Mr Bulkin called – one doesn't say 'rang' here, for some reason – and seemed sorry to hear about Fergus Henson Jr. He has to go on to Denver, being all snarled up just now, to use his own words, with one wild Professor of Comparative Philology who could *not* be less well adjusted. However, he thought he had a couple of talks lined up for me, and was I making out all right meantime?

I asked him, in case he ran across a man called Ginger Brown while he was in Denver, if he could possibly find out whether Mr Brown was really expecting me on Wednesday week, and he said he would make a note of it. 'It is a little confusing,' I explained, 'because Mr and Mrs Riggery of Colorado Springs –'. But he cut me short with a promise to be back inside two days, and then we would soon have everything sorted out.

I suppose I must accommodate myself to the pace of life in this country, but it is a little worrying not to be doing anything definite yet in return for all the money. Still, as Mr Bulkin pointed out before he rang off (called off can hardly be right, surely?), I am moving about and getting to know the natives, which is half the battle.

I had hardly put the receiver down before George Mopus came through, and as a result I had my first taste of clam juice, which is about the same as sea water drunk through the nose. It is all experience, though. But before that he took me into an Automat, to explain how it worked, and did not seem to believe me when I said we had the same sort of thing in England. 'Now this man is having beans on toast,' he told me, pausing by a table, and I must say I felt a good deal of embarrassment. It is a different matter when the boys are eating at school and the Headmaster says, as he sometimes does when showing parents round, 'They are having roast lamb today, as you see.' People in restaurants are a different kettle of fish. Nobody seemed to mind, though, and the man just went on eating his beans – which is more than the boys can be persuaded to do in similar circumstances. They are all more free and easy over here. People seem to have nothing to hide, and I dare say it is all part of the same thing as having no fences round their gardens and being so ready to talk about their egos.

They are not ashamed of money, either. I am not sure where Mr Mopus fits into the organization that brought me over, if at all. He merely said, 'Oh, *that* one!' when I mentioned Herbert S. Bulkin and let the subject drop. But he insisted on paying for our luncheon, and though I naturally averted my eyes when the time came I could not help seeing how he did it. In England it is always an embarrassment – though not one to which a schoolmaster is often subjected – to be paid for at a restaurant table. Americans, instead of fingering one or two flat notes out of a slim wallet in a furtive sort of way, seem to be able to produce rolls of dollars from any part of their person. They strip off half-a-dozen quite openly, leaving plenty; and of course there is the comfort of not being able to tell whether the notes are ones, fives or tens. In England a five-pound note on a plate is unmistakable; and the only people who have rolls in their pockets are bookmakers, coal miners on holiday and, I dare say, car salesmen, with whom I have never lunched. At any rate, I felt quite at my ease while George Mopus was paying, and did not hesitate afterwards to show him, at his request, the little memo I made at the time on an old envelope.

' "Arthur James Wentworth, Esquire, B.A." ' he read out. 'Why, surely –'

'It's on the back,' I said. 'It only says "Makes no bones about it".'

'About what?'

'About paying.'

'I see,' he said. But I am not sure that he understood.

'I make little notes about the things that interest me,' I explained. 'Otherwise one forgets.'

'Oh sure, sure,' he said, and we went on to talk of other things. He criticized the late President Roosevelt in a way that seemed to me to show a lack of proper respect. It is my firm resolve not to interfere in any way in the internal politics of a country where I am a guest, and paid for into the bargain; so I merely remarked, 'In Britain we happen to think he was the greatest President your country has ever had,' and after a glance at my watch to suggest I had another appointment, walked out into the stir and bustle of Fifth Avenue.

Some Impressions of New York

One has read about New York and seen photographs and so on, so that the height of the buildings is not really a surprise, high as they are. One simply looks up, and there they are, and the only surprise in a way is why they stop when they do. It is not as if all of them tapered to a point like the spire of Salisbury Cathedral, which obviously cannot go any further. Still, I am no architect, and no doubt there are reasons – though an Englishman is hard put to it at times to understand why some of the things Americans do are done as they are, unless it is just to be different, which hardly seems worthy of a great democracy. The proper place for a telephone, I should have thought, is a telephone kiosk, not at the back of a shop where it hardly seems fair to make a call without buying something, which I cannot of course afford. This would be a nuisance if one had any calls to make.

I am the last person, I think I may claim, to be accused of insularity or narrow-mindedness, but what is the point of selling you a ticket and then taking it away and giving you another? I was astonished, when making a short train journey from Grand Central station (where the trains are all, rather inconveniently, in the basement – another needless eccentricity), to have my ticket taken from me almost at once by a tall, thin official, who gave me a longer one in exchange; or rather, instead of giving me the longer one he slipped it into a kind of bracket on the back of the seat in front. I said nothing of course, being in a foreign country, and a little later on the same official came back and took the long ticket away, giving me nothing in return. This left me with no ticket at all, whereas the inspector had two, a situation that could never have arisen in my own country. I should certainly not have objected to my original ticket being taken away, for that used to be done on the Great Western many years ago when I was a lad. But to exchange the ticket for another one and then take *that* away is arrant tomfoolery, look at it how you will. It is no part of my business over here to teach the Americans how to run their affairs; otherwise I might well suggest that these ticket exchangers would be better employed as conductors on the New York buses, on which all the work is at present done by the drivers. And what work! Money is put by passengers as they enter into a machine at the driver's right side, which would be sensible enough if the machine issued a ticket in return – except that that, I suppose, if the railway system is any guide, would involve another machine to take the ticket away again in exchange for a bigger one, and so on... The machine in fact does nothing in return for money except to make a thin tinkling or rattling noise, yet it is a constant worry to the driver, who has repeatedly to wind a handle attached to it without producing any visible result. He has also to sort out the money which the machine from time to time disgorges into a receptable, and stack the coins in racks in front of him. As a mathematician I am naturally interested to know what the machine is for, how it works and so on, but the drivers I have so far asked have been too busy steering with one hand and winding

and stacking with the other to make any very detailed reply. One of them
indeed spoke to me with some discourtesy, not realizing I dare say that I was
an Englishman.

These are just a few of my first impressions of America. Of course I realize
that the same points may have been noted by previous visitors to this great
continent; but then if we were all careful never to say anything that had been
said before there would be some pretty long silences, as I remember my
Headmaster saying once apropos the end-of-term reports.

Another odd thing is that the letter-boxes on the sidewalks (one soon picks
up the lingo here) are not very easy to distinguish from the rubbish bins. I
pointed this out to a policeman ('cop', eh?), who reprimanded me for posting
a piece of chewing gum that had somehow got stuck to my shoe, and he said,
'Is that a fact?' in a surprised tone of voice, which only shows that it takes a
fresh eye to see what is going on under your own nose. 'Go ahead and drop
your mail in the trash-can,' he told me. 'Just to square things up.' We both
laughed at that, and I really began to feel at home in this extraordinary
country. I said I had met one or two fellow-countrymen of his during the
war, and he seemed very interested, telling me in return that his wife once
had a canary she bought from an English lady. One lives and learns. I must
say he did not seem at all the type of man to take bribes or hit people on the
head with rubber hosepipes.

I was standing in front of a shop on Fifth Avenue, reading an advertisement
that said 'Not Just Leisure Togs ... *but* Star Studded Groups of *Newsmaking
Sportswear*' and thinking for some reason of Oliver Wendell Holmes, when a
total stranger came up and addressed me.

'How's it go then?' he said. 'How d'you find it?'

'Find it?' I asked.

'All this,' he said. 'New York. Different to London, eh?'

'Yes, indeed. Yes. Oh yes. Different from London certainly.' I agreed,
taking care not to stress the corrected preposition. 'Rather!'

At home I do not often say 'Rather!', but they expect it over here, so I am
told.

'Well?' he said. 'Such as what? What's the impression, tell me?'

'Well,' I said, thinking back over my walk, 'your sewers steam more than
ours do. Not that –'

'For God's sake!' he said.

'It comes up out of the manholes,' I told him. 'It's just a thing one notices, walking along.'

'Sanitation man?' he asked.

'Certainly not. I am a schoolmaster, as it happens.'

'I see,' he said. 'Anything else strike you?'

I told him how surprised I was to see so few men wearing hats – on Fifth Avenue, that is. They seemed to start wearing them on Fourth Avenue, and the further east you went the more there were to be seen. 'I walked down to the river, you know,' I explained, tracing the route with the point of my umbrella, and added, without thinking, that there were clumps of grass growing out of the pavement, or sidewalk, on First Avenue. 'A kind of barley, I think,' I said, hoping he would not suppose any criticism was intended.

'Is that so?' he asked, and I was about to say a tactful word about the weeds in bomb-damaged areas near St Paul's when a new voice remarked, 'Went right down to First, so he says,' and I looked up to find that quite a group had gathered to listen to our conversation. Well, really! I suppose it is natural that people should want to hear what an Englishman thinks of their country, but all the same!

'It's not much of a walk, madam,' I remarked, and told her, just to be friendly (one has to do what one can to kill the absurd canard that the English are stand-offish), that I intended to walk the other way in the afternoon, right down to Eleventh.

'I'd certainly be glad to hear your impressions after *that* trip,' the first man said.

'How so?' I asked, pricking up my ears in the hope of a few tips about items of special interest to look out for.

'Well,' he said, 'there's a devil of a lot of steam comes out of the manholes in those parts.'

There was a general laugh at this, and another when I put a question that had been bothering me since the beginning of our walk, namely just how I had been recognized as an Englishman before I had even opened my mouth. This habit of laughing for little or no reason is a form of shyness, I think. My IIIA boys back at Burgrove often break out in much the same way, when nothing funny has been said. Still, it all makes for friendliness. 'Mind you don't trip over the grass,' somebody called out when I eventually went on my way – to which I retaliated by pretending to clear a path along the sidewalk with swishes of my umbrella. I found myself humming a little tune as I strolled along, always a sign that I am enjoying myself. These informal encounters, so typical of this great country, are very warming to a stranger,

and do a great deal I am sure to foster mutual understanding. I certainly
intend to speak to as many Americans as I can while I am over here. It will at
least prove to them, other things apart, that not all Englishmen are
nincompoops with monocles.

A drawing of a cat caught my eye at what these extraordinary people call a
traffic intersection. I have never cared for the use of dumb animals, pets,
manikins and so on to give warning or advice; words put into the mouths of
squirrels or bears seem to me to lose rather than gain authority. So that I was
somewhat shocked to read, in the very heart of what we must now regard as
the capital of the Western world, the legend.

> 'Tweets' says HEY! that light's gonna change.
> Cross at the start of the green, not in between

'This is worse than the Whispering Fish,' I remarked to a bystander in
overalls, momentarily forgetting that he would not in all probability be
familiar with the advertisements issued some time ago by our own White
Fish Authority. He looked nonplussed and put a hand up to the back of his
curious cap, which had flaps, I noticed, buttoned up at the sides. 'It gives
recipes for cod and so on,' I explained. 'In a kind of balloon.' The fish has a
fin up to its mouth, actually, to show that it is whispering, and I was trying to
make this clear when the lights changed and the man rapidly crossed the
street, as instructed, at the start of the green. Americans are surprisingly law-
abiding in many ways, which is a good thing I suppose; but it is
disconcerting when they move off suddenly before you have made your point
clear.

I did not get to Eleventh actually, as there was a message at my hotel from
Mr Bulkin, asking me to call him back. It looks as though the more serious
side of my trip is about to begin.

The Gentleman and his Domestic Habits

Douglas Sutherland

You Gentlemen of England who live at home at ease
MARTIN PARKER

Gentlemen do not, unless it cannot be avoided, eat out in restaurants. The exceptions to this rule are a few exclusive hotels in the West End of London where they can, at great expense, get such delicacies as Brown Windsor, a thin tasteless soup traditionally served by the Royal Family, and milk puddings like rice and sago which are a relic of their nursery days. They do not like food which has been 'messed about with'. Continental cooking gives them diarrhoea.

Home Food

At home they like to eat poultry, fish or game which they themselves have reared, caught or shot. In the old days salmon and venison appeared so regularly on the menus of Scottish households that the servants, who were stuck with the same fare as their masters, rebelled and stipulated that they should not be required to eat such delicacies more than twice a week. Now all the salmon is put on fast trains to London, venison is sent to Germany and the servants are lucky if they get a look in at the tinned Snoek.

If a gentleman has a cook or his wife has a penchant for cooking they are allowed to run the whole gamut of the culinary arts in such matters as whether the pheasant should be served with bread sauce or fried bread-crumbs. If there are guests for dinner, extravagances such as savouries are sometimes permitted. Gentlemen are very fond of savouries. If there are any left over they are apt to shovel them all onto their own plates in spite of agonized signals from their wives. Then they want to know why the guests are not having any more and they had to pretend that they do not want any more.

Vulgarities

There are certain objects which are never seen on a gentleman's dining table – fish forks and knives for example, which are regarded as a Victorian vulgarity except by those whose fortunes were made in Victorian times. Another are napkin rings. I remember a gentleman asking to be enlightened as to the use of napkin rings. It was explained to him that some people rolled up their napkins and placed them inside the ring to be kept ready for the next meal. 'Good God!' he exploded, 'D'ye mean to tell me they use the same napkin for two meals running!'

Wine Drinking

Gentlemen are very concerned about maintaining a good cellar and by and large know what they are talking about when dealing with their wine merchants. Some wealthy gentlemen even still preserve the tradition of laying down a pipe of port to be enjoyed by their sons when they come of age.

At the same time gentlemen are singularly free from wine snobbery. They acquire any reasonable plonk for their day-to-day requirements and, if it so happens that they have a preference for, say red wine, they will drink it with anything, regardless of the vapourings of professional wine writers about white wine with fish and so on.

Cigar Smoking

Most gentlemen smoke cigars but it is a practice which has its pitfalls. Originally the band was put around the cigar by the manufacturer to protect the white gloves worn by gentlemen from nicotine stains. With the falling out of fashion of white gloves the band was often removed, particularly by those who liked to get their money's worth and smoke the thing to the very end. Now only the most traditionally minded and gentlemanly of gentlemen and ostentatious bookmakers do not remove the band. Thus, nowadays, not to do so is to be taken by the observer to being either very upper class or a bookmaker. Most fear that the wrong conclusion will be reached and remove the band.

Punctuality

One of the characteristics of a gentleman is that he is punctual to a fault. He sits down to his meals exactly at the appointed hour and expects to be served even if there has been a power cut or the cook has run off with the second footman. This rule also applies to guests staying the night. If they are not downstairs by the time breakfast is served they have to put up with cold coffee and congealed bacon and eggs.

The same punctuality rules his drinking habits. He pours his first drink at the same hour every day and drinks precisely his quota. If it is his custom to get drunk after dinner, he does so every night whether he is in his own house or somebody else's. This practice can cause consternation if he is so rash as to move outside his own circle. In fact, a gentleman seldom dines out with any but his closest friends, any more than he has a casual acquaintance to dinner in his own house. Acquaintances are asked to drinks only, when they are offered the alternative of dry sherry or gin and tonic without ice.

Dinner Parties

On the whole, gentlemen give dinner parties in order to fraternize with other gentlemen. It is considered polite to make conversation with ladies who are seated next to you at table but that is as far as communication between the sexes is allowed to go. After dinner the ladies 'must' retire to the drawing room for their coffee while the gentlemen settle down to the port and brandy. Contrary to general belief, they do not tell each other dubious stories when they are left together. This is not from any form of prudishness but because they have not heard any new stories since they left school, where they used to giggle over them in the latrines. Everyone knows that the only new stories originate in the Stock Exchange and are repeated by stockbrokers to their cronies in the golf club. Gentlemen are not stockbrockers and do not play golf often.

The final ritual for gentleman before they rejoin the ladies is for their host to lead them outside to urinate in the garden. The resultant patches of dead grass on the lawn are put down to wireworm and the blighted roses are blamed on the damned greenfly.

The Three Fat Women of Antibes

W. Somerset Maugham

One was called Mrs Richman and she was a widow. The second was called Mrs Sutcliffe; she was American and she had divorced two husbands. The third was called Miss Hickson and she was a spinster. They were all in the comfortable forties and they were all well off. Mrs Sutcliffe had the odd first name of Arrow. When she was young and slender she had liked it well enough. It suited her and the jests it occasioned though too often repeated were very flattering; she was not disinclined to believe that it suited her character too: it suggested directness, speed and purpose. She liked it less now that her delicate features had grown muzzy with fat, that her arms and shoulders were so substantial and her hips so massive. It was increasingly difficult to find dresses to make her look as she liked to look. The jests her name gave rise to now were made behind her back and she very well knew that they were far from obliging. But she was by no means resigned to middle age. She still wore blue to bring out the colour of her eyes and, with the help of art, her fair hair had kept its lustre. What she liked about Beatrice Richman and Frances Hickson was that they were both so much fatter than she, it made her look quite slim; they were both of them older and much inclined to treat her as a little young thing. It was not disagreeable. They were good-natured women and they chaffed her pleasantly about her beaux; they had both given up the thought of that kind of nonsense, indeed Miss Hickson had never given it a moment's consideration, but they were sympathetic to her flirtations. It was understood that one of these days Arrow would make a third man happy.

'Only you mustn't get any heavier, darling,' said Mrs Richman.

'And for goodness' sake make certain of his bridge,' said Miss Hickson.

They saw for her a man of about forty, but well-preserved and of distinguished carriage, an admiral on the retired list and a good golfer, or a widower without encumbrances, but in any case with a substantial income.

Arrow listened to them amiably, and kept to herself that fact that this was not at all her idea. It was true that she would have liked to marry again, but her fancy turned to a dark slim Italian with flashing eyes and a sonorous title or to a Spanish don of noble lineage; and not a day more than thirty. There were times when, looking at herself in her mirror, she was certain she did not look any more than that herself.

They were great friends, Miss Hickson, Mrs Richman and Arrow Sutcliffe. It was their fat that had brought them together and bridge that had cemented their alliance. They had met first at Carlsbad, where they were staying at the same hotel and were treated by the same doctor who used them with the same ruthlessness. Beatrice Richman was enormous. She was a handsome woman, with fine eyes, rouged cheeks and painted lips. She was very well content to be a widow with a handsome fortune. She adored her food. She liked bread and butter, cream, potatoes and suet puddings, and for eleven months of the year ate pretty well everything she had a mind to, and for one month went to Carlsbad to reduce. But every year she grew fatter. She upbraided the doctor, but got no sympathy from him. He pointed out to her various plain and simple facts.

'But if I'm never to eat a thing I like, life isn't worth living,' she expostulated.

He shrugged his disapproving shoulders. Afterwards she told Miss Hickson that she was beginning to suspect he wasn't so clever as she had thought. Miss Hickson gave a great guffaw. She was that sort of woman. She had a deep bass voice, a large flat sallow face from which twinkled little bright eyes; she walked with a slouch, her hands in her pockets, and when she could do so without exciting attention smoked a long cigar. She dressed as like a man as she could.

'What the deuce should I look like in frills and furbelows?' she said. 'When you're as fat as I am you may just as well be comfortable.'

She wore tweeds and heavy boots and whenever she could went about bareheaded. But she was as strong as an ox and boasted that few men could drive a longer ball than she. She was plain of speech, and she could swear more variously than a stevedore. Though her name was Frances she preferred to be called Frank. Masterful, but with tact, it was her jovial strength of character that held the three together. They drank their waters together, had their baths at the same hour, they took their strenuous walks together, pounded about the tennis court with a professional to make them run, and ate at the same table their sparse and regulated meals. Nothing impaired their good humour but the scales, and when one or other of them weighed as much on one day as she had the day before neither Frank's coarse jokes, the *bonhomie* of Beatrice nor Arrow's pretty kittenish ways sufficed to dispel the gloom. Then drastic measures were resorted to, the culprit went to bed for twenty-four hours and nothing passed her lips but the doctor's famous vegetable soup which tasted like hot water in which a cabbage had been well rinsed.

Never were three women greater friends. They would have been independent of anyone else if they had not needed a fourth at bridge. They were fierce, enthusiastic players and the moment the day's cure was over they sat down at the bridge table. Arrow, feminine as she was, played the best game of the three, a hard, brilliant game, in which she showed no mercy and never conceded a point or failed to take advantage of a mistake. Beatrice was solid and reliable. Frank was dashing; she was a great theorist and had all the authorities at the tip of her tongue. They had long arguments over the rival systems. They bombarded one another with Culbertson and Sims. It was obvious that not one of them ever played a card without fifteen good reasons, but it was also obvious from the subsequent conversation that there were fifteen equally good reasons why she should not have played it. Life would have been perfect, even with the prospect of twenty-four hours of that filthy soup when the doctor's rotten (Beatrice) bloody (Frank) lousy (Arrow) scales pretended one hadn't lost an ounce in two days, if only there had not been this constant difficulty of finding someone to play with them who was in their class.

It was for this reason that on the occasion with which this narrative deals Frank invited Lena Finch to come and stay with them at Antibes. They were spending some weeks there on Frank's suggestion. It seemed absurd to her, with her common sense, that immediately the cure was over Beatrice who always lost twenty pounds should by giving way to her ungovernable appetite put it all on again. Beatrice was weak. She needed a person of strong will to watch her diet. She proposed then that on leaving Carlsbad they should take a house at Antibes, where they could get plenty of exercise – everyone knew that nothing slimmed you like swimming – and as far as possible could go on with the cure. With a cook of their own they could at least avoid things that were obviously fattening. There was no reason why they should not all lose several pounds more. It seemed a very good idea. Beatrice knew what was good for her, and she could resist temptation well enough if temptation was not put right under her nose. Besides, she liked gambling, and a flutter at the Casino two or three times a week would pass the time very pleasantly. Arrow adored Antibes, and she would be looking her best after a month at Carlsbad. She could just pick and choose among the young Italians, the passionate Spaniards, the gallant Frenchmen, and the long-limbed English who sauntered about all day in bathing trunks and gay-coloured dressing-gowns. The plan worked very well. They had a grand time. Two days a week they ate nothing but hard-boiled eggs and raw tomatoes and they mounted the scales every morning with light hearts. Arrow got down to eleven stone and felt just like a girl; Beatrice and Frank by standing in a certain way just avoided the thirteen. The machine they had bought registered kilogrammes, and they got extraordinarily clever at translating these in the twinkling of an eye to pounds and ounces.

But the fourth at bridge continued to be the difficulty. This person played like a fool, the other was so slow that it drove you frantic, one was quarrelsome, another was a bad loser, a third was next door to a crook. It was strange how hard it was to find exactly the player you wanted.

One morning when they were sitting in pyjamas on the terrace overlooking the sea, drinking their tea (without milk or sugar) and eating a rusk prepared by Dr Hudebert and guaranteed not to be fattening, Frank looked up from her letters.

'Lena Finch is coming down to the Riviera,' she said.

'Who's she?' asked Arrow.

'She married a cousin of mine. He died a couple of months ago and she's just recovering from a nervous breakdown. What about asking her to come here for a fortnight?'

'Does she play bridge?' asked Beatrice.

'You bet your life she does,' boomed Frank in her deep voice. 'And a damned good game too. We should be absolutely independent of outsiders.'

'How old is she?' asked Arrow.

'Same age as I am.'

'That sounds all right.'

It was settled. Frank, with her usual decisiveness, stalked out as soon as she had finished her breakfast to send a wire, and three days later Lena Finch arrived. Frank met her at the station. She was in deep but not obtrusive mourning for the recent death of her husband. Frank had not seen her for two years. She kissed her warmly and took a good look at her.

'You're very thin, darling,' she said.

Lena smiled bravely.

'I've been through a good deal lately. I've lost a lot of weight.'

Frank sighed, but whether from sympathy with her cousin's sad loss, or from envy, was not obvious.

Lena was not, however, unduly depressed, and after a quick bath was quite ready to accompany Frank to Eden Roc. Frank introduced the stranger to her two friends and they sat down in what was known as the Monkey House. It was an enclosure covered with glass overlooking the sea, with a bar at the back, and it was crowded with chattering people in bathing costumes, pyjamas or dressing-gowns, who were seated at the tables having drinks. Beatrice's soft heart went out to the lorn widow, and Arrow, seeing that she was pale, quite ordinary to look at and probably forty-eight, was prepared to like her very much. A waiter approached them.

'What will you have, Lena dear?' Frank asked.

'Oh, I don't know, what you all have, a dry Martini or a White Lady.'

Arrow and Beatrice gave her a quick look. Everyone knows how fattening cocktails are.

'I daresay you're tired after your journey,' said Frank kindly.

She ordered a dry Martini for Lena and a mixed lemon and orange juice for herself and her two friends.

'We find alcohol isn't very good in all this heat,' she explained.

'Oh, it never affects me at all,' Lena answered airily. 'I like cocktails.'

Arrow went very slightly pale under her rouge (neither she nor Beatrice ever wet their faces when they bathed and they thought it absurd of Frank, a woman of her size, to pretend she liked diving) but she said nothing. The conversation was gay and easy, they all said the obvious things with gusto, and presently they strolled back to the villa for luncheon.

In each napkin were two little antifat rusks. Lena gave a bright smile as she put them by the side of her plate.

'May I have some bread?' she asked.

The grossest indecency would not have fallen on the ears of those three women with such a shock. Not one of them had eaten bread for ten years. Even Beatrice, greedy as she was, drew the line there. Frank, the good hostess, recovered herself first.

'Of course, darling,' she said and turning to the butler asked him to bring some.

'And some butter,' said Lena in that pleasant easy way of hers.

There was a moment's embarrassed silence.

'I don't know if there's any in the house,' said Frank, 'but I'll enquire.

There may be some in the kitchen.'

'I adore bread and butter, don't you?' said Lena, turning to Beatrice.

Beatrice gave a sickly smile and an evasive reply. The butler brought a long crisp roll of French bread. Lena slit it in two and plastered it with the butter which was miraculously produced. A grilled sole was served.

'We eat very simply here,' said Frank. 'I hope you won't mind.'

'Oh, no, I like my food very plain,' said Lena as she took some butter and spread it over her fish. 'As long as I can have bread and butter and potatoes and cream I'm quite happy.'

The three friends exchanged a glance. Frank's great sallow face sagged a little and she looked with distaste at the dry, insipid sole on her plate. Beatrice came to the rescue.

'It's such a bore, we can't get cream here,' she said. 'It's one of the things one has to do without on the Riviera.'

'What a pity,' said Lena.

The rest of the luncheon consisted of lamb cutlets, with the fat carefully removed so that Beatrice should not be led astray, and spinach boiled in water, with stewed pears to end up with. Lena tasted her pears and gave the butler a look of enquiry. That resourceful man understood her at once and though powdered sugar had never been served at that table before handed her without a moment's hesitation a bowl of it. She helped herself liberally. The other three pretended not to notice. Coffee was served and Lena took three lumps of sugar in hers.

'You have a very sweet tooth,' said Arrow in a tone which she struggled to keep friendly.

'We think saccharine so much more sweetening,' said Frank, as she put a tiny tablet of it into her coffee.

'Disgusting stuff,' said Lena.

Beatrice's mouth drooped at the corners, and she gave the lump sugar a yearning look.

'Beatrice,' boomed Frank sternly.

Beatrice stifled a sigh, and reached for the saccharine.

Frank was relieved when they could sit down to the bridge table. It was plain to her that Arrow and Beatrice were upset. She wanted them to like Lena and she was anxious that Lena should enjoy her fortnight with them. For the first rubber Arrow cut with the newcomer.

'Do you play Vanderbilt or Culbertson?' she asked her.

'I have no conventions,' Lena answered in a happy-go-lucky way, 'I play by the light of nature.'

'I play strict Culbertson,' said Arrow acidly.

The three fat women braced themselves to the fray. No conventions indeed! They'd learn her. When it came to bridge even Frank's family feeling was forgotten and she settled down with the same determination as the others to trim the stranger in their midst. But the light of nature served Lena very well. She had a natural gift for the game and great experience. She played with imagination, quickly, boldly, and with assurance. The other players were in too high a class not to realise very soon that Lena knew what she was about, and since they were all thoroughly good-natured, generous women, they were gradually mollified. This was real bridge. They all enjoyed themselves. Arrow and Beatrice began to feel more kindly towards Lena, and Frank, noticing this, heaved a fat sigh of relief. It was going to be a success.

After a couple of hours they parted, Frank and Beatrice to have a round of golf, and Arrow to take a brisk walk with a young Prince Roccamare whose acquaintance she had lately made. He was very sweet and young and good-looking. Lena said she would rest.

They met again just before dinner.

'I hope you've been all right, Lena dear,' said Frank. 'I was rather conscience-stricken at leaving you with nothing to do all this time.'

'Oh, don't apologise. I had a lovely sleep and then I went down to Juan and had a cocktail. And d'you know what I discovered? You'll be so pleased. I found a dear little tea-shop where they've got the most beautiful thick fresh cream. I've ordered half a pint to be sent every day. I thought it would be my little contribution to the household.'

Her eyes were shining. She was evidently expecting them to be delighted.

'How very kind of you,' said Frank, with a look that sought to quell the indignation that she saw on the faces of her two friends. 'But we never eat cream. In this climate it makes one so bilious.'

'I shall have to eat it all myself then,' said Lena cheerfully.

'Don't you ever think of your figure?' Arrow asked with icy deliberation.

'The doctor said I must eat.'

'Did he say you must eat bread and butter and potatoes and cream?'

'Yes. That's what I thought you meant when you said you had simple food.'

'You'll get simply enormous,' said Beatrice.

Lena laughed gaily.

'No, I shan't. You see, nothing ever makes me fat. I've always eaten everything I wanted to and it's never had the slightest effect on me.'

The stony silence that followed this speech was only broken by the entrance of the butler.

'*Mademoiselle est servie*,' he announced.

They talked the matter over late that night, after Lena had gone to bed, in Frank's room. During the evening they had been furiously cheerful, and they had chaffed one another with a friendliness that would have taken in the keenest observer. But now they dropped the mask. Beatrice was sullen, Arrow was spiteful and Frank was unmanned.

'It's not very nice for me to sit there and see her eat all the things I particularly like,' said Beatrice plaintively.

'It's not very nice for any of us,' Frank snapped back.

'You should never have asked her here,' said Arrow.

'How was I to know?' cried Frank.

'I can't help thinking that if she really cared for her husband she would hardly eat so much,' said Beatrice. 'He's only been buried two months. I mean, I think you ought to show some respect for the dead.'

'Why can't she eat the same as we do?' asked Arrow viciously. 'She's a guest.'

'Well, you heard what she said. The doctor told her she must eat.'

'Then she ought to go to a sanatorium.'

'It's more than flesh and blood can stand, Frank,' moaned Beatrice.

'If I can stand it you can stand it.'

'She's your cousin, she's not our cousin,' said Arrow. 'I'm not going to sit there for fourteen days and watch that woman make a hog of herself.'

'It's so vulgar to attach all this importance to food,' Frank boomed, and her voice was deeper than ever. 'After all the only thing that counts really is spirit.'

'Are you calling *me* vulgar, Frank?' asked Arrow with flashing eyes.

'No, of course she isn't,' interrupted Beatrice.

'I wouldn't put it past you to go down in the kitchen when we're all in bed and have a good square meal on the sly.'

Frank sprang to her feet.

'How dare you say that, Arrow! I'd never ask anybody to do what I'm not prepared to do myself. Have you known me all these years and do you think me capable of such a mean thing.'

'How is it you never take off any weight then?'

Frank gave a gasp and burst into a flood of tears.

'What a cruel thing to say! I've lost pounds and pounds.'

She wept like a child. Her vast body shook and great tears splashed on her mountainous bosom.

'Darling, I didn't mean it,' cried Arrow.

She threw herself on her knees and enveloped what she could of Frank in her plump arms. She wept and the mascara ran down her cheeks.

'D'you mean to say I don't look thinner?' Frank sobbed. 'After all I've gone through.'

'Yes, dear, of course you do,' cried Arrow through her tears. 'Everybody's noticed it.'

Beatrice, though naturally of a placid disposition, began to cry gently. It was very pathetic. Indeed, it would have been a hard heart that failed to be moved by the sight of Frank, that lion-hearted woman, crying her eyes out. Presently, however, they dried their tears and had a little brandy and water, which every doctor had told them was the least fattening thing they could drink, and then they felt much better. They decided that Lena should have the nourishing food that had been ordered her and they made a solemn resolution not to let it disturb their equanimity. She was certainly a first-rate bridge player and after all it was only for a fortnight. They would do whatever they could to make her stay enjoyable. They kissed one another warmly and separated for the night feeling strangely uplifted. Nothing should interfere with the wonderful friendship that had brought so much happiness into their three lives.

But human nature is weak. You must not ask too much of it. They ate grilled fish while Lena ate macaroni sizzling with cheese and butter; they ate grilled cutlets and boiled spinach while Lena ate *pâté de foie gras;* twice a week they ate hard-boiled eggs and raw tomatoes, while Lena ate peas swimming in cream and potatoes cooked in all sorts of delicious ways. The chef was a good chef and he leapt at the opportunity afforded him to send up one dish more rich, tasty and succulent than the other.

'Poor Jim,' sighed Lena, thinking of her husband, 'he loved French cooking.'

The butler disclosed the fact that he could make half a dozen kinds of cocktail and Lena informed them that the doctor had recommended her to drink burgundy at luncheon and champagne at dinner. The three fat women persevered. They were gay, chatty and even hilarious (such is the natural gift that women have for deception) but Beatrice grew limp and forlorn, and Arrow's tender blue eyes acquired a steely glint. Frank's deep voice grew more raucous. It was when they played bridge that the strain showed itself. They had always been fond of talking over their hands, but their discussions had been friendly. Now a distinct bitterness crept in and sometimes one pointed out a mistake to another with quite unnecessary frankness. Discussion turned to argument and argument to altercation. Sometimes the session ended in angry silence. Once Frank accused Arrow of deliberately letting her down. Two or three times Beatrice, the softest of the three, was reduced to tears. On another occasion Arrow flung down her cards and swept out of the room in a pet. Their tempers were getting frayed. Lena was the peacemaker.

'I think it's such a pity to quarrel over bridge,' she said. 'After all, it's only a game.'

It was all very well for her. She had had a square meal and half a bottle of champagne. Besides, she had phenomenal luck. She was winning all their money. The score was put down in a book after each session, and hers mounted up day after day with unfailing regularity. Was there no justice in the world? They began to hate one another. And though they hated her too they could not resist confiding in her. Each of them went to her separately and told her how detestable the others were. Arrow said she was sure it was bad for her to see so much of women so much older than herself. She had a good mind to sacrifice her share of the lease and go to Venice for the rest of the summer. Frank told Lena that with her masculine mind it was too much to expect that she could be satisfied with anyone so frivolous as Arrow and so frankly stupid as Beatrice.

'I must have intellectual conversation,' she boomed. 'When you have a brain like mine you've got to consort with your intellectual equals.'

Beatrice only wanted peace and quiet.

'Really I hate women,' she said. 'They're so unreliable; they're so malicious.'

By the time Lena's fortnight drew to its close the three fat women were barely on speaking terms. They kept up appearances before Lena, but when she was not there made no pretences. They had got past quarrelling. They ignored one another, and when this was not possible treated each other with icy politeness.

Lena was going to stay with friends on the Italian Riviera and Frank saw her off by the same train as that by which she had arrived. She was taking away with her a lot of their money.

'I don't know how to thank you,' she said, as she got into the carriage. 'I've had a wonderful visit.'

If there was one thing that Frank Hickson prided herself on more than on being a match for any man it was that she was a gentlewoman, and her reply was perfect in its combination of majesty and graciousness.

'We've all enjoyed having you here, Lena,' she said. 'It's been a real treat.'

But when she turned away from the departing train she heaved such a vast sigh of relief that the platform shook beneath her. She flung back her massive shoulders and strode home to the villa.

'Ouf!' she roared at intervals. 'Ouf!'

She changed into her one-piece bathing-suit, put on her espadrilles and a man's dressing-gown (no nonsense about it) and went to Eden Roc. There was still time for a bathe before luncheon. She passed through the Monkey House, looking about her to say good morning to anyone she knew, for she felt on a sudden at peace with mankind, and then stopped dead still. She could not believe her eyes. Beatrice was sitting at one of the tables, by herself; she wore the pyjamas she had bought at Molyneux's a day or two before, she had a string of pearls round her neck, and Frank's quick eyes saw that she had just had her hair waved; her cheeks, her eyes, her lips were made up. Fat, nay vast, as she was, none could deny that she was an extremely handsome woman. But what was she doing? With the slouching gait of the Neanderthal man which was Frank's characteristic walk she went up to Beatrice. In her black bathing-dress Frank looked like a huge cetacean which the Japanese catch in the Torres Straits and which the vulgar call a sea-cow.

'Beatrice, what are you doing?' she cried in her deep voice.

It was like the roll of thunder in the distant mountains. Beatrice looked at her coolly.

'Eating,' she answered.

'Damn it, I can see you're eating.'

In front of Beatrice was a plate of *croissants* and a plate of butter, a pot of strawberry jam, coffee and a jug of cream. Beatrice was spreading butter thick on the delicious hot bread, covering this with jam, and then pouring the thick cream over all.

'You'll kill yourself,' said Frank.

'I don't care,' mumbled Beatrice with her mouth full.

'You'll put on pounds and pounds.'

'Go to hell!'

She actually laughed in Frank's face. My God, how good those *croissants* smelt!

'I'm disappointed in you, Beatrice. I thought you had more character.'

'It's your fault. That blasted woman. You would have her down. For a fortnight I've watched her gorge like a hog. It's more than flesh and blood can stand. I'm going to have one square meal if I bust.'

The tears welled up to Frank's eyes. Suddenly she felt very weak and womanly. She would have liked a strong man to take her on his knee and pet her and cuddle her and call her little baby names. Speechless she sank down on a chair by Beatrice's side. A waiter came up. With a pathetic gesture she waved towards the coffee and *croissants*.

'I'll have the same,' she sighed.

She listlessly reached out her hand to take a roll, but Beatrice snatched away the plate.

'No, you don't,' she said. 'You wait till you get your own.'

Frank called her a name which ladies seldom apply to one another in affection. In a moment the waiter brought her *croissants* butter, jam and coffee.

'Where's the cream, you fool?' she roared like a lioness at bay.

She began to eat. She ate gluttonously. The place was beginning to fill up with bathers coming to enjoy a cocktail or two after having done their duty by the sun and the sea. Presently Arrow strolled along with Prince Roccamare. She had on a beautiful silk wrap which she held tightly round her with one hand in order to look as slim as possible and she bore her head high so that he should not see her double chin. She was laughing gaily. She felt like a girl. He had just told her (in Italian) that her eyes made the blue of the Mediterranean look like pea-soup. He left her to go into the men's room to brush his sleek black hair and they arranged to meet in five minutes for a drink. Arrow walked on to the women's room to put a little more rouge on her cheeks and a little more red on her lips. On her way she caught sight of Frank and Beatrice. She stopped. She could hardly believe her eyes.

'My God!' she cried. 'You beasts. You hogs.' She seized a chair. 'Waiter.'

Her appointment went clean out of her head. In the twinkling of an eye the waiter was at her side.

'Bring me what these ladies are having,' she ordered.

Frank lifted her great heavy head from her plate.

'Bring me some *pâté de foie gras*,' she boomed.

'Frank!' cried Beatrice.

'Shut up.'

'All right. I'll have some too.'

The coffee was brought and the hot rolls and cream and the *pâté de foie gras* and they set to. They spread the cream on the *pâté* and they ate it. They devoured great spoonfuls of jam. They crunched the delicious crisp bread voluptuously. What was love to Arrow then? Let the Prince keep his palace in Rome and his castle in the Apennines. They did not speak. What they were about was much too serious. They ate with solemn, ecstatic fervour.

'I haven't eaten potatoes for twenty-five years,' said Frank in a far-off brooding tone.

'Waiter,' cried Beatrice, 'bring fried potatoes for three.'

'*Très bien, Madame.*'

The potatoes were brought. Not all the perfumes of Arabia smelt so sweet. They ate them with their fingers.

'Bring me a dry Martini!' said Arrow.

'You can't have a dry Martini in the middle of a meal, Arrow,' said Frank.

'Can't I? You wait and see.'

'All right then. Bring me a double dry Martini,' said Frank.

'Bring three double dry Martinis,' said Beatrice.

They were brought and drunk at a gulp. The women looked at one another and sighed. The misunderstandings of the last fortnight dissolved and the sincere affection each had for the other welled up again in their hearts. They could hardly believe that they had ever contemplated the possibility of severing a friendship that had brought them so much solid satisfaction. They finished the potatoes.

'I wonder if they've got any chocolate éclairs,' said Beatrice.

'Of course they have.'

And of course they had. Frank thrust one whole into her huge mouth, swallowed it and seized another, but before she ate it she looked at the other two and plunged a vindictive dagger into the heart of the monstrous Lena.

'You can say what you like, but the truth is she played a damned rotten game of bridge, really.'

'Lousy,' agreed Arrow.

But Beatrice suddenly thought she would like a meringue.

A Dissertation upon Roast Pig

Charles Lamb

Mankind, says a Chinese manuscript, which my friend M[1] was obliging enough to read and explain to me, for the first seventy thousand ages
ate their meat raw, clawing or biting it from the living animal, just as
they do in Abyssinia to this day. This period is not obscurely hinted at by
their great Confucius in the second chapter of his Mundane Mutations,
where he designates a kind of golden age by the term Cho-fang, literally the
Cook's holiday. The manuscript goes on to say, that the art of roasting, or
rather broiling (which I take to be the elder brother) was accidentally
discovered in the manner following. The swineherd, Ho-ti, having gone out
into the woods one morning, as his manner was, to collect mast for his hogs,
left his cottage in the care of his eldest son Bo-bo, a great lubberly boy,
who being fond of playing with fire, as younkers of his age commonly are, let
some sparks escape into a bundle of straw, which kindling quickly, spread
the conflagration over every part of their poor mansion, till it was reduced
to ashes. Together with the cottage (a sorry antediluvian make-shift of a
building, you may think it), what was of much more importance, a fine litter
of new-farrowed pigs, no less than nine in number, perished. China pigs have
been esteemed a luxury all over the East from the remotest periods that we
read of. Bo-bo was in utmost consternation, as you may think, not so much
for the sake of the tenement, which his father and he could easily build
up again with a few dry branches, and the labour of an hour or two, at any
time, as for the loss of the pigs. While he was thinking what he should say
to his father, and wringing his hands over the smoking remnants of one of
those untimely sufferers, an odour assailed his nostrils, unlike any scent
which he had before experienced. What could it proceed from? – not from the
burnt cottage – he had smelt that smell before – indeed this was by no means
the first accident of the kind which had occurred through the negligence of

[1 Thomas Manning.]

this unlucky young fire-brand. Much less did it resemble that of any known herb, weed, or flower. A premonitory moistening at the same time overflowed his nether lip. He knew not what to think. He next stooped down to feel the pig, if there were any signs of life in it. He burnt his fingers, and to cool them he applied them in his booby fashion to his mouth. Some of the crums of the scorched skin had come away with his fingers, and for the first time in his life (in the world's life indeed, for before him no man had known it) he tasted – *crackling!* Again he felt and fumbled at the pig. It did not burn him so much now, still he licked his fingers from a sort of habit. The truth at length broke into his slow understanding, that it was the pig that smelt so, and the pig that tasted so delicious; and, surrendering himself up to the newborn pleasure, he fell to tearing up whole handfuls of the scorched skin with the flesh next it, and was cramming it down his throat in his beastly fashion, when his sire entered amid the smoking rafters, armed with retributory cudgel, and finding how affairs stood, began to rain blows upon the young rogue's shoulders, as thick as hailstones, which Bo-bo heeded not any more than if they had been flies. The tickling pleasure which he experienced in his lower regions, had rendered him quite callous to any inconveniences he might feel in those remote quarters. His father might lay on, but he could not beat him from his pig, till he had fairly made an end of it, when, becoming a little more sensible of his situation, something like the following dialogue ensued.

'You graceless whelp, what have you got there devouring? Is it not enough that you have burnt me down three houses with your dog's tricks, and be hanged to you, but you must be eating fire, and I know not what – what have you got there, I say?'

'O, father, the pig, the pig, do come and taste how nice the burnt pig eats.'

The ears of Ho-ti tingled with horror. He cursed his son, and he cursed himself that ever he should beget a son that should eat burnt pig.

Bo-bo, whose scent was wonderfully sharpened since morning, soon raked out another pig, and fairly rending it asunder, thrust the lesser half by main force into the fists of Ho-ti, still shouting out 'Eat, eat, eat the burnt pig, father, only taste – O Lord,' – with such-like barbarous ejaculations, cramming all the while as if he would choke.

Ho-ti trembled every joint while he grasped the abominable thing, wavering whether he should not put his son to death for an unnatural young monster, when the crackling scorched his fingers, as it had done his son's, and applying the same remedy to them, he in his turn tasted some of its flavour, which, make what sour mouths he would for a pretence, proved not altogether displeasing to him. In conclusion (for the manuscript here is a little tedious), both father and son fairly sat down to the mess, and never left off till they had despatched all that remained of the litter.

Bo-bo was strictly enjoined not to let the secret escape, for the neighbours would certainly have stoned them for a couple of abominable wretches, who could think of improving upon the good meat which God had sent them. Nevertheless, strange stories got about. It was observed that Ho-ti's cottage was burnt down now more frequently than ever. Nothing but fires from this time forward. Some would break out in broad day, others in the night-time. As often as the sow farrowed, so sure was the house of Ho-ti to be in a blaze; and Ho-ti himself, which was the more remarkable, instead of chastising his son, seemed to grow more indulgent to him than ever. At length they were watched, the terrible mystery discovered, and father and son summoned to take their trial at Pekin, then an inconsiderable assize town. Evidence was given, the obnoxious food itself produced in court, and verdict about to be pronounced, when the foreman of the jury begged that some of the burnt pig, of which the culprits stood accused, might be handed into the box. He handled it, and they all handled it, and burning their fingers, as Bo-bo and his father had done before them, and nature prompting to each of them the same remedy, against the face of all the facts, and the clearest charge which judge had ever given, – to the surprise of the whole court, townsfolk, strangers, reporters, and all present – without leaving the box, or any manner of consultation whatever, they brought in a simultaneous verdict of Not Guilty.

The judge, who was a shrewd fellow, winked at the manifest iniquity of the decision: and, when the court was dismissed, went privily, and bought up all the pigs that could be had for love or money. In a few days his Lordship's town house was observed to be on fire. The thing took wing, and now there was nothing to be seen but fires in every direction. Fuel and pigs grew enormously dear all over the district. The insurance offices one and all shut up shop. People built slighter and slighter every day, until it was feared that the very science of architecture would in no long time be lost to the world. Thus this custom of firing houses continued, till in process of time, says my manuscript, a sage arose, like our Locke, who made a discovery, that the flesh of swine, or indeed of any other animal, might be cooked (*burnt*, as they called it) without the necessity of consuming a whole house to dress it. Then first began the rude form of a gridiron. Roasting by the string, or spit, came in a century or two later, I forget in whose dynasty. By such slow degrees, concludes the manuscript, do the most useful, and seemingly the most obvious arts, make their way among mankind. –

Without placing too implicit faith in the account above given, it must be agreed, that if a worthy pretext for so dangerous an experiment as setting houses on fire (especially in these days) could be assigned in favour of any culinary object, that pretext and excuse might be found in ROAST PIG.

Of all the delicacies in the whole *mundus edibilis*, I will maintain it to be the most delicate – *princeps obsoniorum.*

I speak not of your grown porkers – things between pig and pork – those hobbydehoys – but a young and tender suckling – under a moon old – guiltless as yet of the sty – with no original speck of the *amor immunditiæ*, the hereditary failing of the first parent, yet manifest – his voice as yet not broken, but something between a childish treble, and a grumble – the mild forerunner, or *præludium*, of a grunt.

He must be roasted. I am not ignorant that our ancestors ate them seethed, or boiled – but what a sacrifice of the exterior tegument!

There is no flavour comparable, I will contend, to that of the crisp, tawny, well-watched, not over-roasted, *crackling*, as it is well called – the very teeth are invited to their share of the pleasure at this banquet in overcoming the coy, brittle resistance – with the adhesive oleaginous – O call it not fat – but an indefinable sweetness growing up to it – the tender blossoming of fat – fat cropped in the bud – taken in the shoot – in the first innocence – the cream and quintessence of the child-pig's yet pure food – the lean, no lean, but a kind of animal manna – or rather, fat and lean, (if it must be so) so blended and running into each other, that both together make but one ambrosian result, or common substance.

Behold him, while he is doing – it seemeth rather a refreshing warmth, than a scorching heat, that he is so passive to. How equably he twirleth round the string! – Now he is just done. To see the extreme sensibility of that tender age, he hath wept out his pretty eyes – radiant jellies – shooting stars –

See him in the dish, his second cradle, how meek he lieth! – wouldst thou have had this innocent grow up to the grossness and indocility which too often accompany maturer swinehood? Ten to one he would have proved a glutton, a sloven, an obstinate, disagreeable animal – wallowing in all manner of filthy conversation – from these sins he is happily snatched away –

> Ere sin could blight, or sorrow fade,
> Death came with timely care –

his memory is odoriferous – no clown curseth, while his stomach half rejecteth, the rank bacon – no coalheaver bolteth him in reeking sausages – he hath a fair sepulchre in the grateful stomach of the judicious epicure – and for such a tomb might be content to die.

He is the best of sapors. Pine-apple is great. She is indeed almost too transcendent – a delight, if not sinful, yet so like to sinning, that really a tender-conscienced person would do well to pause – too ravishing for mortal taste, she woundeth and excoriateth the lips that approach her – like lovers' kisses, she biteth – she is a pleasure bordering on pain from the fierceness and insanity of her relish – but she stoppeth at the palate – she meddleth not with the appetite – and the coarsest hunger might barter her consistently for a mutton chop.

Pig – let me speak his praise – is no less provocative of the appetite, than he is satisfactory to the criticalness of the censorious palate. The strong man may batten on him, and the weakling refuseth not his mild juices.

Unlike to mankind's mixed characters, a bundle of virtues and vices, inexplicably intertwisted, and not to be unravelled without hazard, he is – good throughout. No part of him is better or worse than another. He helpeth, as far as his little means extend, all around. He is the least envious of banquets. He is all neighbours' fare.

I am one of those, who freely and ungrudgingly impart a share of the good things of this life which fall to their lot (few as mine are in this kind) to a friend. I protest I take as great an interest in my friend's pleasures, his relishes, and proper satisfactions, as in mine own. 'Presents,' I often say, 'endear Absents.' Hares, pheasants, partridges, snipes, barn-door chickens (those 'tame villatic fowl'), capons, plovers, brawn, barrels of oysters, I dispense as freely as I receive them. I love to taste them, as it were, upon the tongue of my friend. But a stop must be put somewhere. One would not, like Lear, 'give everything.' I make my stand upon pig. Methinks it is an ingratitude to the Giver of all good flavours, to extra-domiciliate, or send out of the house, slightingly (under pretext of friendship, or I know not what), a blessing so particularly adapted, predestined, I may say, to my individual palate – It argues an insensibility.

I remember a touch of conscience in this kind at school. My good old aunt, who never parted from me at the end of a holiday without stuffing a sweetmeat, or some nice thing, into my pocket, had dismissed me one evening with a smoking plum-cake, fresh from the oven. In my way to school (it was over London Bridge) a grey-headed old beggar saluted me (I have no doubt at this time of day that he was a counterfeit). I had no pence to console him with, and in the vanity of self-denial, and the very coxcombry of charity, school-boy-like, I made him a present of – the whole cake! I walked on a little, buoyed up, as one is on such occasions, with a sweet soothing of self-satisfaction; but before I had got to the end of the bridge, my better feelings returned, and I burst into tears, thinking how ungrateful I had been to my good aunt, to go and give her good gift away to a stranger, that I had never seen before, and who might be a bad man for aught I knew; and then I thought of the pleasure my aunt would be taking in thinking that I – I myself, and not another – would eat her nice cake – and what should I say to her the next time I saw her – how naughty I was to part with her pretty present – and the odour of that spicy cake came back upon my recollection, and the pleasure and the curiosity I had taken in seeing her make it, and her joy when she sent it to the oven, and how disappointed she would feel that I had never had a bit of it in my mouth at last – and I blamed my impertinent spirit of alms-giving, and out-of-place hypocrisy of goodness, and above all I wished never to see the face again of that insidious, good-for-nothing, old grey impostor.

Our ancestors were nice in their method of sacrificing these tender victims. We read of pigs whipt to death with something of a shock, as we hear of any other obsolete custom. The age of discipline is gone by, or it would be curious to inquire (in a philosophical light merely) what effect this process might have towards intenerating and dulcifying a substance, naturally so mild and dulcet as the flesh of young pigs. It looks like refining a violet. Yet we should be cautious, while we condemn the inhumanity, how we censure the wisdom of the practice. It might impart a gusto –

I remember an hypothesis, argued upon by the young students, when I was at St Omer's, and maintained with much learning and pleasantry on both sides, 'Whether, supposing that the flavour of a pig who obtained his death by whipping (*per flagellationem extremam*) superadded a pleasure upon the palate of a man more intense than any possible suffering we can conceive in the animal, is man justified in using that method of putting the animal to death?' I forget the decision.

His sauce should be considered. Decidedly, a few bread crumbs, done up with his liver and brains, and a dash of mild sage. But, banish, dear Mrs Cook, I beseech you, the whole onion tribe. Barbecue your whole hogs to your palate, steep them in shalots, stuff them out with plantations of the rank and guilty garlic; you cannot poison them, or make them stronger than they are – but consider, he is a weakling – a flower.

A Terrible Worrier

Joyce Grenfell

Scene: the small and cosy kitchen-living-room of number 2
Alma Cottages, Bull Lane, in a rural village in Bucking-
hamshire. Mrs Moss lives there. Her crony, Mrs Ingstone,
from number 1 next door, is a mite hard of hearing.

There he is, Mrs Ingstone. That's his car. I'd know it anywhere. It is good of
him to come round so soon. Look, dear, you let him in – I know it's my
cottage but you're nearer the door, and I feel funny.

Oh, there you are, Mr Molder. Come in. You know Mrs Ingstone? I was
just telling her it's very good of you to come round so soon. Now, where will
you sit? Will you be all right on the settee? I think it's nice for a big man.
Don't sit on Kipper!

You silly old pussy-cat. Gut up off that nice settee and go and sit up on
your window-sill – there's a good boy. He likes to sit on the window-sill and
purr through the geraniums.

It's ever so good of you to come round so soon. I've been so worried. *I
haven't been able to sleep, Have I?* I told her. *I told you, didn't I?* I haven't been
able to sleep.

Mr Molder, I've done a wrong thing.

Well, we don't know how wrong, DO WE? It could be criminal, but you
don't know, do you?

I know you've got to get back to your lawyer's office, so I'll tell you right
away.

The other evening I was sitting in here when two young people come
round selling tickets for a raffle, and I took two. No sooner did I have them in
my hand than I realised I'd done a wrong thing.

No, that's not *the* wrong thing I've done. Oh, I've done two. Well a raffle is
gambling, isn't it? I don't like the idea of gambling – I don't mind having a

go at hoopla at a garden fête or that – but a raffle is proper gambling. But oh! The prizes were *lovely!*

First prize is a cruise for two to Madeeria – there and back. And the second prize was a cocktail cabinet with all beautiful crystal goblets. And there was littler prizes – a brace of pheasants and a rabbit, and boxes of this and that and all for ten new p.

I told Mrs Ingstone when she come back to her cottage next door that I'd got the tickets, and she said, 'Mind you win that cruise for two and I'll go with you.' We had a good laugh!

But then I started to worry.

Because I might *win*.

Well, they could make you go, couldn't they? No, I wouldn't like it, because a cruise is on the sea, isn't it? I don't like the idea of being *on* the sea. I don't mind looking at it from the side, but I wouldn't want to be on it. Well, I mean, there could be a bad storm and would there be enough lifejackets to go round? And would they expect me to undress at night? And what are you supposed to do with your dentures?

Oh, I did worry.

And then I worried about this cottage. It's a council cottage, you know, and they might think, well, if she can afford to go off on a cruise . . . you see *they* wouldn't know I hadn't paid for it. They might put up the rent, or the rates. I mean they could turn you out, couldn't they? You don't know where you are with them. I shan't vote for them next time, whoever they are.

Well, the day come for the bazaar where they was going to draw the raffle, and I'd asked Mrs Ingstone to go with me, *didn't I, but you couldn't come, could you?*

She was going to a lecture at the Women's Institute with her niece on hormones. *But you didn't like it. Did you?* Well, they're not very nice, hormones. But did you know we was all supposed to have them? It was news to me. I don't think I've got any.

Well, I thought to meself, I'll just pop down on the bus to the Town Hall where the bazaar was and I'll just pop in and see them draw the raffle and then pop off home again on the bus. But when I get to the door of the Town Hall there was that Mrs Amblecrumbie or whatever she's called – you know, that lively little woman with the short legs, goes to St Luke's. She spots me and she says, 'Oh it's one of my Old Age Pensioners from the club. Let her in half price.' You don't mind the half price, but you don't like the attention being drawn. Still, I got a nice place up by the platform so I could see it all going on. A woman come on to do the draw, and she makes a great palaver of it, muddling up all the little ticketty bits in a container and then she puts her hand in and makes her selection.

'First prize – a cruise for two to Madeeria.'

She took all day undoing it, and I thought to meself – get on with it.

Then she opens the ticket and says 'First Price, Lady Clutton-Taylor.'

Lady Clutton-Taylor! Well – she can afford to go on a cruise any day of the week. Nobody much clapped.

I didn't know whether to laugh or cry. I was disappointed and relieved at one and the same time. I was just bending down to pick meself up to go home when I heard my name called.

'Mrs Moss, 2 Alma Cottages, Bull Lane, a lovely rabbit.'

I looked up and there was this woman standing on the platform with a rabbit in her hand – dead – but still in its fur. Oh, I thought to meself, I'm not going to be bothered with *that*, so I won't say anything. I'll just sit here, numb. But that Mrs Amblecrumbie...

'Bravo, Mrs Moss, you've won a lovely rabbit.'

Mr Molder, I had to get up out of my seat in the body of the hall and go all the way up to the platform to receive this said rabbit, and as she put it into a carrier bag for me to take off home I could see it had still got its eyes open.

No, I did *not* want it. Because you have to *do* a rabbit. No, I've never done a rabbit. Perhaps it is funny for a country woman never to of done a rabbit. Mark you, I've seen many a rabbit done. My mother must of done twelve a year if she did a dozen, and you'd be surprised what goes on under all that fur.

Well, I'm on the bus now, and I'm worrying all the time. How am I going to get rid of this blessed rabbit? I couldn't leave it on the bus because some nosey parker would come running after me, 'Oh, you've left your rabbit on the bus.' And I couldn't drop it into the gutter because it was raining. And I couldn't put it in my bin because they'd cleared it that morning, and you know what they are – once a week – if that – because they please themselves nowadays.

Oh, I did worry.

Well, I'm off the bus now, walking up Queen's Hill, and I pause to get my breath. I notice I'm standing alongside a little red car. It was parked, like, up against the kerb and its window was open about eight inches. And before I knew what I was doing I'd posted that rabbit.

As I done so a young man is coming down the hill and he says 'Good

evening' to me so I know he's seen me do it. I say 'Good evening' back at him
and I wait till he's out of sight and then I try the door. Locked!

I couldn't get my rabbit back.

I went up home and I didn't sleep one wink all night, DID I? I told her. *I told
you, didn't I?* Not one wink, and at first light I'm down there and the car is
gone. And that's the wrong thing I done, posting that rabbit. Mr Molder,
what I need to know is this: Was it an abuse of personal, private property
and could any person inform against?

You don't think so?

But are you sure?

'Well, that's all right then. *You won't have to come and visit me in Dartmoor, will
you?*

Kipper. Don't you dare scratch that nice white paint.

No, don't move, Mr Molder. I'm going to put the kettle on and we'll have
a cup of tea. He has to go out a lot now. Don't you? He's an old boy. But he
knows what he's going out for, and he's going to be quick about it because it's
cold out there. That's a clever boy. You hurry up and then we'll have a nice
cup of tea.

How Will Noggin was Fooled, and Berry Rode Forth against his Will

Dornford Yates

'Who's going to church?' said Daphne, consulting her wrist-watch.

There was a profound silence.

My sister turned to Jill.

'Are you coming?' she said. 'Berry and I are.'

'I beg your pardon,' said her husband.

'Of course you're coming,' said Daphne.

'Not in these trousers. This is the first time I've worn them, and I'm not going to kneel in them for any one.'

'Then you'll change,' said his wife. 'You've plenty of time.' Berry groaned.

'This is sheer Bolshevism,' he said. 'Is not my soul my own?'

'We shall start,' said Daphne, 'in twenty minutes.'

It was nearly half-past ten in the morning of a beautiful summer day, and we were all taking our ease in the sunshine upon the terrace. It was the first Sunday which we had spent all together at White Ladies for nearly five years.

So far as the eye could see, nothing had changed.

At the foot of the steps the great smooth lawn stretched like a fine green carpet, its shadowed patches yet bright with dew. There were the tall elms and the copper beech and all the proud company of spreading giants – what were five years to them? There was the clump of rhododendrons, a ragged blotch of crimson, seemingly spilled upon the green turf, and there the close box hedge that walled away the rose-garden. Beyond the sun fence a gap showed an acre or so of Bull's Mead – a great deep meadow, and in it two horses beneath a chestnut tree, their long tails a-swish, sleepily nosing each other to rout the flies; while in the distance the haze of heat hung like a film over the rolling hills. Close at hand echoed the soft impertinence of a cuckoo, and two fat-pigeons waddled about the lawn, picking and stealing as they went. The sky was cloudless and there was not a breath of wind.

The stable clock chimed the half-hour.

My sister returned to the attack.

'Are you coming, Boy?'

'Yes,' said I. 'I am.'

Berry sat up and stared at me.

'Don't be silly,' he said. 'There's a service this morning. Besides, they've changed the lock of the poor-box.'

'I want to watch the Vicar's face when he sees you,' said I.

'It will be a bit of a shock,' said Jonah, looking up from the paper. 'Is his heart all right?'

'Rotten,' said Daphne. 'But that doesn't matter. I sent him a note to warn him yesterday.'

'What did you say?' demanded her husband.

'I said, *"We're back at last, and – don't faint – we're all coming to Church tomorrow, and you've got to come back to lunch."* And now, for goodness' sake, go and change.'

'But we shall perspire,' said Berry. 'Profusely. To walk half a mile in this sun is simply asking for it. Besides –'

'What's the car done?' said Jonah. 'I'm going, and I can't hurry with this.' He tapped his short leg affectionately. 'We needn't take Fitch. Boy or I can drive.'

'Right oh,' said my sister, rising. 'Is ten-minutes-to early enough?'

Jonah nodded.

'This,' said Berry, 'is a conspiracy for which you will pay. Literally. I shall take the plate round, and from you four I shall accept nothing but paper. Possibly I shall –'

Here the girls fell upon him and bore him protesting into the house and out of earshot.

'Who's going to look after the car while we're in church?' said I.

'There's sure to be somebody ready to earn a couple of bob,' said Jonah. 'Besides, we can always the disconnect the north-east trunnion, or jack her up and put the wheels in the vestry or something.'

'All right. Only we don't want her pinched.' With a yawn I rose to my feet. 'And now I suppose I'd better go and turn her out.'

'Right oh,' said Jonah, picking up his paper again.

I strolled into the house.

We were proud of the car. She was a 1914 Rolls, and we had bought her at a long price less than a week ago. Fresh from the coach-builder's, her touring body was painted silver-grey, while her bonnet was of polished aluminium. Fitted with every conceivable accessory, she was very good-looking, charming alike to ride or drive, and she went like the wind. In a word, she did as handsome as she was.

It was eight minutes to eleven as we slid past the lodge and on to the Bilberry road.

Before we had covered two furlongs, we swung round a corner to see a smart two-seater at rest by the dusty hedgerow, and a slight dark girl in fresh blue and white standing one foot on the step, wiping her dainty fingers on a handful of cotton-waste.

'Agatha!' cried Daphne and Jill. 'Stop, Boy, stop!'

Obediently I slowed to a standstill, as my lady came running after us.

'You might have told me,' she panted. 'I never knew you were back. And I am so glad.'

'We only arrived on Friday, dear,' said Daphne, and introduced Berry and me. Jonah, it appeared, had met Miss Deriot at tennis in 1914.

'But you had your hair down then,' he said gravely.

'It's a wonder I haven't got it down now,' said Miss Deriot. 'Why didn't you come along ten minutes earlier? Then you could have changed my tyre.'

'And why are you driving away from church?' said Jill.

'One of the colts has sprained his shoulder, and we're out of embrocation; so I'm going to get some from Brooch.'

'I'll come with you,' said Berry eagerly, preparing to leave the car. 'I don't like to think of you—'

'Nonsense,' said Daphne, detaining him.

'But supposing she has another puncture?'

'Yes, I can see you mending it on a day like this.'

'It's very kind of you,' said Miss Deriot, with a puzzled smile.

'Don't thank the fool,' said my sister. 'If I thought he'd be the slightest use to you, I'd send him; but he only wants an excuse to get out of going to church.'

'Poor jade,' said her husband. 'I am a knight, a simple starlit knight, a Quixote of today. Your brutish instincts—'

'Carry on, Boy,' said Daphne. I let in the clutch. 'And come over this afternoon, Agatha, and we'll tell you all about everything.'

'Yes, do,' cried Jill.

'All right,' said Miss Deriot. 'So long.'

Three minutes later I was berthing the car close to the lichgate in the shade of sweet-smelling limes, that made a trembling screen of foliage within the churchyard wall.

As luck would have it, Will Noggin, once a groom in our service and now a trooper of the Dragoon Guards, was leaning lazily against the grey wall, taking his ease. As we drew abreast of him, he stood to attention and saluted, a pleased grin of recognition lighting his healthy face. We greeted him gladly.

'Glad to see you're all right, Will,' said Jill.

'Thank you, miss.'

'Aren't you going to church?' said Daphne.

'Not today, m'm. I'm on leave, and I've 'ad my share o' church parades i' the last four years, m'm.'

We all laughed.

'Well, if you're not going,' said I, 'we want someone to keep an eye on the car.'

'I'll do it gladly, sir.'

'Right oh! She's a pretty piece of goods isn't she?'

'She is that, sir,' said Will, visibly impressed.

As I followed the others into the porch, I glanced back to see our sentinel walking about his charge, bending an appreciative gaze upon her points.

They were singing the *Venite*.

On the ledge of our old pew lay a note addressed to 'Major Pleydell' in the Vicar's handwriting. When Berry had read it he passed it to Daphne, and I was able to read it over her shoulder.

Dear Major,

Sometimes in the old days you used to read the Lessons. I think we should all like it if you would do so today; but don't, if you don't want to.

Yours very sincerely,

John Bagot

In a postscript the writer named the appointed passages of Holy Writ.

So soon as the first Psalm had started Berry stepped to the lectern, found his places and cast his eye over the text. Before the second Psalm was finished, he was once more in his place.

Doors and windows were open as wide as they could be set, and the little church was flooded with light and fresh warm air, that coaxed the edge from the chill of thick stone walls and pillars, and made the frozen pavements cool and refreshing. Mustiness was clean gone, swept from her frequent haunts by the sweet breath of Nature. The 'dim, religious light' of Milton's ordering was this day displaced by Summer's honest smile, simpler maybe, but no less reverent. And, when the singing was stilled, you overheard the ceaseless sleepy murmur of that country choir of birds and beasts and insects that keep its rare contented symphony for summer days in which you can find no fault.

My impious eyes wandered affectionately over familiar friends – the old oak pews, almost chin-high, the Spanish organ, the reluctant gift of a proud galleon wrecked on the snarling coast ten miles away, the old 'three-decker' with its dull crimson cushions and the fringed cloths that hung so stiffly. A shaft of sunlight beat full on an old black hatchment, making known the faded quarterings, while, underneath, a slender panel of brass, but two years old, showed that the teaching of its grim forbear had not been vain.

For so fair a morning, Bilberry village had done well. The church was two-thirds full, and, though there were many strange faces, it was pleasant here and there to recognize one we had known in the old days, and to learn from an involuntary smile that we had not been forgotten.

It was just after the beginning of the Second Lesson that we heard the engine start. There was no mistaking the purr of our Rolls-Royce. For a second the girls and Jonah and I stared at one another, panic-stricken. Then with one impulse we all started instinctively to our feet. As I left the pew I heard Daphne whisper, 'Hsh! We can't all –' and she and Jonah and Jill sank back twittering. Berry's eyes met mine for an instant as I stepped into the aisle. They spoke volumes, but to his eternal credit his voice never faltered.

I almost ran to the porch, and I reached the lich-gate to see our beautiful car, piloted by a man in a grey hat, scudding up the straight white road, while in her wake tore a gesticulating trooper, shouting impotently, ridiculously out-distanced. Even as I watched, the car flashed round a bend and disappeared.

For a moment I stood still in the middle of the road, stupefied. Then I heard a horn sounded behind me, and I mechanically stepped to one side. Fifty yards away was the two-seater we had encountered on our way to church.

Frantically I signalled to the girl at the wheel. As I did so, a burst of music signified that the Second Lesson had come to an end.

'Whatever's the matter?' cried Miss Deriot, as she pulled up.

'Somebody's pinched the Rolls. Will you –'

'Of course. Get in. Which way did they go?'

'Straight ahead,' said I, opening the door.

We were well under way before I had taken my seat. As we came to the bend I threw a glance over my shoulder, to see four figures that I knew standing without the lich-gate. They appeared to be arguing. As we turned the corner a stentorian voice yelled – 'The Bloodstock road, sir! I can see their blinkin' dust.'

Perched on one of the lower brances of a wayside oak, Will Noggin was pointing a shaking finger in the direction he named.

We were less than three miles from Bloodstock when the off hind tyre burst. Miss Deriot brought the car to the side of the road and stopped in the shadow of an old barn.

'That,' she said, 'has just done it.'

I opened the door and stepped down into the road.

'It means a delay when we least want it,' said I ruefully.

'Worse. I've had one burst already, and I only brought one spare wheel.'

I whistled.

'Then we are indeed done,' said I. 'I'm awfully sorry. Heaven knows how far you are from your home. This comes of helping a comparative stranger. Let it be a lesson to you.'

My companion smiled.

'I don't mind for myself,' she said, 'but what about your car?'

I spread out my hands.

'Reason dictates that I should foot-slog it to Bloodstock and try and get the police moving; but I can't leave you here.'

'You can easily, but you're not going to. I don't want to sit here for the rest of the day.' She pointed to the barn. 'Help me to get her in here, and then we'll push off to Bloodstock together.'

A hurried reconnaissance led to the discovery of a little farmhouse, and two minutes later I was making urgent representations to the owner of the barn. To our relief the latter proved sympathetic and obliging, and before we again took to the road the two-seater was safely under lock and key.

'And now,' said Miss Deriot, 'how did it happen?'

'The theft? I can't imagine. We left that fool who yelled at us in charge. I suppose he left her to get a drink or something. This is only the fourth time we've had her out,' I added gloomily.

'Oh, I say! Never mind. You're bound to get her again. Look at that meadow-sweet. Isn't it lovely? I wish I could paint. Can you?'

'I painted a key-cupboard once. It was hung, too. Outside the stillroom.'

'Pity you didn't keep it up,' said Miss Deriot. 'It's a shame to waste talent like that. Isn't it just broiling? I should love a bathe now.'

'I hope you don't wear stockings in the water,' said I.

Miss Deriot glanced at her white ankles.

'Is that a reflection?' she demanded.

I shook my head.

'By no manner of means. But there's a place for everything, isn't there? I mean –'

We both laughed.

'That's better,' said my companion. 'I couldn't bear to see you so worried this beautiful morning.'

'My dear,' said I, 'you've a nice kind heart, and I thank you.'

'Don't mention it,' said Miss Deriot.

From the crown of her broad-rimmed hat to the soles of her buckskin shoes she was the pink of daintiness. Health was springing in her fresh cheeks, eagerness danced in her eyes, energy leapt from her carriage. Had she been haughty, you would have labelled her 'Diana', and have done with it; but her eyes were gentle, and there was a tenderness about her small mouth that must have pardoned Actaeon. A plain gold wrist-watch on a black silk strap was all her jewellery.

'We'd better strike across the next field,' said Miss Deriot. 'There's a path that'll bring us out opposite *The Thatcher*. It'll save us about five minutes.'

'You might have been born here,' said I.

'I was,' said Agatha. She nodded towards a beech wood that stood a furlong away. 'The trees hide the house. But we left when I was seven, and only came back to the County five years ago. And here's our field.'

The five-barred gate was padlocked. I looked at my companion.

'Shall I get over, advance ten paces, and gaze into the middle distance? Or aren't you that sort?'

Miss Deriot flung back her head and laughed.

'I'd rather you gave me a leg up,' she said.

With a hand on my shoulder and foot in my hand, she was up and over in an instant. I vaulted after her.

'You know,' I said, 'we ought to perform, you and I. With a painter's ladder, a slack wire, and a little practice, we should do wonders. On non-matinée days I might even lift you with my teeth. That always goes well, and no one would know you were as light as a rose-leaf.'

'Seven stone three in the bathroom,' said Agatha. 'Without stockings. Some rose-leaf.'

We were going uphill. The meadow through which we were passing sloped to an oaken fence, stoutly constructed to save the cattle from a perilous fall. For on its farther side the ground fell away sheer, so that at this point a bluff formed one high wall of the sunken road for which we were making. *The Thatcher*, I remembered, stood immediately opposite to the rough grass-grown steps, hewn years ago for the convenience of such passengers as we. There was a little stile set in the fence, and as I swung myself over I glanced down past the edge of the bluff and in the road below.

In the little curved space that fronted the inn the Rolls was standing silent and unoccupied.

I must have exclaimed for Agatha was over the stile in an instant, and asking me what was the matter. Then she saw, and the words died on her lips. Together we stood spell-bound.

The door of the inn was shut, and there was no one in sight.

My first impulse was to dart down the steps, beat upon the door of the tavern, and confront the thief. But valour yielded to discretion. The great thing was to recover the car. I had but a slip of a girl with me, the spot was a lonely one, and it was more than likely that the highwayman was not working alone. Besides, Agatha must not be involved in any violence.

I turned to my lady.

'You stay here. I'm going to take her and drive straight to the police station. I'll pick up some police and come back just as quickly as ever I can.'

Miss Deriot shook her pretty head.

'I'm coming with you,' she said. 'Carry on.'

'But, my dear—'

'I often wish I wasn't so obstinate.' She spoke meditatively. 'But we're all like that. Mules aren't in it with the Deriots,' she added, with a dazzling smile.

'Neither, apparently, are cucumbers,' said I, and with that I began to descend the rough stairs, stepping as delicately as I could.

Half-way down I turned to look at my companion, and at that moment the step upon which I was standing gave way. The scrambling sounds which proclaimed my fall were followed by the rasping protest of yielding cloth, and I came to rest six feet from the road at the expense of a pre-War coat, which had caught the corner of one of the unplaned risers. All had been so still, that in that hollow place the noise could not have failed to attract the attention of any one who was within earshot, and I lay for a moment where I had fallen, straining my ears for the sound of footsteps or voices.

'Are you all right?' whispered a soft voice above me.

I turned my head and nodded. Miss Deriot, standing with clasped hands, heaved a sigh of relief and prepared to continue her descent.

Gingerly I stepped down into the sandy road and started to cross it a-tiptoe.

Facing towards Bloodstock, the car presented her off-side to us.

With the utmost caution I proceeded to negotiate the two spare wheels and clamber into the driver's seat. As I sat down, Miss Deriot slipped in front of the bonnet and round to the near side. She was opening the high side-door and my foot was on the self-starter, when I heard the murmur of voices.

We were not a second too soon.

The moment I had started the engine there was a cry, followed by the clattering of heavy shoes upon cobbles, and as the car slid into the road a man in a grey hat came tearing out of the inn's courtyard, waving his arms and yelling like one possessed. Hard on his heels came pounding his supporters, three of them, all bellowing like bulls.

So much I saw for myself. Agatha, kneeling on the seat by my side, kept me informed of their movements till we swept out of sight.

'He's simply dancing. The one in the grey hat, I mean. Now he's shaking his fist at us. Oh, he's mad. He's thrown his hat on the ground. O-o-o, Boy, he's trying to kick one of the others. Oh, I wish you could see. . .' The merry voice dissolved into peals of laughter.

Then the road curled, and Agatha turned left about and settled herself by my side.

'How did you know my Christian name?' I demanded.

'Your sister used it this morning. You see, I've forgotten your other and I can't keep on saying "you". But I won't do it again.'

'Please, Agatha.'

'Deriot. One "r". I say, you've torn your coat properly.'

'It feels as if it was in two pieces,' said I.

'If it wasn't for the collar, it would be,' said Agatha. 'Never mind. Bare backs are still fashionable. And what's a torn coat, when you've got the car again?'

'You're right,' I agreed. 'You'd hardly believe it,' I added, 'but I can tell from the feel of her that some stranger's been driving.'

'I can believe it. After all, a car's just like a horse.'

As she spoke, we sped into the market square of Bloodstock. The police station stood in Love Lane, a couple of streets away.

Here a disappointment was in store. The sole representative of the Law was a station sergeant in his shirt-sleeves and a state of profuse perspiration. Between his lips was a penholder, and he held a telephone receiver to his left ear. In an adjoining room the bell of another telephone was ringing violently in long regular spasms, while, somewhere quite close, a dog was giving ceaseless vent to those short sharp barks which denote impatience of detention.

A sudden elevation of the sergeant's eyebrows invited me to state my business, but before I had spoken two sentences he shifted the penholder from his mouth and shook his head.

''Fraid I can't 'elp you at the moment sir. That's the third car what's been stole in this distric' this mornin'. There's a 'ole gang of 'em about. Every one excep' me's out after 'em now. 'Eaven knows when they'll come in. An' there's that other telephone goin' like mad, an' the Chief Constable's lef' his bulldawg tied up there, an' 'e won't let me within six foot of it.' He turned to blare into the mouthpiece. ''Ullo! 'oo *are* you? 'Oo *are* you? Wot! Oh, I can't bear it. 'Ere, for 'Eavens sake, 'old the line.' He set down the receiver, shook the sweat out of his eyes, and sank on to a stool. 'Another blinkin' car gone,' he said hoarsely. 'I dunno wot's the matter with the world. I wish I was back in France.'

Love Lane was a narrow street, so I did not attempt to turn the car, but drove on and presently out of the town by back streets on to the Bilberry road.

It would have been better if I had telephoned White Ladies before leaving Bloodstock, to announce my recovery of the car; but I was expecting to be back there so soon that it seemed unnecessary.

Indeed, it was only when we were once more under way that I thought of the colt and the embrocation, to say nothing of my lady's two-seater, now standing helpless in the gloom of the wayside barn.

'I tell you what,' said I. 'We'll drive to the barn and pick up the lotion, and then I'll take you home. Then I can run your chauffeur back to the barn with a spare cover, drop him there, and push off to White Ladies.'

'I can improve on that,' said Agatha, with a glance at her wrist. 'It'll be past one by the time we get home, so you must stay to lunch. You can

telephone to White Ladies from there. And afterwards I'll go back with you –
I was to come over this afternoon, wasn't I? – and we can drop the chauffeur
at the barn on the way. And he can come for me in the evening.'

Agatha was living at Broadacre, a fine old place on the edge of the forest
itself, and thither we came without incident, just as an old-fashioned gong
was summoning the household to meat.

Admiral and Mrs Deriot were kindness itself. First I was given a long,
cold, grateful drink. Then the old sailor led me to his own chamber and
ministered personally to my wants. My coat was given to a maid to be
roughly stitched, and when I appeard at luncheon it was in a jacket
belonging to my host. Our story was told and retold, the lawlessness of the
year of Grace 1919 was bewailed, and a violent denunciation of motor-
thieves was succeeded by a bitter proscription of the County Police.

In the midst of my entertainment I remembered that I had not telephoned
to White Ladies, but the servant sent to make the connection was informed
by the Exchange that the line was out of order.

'I expect it's fused,' said I. 'With Berry at one end and that station
sergeant at the other, the strain must have been fearful.'

It was half-past two before we were once more in the car. On the back seat
sat the Deriots' chauffeur, holding a spare wheel between his knees.

It did not take us long to reach the barn, and, so soon as we had once
unearthed the farmer, authorized him to suffer the chauffeur to remove the
two-seater, and discharged our debt for 'accommodation', I turned the Rolls
round and headed for White Ladies.

'She's certainly a beautiful car,' said Agatha, as the Rolls sailed up a
treachcrously steep gradient in top. 'It's like being in a lift.'

'And, but for you, we might never have seen her again. Shall I give you a
stamp album, or would you like to drive?'

'D'you really mean that?' said Miss Deriot.

I shot her a glance. There was no mistaking the eagerness of her parted
lips and the sparkle of her gay brown eyes. By way of replying I brought the
car to a standstill. A moment later we had changed places.

'It's awfully kind of you,' said Agatha delightedly, as she let in the clutch.
'I've always wanted to drive a Rolls. I hope I shan't hurt her.'

'You'll do her good,' said I. 'I watched you in the two-seater. You've got
beautiful hands.'

'Thank you, Boy.'

'Now you shall have a stamp album as well. Go carefully here. There used to be a wasps' nest in that bank, but it's closed now, same as the German banks. What a war!'

'But I don't collect stamps.'

'Then she shall have a dog. What about a Sealyham to sleep on your bed and bite the postman?'

'I'd love one,' said Agatha.

'And you'll sit up in bed in the morning, with your hair all about your eyes, and smile at him, and he'll growl back at you – I can just see you.'

'Thanks awfully. But you're wrong about my hair.'

'Is it never unruly?'

'Only by day. I wish to goodness I could wear it down.'

'So do I. Then we could all sit on it when the grass was wet. At the moment there's a particularly beautiful tress caressing your left shoulder. And I think you ought to know that the wind is kissing it quite openly. It's all very embarrassing. I hope I shan't catch it,' I added cheerfully.

Miss Deriot made a supreme effort to look severe.

'If you do,' she said uncertainly, 'I shall drive straight into the horse-pond.'

''Sh!' said I reprovingly. 'You oughtn't to jest about such things. You might catch it yourself. Easily.' Here we passed the horse-pond. 'You know you'll never be able to look fierce so long as you have that dimple. You'll have to fill it up or something. I suppose it's full of dew every morning now.'

Without a word Agatha slowed down, turned up a by-road, and stopped. Then she proceeded to back the car.

'What on earth is she doing?' said I.

She turned a glowing face to mine.

'Going back to the horse-pond,' she flashed.

I laid a hand on her arm and she stopped.

'My dear, if you must have a bath, you shall have one directly you get to White Ladies. I'll turn on the water for you. But let me beg of you –'

'If I go on, will you promise to behave?'

'Faithfully.'

'And fold your arms and sit like a groom all the way?'

'I suppose you couldn't make it a footman? Then I could stand on the petrol tank. However, as it's your birthday –'

I folded my arms with a sigh. Instantly Agatha leaned towards me with a dazzling smile.

'Good Boy,' she said in a caressing tone. 'Now he shall have a stamp album.'

'But I don't collect stamps.'

The smile deepened. But for her red mouth, her little white teeth would have been the prettiest things in the world.

'Well, I'd thought of a stamp album,' she said slowly. 'However, as it's your birthday—'

A minute later we were back in the main road.

By my direction Miss Deriot drove straight to the stables, and left the car standing in the middle of the yard.

As we walked round to the front of the house, 'We won't tell the others that we've found her just yet,' said I. 'We'll hear what they've got to say first.'

'Perhaps they're all out looking for her,' said Agatha.

'Not all. Daphne's sure to be here somewhere.'

As I spoke we rounded a clump of laurels to see the lady in question comfortably ensconced in a deck-chair upon the lawn. By her side was Jill, seated upon a cushion, one little foot tucked under her, nursing the other's instep with her slim, brown hand. On a rug at her feet lay Jonah, his chin propped between his two palms and a pipe in his mouth.

All three were gazing contentedly across the grass to where the drive swept wide to the foot of the broad grey steps. *There stood a handsome Rolls-Royce, the facsimile of the one from which we had just alighted.*

With a great gasp Agatha stopped dead, and I recoiled as from a spectre. Instinctively we clasped one another.

'It's all right,' I whispered. 'I've seen it too. It'll go away in a moment. Shows what imagination will do.'

'But — but it's real!' cried Agatha.

'Real enough, my lady,' said Jonah's voice. He seemed to be speaking from a great distance. 'And I'll bet you never expected to see her again so soon,' he added, looking at me with a smile.

'To tell you the truth,' said I, 'we didn't.'

As in a dream I watched a dazed and stammering Agatha made welcome and set in a chair by my sister's side. Somebody — Jill, I fancy — led me to the rug and persuaded me to sit down. Mechanically I started to fumble for a cigarette. Then I heard Jonah talking, and I came to my senses.

'We thought you'd be surprised,' he was saying, 'but I didn't think it'd take you like this. After all, there's nothing uncanny about it.'

'I don't understand—'

'Listen. Will Noggin was sitting in the car when he heard a crash, and there was this fellow lying in the middle of the road about fifty yards away, with a push-bike beside him. Naturally Will jumped out and ran to his help. The man seemed to be having a fit, and Will was just loosening his collar, when he heard the engine start and saw the Rolls moving. He left the chap in the road and ran like mad, but he was too late. Nobody ever saw the fellow with the push-bike again. Of course he was one of the gang, and his fall was a put-up job to get Will out of the way. Pretty smart — what?

'Well, you hadn't been gone five minutes when Fitch arrived on his motor-bike. He'd come to bring us a can of petrol, for after we'd left he remembered the tank was almost empty.

'That gave me a bit of hope. If they stuck to the main road you were pretty well bound to catch them, for Fitch swore they'd never get five miles. But, of course, they might turn off. So I thought the rest of us had better follow and search the by-roads for all we were worth. So I sat on Fitch's carrier with the can under one arm, and Daphne commandeered the curate's push-bike and sent Berry after us.'

'Isn't he back yet?' said I looking round.

'Not yet,' said Jonah, with a grin.

'And doesn't he know she's found?'

'That pleasure is still awaiting him. Well, Fitch was right. We left the Bloodstock road for the second time at Dew Thicket, and at the foot of the hill there she was, dry as a bone, but as right as rain.'

'Abandoned?'

'Apparently. Anyway, there was no one in sight. I sent Fitch after you and drove her home. Fitch had a burst directly he'd left me, and had to walk back to Bilberry.'

'Is that all?' said I.

'Well, it's enough, isn't it?'

'Not nearly,' said I, rising to my feet. 'Kindly accompany me to the stables.'

'What d'you mean, Boy?' cried Jill.

''Sh!' said I. 'Come and see.'

In silence I led the way, Agatha treading solemnly by my side. As we turned under the archway that led to the stable-yard—

'You see,' I said carelessly, 'we, too, have met with some success.'

The Rolls was standing where I had left her, waiting to be back into the garage.

My sister gave a cry and caught at Jonah's arm. Jonah started violently and smothered an exclamation. Jill put one hand to her eyes, as if to brush away a vision.

There was a long silence.

At length I turned to Jonah.

'I fear that you were hasty, brother. A moment's reflection will show you that you and Fitch have spoiled some poor car-owner's day. Let me suggest that you return your ill-gotten gains to the foot of the hill beyond Dew Thicket without delay. As a matter of fact, I know the police are very concerned about this theft. It was the fourth in this district this morning.'

Fitch came forward, touching his hat.

'It's a mistake anybody might make, sir. They're as like as two pins.' He pointed to the car. 'She's the spit of ours, she is.'

'Don't be silly,' said I. 'I admit they're exactly alike, but that's ours.'

Fitch shook his head.

'Different chassis number, sir, to say nothing of the number-plates.'

I stared at him. Then—

'Nonsense,' I said sturdily.

'It's a fact, sir. The one in the front's ours. I'm afraid you've stole somebody else's car.'

We had returned to the front of the house and we were wondering what to do, when our attention was attracted by a sudden outburst of cries and the noise of a car's tyres tearing at the road. This lay but a hundred odd yards away on the farther side of the brown stream by which the lawn was edged. For the length of a cricket pitch the hedgerow bounding the highway was visible from where we stood, and as this was not more than four feet high, we were able to observe a scene which was clearly but the prologue to a drama in which we were presently to appear.

Under the explosive directions of a man in a grey hat, who was standing upright and holding on to the wind-screen, frantic efforts were being made to turn what seemed to be a small touring car. Even as we looked, a savage gesture in our direction suggested that our friend was identifying the Rolls by our side as stolen property for the benefit of four individuals who crouched timorously behind him. To my consternation I observed that these were no less than an inspector and three constables of the County Police.

The next minute the car had been turned round and was being driven rapidly back to our lodge-gates.

'Leave them to me,' said Jonah quietly. 'Go and sit down on the lawn, all of you. I'll fix them.'

'That's the fellow,' said Grey Hat, in a shaking voice, 'and that's his accomplice.' He pointed a fat hand at myself and Agatha in turn.

'I beg your pardon,' said Jonah. Grey Hat turned and looked him up and down. 'Were you wanting anything? I mean, I live here.'

'I don't know who you are,' came the reply. 'But that's my car, and those are the people who stole it.'

'One thing at a time. My name's Mansel.'

'I'm the Chief Constable of the County.'

'Good. Now, about the car. I was under the impression that it was mine.'

'Don't try and bluff me, sir,' roared the other. 'You know perfectly well that that car was stolen from the outskirts of Bloodstock only a few hours ago. You're a receiver, sir, a common–' He checked himself with an effort. 'Inspector!' The officer addressed came forward and saluted. 'Caution the three of them.'

'Hadn't you better identify your property first?' said Jonah. 'I mean, I don't want to interfere, but if it's a question of our arrest–'

The inspector hesitated, and the Chief Constable's face took on a darker shade of red. He was a coarse-looking man, generously designed and expensively over-dressed. For a moment I thought he was going to strike Jonah. Then he caught a heavy underlip in his teeth, turned on his heel, and strode to the Rolls-Royce.

He cast a proprietor's eye over her points. Then he stepped behind her as though to come to her other side. The next second he was back and shaking his fist in Jonah's face.

'So you've had the infernal audacity to alter the number-plates, have you?' he yelled. 'Thought to bluff me, I suppose. You impudent–'

'One moment,' said Jonah steadily. 'Without looking at the dash, tell me your chassis number. Your chauffeur should know it.'

'One double seven eight,' came parrot-wise from the lips of the gentleman referred to.

Grey Hat almost ran to Rolls, tore open the bonnet, and stared at the dash – stared...

We waited in a silence so charged with expectancy as to be almost unbearable.

At last the Chief Constable straightened his back. His eyes were bulging and his face redder than ever. Twice he essayed to speak without success. Then –

'I said it was my car,' said Jonah placidly.

For a moment Grey Hat stood glaring at him. Then, muttering something about 'a mistake', he started to lurch towards the police car. As the officers turned shamefacedly to follow their chief, Jonah's parade voice rang out.

'Stop!' At the word of command, master and men alike stood where they were. 'My friends and I have been openly accused of felony and threatened with arrest.'

The Chief Constable swallowed before replying.

'I was mistaken,' he said quickly. 'I – I apologize.'

'You mean to say you believed that to be your car?'

'I did.'

'Why?'

'It's exactly like it.'

'There must be some difference.'

'There's no difference at all. If mine were here, I'd defy you to tell them apart.'

'Do you seriously suggest that I shouldn't know my own car?'

'I do.'

'And that such a mistake on my part would be excusable?'

'Certainly.'

'Thank you,' said Jonah. 'That excusable mistake was made this morning. My car was stolen and sought for. Your car was found. If you will accompany me to the stables, I shall be happy to restore it to you at once.'

Grey Hat started to move forward, his face transfigured with excitement and relief.

'You mean to say –' he began.

'Come sir,' said Jonah icily. 'I feel sure that the ladies will excuse your withdrawal.'

It was half an hour later, just when we were finishing tea, that a cry from Jill made us all turn to follow her gaze down the curling drive.

Twenty paces away was Berry, plodding slowly in our direction, wheeling a tired-looking bicycle. His clothes were thick with dust, his collar was like a piece of wet rag, and on his face there was a look of utter and profound resignation.

As we started to our feet—

'Don't touch me,' he said. 'I'm leading in the Marathon race. The conditions are fearful. Competitors are required not only to walk, but at the same time to propel a bicycle, the hind tyre of which must be deflated. You're only allowed five falls, and I've used four of them.' With a final effort he reached the edge of the lawn and laid the bicycle gently on its side. '"How we brought the good news from Aix to Ghent,"' he continued. 'Yes, I see the car, but I'm not interested. During the last five hours my life has been so crowded with incident that there is no room for anything else. Isn't there a cycling club about here I can join? I've always fancied a grey sweater.'

'Did I hear you say that you had fallen, brother?' said I.

'You did. Four times were these noble limbs prostrated in the dust. The first time was when the handle-bars came off. Oh, it's a beautiful machine.' Solemnly he waited for the laughter to subside. 'But she doesn't turn easily. If my blood counts, there are at least three corners in the County that are for ever England. And now will somebody fetch the Vicar? I shan't last long. And some drinks.' He stretched himself upon the grass. 'Several drinks. All together in a large vessel.'

Jill fled, weak with laughter, to execute his commands. Berry proceeded to remove his collar and tie.

'I can't think,' he said suddenly, 'why they call them safety bicycles. I suppose it's because they strike only on the box.' He turned to Daphne. 'Since I left you this morning, woman, I have walked with Death. Oh, more than once. Of course I've walked without him, too. Miles and miles.' He groaned. 'I never knew there was so much road.'

'Didn't you do any riding?' said Jonah. 'I know they're called push-bikes, but that's misleading. Lots of people ride them. That's what the saddle's for.'

'Foul drain,' said my brother-in-law, 'your venomous bile pollutes the crystal flood of my narration. Did I ride? That was the undoing of the sage. When he recovered consciousness for the second time, it was to discover that the chain was missing and that the back tyre was windless. In my endeavours to find the chain I lost myself. That reminds me. I must put an advertisement in *The Times* to the effect that any one returning a bicycle-chain to White Ladies will be assaulted. I have no desire to be reminded of today. If anybody had told me you could cover about fifty miles of open road in England without meeting anything but road hogs, who not only failed to stop when I hailed them, but choked and blinded me with their filthy dust, I should have prayed for his soul. And not a pub open!'

He stopped to watch with a glistening eye the approach of Jill, bearing a tankard in one hand and a large jug of some beverage in the other.

'What is it?' he said.

'Shandy-gaff.'

'Heaven will reward you, darling, as I shan't.' He took a long draught. 'And yet I don't know. I've got an old pair of riding-breeches I don't want, if they're of any use to you.'

There was a shriek from Agatha and Jill.

'Is anybody going to church?' said Daphne, consulting her wrist-watch.

Berry choked.

Gravely I regarded him.

'Run along and change,' said I. 'And you can return the curate his bicycle at the same time. Besides, a walk'll do you good.'

'Don't tempt me,' he replied. 'Two hours ago I registered a vow. I shall drink no water till it is accomplished.'

'Let's hear it,' said I.

'To offer no violence to a fool for six months,' said Berry, refilling his tankard. 'By the way, you'll have to be very careful when you take off my boots. They're very full of foot this evening.' He sank back and closed his eyes. 'You know I never look at the almanac, but before I was up this morning I knew that this was a blue-letter day.'

'How?' said his wife.

'I left a stud within the bath, and heard Jonah find it.' He spread out a dramatic arm.

> And he thereon did only sit,
>   So blind he couldn't see,
> And then the fat-head yelled and swore,
>   Not at himself, but me.

Early Married Life

W. Heath Robinson

As every lion-tamer knows, the King of Beasts cannot be expected to jump through paper hoops without a little preliminary tuition; and what applies to lions applies equally to wives. It is during the early days of his married life – when the honeymoon is but a fragrant memory and every pawnable wedding-present has gone to its new home – that the wise husband will train his wife in the way that she should go – not so much with blows and curses as by the power of suggestion and example. Once a woman gets set in her ways, it is practically impossible to pry her loose without the help of gun-cotton; and it is therefore up to her husband to see that she steps off, so to speak, on the right foot.

The most important of a wife's duties is, of course, the supervision of the culinary department – or 'kitchen', as it is technically termed. In households where expense is no object, thanks to a bequest from a rich uncle or a lucky investment in an Irish Sweep, the actual work is usually done by a gaggle of assorted serfs, churls, scullions, etc. Nevertheless, it is essential that the housewife should at least know how to boil an egg, as otherwise starvation will stare the family in the face whenever a strike or an epidemic of mumps breaks out in the basement.

The young husband, therefore, should assist the little woman to master the elements of cookery, either by standing her a course of training or by giving her a few tips himself. (Banana-frittering by the Heath Robinson method, for example, is seldom taught in schools, for some reason.) At the same time he should acquaint her with his own personal preferences in the matter of victuals, and give her a list of those dishes – e.g. tapioca, spinach, homemade seed-cake, cold stewed fish, and so forth – which have only to appear on the table to make him bubble at the eyes with rage.

More than one marriage has gone up in a cloud of smoke owing to the wife's inability to understand that an occasional night out with the boys is what every husband needs to preserve his reason and keep him from brooding on his care-free past. In the life of every man above the rank of moron there are times when the urge to go mildly gay in exclusively masculine company becomes too strong to be withstood; and it is by her behaviour at such moments that the young wife proves herself.

If, when her spouse timidly applies for the necessary leave, she at once assumes that his love is dead and scampers weeping to her mother, she may be held to have failed at her job. If, on the other hand, she acquiesces smilingly and allows him an extra shilling from his wages for buns, lemonade, etc., she can be accounted not only a good wife, but a highly unusual one.

The husband who knows what is good for him will take pains to make this point very clear to his little old haybag – as he calls her affectionately – almost before he has scooped the last of the confetti from his ears. In return, the least he can do is to promise to remove his boots in the hall when he comes home, singing slightly, from his refined carousals, or to hoist himself silently to bed by an ingenious apparatus which can be erected in a few moments by any reliable carpenter. It is on this basis of mutual give-and-take that all the most successful marriages, such as that of – er – such as that of – well, all the most successful marriages are founded.

There are, of course, certain minor matters in which every young wife needs a little kindly instruction. She must be taught, for one thing, that the correct way to squeeze a tube of toothpaste is upwards from the bottom, *not* sideways from the middle. She must learn also that as a protection for carpets against the ravages of moths there is nothing cheaper or more effective than cigarette-ash. And lastly, she should be trained to exhibit no temperament when her soul-mate brings home unexpected guests to dine – or when they have gone, for that matter.

Yes, but – as some lady in black bombazine and a bonnet with bugles will almost certainly demand – what about the husband, hey? Does *he* contribute nothing to the success or failure of the deal? Is his life to be roses, roses all the way, while his wife turns somersaults at his command and wears her pretty fingers to the bone to keep him neatly underclothed and socked?

Not by a long shot, lady. As I have already implied, give-and-take is the thing that matters, and the wise husband knows that he, too, must play his part if his home-life is not to degenerate into a species of running dog-fight. There are many little ways in which, without unduly exerting himself or missing his nightly mug of buttermilk at the 'Archdeacon's Arms', he can make himself useful about the house and earn a reputation for thoughtfulness that will stand him in good stead whenever he wishes to touch his mother-in-law for a fiver.

Peeling onions is one of several domestic duties which any woman will gladly delegate to anybody who cares to take it on. Few men are born onion-peelers, the majority being designed rather for the manipulation of cork-screws, but with the help of an arrangement of mirrors this sad-making task can be carried out with the minimum of inconvenience to the tear-ducts.

Again, experiment has shown that many lengthy husbands make admirable emergency clothes-props. A man of normal physique looks more than usually dignified at the end of a clothes-line, the more so as he can use the opportunity to study some improving book, from which informative extracts can be read aloud to the little woman as she pegs out the winter woollies. Husbands who suffer with their feet, however, should not volunteer for clothes-line duty more than once a fortnight.

In homes where the finances will not run to a vacuum cleaner, the husband who wishes to win an approving nod can either seize the dustpan and brush and do the job himself, thereby imposing a grave strain on his braces, or – if he is an indifferent stooper and of a mechanical turn of mind – devise an efficient substitute from the following simple ingredients, most of which will be found lying about in the attic: a disused saucepan, the bag part of a bagpipe, two-thirds of a chair, two short lengths of stove-pipe, a little horse-blanket, some stout twine, and divers portions of an old iron bedstead. With these he can construct a vacuum cleaner that will evoke gasps of admiration from the neighbours and swallow anything from a smallish Pekinese downwards.

In the same way, he need neither overwork his wife by commanding her to press his trousers - a job no woman is really keen on, or even good at – nor pawn the family plate to acquire a trouser-press. All he needs to preserve that knife-like crease which is the hall-mark of the snappy dresser is a garden roller and a fine afternoon, the first of which can usually be borrowed, while the latter is bound to occur eventually. Many self-made men attribute their success to their lifelong habit of pressing their trousers in this manner and investing the money saved in sound Government stocks.

The above mentioned are but a few of the dodges whereby the thoughtful husband can endear himself to his wife and get himself pointed out in church as a model Benedict. ('*So* helpful about the house, my dear, and hardly *ever* beats her.') Many other little attentions – such as installing a Heath

Robinson 'Lettasleep Roofalarm', being every ready to wind wool with the help of a Heath Robinson 'Eziwynda', and carrying always about his person a supply of those aids to beauty which every woman is liable to need at any moment – will doubtless suggest themselves; but I have said more than enough, I think, to give him the right idea.

(It should be remembered, however, that there are certain domestic provinces which the most helpless of wives regards as her very own. An occasional hint *re* the frying of bacon is unlikely to be resented, but a husband who repeatedly elbows the cook aside in order to demonstrate the right way of cooking this or that is apt to find himself cookless – and possibly even wifeless – within a month at the most. Nor should he, if he likes a quiet life, ever presume to criticize his partner's choice of curtains, carpets, or spring hats.)

Anyway, if any young married couple who (or which) faithfully obeys the precepts I have here laid down – if any such young couple (I repeat, taking a new breath) fails to live in perfect amity for at least eleven months, nobody will be less dumbfounded than myself.

And that goes for Mr Heath Robinson too, I shouldn't wonder.

The Eternal Combustion Engine

Patrick Campbell

Little Springs and Ratchets

It was time for iron self-control, a time for cool, rational thinking, a time to begin cleaning the windows or polishing shoes, a time to smash the screwdriver into two or more pieces with the hammer. In particular, it was a time not to read the news story again.

I read it again.

An investigation has been ordered by the British Motor Corporation into the safety of door handles used in their mini-car range. This follows complaints and reports of serious accidents in which the door handles figured.

The eye skittered down the column, towards the forbidden paragraph at the end:

... a million mini-cars have been fitted with forward-pointing handles ... there is no particular reason why the door handles were designed in this way ... our design experts are carrying out tests...

And then the final paragraph, the forbidden one, the bottle of whisky lurking in the cupboard that croons to the reformed alcoholic. It read:

One Birmingham driver who has already made the modification on his own car said last night: 'The operation takes only two or three minutes and involves removing two screws. It makes it easier to open the door and if anything improves the appearance.'

What a filthy thing to say. What a foul revelation to make. What a disgusting temptation to spread in the path of the innocent. On a level with disseminating erotic postcards in the kindergarten, encouraging Boy Scouts to examine advertising material in the vestibules of night clubs.

The operation takes only two or three minutes and involves removing two screws.

The original siren song, sweet and simple, the irresistible lure to disaster.

'Don't listen to it, dear,' I said to myself. 'Clean the windows, polish our shoes, dismantle the screwdriver. Do not touch pitch.'

'But listen, dear,' the other half said, 'it's a perfectly simple operation. The man says so. It's only a matter of removing two screws, reversing the handle and there you are.'

'You listen to me, my friend,' I said. '*Think*. You know about door handles. When you depress a door handle, to open a door, you compress a spring and the tongue of the lock goes in. When you release the door handle the tongue protrudes again automatically. It's the way doors work –'

'Oh, Lord,' I said, 'everyone knows that. Let's just nip down and have a look at the car. See if the two screws are on the inside. We wouldn't have to bring the screwdriver –'

'Will you never learn?' I said. 'Does experience mean nothing to you? Do you not recall the last time you dismantled the lock on the bathroom door? If you remember, it wasn't engaging properly so, proceeding with the greatest care, we removed the screw that held the door knob on the axle, and then gently pulled out the axle and then with infinite precision we unscrewed the four screws from the plate on the inside of the door and with extreme delicacy eased off the plate and suddenly there was an explosion and the bathroom was filled with little ratchets and springs and levers in such profusion that we could scarcely imagine where they'd all come from –'

'But probably,' I said, 'the lock on the car door is much simpler –'

'And then,' I said, 'for hours and hours we tried to put all the little springs and ratchets and levers back again, telling ourselves over and over again that it was a perfectly simple piece of mechanism that a half-way competent child could instantly perceive how it worked –'

'We could just,' I said, 'have a little rootle at the door on the passenger side. That's the easy one –'

'And hours and hours later,' I said, 'we decided we'd have to leave out the spring and we reassembled the lock without it and we put the plate back on again and we inserted the axle and screwed on the door knob and then we shut the door from the inside and hours and hours after that a kindly person broke the door down to let us out again –'

'Anyway,' I said, 'let's just go down and have a look at it. Think of the rather special distinction of having a Mini with the handles facing backwards . . .'

It was irresistible. I went down, taking the screwdriver with me, just in case, and there was the man next door, with a screwdriver, doing something to the handle of his Mini. He looked hot, and tormented. When he saw me he got into his car, with an appearance of nonchalance, and slammed the door. It failed to shut.

I went straight back upstairs again, gleaming with virtue.

A Car was Cleaned Today

There was an aura of instability about the lady. I could see only the back of her head through the rear window of her car, but even her hair looked uneasy, as though it had been subjected to some experimental cutting that hadn't quite worked.

Also, she was busy, in a quietly desperate way, trying to fix one of the huge new residents' parking confusions to the windscreen.

As the next customer disappeared into the maelstrom of the car-wash emporium I gave her a little toot on the horn, inviting her to move up in the queue.

It had a bad effect. The parking thing fell off the windscreen, the lady shot a terrified glance at her driving mirror, found it was out of alignment, threw up a hand to adjust it and dropped what was probably her handbag on the floor. At any rate, she disappeared downwards, from sight.

The man behind me gave an impatient blast on his horn, so I gave the lady another little tootle on mine. The difficult looking hair suddenly appeared again, jerking from one side to the other as the lady looked for the starter, which had evidently moved since she'd last seen it.

The man behind me gave me two blasts, I gave him a couple of digits in reverse, the lady's car, in a series of short, compact leaps entered the maw of the car-wash place and halted just in time in front of the two enormous, woolly rollers.

As usual, the laundry staff had altered completely since the previous week. In place of the three cheerful Africans there were now a couple of indolent white natives, round about seventeen years of age. One of them, in rubber boots, pressed the button and the rollers began to whirl, flinging out sheets of water. The lady sat there, in her car, without moving, terrified of the spray.

The lad in the boots switched off the machinery. 'Come on in, missus,' he bawled, waving his arm. He switched on again. The lady, blinded by the water, drove straight into one of the rollers, instead of between them, stalled her engine and came to a halt. She became invisible in the heart of the cascade, with her radiator jammed up against the whirling roller.

The booted boy switched off again. In a frenzy of indignation he pounded the windscreen of the lady's car, once again waving his arms. She opened her window, and they held a short conversation. At the end of it the boy pushed the car back, away from the roller, lined it up straight through the window, switched on again and then let out a great cry of, 'MISSUS!' The lady, edging forward into the spray, almost had time to shut her window but not quite. It must have caught her in the ear, because I saw her shoot up a protective hand before she disappeared into the Niagara.

When the boy switched off again I saw that the lady had got through to the other side, and was trying to make adjustments to her sodden hair, in the driving mirror. The lad, on the other hand, was leaning against the wall, holding his stomach in an agony of laughter. After a while, he recovered, and both lads soaped down the lady's car. While I passed through the rollers she survived another deluge of water, this time apparently without damage, and moved on into the drying tunnel.

I had a clear view of what happened next. The lady, probably seeking instruction, opened her window again and got, straight into her affected ear, the full blast of the hurricane generated by the machine. Among the other things in the car that rose into the air and whirled around like demented birds was her residents' parking placard, which fastened itself grimly to the back of her neck.

Both lads leant against the wall, this time, sobbing with laughter, their knees visibly giving way.

The lady got her window closed. She sat at the wheel, her head bowed over it, her very soul soaked in water and shredded by the recent typhoon. After nearly a minute she recovered enough to put the car into gear. It leaped forward out of the tunnel, took another buck-jump into the forecourt of the garage and stopped stone dead, the engine once again stalled. The lady made gestures indicating that she was unable to re-start it. The two lads, holding on to one another, staggered forward and gave her a push. The engine started with a roar. The booted lad, already weakened, fell down. The lady, perhaps with the intention of thanking them, threw open her door. It struck the fallen lad on the head.

The lady drove away, disorientated beyond recall. That evening, her husband probably said brightly, 'I see you had the car cleaned today.'

The Delicate, Awful Angels

This is certainly going to provoke another revolution.

This is the absolute end.

They'll simply have to think again. It's a wise statesman who, seeing that he has made an unpardonable blob, apologises handsomely to the nation and quietly erases it. So get on with it, M. Chalandon, *de suite*.

Let me explain, if this sudden dryness in my throat will permit it.

M. Chalandon is the new Minister for Equipment and Housing in the Pompidou Government – and I don't know what sort of Equipment he looks after either but that doesn't matter because this M. Chalandon has just forbidden the sale of alcohol on all the autoroutes in France.

This also doesn't really matter because it seems that there are only five bars in the whole autoroute network, so to make tolerable the endless kilometres ahead nearly all French drivers have filled themselves to the brim before starting out, just in case one of these five bars doesn't lie somewhere ahead, but the really unpardonable thing that M. Chalandon has done is to issue 120,000 breathalysers to the police.

Breathalysers, in France, to be used by the police against hardworking French – and other – citizens who have merely been using their inalienable privilege to take three hours off for lunch with, naturally, *quelques apéritifs*, followed by a litre or two of the good *rouge maison*, topped up with as many fortified coffees as may be necessary to ward off sleep so that we may hit the road again in racing condition.

Breathalysers, in France!

Incredible.

As yet, M. Chalandon has not fixed the permissible level of alcohol in the blood, but even if it's four times the British allowance it will still prove a crushing burden upon the *liberté* of the French motorist, to say nothing of the hundreds of thousands of auberges, cafés, bistros, estaminets, restaurants and bars who keep him going.

The breathalysers – they are called 'alcootest' – will provide the police with the equivalent of the nuclear bomb, as if they weren't sufficiently heavily armed already.

In France the motorcycle cops, who will presumably be empowered to use the bomb, are known as the Angels of the Road – *les Anges des Routes*. Even in the good old days, before the *alcootest*, it was a joke that made Frenchmen – and others – smile between tightly clenched teeth, because the Angels give the impression of being as angelic as barbed wire.

They always travel in pairs, on huge black German motorbikes. They wear white crash helmets and jet-black sunglasses, even in the middle of winter. They have blue shirts, black riding-breeches and black boots and they're slung around with white Sam Browne belts with an enormous revolver in a white holster convenient to their right hand. To see them in the rear mirror makes the heart stop beating altogether. Even a glimpse of them, dismounted and chatting amiably together, causes people to drive into walls.

They have a method of nicking you that deprives you of the power of speech. While the second one waves you in to the side the first one goes on ahead, in case you're mad enough to make a break for it, and stops some way down the road.

Then the second one takes exactly nine minutes to get off his bike. He's precisely ten yards ahead of you, and throughout the performance he keeps his back turned. A booted leg is swung over the saddle, the bike is carefully elevated on to its stand. Then we have the glove removal business, one finger pulled slowly and deliberately at a time, until both gloves are ready to be laid side by side on the petrol tank, and adjusted for alignment. Then we have the hitching of the belt and the easing of the revolver holster and then – and only then – does he turn and come walking back purposefully towards you. Nor are the bloodcurdling preliminaries yet over.

He stands beside the window and then very slowly touches his hand to his crash helmet. 'M'sieu,' he says.

At this point I've seen grown men bury their faces in the steering wheel and sob like terrified little children.

Now we are to have the *alcootest* on top of this conglomeration of horror, shoving Liberté, Egalité and Fraternité right down the pipe.

There's another bitter blow. The Chief of Police in Paris is M. Perrier. The tormented motorist might like to think that he's a member of that distinguished mineral water family but he certainly won't be allowed to say it.

Klaxonnez et Clignotez

At a time in France when the *autoroutes*, the *routes à grande circulation*, the *routes secondaires*, all the *agglomérations* and even the *pistes* are jampacked with cars with camping equipment on the roof or rubber dinghies, or others towing caravans or whole yachts, or cycling clubs travelling at 40 m.p.h., and all of them hounded not only by the police but also by the Army, I feel that the time is coming for me to take a French driving test.

It's a wise decision prompted by hysterical terror. The fact is that I've got quite a little nasty on my British driving licence and I don't want to have to spell it out in French to a motor cycle cop wearing a white crash helmet, black glasses and a huge gun.

In France the amber section of the traffic lights is almost beyond question operated in some secret fashion by the police themselves, in that the green always changes the moment one is passing through at more than 15 m.p.h., and is red a split second later. My belief that these lights are controlled by the police is buttressed by the fact that one of them is always concealed behind a stationary car and blows his whistle piercingly as one trundles helplessly through against the *Rouge*.

The fine, payable on the spot, is usually about £2 10s., enough in all conscience, but it's the filling out of the charge sheet that kills. It includes your mother's maiden name and takes about twenty minutes to complete and you're always in a hurry to get to the airport while it's being done.

It's not the time to have quite a little nasty even on a British driving licence, so that I have come to the wise, terrified decision to obtain a nice clean French one.

Seeing that I have been driving a car with only some minor bing-bongs and buffets for nearly forty years it would seem that I should have no difficulty in passing the French test. I actually like driving and, though I say it myself, I am neat, quick and efficient and give the minimum amount of offence to other users of the road. I am also about eighty-nine road signs short of receiving a French permission to conduct, or a *permis de conduire*.

There are indeed eighty-nine of them and when you look at them, illustrated in glaring primary colours in the driving school handbook, you can hear – as surely as though it were actually happening – the scream of brakes, the crash of glass and the shrilling whistles of the police. There's one picture of four cars and two huge lorries with trailers boiling along in different directions on an autoroute that makes me lose my balance even when I'm sitting down.

Part of the trouble is, of course, the language. I think of *l'agglomération* as 'the agglomeration', instead of the simple 'built-up area'. The agglomeration sounds like a boiling cauldron of traffic hemmed in to bursting point by endless barricades of one-way streets, and I never want to be in one as long as I live.

To blow the horn is to *klaxonner* and conjures up an instant vision of a mad motorist with an enormous moustache and his cap turned back to front thundering down upon you while he pumps the long cast-iron lever of a screeching Klaxon horn.

To put out the direction indicator, in English, is admittedly a somewhat cumbersome and elongated phrase, but it's blessedly calm in comparison with the French *clignoter*, which sounds like an absolutely desperate emergency, full of sharp spikes. The thought of being on a *route à grande circulation* when some lunatic suddenly shoots out of a *route secondaire*, ignoring *le Stop*, and you've got to *klaxonner* and *clignoter* all at the same time makes me want to stay in bed.

Level-crossings, which seem to be everywhere, are another source of panic. There's the level-crossing armed with barriers and looked after by a custodian. There's another one armed with a luminous, automatic, sonorous signalling with automatic half barriers where a red light begins to *clignoter* like crazy only 20 seconds before the arrival of the train. There is also another kind. It's without barriers and without automatic signalling and the handbook advises you not to get on to the iron way until you're sure that the train will not be there at the same time.

In case, when if ever I take the test, the worst comes to the worse, I have armoured myself against disappointment with a small jest.

An English girl, an expert driver, failed hers the other day. The examiner told her, in English, 'Your driveeng ees magnifique but your Code ees terribul.'

If the same thing happens to me I propose to say, 'I dough. I'b had id for weegs.'

And walk home.

P.S. The French Government has just announced that the possession of a British driving licence entitles one to apply for a French one, without enduring the trials of a test.

They would.

A Carload of Paint and Porn

A couple of hundred yards ahead, on the left-hand side of the road, the sudden heart-stopping spectacle of people activity presented itself.

Five or six policemen, three or four cars and some curious looking equipment. Perhaps lifting gear, after some appalling mass accident.

As is normal for the motorist under these circumstances I began to make a number of swift modifications in behaviour. Having been bowling along happily in the middle of the road at some 50 m.p.h. I slowed rapidly to 30, drawing in towards my own side. I threw away a cigarette, removed my elbow from the window and placed my hands on the wheel in the ten-to-two position as advised and practised by the constabulary themselves.

When there are five or six policemen ahead with some curious looking equipment it is wise for the motorist to behave in a manner so unobtrusive as to be almost invisible.

The immediate effect of all these precautions was to let hell loose behind and then immediately beside me.

A horn screamed and suddenly a vulgarly red sports car drew level with me on the outside. The swine driving it made filthy gestures to me and shouted dreadful words. I judged that he had been frightened, probably having been about to pass me on the inside, by my slowing down fairly abruptly and drawing over into that lane, and was taking his revenge in the only way he knew.

In normal circumstances, of course, I would have rebuked his bad manners with an answering blast on *my* horn, various fingers in the air and the headlights blazing into his driving mirror, but this time I let the vulgarian go in peace, being more concerned about the Heat ahead.

It turned out that they were engaged in an innocent and even kindly enterprise, beneath a large notice which said that they were prepared to give any motorist who dropped in a free test of all his lighting equipment, while at the same time passing an eye over his windscreen wiper and tyres.

For a single split-second I thought I'd been successfully wooed. It seemed to be such a nice thing to do – drawing into the lay-by, giving a friendly greeting to the police and then thanking them in advance for offering – free of charge – all these generous services. So different from the normal cowering terror. Mercifully, a moment later I came to my senses and drove past the testing station with averted eyes and both hands on the wheel at ten-to-two, just like they do it themselves.

The fact of the matter is that I don't want anyone to take a close look at my car – and least of all the police – because I can scarcely bear to look at it myself.

It's in good running order – a great little goer – but it has gathered to itself, both inside and out, a number of curiosities that would be difficult to explain to someone else.

For a start, the outside is almost completely covered with the paw marks of the cat Griselda, who has taken to sleeping on the roof-rack. She sleeps there, disdainfully, because the other cat, Pompom, is pregnant again and she herself can't have any, but I wouldn't care to have to explain all that to the police who, if they got the chance, might like to warn me of the danger of driving with a windscreen almost opaque with cat's pads.

There's no point in cleaning it because Griselda just tramples all over it again that night and the windscreen washer doesn't work because the plastic bag that holds the water for it is full of white paint.

This great little goer has the engine at the back so that the boot, with the plastic bag in it, is at the front. Some time ago I bought a huge 2-gallon can of white paint, for some home decoration, and when I got it there Madame said it was too yellowy so I threw it back into the boot in a fury and the lid came off and the windscreen washer hasn't since.

There's a shelf behind the back seat which is covered with paperback books with pornographic covers in full colour which were lent to us by a friend who has moved. I don't like to bring them into the house, so there they remain for ever. A saucepan of pea soup fell off the kitchen windowsill and filled the louvres of the engine cover and I don't have the strength to remove it either. What's under the back seat I do not wish to know, but the lighting equipment is quite good.

Or, at least, good enough for me.

Too High in a Bare Sky

Instead of turning south in Turin we carried straight on in the direction of a town called Susa.

I'd had enough of the endless tunnels on the autostrada that runs along the coast behind Genoa, Savona and so on, particularly as there always seemed to be at least two cars that had run into one another – police, documents, gesticulations – at the end of every tunnel, so that our own personal buffeting must surely be on the way, probably by a fifty-ton lorry, with a trailer to execute the *coup de grâce*.

Perfectly simple route on the map. Susa, then Sestrière, crossing the border into France at Clavière and then all down-hill into Briançon for a dinner gastronomic and an early night.

After Susa Madame became totally absorbed in the map, paying no attention of any kind to the scenery, as we swirled upwards round a long, long series of hairpin bends.

'After you've looked at it,' I said, 'you might care to describe the scenery as majestic.'

She looked at me instead, and spoke gloomily. 'We're on the wrong road.'

I hauled the car round two more hairpins, following the colossal lorry

ahead and trying to keep away from the even bigger one behind. In the brief
interval before the next bend I said, 'There's nothing I can do about it.'

'In that case,' she said, 'I give up.' Glasses off, map put away, arms folded
– perfect posture for the infallible map-reading wife led into the wilderness by
the wilful idiocy and blindness of the car driving husband.

Hours later, still sandwiched between the giant lorries, we came out on a
flat bit, and the Customs post. I stopped and looked at the map myself. An
error had indeed been made. A right instead of a left turn in Susa. And before
us, inescapably, the pass of Mont Cenis – 6000 feet above sea level and going
due north towards Switzerland.

I started off and instantly got the two giant lorries glued on fore and aft, as
before. The three vehicles ground upwards into the clouds, and then all three
of us swirled down the other side of the mountain, still irrevocably glued
together. At the end of the second hour I said, 'On the map, just after a place
called Modane, there's a squiggly little yellow road that turns south.'

She said, 'At this hour of the evening I am not turning south on any
squiggly little yellow road. I am staying the night in Modane, even if it hasn't
got an hotel.'

It had an hotel, quite a nice little one, even if it was in eternal danger of
having the awful mountains fall upon it. We went for a walk and saw a train
leaving the station. There were four cars full of people on the flat trucks
behind the engine. They were all peering ahead through their windscreens as
the engine plunged into the bowels of an alp. We held on to one another. We
were far, far too high in the thin, bare sky.

By ten o'clock the following morning we were even higher. On the map the
squiggly little yellow road for some reason looked as if it was all downhill, but
it wasn't. It climbed and climbed, squirming, doubling on itself, redoubling,
resquirming, until it straightened out for a moment at the very top of the Col
du Galibier. There was a house there, a kind of restaurant and souvenir shop.
There was a man outside it sitting on a bench and reading a newspaper. *We
were all nearly 8000 feet up in the air.*

I said, 'Like – brandy?'

Her eyes were closed. She said, 'Just get me down.'

We began to descend. Suddenly, she cried in a low, urgent voice, 'No! No –
it's not! *Stop* it!'

'What?'

'Aeroplane. *Underneath. . .*'

Flying, apparently very slowly, up the valley below us was a light aeroplane. Creeping along the edge of the cliff, in the car, we could look down upon it. She said, very thinly, 'We've only got – wheels.' The plane banked, turned and flew off down the valley again. I wrenched the wheel to the left to stop myself taking off from the road and following it. When we saw the sea again late that afternoon it looked like terra firma.

By now, of course, these revolting, vertiginous Alps are covered with screaming slippery snow. And people are sliding about all over them, 8000 feet in the sky, and actually enjoying themselves.

I like it here, under the bed, holding on to the floor.

Buttercups and Daisies

Compton Mackenzie

Curiosity rather than conviction or a desire to be convinced is likely to be the motive force which drives people into attending public meetings. The only settlers on the Oak Farm Estate (the chronicler must try by sticking to the recognized name not to prejudice the issue) who cared a jot whether it was to be known in future as Oak or Oaktown were Mr Robert Waterall and Major Wilberforce Kettlewell. There was not any real interest in the elimination of the clumsy name Oak Farm Estate, for hardly any of the settlers received enough telegrams during the year to feel the iniquity of having to pay a penny for those unnecessary two extra words or the exhorbitant porterage on telegrams brought out from Galton. And even the establishment of a post-office was not felt as a vital need by the happy-go-lucky population of oddities who had escaped to the Oak Farm Estate from the ever-growing complicacy of modern life. Nevertheless, in spite of this indifference to the issues at stake there was hardly one of the settlers absent from the meeting convened by Mr Waterall in the big barn of the old Oak Farm on that August evening.

Some came because a strong rumour had gone round that Major Kettlewell and Mr Waterall were likely to fight it out with fists before the evening was over. Some came because an equally strong rumour was prevalent that refreshments would be served free when the meeting was over. Some came because they had not had an evening off since they exchanged the soul-destroying demands of urban existence for the back-breaking demands of a country livelihood. Some came to stare at neighbours of whose extraordinary behaviour they had heard lurid tales, but whom they had not yet had an opportunity to know even by sight. Some came because it was a fine evening. And one came – it was old Mrs Felton of Windermere Cottage – because she had been told that it was a religious gathering, and church or chapel being so far away she thought it would be a nice opportunity to

perform an act of worship. In addition to the settlers, there was a sprinkling
of young farm-labourers from various farms in the neighbourhood, who
made a habit of attending meetings for the purpose of shouting observations
to the speakers, talking to one another in the back rows, and smoking
cigarettes in defiance of the stewards. Finally there was the Press which
consisted of a spotty-faced youth of seventeen with ink-stained fingers and a
pencil he had bitten down to a pulp. To his four-line report of the meeting
two days later in the *Galton Advertiser* no attention was paid at the time, and
no attention need be paid now.

Hobday, with the help of planks, barrels, chopping-blocks, and hurdles
had provided an excellent imitation of seating accommodation; and of the
raised threshing-floor at the end of the barn he had made an almost lifelike
representation of a real platform with two pots of ferns, a Union Jack, a table
with a jug of water and five wicker chairs.

'You'd better come up on the platform with me, my dear,' Mr Waterall
murmured to his wife as they passed from the spangled gold of the westering
August sun into the austere shade of the old barn.

'Oh, no, Robert, please,' she protested.

'Well, somebody must sit in those wicker chairs,' he said. 'Hobday may be
offended if we show no appreciation of all the trouble he has taken.'

'Well, I should ask old Mr Chilcott,' she suggested, 'and Hobday himself.
But not me, please, Robert, I've never sat on a platform in my life, and I
don't like to leave little Phyllis. She is feeling very nervous, and I've promised
to let her hold my hand all the time.'

The Reverend Nehemiah Chilcott was a plump and venerable old
gentleman dressed in a clerical frock coat. He had a long white beard, and
like many old gentlemen with beards he considered it superfluous to wear a
tie, supposing that the glazed surface of his dicky was sufficiently garnished
by his white hairs.

'Mr Chilcott,' said Mr Waterall, the graciousness in his voice already
betraying a tendency to be all things to all men, the effect of becoming a
public character. 'Mr Chilcott, may I beg that you will do me the favour of
occupying a seat on my right?'

Mr Chilcott indicated his willingness by an inclination of his venerable
head and on reaching the platform sat looking down at the audience with the
expression of a prophet faced by one of the periodic flirtations of the Children
of Israel with strange gods.

'Mr Hobday, I think you'd better take the chair on my left,' said Mr

Waterall, 'You're used to this sort of thing.'

'As you like,' said the owner of the Emporium.

Whereupon he stumped heavily up on the platform, sat down firmly in his wicker chair, wiped his mouth with the back of his hand and looked fiercely across at the group of young farm-labourers shuffling their feet at the far end of the audience.

It should have been mentioned before that a considerable proportion of this audience consisted of dogs, some of whom had accompanied their owners, while others had just wandered in because the big doors of the barn were wide open. Among these dogs was Peter. There had been of course already a good deal of the low snarling and growling with which dogs express their contempt for each other's personalities and political opinions; but the quantity of dogs present was not revealed until the entrance of Major Kettlewell when every dog in the barn forgot to snarl at its nearest neighbour and barked loudly at the new-comer. Why all the dogs should have shown such resentment at the Major's appearance would have been difficult to say. Many figures outwardly much more eccentric than the Major had entered their seats without a word of canine protest; yet there was something about the way he came in which made every dog long to chase him out again. It was lucky that Lieutenant Green and his seven fox-terriers had not yet arrived, for they would undoubtedly have proceeded from words to action. However, they arrived later and they were too busy expressing their opinion of the dogs already there to notice the Major who by then had taken his seat.

'Shut up Peter, you ass,' said Roger.

'Can't I really put that bottle-nosed bounder out of the barn?' Peter asked.

'Lie down, Peter you, fool,' said Ralph severely.

'Every dog in the place agrees with me,' Peter grumbled, as he settled down unwillingly at the feet of the two boys.

'I think we might open the proceedings now,' Mr Waterall on the platform murmured to Mr Hobday. 'It's five minutes after the half-four.'

Mr Hobday agreed, and Mr Waterall produced from his pocket a hand-bell which he rang for silence. This started every dog in the place off again, for being unable to see from where they were lying what was happening on the platform they decided unanimously to suppose that a door bell had been rung and that it was now imperative to fill their visitor's heart with terror of their sagacious ferocity and with awe of their noble devotion to property.

'I wish he wouldn't show off like that,' Ralph muttered to his brother. 'It's bad enough making an ass of himself by getting up and jawing, without ringing bells.'

'Ladies and gentlemen, or may I not say, fellow-searchers after the simple life...'

A loud 'Hear, hear,' from Hobday almost at his elbow nearly threw Mr Waterall off his rhetorical balance, and he bent over hastily to consult the note he had of his opening.

Ralph and Roger, blushing hotly at the parental spectacle, leaned down to bury their shame in Peter's shaggy coat. Farther along the row they could hear a faint whimpering from where Phyllis sat, clasping her mother's hand in an agony of filial apprehension.

Mr Waterall recovered from Hobday's sudden endorsement and proceeded more easily:

'I have taken upon myself to invite you here this evening in order that you may signify in no uncertain fashion what is your will.'

'Ask old Will Poley, if his missus don't object,' a voice cried from the back of the barn amid loud guffaws from the group of farm-labourers in a smoke-screen of Woodbines.

'Order, at the back there,' cried Hobday.

'Order!' cried several members of the audience in front.

'Hogs,' whispered Mrs Poley to her husband.

'What can you expect, Maria? I told you before we come out that it would be all hoggishness. Pay no attention to them.'

'I do not want at this early stage of the proceedings,' said Mr Waterall, 'to introduce a note of bitterness, but I must ask those gentlemen at the back of the barn either to avoid the introduction of personalities or to leave the barn.

'Hurrah, Poley for ever and free speech!' a concealed wag cried. 'Stand up, Poley, and show us your face.'

'You sit still, Will,' said his wife. 'Don't you dare move.'

'I wouldn't move a finger for such hogs,' Poley answered her, sitting poker-backed with dignity.

'When I look round at this sea of upturned faces,' Mr Waterall went on, 'I am filled with a deep sense of my own unworthiness. Who am I that I should venture to offer myself as spokesman of your most intimate hopes upon this momentous occasion? Ladies and gentlemen, I have no desire to arrogate to myself a position to which I have no claim. Like yourselves I am but another humble seeker after the simple life that was led by our rude forefathers.'

This remark was greeted by some stamping of feet at the back of the barn, but whether in approval of the poetical allusions or whether to express their surprise at hearing their relations called rude was not clear.

'Like you,' Mr Waterall continued, 'I am sick, mortally sick of the artificial conditions of modern city life and whenever I can flee with my family to lovely Hampshire, there to commune with nature in a tranquillity of mind and a contentment of body which no city can provide. God, ladies and gentlemen, made the country, but it was man, ladies and gentlemen, man who made the town. But to pass from the poets and confront the grim facts of this workaday existence of ours. We are met here this evening to determine what we wish to be called. How many of us in later life have oft-times wished that we could have had a say in our names when they were first bestowed upon us by doting parents.'

At this point a very loud 'Hear, hear' rang out from that part of the barn where Micha and Rehob Chilcott were sitting; but, as both the young men immediately looked round to see who it was behind them that could have endorsed this opinion from the platform so enthusiastically, the Reverend Nehemiah Chilcott sitting with folded arms on Mr Waterall's right, was unmoved.

'Do not let me impute to our parents any neglect of their duties, ladies and gentlemen. Whatever names they bestowed upon us were given in the full belief that they were the names we ought to have.'

A cry of 'Shame' from somewhere near the Chilcott brothers again roused a suspicion that they were not in complete agreement with the speaker.

'But there have been parents,' Mr Waterall resumed, 'who have gratified their own love of eccentricity at their children's expense and there have been parents who have given to their children the first names that came into their heads. In some such spirit have those acted who propose to contaminate this lovely part of Hampshire with a name like Oaktown.'

Here Major Kettlewell leapt to his feet shouting 'Monstrous!' Much of the effect of his intervention was destroyed by the fact that he was sitting at the very end of a bench and that unknown to himself his seat upon it was the only thing that counterbalanced the weight of four or five children who were sitting at the other end of it. Consequently when Major Kettlewell leapt up to cry 'Monstrous!' at Mr Waterall's interpretation of the spirit in which the name 'Oaktown' had been chosen, the rest of the occupants of the bench collapsed in a heap on the floor. Not only this, but every dog in the barn which had been drowsing quietly through Mr Waterall's speech immediately started to bark furiously.

'Sit down, sir,' said Mr Waterall majestically. 'Sit down, sir. You shall have an opportunity later to put your views before the meeting. There is no intention to curb the freedom of speech. We welcome discussion, but we will not tolerate interruptions.' Then he turned to the audience. 'Our friend takes exception to my use of the word 'contaminate'; but I appeal to you, ladies and gentlemen, is contaminate too strong a word for a name like Oaktown, a name which deliberately introduces into the sylvan atmosphere of Oak the harsh and discordant suggestion of city life? We do not want towns here. We have come here to avoid towns. And I say deliberately that for any resident upon the Oak Farm Estate to attempt to rob us of our rusticity will be strongly and justifiably resented. Not that I put forward any plea for such a clumsy name as Oak Farm Estate. Indeed, I will go so far as to say to my gallant friend down there, that if it were a question of choosing between the Oak Farm Estate and Oaktown I might be puzzled to know how to make my decision. Fortunately there is an alternative, and the alternative, ladies and gentlemen, is the simple yet picturesque monosyllable Oak. Surely there is no word in the language which appeals quite so-so – so — so . . .' the speaker struggled to catch the resplendent adverb which was eluding the net of his eloquence . . . 'quite so much,' he gulped out finally, surrendering to the necessity that compels the orator to get on at any cost, 'which appeals quite so much to the deeper feelings of every Englishman. And whatever may be our different professions, occupations, and trades, we are all of us here, English men and women, and, let me add, we are all of us proud of it.'

Here the audience broke into that cordial applause which always greets a blatantly obvious statement reflecting credit upon itself. Even Major Kettlewell called out a bluff and gruff 'Hear, hear,' and Mr Waterall was just going to continue in a mood of refreshed complacency, when from the middle of the gathering bobbed up the hirsute face and head of Mr Augustus Ryan in the way that a seal will suddenly bob up from the middle of its pond at the Zoo.

For a moment Mr Waterall was possessed by an over-mastering impulse to fling his silk hat at Mr Ryan, for there was something about that mop of untidy hair and untrimmed beard which roused feelings in Mr Waterall's breast not far from murderous.

'There will be an opportunity for you to address any questions to the chair later,' he said sternly.

'I've no desire to talk to any chair, now or later,' Mr Ryan insisted. 'I get quite enough back answers from my own furniture without talking to chairs I haven't met. What I wish to say is not meant for chairs. Far from it. What I wish to say is that I am of Irish extraction and that my nephew, Texas Bill . . .'

'Sit down,' Mr Waterall shouted.

'Thanks very much,' said Mr Ryan, his hirsute face and beard vanishing as he sat back in his place again.

'We were talking about the beauty of Oak, ladies and gentlemen, when we were interrupted by the shamrock.' Mr Waterall paused for a laugh but none was forthcoming, and he went on quickly. 'My contention is that Oak was the original name of this district. The Oak Farm. So called because it was the farm in Oak, not because it was built of Oak. When it ceases to be a farm what remains? Why Oak. What need to drag in "town"? Already the wags of Galton have christened us Tintown. Let us beware that they do not presently call us Joketown.'

'Why shouldn't they call it Joke instead of Oak?' demanded Major Kettlewell angrily.

'They don't call it Joke Farm.'

'Why should they call it Joketown then?' the Major pressed.

'There's no analogy.'

'Never mind about analogies, sir. We're discussing facts.'

'Then discuss facts,' said Mr Waterall hotly.

'I don't intend to be bullied by you,' the Major rattled.

'And I don't intend to be bullied by you,' Mr Waterall retorted with dignified calm. 'I have convened this meeting in order to give the people of Oak an opportunity to express their opinion without let or hindrance, and I will not be deterred from carrying out my intentions by ill-timed interruptions. In due course as chairman I shall invite you to step up here on the platform and contribute to the discussion. Meanwhile, I must therefore ask you to abstain from interjecting irrelevant remarks from the body of the hall.'

'Hear, hear,' said Mr Hobday, who had been gazing fixedly at the Major throughout this interlude in the hope of conveying what he thought of him for dealing at the Army and Navy Stores instead of the local Emporium.

'What's in a name, ladies and gentlemen?' Mr Waterall resumed, 'You may say with gentle Shakespeare, "a rose by any other name would smell as sweet." That is true. Not even a name like Oaktown could successfully deprive this countryside of its loveliness. It could not rob the green from our hedgerows. It could not . . .'

'You're safe, Lootenant,' one of the young men at the back called out. But

Lieutenant Green had found a seat with something to lean against and he was fast asleep.

'But though an ugly name could not destroy the beauty of Oak,' Mr Waterall continued, 'why should we repay the prodigal abundance of nature so ungratefully? Ladies and gentlemen, there is much more that I could say in favour of Oak as a name, much more that I could urge against Oaktown as a name. But there are other speakers beside myself here tonight, more eloquent, I know, though not, I venture to think, more sincere.'

Mr Waterall resumed his seat amid the applause which an audience finds it so difficult to withhold from anything that is finished. He had no sooner sat down than he rose again.

'Excuse me ladies and gentlemen, but in the emotion of the occasion I completely forgot that I had not said a word about the post-office which we all needed so much. I shall not detain you long, however. The arguments in favour of a post-office nearer than three miles away do not require elaboration by me. They can be appreciated by the lowest intelligence. In the middle of the night one of our loved ones is taken seriously ill. Where is the post-office? Three miles away. On an afternoon of wind and rain we are anxious to communicate with friends, with relations, with our associates in business perhaps, and where is the post-office? Three miles away. In order to obtain one of those small mauve stamps which hold the likeness of our beloved Queen and which at the cost of one penny sends our message forth to the uttermost parts of the British Isles we must walk three miles. Ladies and gentlemen, such a state of affairs is not to be tolerated any longer. You will be invited to pass a strongly worded motion this evening, affirming your fixed and unalterable determination not to rest until the postal facilities to which, as citizens of this mighty Empire, you are entitled, have been granted to you. Do not the telegraph poles which connect Medworth with Galton pass some of your very doors? They do. And yet we are condemned to pay porterage of one shilling and sixpence on every telegram delivered in Oak. Not only that, but we have to pay an unnecessary halfpenny for the word "farm", another unnecessary halfpenny for the word "estate", another unnecessary halfpenny for the word "Galton", and a fourth unnecessary halfpenny for the word "Hants", because forsooth there is another Galton in the county of Worcestershire. But Oak, ladies and gentlemen, would be unique. Oak would require no Galton and no Hants...'

At this a bullet-headed little cobbler called Pluepott who had recently left Bedford to settle here and who had already shown signs of becoming the chief handy man for the neighbourhood, being an adept at everything from carpentry to bee-keeping, rose from his seat.

'On a point of order, Mr Chairman, why not?' he asked.

'Surely I made that clear?' Mr Waterall. 'Because there would only be one place in the whole of these islands called Oak, and therefore the addition of Galton or Hants would be superfluous.'

'On a point of order, Mr Chairman, I still do not understand why,' Mr Pluepott persisted.

'Don't answer him,' growled Hobday, who regarded Pluepott with some jealousy as likely to become a serious rival. 'Don't answer him. He'd argue with the hind legs of a donkey.'

'I have given you a perfectly good explanation,' said Mr Waterall. 'And as I am sure that everybody else present understands perfectly well why Galton and Hants would be superfluous I do not propose to discuss the matter further.'

'But on a point of order, Mr Chairman...'

Mr Waterall rang his bell and every dog in the place started barking. When they had been cajoled or threatened into silence Mr Pluepott was still upon his feet, and Mr Waterall did not like to ring the bell for fear of starting off the dogs again.

'On a point of order Mr Chairman...'

This was too much for Hobday. He rose from his seat and stepped forward to the front of the platform.

'What right you have got to go on blaring away when you've been ruled out of order?' he demanded.

'I'm not speaking to you, Hobday,' said Mr Pluepott contemptuously. 'I'm rising on a point of order, Mr Chairman.'

'How can you rise on a point of order when you've been ruled out of order. Be more civilized, Pluepott,' said his rival.

The Woodbine-smoking group at the back began to hope that there would be a fight after all and they cheered.

'That's right, Hobday, don't you be flummoxed,' they shouted.

'I call upon the Reverend Nehemiah Chilcott to address the meeting,' Mr Waterall said firmly. 'Perhaps he will be able to make the situation clearer to our friend than I have been able to. Mr Chilcott!'

Ralph and Roger looked across to where the Chilcott brothers were sitting. They felt genuinely sorry for them.

The old gentleman advanced to the front of the platform, and gazed down

sternly at the audience. Then he cleared his throat loudly, thereby causing
several dogs to growl and a small child to burst into tears, before he boomed
out in a deep voice:

'Wandering sheep!'

The young men at the back baaed once or twice behind their smoke-
screen, but something in the old man's eye checked them when he repeated:

'Lost and wandering sheep! Whatever name in your pride you give to this
place where you have pitched your tents I beg you before it is too late
to ask yourselves what is the name the Lord Jehovah has given to it. And I
will tell you. The Lord Jehovah has sent me His unworthy servant to make
known unto you that He will call this place New Sodom unless you turn
from your abominations. Of what avail to petition for a post-office when
one amongst you is seeking a licence to sell intoxicating liquor? Neither
Oak nor Oaktown shall you be called in the ears of the Lord Jehovah, but
Soak and Soaktown.'

Hobday leaned over and twitched Mr Waterall's coat.

'I know, I know,' the chairman muttered, 'it's very awkward. I'll try to
stop him. Ahem! Mr Chilcott.'

But the venerable minister without turning waved Mr Waterall's interruption behind him.

'Lost and wandering sheep, come back,' he cried sonorously. 'Forsake
strong drink. Seal the covenant. The Reformed Children of Israel abominate
the juice of the grape. The Reformed Children of Israel...'

'Excuse me,' said Mr Waterall, 'nobody is more sympathetic than I am
with the cause of true temperance, Mr Chilcott; but this is not a temperance
meeting, and as chairman I must ask you to keep to the point at issue. We are
debating a suitable name for what is now known officially as the Oak Farm
Estate and we are calling upon the authorities to take immediate steps to
provide us with postal, and telegraphic facilities. The question of the
proposed off-licence is not upon the agenda.'

'The question of an off-licence may not be on your agenda,' said Mr
Chilcott sternly. 'But it is on the agenda of the Recording Angel.' He turned
again to the audience. 'Lost and wandering sheep...'

'I call upon Major Kettlewell to address the meeting,' said Mr Waterall.
'We have all listened with great respect to what the Reverend Mr Chilcott
has had to tell us, but I'm sure that...'

'Lost and wandering sheep,' the old gentleman boomed out, entirely
disregarding Mr Waterall.

'I should think Micha and Rehob are feeling pretty awful,' Ralph observed to his brother.

'Frightful,' Roger murmured.

'Major Kettlewell,' Mr Waterall called down. 'Will you take the platform?'

But the Major gave no sign of having heard the invitation, and the chairman tried once more to stop old Mr Chilcott.

'I must beg you, sir, to give somebody else an opportunity of letting us hear his views.'

'Obey the chairman's ruling,' Mr Hobday shouted angrily; but the old gentleman was impervious.

'Lost and wandering sheep, seal the covenant. The Reformed Children of Israel call you to return to the fold. You do not require a post-office to reach the Lord Jehovah...'

'Go down and ask his sons if they can get him off the platform,' Mr Waterall whispered to Mr Hobday.

'We can't do anything with him,' Micha and Rehob assured Hobday when he made his appeal. 'You shouldn't have asked him to stand up and spout. It's your own fault.'

'Lost and wandering sheep,' boomed that relentless voice again.

'I'll stand no more of it, Will,' Mrs Poley was heard to wheeze in her penetrating whisper. 'I'll not be called a sheep by anybody who isn't Church of England. I'm going home. You stay if you like, but I'm going home.'

Whereupon Mrs Poley rose majestically and left the meeting followed by her husband to the chagrin of Mr Waterall who had been counting on Poley's support for his motion.

For another ten minutes old Mr Chilcott held forth on the evils of strong drink, and he might have gone on for another half-hour if a bat had not left the upper glooms of the barn and started to flitter round and round him so close sometimes as almost to run the risk of being entangled in his venerable beard. Even Mr Chilcott's concentration was disturbed at last, and he was driven to take refuge in his chair and put a large red handkerchief over his face.

'Infallible,' Mr Ryan was heard to say. 'There's nothing like it for distracting anybody's attention. It's a pity Mr Waterall didn't call on me, I'd have stopped him in a minute if he'd asked me to. I'd have been up on the platform and running round that elderly gentleman till he'd have been glad to go home and sleep it off.'

'Well, ladies and gentlemen,' said the chairman, 'I feel sure that some of you will now wish to hear a few arguments from the other side, and I have much pleasure in calling upon Major Kettlewell.'

'I'm not coming up on the platform,' snapped the Major. 'I decline absolutely to come up on your platform. Nothing will induce me to come up on your platform. I deny your right to summon the meeting at all. You are not the senior resident. You are not even a genuine resident at all.'

'What do you mean by that?' Mr Waterall demanded angrily.

'I mean what I say sir. I mean that you are a week-ender. A miserable week-ender. And for you to put forward your name in opposition to mine shows a most unneighbourly spirit. Not only did you call this meeting, but you caused a printed announcement of it to be affixed to my front door. You shall hear of that again, sir. Are you aware that I have already addressed a petition to the authorities, asking for the name Oaktown to be recognized as a fit and proper telegraphic address?'

'I refuse to accept the name Oaktown,' said Mr Waterall. 'I regard Oaktown as an essentially vulgar name. Oak, sir, Oak is the only name I will support.'

'Oaktown!' the Major roared.

At this moment Peter, who had been sleeping quietly at the feet of Ralph and Roger, stirred.

'I say, Oak, Oak, Oak,' Mr Waterall shouted.

There was loud applause, not because the audience really cared a jot whether it was Oak or Oaktown, but because Mr Waterall had succeeded in shouting more loudly than the Major, who, enraged by what he thought was the tide of public opinion rising in favour of his rival, bellowed:

'Oaktown!'

It may be remembered that Peter had been taught by Mr Bellamy that Oaktown was a word in which he should show disapproval. On hearing it now bellowed forth like this by Major Kettlewell with whom he had already had a passage of arms this week, he rushed along between the benches and seizing Major Kettlewell's coat between his teeth he shook it with furious growls. It was not to be expected that the other dogs in the barn would allow Peter to occupy the centre of the stage without competition. Some attacked one another. Some barked wildly at the air. Some like Lieutenant Green's fox-terriers tore round after imaginary rats. To add to the confusion an owl, roused by the clamour, swooped down from where it was roosting and, bewildered by the light, brushed the heads of the audience with its great

wings as it continued to swoop wildly hither and thither about the barn.
Women and children screamed. The dogs barked more loudly. About twenty
bats disturbed by the owl began flittering around with the original bat which
had silenced old Mr Chilcott. One of them got caught in Mrs Gnathead's
bonnet. Gnathead in trying to knock it out, upset a plank on to the toes of
about six young Hobdays. Mr Waterall on the platform rang his bell. The
young men at the back shouted 'Yoicks!' and 'Tally-ho!' The dogs barked
louder than ever, and above all the din the voice of Major Kettlewell was
heard bawling at Peter to let go of his coat and threatening Mr Waterall with
dreadful penalties for deliberately inciting a savage dog to attack him. Old
Mrs Felton of Windermere Cottage was seized with palpitations, which were
not diminished by the caving in of the lid of the barrel on which she was
sitting and what looked in consequence like the probable attachment of the
barrel to Mrs Felton for the rest of her life. Lieutenant Green produced a
whistle which he began to blow as hard as he could with the idea of gathering
his dogs to heel, but which sounded much more as if he were blowing for the
police. Anyway his dogs paid no attention, but continued to scamper up and
down after imaginary rats. Ralph and Roger were shouting at Peter to let go
of Major Kettlewell's coat, but their shouts added little to the general noise
because they were too much stifled by mirth.

'I didn't think this would be such a lark, did you?' Ralph observed to
Roger.

'No, it's a jolly good lark, isn't it?' the younger one agreed.

'Look at that little funk Phyllis. She's blubbing like anything.'

'I've caught a bat! I've caught a bat!' Ralph cried in ecstasy.

'Where?'

'In my hat.'

'I say, how ripping! Let's tame it.'

'Of course, I'm going to,' said Ralph. 'Look out, don't squash it with your
great beefy paws, you clumsy hog.'

'We can put it in that canary-cage of Phyllis's,' Roger suggested. 'Do bats
lay eggs?'

'Fish and find out,' said Ralph, whose knowledge of bats was not in excess
of his young brother's.

And at this point the chronicler feels tempted to lay down his pen and to
the kind reader who wants to know more reply ungraciously in the words of
Ralph to Roger.

The farcical chronicles of Oak are not to be contained in a single volume, and if the history of Oak were to be brought down to the present it would merely fade out in a monotone of dull respectability. The post-office was achieved within a year; but the postmaster was not Hobday, who however did obtain his off-licence much to Mr Waterall's regret when he found it meant that every Sunday afternoon about twenty young men would sit along the hedge and on the stile opposite the gate of Dream Days drinking beer, this being the nearest lawful spot to the Emporium where they could be held to be consuming it off the premises. For two years the post-office stamped all letters Oak Farm Estate, which so much angered Mr Waterall that he would not use it and sent all his letters to be posted in Galton. However, the struggle between the supporters of Oak and Oaktown did ultimately finish in a victory for Mr Waterall's side some three years after that meeting in the barn which is at this moment breaking up in such noisy disorder.

Cooper the Trooper

Tommy Cooper

The day I joined the army I was interviewed by a Colour-Sergeant in the Guards. He asked me if I could ride or did I know anything about horses. I said I didn't. He said, 'You seem to me to be a little hoarse,' and put me in the Horse Guards. I then had a test to see if I could swear like a trooper.

I was sent to the cavalry barracks at Aldershot. There was a shortage of space. Most of us shared the stables with the horses. The horses complained. Several soldiers had to be billeted in the fields. They were un-stable. The unit I reported to had only one horse in the beginning. It was a one horse outfit.

Eventually we did get some more horses, but all I got was Raymond, the troop mascot, he was a little donkey. My feet touched the ground on either side of him. Whenever the bugle sounded the charge, off would go the troop in every direction, and Raymond would go trotting off leaving me standing bow-legged. The Corporal would then shout 'Whoa! Hold your horses,' and I would cradle little Raymond in my arms. Eventually I got a horse, and Raymond was transferred. One day the Sergeant-Major yelled to me 'Cooper! What is your donkey doing in the company office?'

'He's been promoted,' I said. 'He was officer material. He's there to do the donkey work.'

'All right,' said the Sergeant-Major, 'but he'll have to watch out for the Adjutant. He might talk the hind leg off him. We haven't much use for a three legged donkey, except, maybe in the inter-regimental three-legged race, which isn't a bad idea at that.'

Most of the troopers were getting bowlegged. If we were going to a dance we used to straighten our legs by clutching a saveloy between our knees and stretching it down between our ankles. Then we would jump up and down to a couple of choruses of 'Knees-up Mother Brown'.

We had a trooper named Skimpole. He was the fastest thing on two legs.

We all felt sorry for his horse. Have you ever seen a horse with a hernia? Another trooper had been transferred from the RAF. He always sat his horse backwards. He had been a tail-gunner. He used to keep falling from his horse so they fastened him to the saddle with a strap. Another trooper was a Pole. He was a gallup Pole.

I soon found that old troopers never tossed a coin to decide anything. They just shouted, 'Heads or tails?' and tossed a horse. One time I was riding an old grey mare, but it turned out she wasn't what she used to be. I was switched to a great big black stallion. This was a horse of a different colour. It was a real dark horse. After him I had a gelding. It was specially cut out for the job.

The Corporal of the Horse was always picking on me. One day as I was walking across the barrack square he yelled, 'Hey, Cooper! I know the regimental mascot died, but that was last year. You don't still have to walk around with your trousers at half mast. And empty your pockets. They look like saddle bags.' My pockets were empty at the time.

The Corporal said he had been born in the saddle. It must have been hard on his mother. He once asked me to go to the store to get him a pair of riding boots.

'Yes, Corp', I said, 'West Riding or South Riding?'

When I came back he complained that the boots squeaked.

'You wouldn't just squeak,' I said, 'you would yell if some clodhopper walked on you.'

We found barrack life very humdrum. Whenever we went on parade there would be a lot of humming and hawing. We would hum and the horses would haw. Sometimes we would just horse about.

Finally I got a horse with a very soft saddle. It was a saddle of mutton. One day I was mounting up. I had one foot in the stirrup when the horse galloped off like balmy. I hopped alongside him for a mile or two but in the end it became quite a drag. I woke up in military hospital. It was so quiet you could hear a pin drop. Then I heard a man singing a sea shanty. He had been in the navy, in the submarine cavalry. They rode sea horses. He was suffering from land sickness.

Our officers were a strange lot. One, we used to call Beryl, was drummed out of the service. He was caught riding sidesaddle. We used to call the officers the 'Scilly Brigade'. We had a captain with a fantastic walrus moustache. How he got it was a closely guarded military secret. Most of the men thought he had pinched it from a real walrus and had it grafted around his nose. But I discovered his secret. He had gone to the doctor with an ingrowing hair up his nostril only to discover it was a complete ingrowing moustache. The doctor had operated on him to turn his face inside out. He had been a schoolmaster and always carried a cane. He would whack anyone within striking distance and shout, 'That hurt me more than it hurt you', and then burst into tears. We believed him. In fact we always felt sorry for him.

We had an officer from the Shetlands who always rode a Shetland pony. He was unpopular because of the deep depression that was always hanging over him. He always wore a superior smile when he went riding. Most everyone else wore riding breeches.

I had a lazy horse. Everything was too much trouble for him. Instead of carrying me, most of the time I had to carry *him*. I was the only trooper with saddle sores on his shoulders. He was a queer animal. He wasn't fond of his oats, but he could stand a lot of chaff.

We were finally mechanized. We were issued with tanks. The men soon got used to them, but the horses found them a bit cramped. So we gave the soldiers farewell to our steeds; our steeds gave us the horse laugh and we soon found ourselves in the Middle East with a war on.

We went into camp near the Suez. It was no holiday camp, not like the posters at all. I went on parade wearing shorts for the first time since my Boy Scout days. My under-pants kept sticking out.

'Cooper!' yelled the corporal, 'your bloomers are sticking out!'

'Never mind the bloomers,' I yelled back, 'my stays are killing me.'

I got seven days jankers.

While in this camp we played cricket against a battalion from Palestine. When our captain yelled for a new ball, they offered to accept the old one in part-exchange.

We had a general visit us at our camp. He came to the men's mess and took a big dollop from a tin.

'Ah! This is very good butter,' he said. 'Very good butter, to be sure.'

One of the officers hurriedly pointed out that it was axle-grease.

'Ah,' exclaimed the general, 'this is very good axle-grease,' and he helped himself to another mouthful.

He spotted me as I was leaving the mess tent.

'Who is that man with the two concertinas hanging from his belt?' he demanded. My trousers did need pressing. He had our Intelligence officer with him. He was disguised as a worm, to worm his way into our confidence. He got me another seven days jankers.

Once we were lost in the middle of the desert. There we were, not knowing in which direction to go. We tried to work it out by a process of elimination. We knew we didn't want to go up. We knew we didn't want to go down. That got rid of two possibilities for a start.

Suddenly we saw a penguin waddling towards us. We thought it must be a mirage. But it turned out to be a waiter from the Normandy Hotel in Cairo. He had stepped out of the kitchen, across the garden and got lost. The steak and chips were cold but it went down all right. We finally reached this little oasis. There were no girls but there were plenty of dates.

The next morning, on the horizon, there was a row of camels. What a sight! It was a caravan site. One of the caravans had an ad in the window, 'Room for rent. Must be willing to travel.'

A little man came up to me and whispered in my ear.

'Psst, effendi! Do you want to buy a piano? It fell off the back of a camel.'

I played in a few shows for the troops in Cairo. One of the most popular ditties at the time was a little number called 'Up your pipe, King Farouk,' dedicated to the then King of Egypt, and which the British Tommies always sang with gusto on every special occasion as a mark of respect. One of my friends, he had a smoke-curing factory in Blighty, opened up a smoke house in Cairo for smoking camel. He reckoned it would be the biggest thing since smoked salmon. He said that smoked camel sandwiches were a natural. He got the idea from an American poster he saw in Cairo which said 'Smoke Camels.'

About that time I started wearing my fez at army shows. I used to grow geraniums in it. I also got up to my old tricks. I didn't pull rabbits out of a hat. They never know when to stop. I pulled a pig out of a poke. Once I pulled a reindeer out of a hat. It was a deerstalker. I tried sawing a lady in half but didn't know what to do with the bits. I wound up the act by letting the cat out of the bag. It was a howling success.

After I left the army I decided to go on the boards. I went to see an agent and showed him my routine.

'Well?' I asked. 'What do you think of that then?'

Funny man! I couldn't understand a word he said. He had a peg on his nose.

While I was there, another man came in for an audition. He actually flew round the room three times whistling 'Only a Bird in a Gilded Cage,' and landed on the ceiling. Marvellous! The agent turned him down. He said that bird acts were two a penny. I also saw him turn down a talking dog who danced the tango, because he didn't like his legs. I later found this agent was a secret agent from MI5. He knew nothing about acts: not even third acts.

But I was soon on the merry-go-round: cabaret, music halls, clubs, TV – the lot. I travelled up and down the country staying at hotels and boarding houses, meeting all kinds of people.

I remember a boarding house in Blackpool where I stayed. The landlord was dogmatic and his wife was bitchy. They hounded me. Every night they used to take each other out, walkies. I must remember to send them a couple of tins of mince chunkies for Christmas.

Sunday dinner there! What a performance! The host would rap out a rapid grace, and then it was every man for himself. Meat, greens and spuds would go flying in all directions. Bits of plastic Yorkshire pudding stuck to the ceiling and gravy slopped all over the table. You had to be quick to dodge the stabbing forks. There's the back of my hand to prove it. For afters there was always something with curdled custard. We never did find out what that something was. We suspected but we didn't care to talk about it.

At one place I stayed in Manchester, we used to have a trapeze artiste who took her meals swinging from the chandelier. There was a contortionist who could look up his own back to see if his hat was on straight. Then there was an hygienic acrobat who used to do handstands on the toilet seat, and a midget who had served in the navy on midget submarines. He was working as a radio repair man inside transistors.

In a Wigan boarding house, we had a man who called himself a lion-tamer. He trained sea-lions. He used to get roaring drunk on sea-shanties. Then there was the xylophone player. He got drunk one night. He tore up a couple of Belisha Beacons and tried to play the overture to *William Tell* on a pedestrian crossing. He had an uncle who was a bird impersonator. He used to go down the Underground and ride round and round the Inner Circle and finally disappear up the Elephant and Castle.

I was once playing in Newcastle when I met a girl who used to be a snake-charmer. She gave it up because the snakes were always messing about. The boarding house where we were staying was strange. All night long I could hear humming but it wasn't until I was bitten I realized it was a humbug. My landlady warned me to watch my step when she found a strange footprint on my hot water-bottle.

While I was at a hotel in Walsall there was a convention going on for fruit growers. The language in the bars was choice and fruity. I was told that the convention turned out to be fruitful. The Shoe Manufacturers' convention, a few weeks before, was a lot of cobblers talking about how they could save their souls. Very religious.

I missed a booking once. I phoned my agent. He said 'What are you getting all steamed up about?' I was phoning from a sauna. He had just booked an ex-policeman who wanted to be an actor. He was tired of being called a pig and preferred to be called a ham for a change. He played straight parts but in the end he turned out to be bent. He stole the show at the Hippodrome, Pudsey.

At Margate I stayed at a hostel. I could tell by the way the tables were laid for dinner that our hostess was well travelled. I had an Iberia knife, an SAS fork and an Air France spoon. It was a jet set. The hostess was blunt about it. She said she didn't like to leave everything in the air. She was an air hostess.

In Wells, the Cathedral town, the landlady at the boarding house where I stayed was a pirate. Her black beard repelled all boarders. The boarders were a motley crowd. There was an impressionist who was always taking off someone or other. One day he took himself off with the wife of his best friend.

There were a couple of acts the talent shows hadn't yet discovered. One even had his own clapometer. An old girl, a Mrs Fargo, known as 'Wells' Fargo, gave drama lessons. She was a stage-coach. She told me about a couple of friars who had gone to work at the local chip shop. One was a fish-friar: the other was a chip-monk.

When I am on tour I like to look around the shops, especially antique shops. I went into one antique shop and bought a music-stand. I couldn't get a note out of it. The shopkeeper tried to sell me a four-poster bed. I didn't like the posters. He said the bed was ideal for antique lovers. I said I might be old but I wasn't antique yet. I picked up a funny looking article.

'What's this?' I asked.

'Why, it's as plain as a pikestaff,' he said. 'It's a pikestaff!'

I was so annoyed I rammed my pipe into my jacket pocket. My jacket caught fire. It was a blazer.

As I left the shop I bumped into an old acquaintance. He was a soft-shoe dancer. He told me that he had taken a job as a postman. He said it was better than walking the streets. He had just had an operation. An ear transplant. He complained to his surgeon that he could now hear violins playing all the time in that ear. The surgeon said he wasn't surprised. The donor had an ear for music.

I played in a market town in the Black Country. It was a black market. What a reception! The locals showered me with eggs, cream, butter and milk. I was a mess. I went to the gents for a wash and brush up. There were four cubicles. It was a fourflusher. I was flustered. I dropped the brush and bent to recover it. The seat fell on my head. I staggered out into the corridor to the bar. I bumped into the stage manager.

'Ah, Tommy!' he said. 'You're looking very flushed. Have one on me.'

There was no answer to that.

I made my debut at the London Palladium in 1952. I met an old fellow in the bar who asked me if I were the Tommy Cooper he had just seen on the stage. I said I was and he said it served me right. It turned out that this man had been a missionary many years ago in the Solomon Islands when the islanders were still cannibals. He said it had been the missionaries who had given the cannibals their first taste of religion.

The old missionary told me that life with the cannibals had never been dull. There was always something cooking. The old cannibal chef would often have acquaintances for dinner. The chef's daughter had written a cookbook called *Jungle Cooking, or Have Your Friends for Dinner.*

While the old missionary and I were talking, there was a sudden disturbance. It was the Mad Cannibal from Canning Town doing the can-can.

I made my first appearance in the USA in 1954. I appeared at the fabulous Hotel Flamingo, Las Vegas. The press said I was the high spot of the show. No wonder. I'm six feet four. The rest of the performers were three feet six. I thought as the hotel was called The Flamingo, I would do my big trick with flamingoes instead of doves, but their legs kept sticking out of my coat-tails. So I did the trick with some cards I had met at the swimming pool, they were only three feet six too.

While I was in Las Vegas I was invited to a cocktail party at a nearby motel. It was close to a huge car cemetery. A big notice outside, said RUST IN PIECES.

There I was with a cocktail in one hand and a toothpick in the other, when a women came hopping up to me. It was Hedda Hopper. She was dodging the column. She was a fifth columnist.

'Ah!' she said, 'you're Mr Cooper I am told. Hi Gary!'

'I'm not that sort of Cooper,' I said.

'Cooper, Cooper!' she said. 'Seen one, seen them all.'

She stuffed an olive in my ear and hopped off.

I met too that great rock-star Rock Hudson, who had just left his uncle upstairs or downstairs with MacMillan and Wife. Some joker was there too. He was jamming bananas into a fruit machine which was tilted upside down, and he was singing 'I'll do it my way.' He had blue eyes.

An American friend of mine then pointed out a lot of Mafia men in the lobby of the hotel. There was this man slapping another man around. I asked my friend what it was all about.

'That guy doing the hitting bit,' he said, 'is the ex-boxer, Slapsy the Schlapper. He's a hit man. And that guy there with the size-twelves, that's Harry the Cobbler. He specializes in making concrete boots. The guy he is talking to is Hugh "rat-tat-tat" Ratzoff. He is a Tommy-gunner, so watch out. As a matter of fact, he is the original Hugh dirty rat, Hugh.'

'I like that,' I said, 'but I like the look of that cracker over there better. Who is she?'

'That,' said my friend, 'is Bridget Cardot. She's a hit woman. They call her Contract Bridget.'

'What about that nervous looking fellow over there?' I asked.

'Oh, him!' said my friend. 'You mean the guy flitting around winking and nudging himself? He's nobody. He's in civil engineering. He just supplies cement to Harry the Cobbler.'

'Do you know that girl who just walked in?' I asked.

'Do I?' said my friend. 'Why, that's nobody but Wanda Downtown, the lady cop. Now, she's really something. Have you ever seen a cop with legs like that? She really knows her stuff. When she heard that the local laundromat was being used by crooked politicians to wash their dirty linen, she went to clean up the joint. She took her knuckle-dusters and her bold automatic tucked down her stocking. A reporter spoke to one of the arrested men. He said he didn't want to talk about it, but it was a fair cop.'

'But of course,' continued my friend, 'the case came to nothing. The prosecuting attorney was bought for a song to the tune of "Who wants to be a millionaire? I do." The judge was sewn up tight. In a sack at the bottom of the lake. And do you see the guy with the ears, the nose and that mouth? That's the big shot, No-face Nolan. He has Grogan, the Chief of Police, in his pocket. Look! That's Grogan peeking out of Nolan's coat-tails.'

I met a woman who owned a night-club in Las Vegas called 'The Igloo.' She told me she was an Eskimo.

'You've got a funny accent for an Eskimo,' I said.

'Well,' she said, 'you've heard of Nanook of the North. Well I'm Eskimo Nell from way down south, you-all. I had a sister Florrie. She was known as Ice-Floe, but things got tough. We had a deep depression over Iceland and there was a wage freeze. Ice-Floe drifted way down south and disappeared. I married an Eskimo called Esky Moe Iceberg, and we lived just north of the North Pole. He was a movie actor and had played 007 Centigrade in the movie *Coldfinger*.

'We first met at an ice-rink in the Street of a Thousand Ice-holes by the sign of the Freezing Mitt. I was wearing the latest Eskimo fashion at the time. Cold pants. The temperature was forty below and not much more above. It was cold. Esky Moe told me it was love at first sight. "Get a load of that dame!" he had said to himself. "What a pair of nostrils! Like pools of pitch in the snow!"

'I tell you, Tommy,' said Eskimo Nell, 'It was a cold romance. Moe seized me in a freezing embrace and crushed me to him like ice. He said, "Your nose is so wonderful. So hard, so cold." I could feel his freezing breath in my face. We rubbed noses with a freezing passion. I agreed to marry him and we sealed it with a sniff.

'Moe took me to see his uncle. He was a big shot. He was on the cold line to Moscow when we walked in. He was actually an Eskimo rajah who had patented a sauce made from ice. It was a chilly sauce. His name was Birra Jam which means Big Jim. He was called B. Jam for short. He owned a frozen foods factory and advertised a lot on ETV (Eskimo Television).

'Moe and I were married and we bought our own igloo. That's an icicle built for two. It had everything as far as convenience. You could get to it on the Arctic Circle or the Northern Line, change at Whitechapel. We were proud of our home. We decided to have a house cooling and invited all our friends for drinks and dinner.

'I told Moe to get the sledge from the garage and nip down to the supermarket. It was a very cold nip. I told him to pick up a penguin, just imported from the South Pole and, maybe, lampoon a whale or two on the way. We would have a whale of a time. I also reminded him to get some cleaning materials – Eskimo Snow and a carton of Cold Automatic.

'Moe put on his ice-cap and went to get the sledge from the garage. It wouldn't start. Moe had to get some anti-freeze to unfreeze the dog from the lamp-post. Moe finally drove off singing, "Sledge dogs and Eskimos go out in the midnight sun."

'All the big shots of the Eskimo community turned up at our house cooling. There were reporters from the *Midnight Sun* and the *Freezing News* lots of people from ETV including Dan-Dan the Weatherman. He looked nervous but was putting up a cold front. Felix Oneupski, the Polish explorer, was there. He told me his brother was exploring the South Pole. The fact that they were both explorers and were both up the pole was all they had in common. Actually they were Poles apart.

'We served snowballs and frozen Daiquiris for drinks. We ran out of ice. I chipped a few cubes from the walls. For dinner, we had blubber paté, followed by deep-frozen penguin. Next we had glacier mince, served with ice chips and greens from Greenland. For dessert, we had chocolate moose, complete with antlers, with a delicious sauce of pink candles. Then there was iced coffee, after which we chatted and sucked frozen peas. The men drank brandy and smoked fish. The party was a great success.

'And so life went on,' said Eskimo Nell. 'Moe pottered about the igloo and thawed logs for the fire in the backyard. We had our snow flakes and whale juice for breakfast in the morning. We kept pets: a polar bear and an arctic fox. Both appeared on ETV in the glacier mint commercial. It brought us in a few extra bucks. We gave parties and discussed art, politics, but tried to avoid talking about the weather. You had only to mention in company that the weather was cold and some patriotic Eskimo would take the cue.

'"Cold? Did you say cold?" he would shout and everyone felt obliged to freeze to attention and sing the Eskimo National Anthem. "The Snow-spangled Banner."

'I will now sing it for you, Tommy!' said Eskimo Nell.

I was touched. I must have been as I listened to her plaintive wail. I forgot the song but remember the touching.

Eskimo Nell paused to chip an icicle from her eye before she carried on. 'I had a boy we called Horatio. He was known to one and all as Horatio, Nell's son. Moe's ambition was for him to be an admiral in the Eskimo Navy. Not much of a future, I thought, to be an admiral of a fleet of canoes. However, Horatio grew up and changed his name to Hornblower. He went off to Hollywood to look for Gregory Peck.

'Life was wonderful for a time, but of course, it couldn't last. Eventually our love began to grow warm and Moe took to giving me melting glances. This, as you know, is not so hot for an Eskimo. So, finally, I told him to go paddle his own canoe. We rubbed noses for the last time and I left him with his nose well out of joint.

'Sometimes, when I get lonesome, I sleep in the deep freeze and dream about Esky Moe Iceberg.'

This, then was the sad ballad of Eskimo Nell. I shed a tear or two and said how sorry I was.

'Don't be,' said Nell. 'Fellas leave me cold. They cut no ice with me nowadays.'

I went home and turned the central heating full up.

While I was in the States I was asked to do a Western film for TV. I've always been crazy about Westerns. I read all the Western comics as a kid – Tom Mix, Rex Ritter, Rocky Lane and Roy Rogers. So when it comes to Westerns I know what I'm talking about.

We went on location way out West to a town called Sleepy Hollow. The windows were yawning, and the doors had dropped off. The only sign of life was some centipedes and these were on their last legs. I went into a store and bought one of the new ten-litre hats. Then I went up Boot Hill for some boots.

I walked across the road to the saloon. There was Granny Croakley, Wild Bill Hiccup and Daniel Goon. I recognized them all.

I made my first mistake when the bartender asked me what I wanted. I said I wanted a couple of shots and held up a couple of fingers. Granny Croakley, who had been dozing, woke up and shouted 'Draw!' She fired two shots and I almost lost two fingers. But I drew her a quick sketch.

Wild Bill Hiccup made for his gun. He was quick on the trigger and slow on the draw. He fired before he had unholstered his pistol. He shot himself in the foot. He was hopping mad. He threw a gun at me. It hit me on the left ear. He was a gunslinger. Daniel Goon pointed a gun at me but he couldn't fire. I had put my finger over the hole.

The Clapham Kid walked in. He had a Colt 45 in one hand a hot 45 in the other. 'How do you like it?' he said. 'Hot or colt?'

I took off. Outside in the street, I saw a cowboy with a horse across his shoulders. He glared at me.

'What's wrong, amigo?' he shouted. 'Haven't you ever seen a cowboy carrying a colt before?'

I went off to find the Indian village. I knew I was getting near it. I could hear the dogs pow-wowing. I met the Red Indian Chief.

'Me, Tommy Cooper.' I said. 'Me come in peace.'

'Me Tommy Hawk,' he answered. 'Soon you go in pieces.'

I offered to smoke the pipe of peace with him.

'Pipe of peace?' he said. 'Me no smokum. Medicine man, he say pipe bad for health. So up your pipe. I give you cigar.'

He was a cigar store Indian. He said: 'White man speak with forked tongue.' I said 'I'm sorry, but I was eating peas and my fork slipped.' It was a slip of the tongue and I slipped away on it.

There was a big tepee. It had been thatched with scalps. It was a wigwam. It had a sign. It was an Indian sign. It said 'The Bombay Restaurant'. There was an Indian outside wearing a turban with a feather. It was a feather in his cap. He was singing 'Curry me back to ol' Virginny.' He told me that the wigwam was the new Indian restaurant and did I want to make an Indian Reservation. He said his name was Smith, alias Kid Curry. He used to be in a TV comedy series for Sunday morning viewers. It was called the *Curry On* series. In one show he had played the part of a cowboy and had been showered with curry pies. It was called *Curry on, Cowboy!* He said he had a partner. His name was Jim Bhowani and he was from up the junction. He was a sacred cowboy and had left England because the taxman was milking him.

There were a couple of Indian scouts hanging about with their scoutmaster. They were waiting to take stones out of horses hooves with their scout knives. They tried to flog me a horse. They said it was the finest horse in the West. It was a sea-horse. It was a Western Super-Mare.

To the Manor Born

Peter Spence

Audrey fforbes-Hamilton, recently widowed and forced to move from her ancestral manor, Grantleigh, is now installed in the old lodge on the estate. Here, in her reduced circumstances, she comes into frequent contact with the new lord of the manor, Richard DeVere, in whose presence she preserves a veneer of civility...

According to Anderson & ffitch, which first brought Richard DeVere to Grantleigh, the old lodge was a 'tasteful conversion'. If this was taken to mean that it had been converted from something tasteful into something tasteless, it would be near the mark. Successive owners had modernized it, obliterating all its old features, and its interior had degenerated into the bland style of a period which Audrey dubbed 'mock Recency'.

Only the hall had retained its original style and dimensions, but it led off into silly little rooms which would have been better placed on a housing estate in Basildon.

Furthermore, a previous owner appeared to have a grudge against heat. First, he'd removed any doors which might have kept it in, in favour of allowing free passage from room to room without let or hindrance, and all the fireplaces were horrid little tiled objects much too small to heat the enlarged rooms.

But of course, it was its position which Audrey found so irresistibly attractive, offering as it did an unobstructed view of the manor, its comings and goings, and even much of what went on behind that stately façade. She was now seeing builders' vans parked outside and workmen coming and going, and was consumed with curiosity as to what DeVere was doing.

Since she had hardly left the manor in body, she certainly hadn't left it in spirit, but was clinging to it like a phantom limb after an amputation.

The triumph of her little deception with DeVere, coupled with her establishing a bridgehead from which she could keep an eye on him, sweetened the pill of her otherwise disastrous change of circumstances. She was also strengthened by her unerring sense of destiny and confidence that one day the worm would turn and she would be back in the manor.

All this apart, it was problems all the way. But they tended not to be the ones she anticipated. She expected, for instance, to find living in a confined space unutterably claustrophobic. But even while her new living quarters were not decorated, carpeted and curtained, and while builders occupied every available space, knocking down walls and tearing up floorboards, she found it bearable. She even found the actual experience of sharing a bathroom much less abhorrent than the theory, except that Brabinger would keep using her Ladyshave.

And then, of course, she gradually became aware of new privations which she had not anticipated at all.

For instance, she could not have foreseen that one of the most painful experiences of the move was to be the trivial act of crossing out 'Grantleigh Manor' from her printed writing paper, when informing her friends of her change of address. This led her to another agony, that of asking herself who her friends were, a question which had never arisen before since in her former position her circle had been rigidly prescribed. This in turn led her to realize that if her friends just included those who had rallied to her in her hour of need, then she only had a handful. And if her friends were those people who were now inviting her to dinner parties and the like to ease the misery of her husbandless state, then she had none. The sudden realization that there were absolutely no invitations on the horrid little mantelpiece was traumatic.

'The mantelpiece at the manor positively bristled with stiffies,' she recalled indignantly to Marjory, who was always round at the old lodge helping her settle in.

'Dinner parties, balls, coming-outs, society weddings, Henley, Ascot, Goodwood, Glyndebourne,' she listed nostalgically, 'to think that I won't be going to Glyndebourne this year, and I used to so enjoy it – apart from having to sit through all those interminable operas. Fair-weather friends all of them – suddenly I'm a social pariah. No invitations – not so much as a Tupperware party in the village.'

Marjory tried to comfort her, and pointed to two conspicuous cards on the mantelpiece.

'What are those two?'

'Oh, real social highlights, these.' She picked them up and read them. 'An

invitation to patronize Fonacar Cabs and to have my drain problem solved.'
She had written 'refused' on both.

Audrey went to her handbag in search of further evidence. She looked at
her diary and flicked its pages under Marjory's nose. The front was crammed
full of tiny writing and the later pages were blank.

'We were really in demand till Marton died – now look what I've got to
look forward to.' She consulted the diary 'The Muslim New Year, and High
Tide in Aberystwyth. And nothing to wear for either.'

Since the last encounter the day she left the manor, Audrey's attitude to
DeVere had mellowed. Part of this was due to her pride that she left the
manor nobly, rather than fall in with his plans. She had delivered one
body blow and was now entrenched in a position from which more could
follow if he stepped out of line. Furthermore, she was in a position to
formulate and execute her own manoeuvres which would lead her back to
her first love – the manor. That DeVere was quite beyond the pale was
without question, but that was not to say that he couldn't eventually be
moulded into a suitable match for her. In this enterprise she must be
circumspect and cautious, lest she rule herself out as a suitable partner for
him. Hence, at this stage in the relationship, she was content to bide her
time, seeming neither overanxious to ingratiate herself nor to appear to
threaten him. But this was easier said than done. Eager though she was
that relations should be cordial, this did not give DeVere the right to
trample all over her.

He was doing this unwittingly, but with Audrey being constantly
reminded of her humbled position in the neighbourhood *vis-à-vis* his exalted
status, he might as well have been trampling in public and in spikes. It was
at their first meeting after the move that things came to a head. The
battleground was at the village post office.

'Really, the price of ninepenny stamps these days,' Audrey complained as
the old harridan pushed the perforated sheet under the grill.

'Always been 9p, dear,' said Mrs Patterson, the postmistress.

'Not nine p. Nine *pence*. A *pea* is a little green vegetable which grows in a
pod. Now, could I pay for my papers, Mrs P?'

'Have to take for them separate, dear.'

It was one of the facts of life in Mrs Patterson's shop that everything had to
be 'took for separate' – the post office, the groceries section, the off-license,
the newspapers department, and she had tills dotted all over the shop, each
guarded by a spiteful-looking cat.

Mrs Patterson was thumbing through her newspaper account book.

'Now, it's Mrs fforbes-Hamilton, isn't it?' she said as if she needed reminding, 'of Grantleigh Manor...?'

'No, it's the old lodge now.' The admission did not come easily.

'Ah, yes – how is it there?'

'Small.'

'And how's Mr DeVere doing up at your old place – they say he's knocking hell out of the old manor.'

'I wouldn't know.'

'Nice man – if you see him, would you tell him his cigars are in and so is his *Horse and Hound.*'

The intimation that DeVere might be a hunting man came as a surprise. She wondered about it as Mrs Patterson took her money for the papers, and then totted up her groceries and 'took separate' for them.

'That'll be £5.16,' she said, bringing a little notice down from the top of some sweet jars. It said, 'Please do not ask for credit – a refusal might offend.' Audrey pretended she hadn't seen it, and paid.

'Was there anything else, dear?' This was only the third time she had been called 'dear' in the last twenty-five years. All of them had been in the last minute or so, a symptom that her reduction in circumstances was being noted.

Audrey bore the slight with fortitude. There was one other thing to buy, and she could see it in the cold display cabinet.

'Could I have that breaded ham, please?'

'I'm sorry, dear,' said Mrs Patterson. 'I'm keeping it back for old Mrs Cartwright. Her Linda's picking it up sometime.'

Audrey boiled. Linda was supposed to be working for her.

'Mrs Cartwright? The herdman's wife? Since when has she taken preference over...'

No, no, Audrey was telling herself. Control. Dignity. Don't give them the satisfaction of seeing that it hurts.

Her sentence was cut short anyway by the ringing of the shop bell. The door opened and DeVere was standing beside Audrey at the counter.

'Morning, Audrey.'

'Good morning, Mr DeVere.'

'Nice weather for the time of day, as the old country saying goes.'

Audrey ignored it and said coldly, 'Your cigars are in.'

'Ah – just passing by on the off chance.'

'And your *Horse and Hound*,' said Mrs Patterson, handing the items over the counter.

DeVere fumbled in his pocket and jangled his money, but Mrs Patterson removed the 'No Credit' notice from him, as deftly as she had displayed it for Audrey. DeVere put his money away.

'Thank you.'

'Was there anything else?'

'Yes. I wonder if you have such a thing as . . .'

The shop bell rang, and he turned round.

Audrey was gone.

She had stepped out into Main Street, that is to say, the only street in Grantleigh village. Parked ostentatiously, or so she thought, was DeVere's Rolls. She looked at it as if contemplating an act of vandalism, but was sufficiently self-aware to realize that her own Rolls parked round the corner by the horse-trough was having much the same effect. She had just come face to face with DeVere for the first time since her departure from the manor, and she had plenty to say to him and he had plenty of information she would like from him.

She hovered outside the shop, and read the display of cards in the window advertising for home-helps to do light cleaning. There seemed to be an extraordinary number of dirty lights in the neighbourhood. She smiled at Mrs Hodge's advertisement – 'Let me do your dressmaking and have a perfect fit.' There was a Grand Carpet Sale in Marlbury, with the inducement to 'get felt free', which sounded interesting. But it was another advertisement which caught her eye:

> *FREE SECRETARIAL COURSE*
> *Offered to any girl in*
> *vicinity likely to be available*
> *for temporary work with local*
> *company.*
> *Apply: Richard DeVere*
> *Cavendish Foods*
> *Grantleigh Manor*

She then walked a little way up the road and back again past the shop door in the hope of their paths crossing. DeVere did not emerge. She tried the same dummy run a second time, and DeVere did not rise to the bait. She had just turned back for a third approach when the shop bell rang and DeVere stepped out into the street and hailed her. Audrey spun round.

'Are you going home, Audrey?'

'Yes.'

DeVere pointed the other way down the road.

'It's that way.'

Audrey did not react to this, because she noticed that DeVere was holding a breaded ham. He noticed her looking at it.

'Now who would have thought you could get a breaded ham just like that' – he flicked his fingers – 'in the middle of the country?'

'Indeed,' agreed Audrey. 'These days, all the best pigs seem to be moving into the towns.'

With that, she set off in the direction DeVere had indicated.

'Are you walking?' he shouted after her, when she was a little way down the road.

Audrey looked at her feet in disbelief.

'So I am. I wondered what it was I was doing.'

'Can I offer you a lift?'

'Oh – if it's not taking you out of your way.'

'I live on the estate, don't I?'

'Oh, I know, Mr DeVere. Believe me, I know.'

She was coming back. DeVere, the perfect gentleman, opened the passenger door without the spur of it being either a new car or a new wife, and ushered her in, a chivalrous act which he then ruined by tossing the breaded ham after her, so that it landed on her lap, shedding a crumb or two. Getting into the driver's seat, he tossed *Horse and Hound* into the back and lit a cigar. He started the engine and the car moved off.

'Home, James, and don't spare the horses,' he yelled, and then, in a voice he thought passed for a west country accent, 'giddy-up'. 'Isn't that what you say?'

'No.'

'Mush.'

'Not to horses.'

'I'm sorry, I forgot I was talking to the Anna Sewell of the Avon Valley.'

Audrey was not amused, but sat there ram-rod stiff, staring ahead of her. She did not know that round the corner by the horse-trough, PC Peaslake had drawn up on his motorcycle, and was slapping a parking ticket on her windscreen. She wondered whether she had made the right decision in choosing this moment to make her first move with DeVere. Now she was in his car, she was no longer on neutral territory.

'The French have a word for it, you know,' said DeVere, after an uneasy silence.

'What?'

'I don't know, but the English word doesn't seem to be getting through. Better out than in, you know.'

Audrey steeled herself for a showdown.

'I don't know where to start,' she said. 'It's one thing after another, isn't it?'

She took a deep breath.

'First you take my ... then you take my ... and then,' words were failing her fast. In an effort to come up with some kind of inventory of the privation she had suffered at his hands, the details had gone completely out of her head. The only one that she could be sure of was a breaded ham which she clutched like a bludgeon, but what really hurt was that she had been called 'dear' by Mrs Patterson.

'I'm sorry,' said DeVere.

'If you were sorry,' she said, 'you would...' she had seen that if he was sorry, there was nothing he could do about it. She changed the subject.

'I must say I'm surprised to see you're doing your own shopping.'

'I wouldn't normally, but I've given my girl the morning off to go to a typing course.'

'Yes, I saw your notice.'

'I'm bringing prosperity to an under-privileged area,' he boasted. 'I could do a lot for this valley.'

'I'm sure you could,' said Audrey acidly.

'I beg your pardon?'

'Nothing.'

DeVere continued his self-advertisement.

'I'm supporting local industry,' he said, puffing cigar smoke, 'like I get my cigars through Mrs Patterson.'

That sounded like hard work. Audrey fanned the fumey air vigorously.

'Who is the girl who does your shopping, by the way?'

'The Cartwright girl.'

'Linda?'

'That's right. The horsey one.'

'I didn't realize she worked for you.'

'Oh, yes. Only today she's on a secretarial course. Come to think of it, I'm surprised to see you doing your own shopping. Who usually does yours?'

'Linda Cartwright.'

This was a bombshell. Linda Cartwright was also Audrey's employee. She adopted a defeatist tone.

'So now you take my domestic. Well, it was only to be expected.'

DeVere looked to the heavens through his automatic sun-roof.

'Oh, my God, so that's it. *Mea culpa*. I'm sorry, Audrey. I had no idea. She didn't say.'

'No, she wouldn't I expect you're paying her far more than I could. You'll have my entire staff before you're through.'

'That's the last thing I want.'

'And it's the last thing I've got.'

DeVere felt himself to be the victim of a malevolent imagination, and he was going to have to get used to it.

'I wouldn't have done that if I'd known. You've got me all wrong. You don't think too much of me, do you?'

'Whatever do you mean? There isn't an uncharitable bone in my body.'

'That leaves the nervous system and the bloodstream. All right, if I've got to prove that I'm no ogre, what would you say to Linda Cartwright being on my payroll to work for you?'

Audrey was tempted by this gesture, but to accept would not be true to the part she was playing. 'No charity' was becoming her motto.

'And then spend the rest of my life making it up to you? No, no, not me. Anyway, that's not my main concern.'

'You mean there's more?' sighed DeVere wearily. 'All right, wheel out the big guns. What is it?'

Audrey was beginning to get the feel of this encounter and a list of grievances was being drawn up in her subconscious which now appeared before her like an agenda.

'Mrs Patterson says you've been, as she puts it, "knocking hell out of the manor". I want to know what you're doing.'

'Nothing drastic. I'm leaving the foundations.'

'Why? They're the worst bits.'

DeVere felt her animosity boring into him. His business experience was that the best way to deal with hostility is to make light of it, and toy with those who harbour it, as cat with mouse.

'Yes, I'm knocking all the walls down. It's a Japanese idea – to make the interior design blend with the outside landscape.'

He laughed as he saw that Audrey appeared to be believing him, and said more seriously. 'No, I'm just doing some things in your husband's study to make it my personal office. We call it functionalizing.'

'That's a big word.'

'It's a big room. Personally, I prefer the more genteel description.'

'Which is?'

'Knocking hell out of it.'

Audrey tightened her grip on the breaded ham.

DeVere was bashing on gaily. 'You'd be surprised how well my computer console blends with the fruitwood panelling in the ballroom.' He looked at her for a reaction, and it was clear from the optic daggers that she returned that he had overstepped the mark.

'I'm sorry, Audrey,' he said in a conciliatory tone, 'it's just that you rise to it, like a trout to a fat fly. Pardon my choice of words. How's your house, by the way?'

'Small!'

She was clearly dissatisfied with the place – a fact which DeVere seized on to atone for his lack of good grace. He might even score more in the likeability rating by pursuing this line of enquiry.

'If there are any alterations you'd like to make, my builders could always be at your disposal, and at my expense, of course, but that goes without saying.'

'That's very kind, but no thank you.'

'Is there anything else you want?'

'A horse!' Audrey was staring wide-eyed at the road ahead of her. 'Slow down for heaven's sake.'

DeVere was driving faster than was customary along these narrow country lanes, and, turning a corner, Audrey had been the first to see a horse and rider coming towards them on the narrow verge.

'Slower, slower,' Audrey was begging. 'Snail's pace.'

DeVere did as he was asked, but without seeing why.

'We're in the country now,' said Audrey as they crept past the horse to the acknowledgement of the amply busted adolescent in its saddle.

'We don't race around the lanes on cubbing days,' she admonished. 'Nor do we brush past horses at 90 mph honking our Colonel Bogey hooters.'

DeVere stood corrected and flicked his fingers in self-deprecation.

'Tch. Of course not,' he said. 'No, that's cows, isn't it?'

They were now past the horse and moving up to the car's former speed.

'Who did you say did your shopping for you?' DeVere asked.

'Linda Cartwright. And who did you say you were paying a fortune to go on a secretarial course today?'

'Linda Cartwright. And who was that on the horse?'

'Linda Cartwright,' they chorused in unison.

Audrey smiled.

'And do you know something? She's on the way to the shop for her mother. To pick up a breaded ham.' She laughed and loosened her grip on the Cartwright Sunday lunch.

For the rest of the journey, they found themselves in complete agreement. This consensus of opinion was that Constable Peaslake was unnecessarily bombastic. The subject arose when a police motorcycle appeared from nowhere as they sped along the main road and hee-hawed them to a halt.

Book in hand, the constable was just giving DeVere the 'you were doing eighty-five – what is it? – is the lady having a baby or something?' recital, when Audrey leant over to make sure Peaslake realized who the lady was.

'Perhaps you haven't met Mr DeVere, constable,' she said, as if Peaslake was on a social call. 'Your father's new employer.'

The notebook went away.

'Just checking you haven't seen any escaped convicts,' the constable improvised rather obviously.

Audrey knew the nearest prison was fifty miles away.

'Just so that if you see anyone hitching, you'll know.'

'Yes,' said Audrey, 'we'll know if they're going this way, they'll be on their way back to prison.'

Peaslake stomped back to his chattering motorcycle and rode off.

Soon they were back in the forecourt of the old lodge.

'Most girls I give lifts to like to play with the gadgets,' said DeVere as he dropped Audrey off.

'Most girls haven't been in Rolls-Royces before.'

'Don't you even want to use the car phone?'

'No, thanks – I'll write. Good-bye, Mr DeVere.'

DeVere drove off to the manor, leaving Audrey standing in the forecourt. She waved a breaded ham at him.

'Yours, I think,' she called after him, faintly lest she be heard. She put it into her basket and walked in the front door.

The hall was in chaos. Floorboards were up and wires were trailing about all over the place, and the house had that dusty atmosphere which denotes the transformation of masonry from wall to rubble. She thought the builders had finished. She heard a thump upstairs.

'Brabinger,' she shouted up the stairwell. Stairwell? Hah!! In this little hutch? Brabinger appeared halfway up the stairs. He wore his leather apron and waistcoat, and it appeared that his sleevegarters had not kept his cuffs, which were wet, out of mischief. He was holding a dead pigeon.

'What on earth are you doing?' demanded Audrey.

'I'm doing the rewiring, madam.'

'I see. With a pigeon?'

'No, no, madam. I found this floating in the water tank.'

'I was going to say! I've heard of detecting gas leaks with canaries, but I didn't realize electricity had any equivalent.'

The implications of Brabinger's find took a little time to percolate.

'In the water tank?' she screamed. 'Oh, how awful!'

'It's all right. It's dead.'

'Yes, but to think that my bath water comes out of that tap. I've washed in it – I've drunk it.' She clutched her throat and choked dramatically.

'Ye Gods, I've arranged flowers in that water.'

'I'm sure they'll grow the better for it.'

'*And* that's the water I took up to the church for the Cartwright christening. What a way to welcome a newborn into the bosom of the church. To dunk his head into the entrails of a dead pigeon.'

'If the baby grows into a seven-footer, you'll know what's done it, madam,' he laughed, adding as an afterthought, 'if I may be allowed to say so.'

'No, you may not – may I remind you that you are still "downstairs" in spite of the shortage of stairs. I feel quite ill. Anyway, what were you doing in the loft – the wiring's all done.'

'It's *my* system, madam.'

'What system?'

'I thought you'd ask. If you'd care to follow me, I'll show you.'

He led her into the kitchen and pointed proudly above the door, where there was now a bell-box where none had been before. Encased in the mahogany frame behind the glass were twenty little portholes marked 'Front Door', 'Back Door', 'Drawing Room', 'Library', 'Morning Room' and 'Bedroom – one to fifteen and so on, each backed by its little red disc just waiting to wag when service was summoned to any of the rooms.

'Well, I never,' exulted Audrey, putting her shopping down on the table. 'Brabinger – you are ingenious. That's assuming it works.'

'Oh, it does, madam, it does. *Regardez*.'

He disappeared into the hall and a few seconds later the bell-box burst into life. The little red disc behind 'Conservatory' oscillated vigorously back and forth.

'There, madam,' said Brabinger returning, 'the front door.'

'Very good. I don't like to criticize, but the bell-box said "Conservatory".'

'You always were a perfectionist, madam. A small matter. I just have to do a bit of fiddling in the junction box to connect the right wire to the conservatory.'

'But Brabinger, we haven't *got* a conservatory.'

'Ah,' said Brabinger. 'Details, details. Soon we'll have a bell-push in every room – the sitting-room, the dining room, all the bedrooms, the bathroom.'

'Why should I want to summon you to the bathroom? Besides, in a house this size, I can always shout.'

'Well, the loft then, if ever you make it into another room.'

'Oh, marvellous – so that the drowning pigeons can summon help.'

'I have only to put the bell mounting in the drawing room, and the job will be done.'

Audrey was very impressed, and felt she was pouring scorn on it.

'Sweet of you to think of it, Brabinger. Congratulations.' She looked at the pigeon. 'Now, do get rid of that thing.'

They were standing face to face when a bell rang. Brabinger was looking beyond Audrey at the back door, where Marjory had appeared, and Audrey was looking at the bell-box.

'Your services appear to be required.'

'It's Miss Frobisher, madam.'

'Then what is she doing in "Bedroom Three"?'

She turned and saw Marjory. Brabinger had already opened the door, and stood with the dead pigeon still dangling from his fingers.

'Morning, Brabinger,' chirped Marjory. 'Yuh!' she recoiled from the pigeon. 'What's that pigeon doing?'

'Not a great deal,' said Audrey.

'Where's it come from?'

Brabinger began, 'I found it in the...' but was soon cut off.

'Brabinger shot it, didn't you, Brabinger?' Audrey interjected.

'But it's drenched,' Marjory objected.

'With a water pistol.'

'Oh, good shot, Brabinger.'

That was all right, then. Audrey swooped on Marjory and engulfed her with pleasantries.

'Oh, Marjory, I'm so thankful to see you. There's something I want to tell you.'

She put her arm around her and bulldozed her through the hall into the drawing room, with a passing instruction to Brabinger-cum-pigeon.

'Oh, when you've got rid of that object, there's something you and Ned can do for me. I forgot something when I drove back from the village.'

'What would that be, madam?'

'The car,' replied Audrey, tossing him the keys.

The drawing room was still in a state of some disarray though it looked considerably more lived in than it had done for weeks. The carpet was down, the furniture was installed. The curtains were not up, though they lay ready, draped over the back of the armchair. It lacked refinements, the homely and personal touches provided by ornaments and pictures. These were still in tea chests in the grate.

'Oh, this room is going to be lovely,' said Marjory.

'Yes, but it will never be Versailles – not with that horrid little fireplace. Would you give me a hand with these?'

They heaved a tea chest into the middle of the room and began to unpack it. Marjory was extracting a marble table lamp complete with shade.

'Like a lucky dip, this – only without the sawdust. Do be careful with that.'

'Any breakages during the move?'

'Only one of those lion's-paw table legs. Nasty chip.'

'Oh, dear, those tables are quite rare.'

'This one is now – can't be many tables with three lion's-paws and one pig's trotter.'

She was extracting a fox's brush mounted on a wooden shield. She grimaced at it.

'No,' she judged, 'I don't think I want hunting trophies all around me. A bit tasteless – perhaps you'd like it – it's more your sort of thing.'

She stopped to watch Marjory putting the lamp on an occasional table.

'Lampshade seams should point *into* the wall, Marjory, and *away* from the door where it can't be seen.' Marjory turned it round.

A horse's hoof, mounted on an inscribed silver plinth, was emerging from its wrapping.

'Ah, that is more like it,' said Audrey as she read the inscription. 'Petronella – one of grandfather's best horses – do you realize that this hoof won the St Leger in 1912?'

'On its own?' gasped Marjory.

'Attached to the horse,' she said with a long-suffering sigh. 'What a way to end up – full of paper clips.' She flipped up the silver lid and paper clips spilled out on to the table.

'Oh, yes, we used to have a little joke with this when Marton and I were children. Watch this, Marjory.'

She picked out a paper clip and held it up in one hand. 'Clip,' she said, then she raised the hoof in the other. 'Clop.' Then she banged them down on the table alternately. 'Clip, clop, clip, clop, clip,' she chanted in the rhythm of horses' hooves breaking from trot to canter. She was laughing but gave up when she realized that Marjory hadn't understood the joke.

'We used to play that for hours when we were children.' She thought for a moment and her smile faded. 'What a tedious childhood we must have had.'

'Ah, I see,' said Marjory, triumphantly and laughed.

'Good.'

'Well, of *course* it was attached to the horse.'

Audrey wondered about Marjory sometimes. She gave Marjory the hoof to put on the mantelpiece.

'The rest of her was probably made into glue,' said Audrey sadly.

'It comes to us all.'

'She was the best runner the family ever had. Even better than Marquis, my favourite.'

'What was he best at? Have you got any mementoes of him?'

'He was a stud horse.'

'No – well, I don't suppose you want one of *those* on your mantelpiece!'

'Don't be vulgar, Marjory.'

Marjory was trying to put the hoof on the mantelpiece which, after several falls into the grate, she accepted to be too wide for the narrow ledge, and put it on the windowsill.

'Did you want to see me about something?'

'Did I? Oh, yes.' She didn't know where to begin, but launched into her grievances obliquely.

'I try – I try – now, don't I try, Marjory?'

'It's Mr DeVere, isn't it?'

'Yes – answer me this, Marjory. I don't mind coming to live here – no, really I don't, even if it does add another line to my address, a sure sign that one is on one's way down. No, I can get used to this little shed and having to turn a corner every two feet and treading in the dog's bowl every five minutes. That I can get used to. But am I very silly if I resent DeVere running off with my domestics and joking about it, about him getting preferential treatment at the shop, where I now get called "dear" not to mention the breaded ham. I mean, the whole fabric of society is becoming irreparably unstitched.'

The tantrum had burnt itself out.

'What was the question again?'

'I've forgotten.'

'As I see it, you just have to steel yourself to a more modest lifestyle.'

'That's what I thought you'd say,' she sighed. 'Oh, well, I suppose I can learn to wear curlers in the Washeteria.'

'You don't have to go mad.'

'I think I am going mad sometimes. Driven to it, mind. By him.' She pointed the accusing finger towards the manor. 'If I'm going to get back to the manor, he holds the key. This is between you and me, Marjory. I want to get on with him. I want to. But I can't have any sort of association with a man who I bend over backwards to accommodate and then tries to patronize me with offers of help, money, builders – and typing lessons.'

'Typing lessons?'

'The latest – paying girls for his own use. Typing, that is. He calls it bringing prosperity to the valley.'

'I think you should accept his offers,' said Marjory.

'No. Not while there's nothing I can do for him. If only there was.'

'There are plenty of things you can do for him.'

Audrey's disconsolate mood suddenly changed with the appearance from the tea chest of her favourite picture of herself.

'Ah, look,' she said admiringly. 'There's Marquis and me at Badminton.'

Marjory looked over her shoulder.

'Good heavens, who's that with you?'

'M'm? Who?'

'Isn't that the Queen you're talking to?'

Audrey managed to compound all the elements of surprise.

'So it is – yes, I remember now, she did just happen to be there. She must have just strayed into the picture.'

Marjory hadn't seen through this one, so Audrey could elaborate on the theme.

'It's funny – you don't really think of royalty as being flesh and blood until they're actually standing right in front of you. It was years before I was prepared to accept that they had to eat. I always used to think that old Queen Mary's toque was to keep chocolates in for when she was hungry.'

As she spoke she went towards the fireplace, opening the flap at the back of the picture, thereby making it too wide for the narrow mantelpiece. It fell into the grate.

'Oh, Christopher Columbus!' she growled.

'I don't think it's DeVere at all,' said Marjory. 'I think this little house is getting on your nerves.'

'It is *not*,' Audrey denied. The picture fell in the second attempt to install it in its pride of place.

'I like it.'

The picture fell.

'Yes, I like it.'

It fell again and the glass broke, as if trying to persuade Audrey to change her mind.

'Oh, hell's whiskers!' she screamed. 'I hate it, I hate it, I hate it.'

She collapsed into the Chesterfield, red-faced and gasping for breath. Marjory mercy-dashed to her aid, seizing a carafe of water and glass from the drinks trolley on her way. She quickly dispensed it and handed the glass to Audrey who drank gratefully.

'Thank you, Marjory,' she sighed. Then a thought dawned. 'Oh, my God – pigeons – I'm being poisoned!'

'What? You're delirious.'

'No, it's all right,' said Audrey, suddenly regaining her composure. 'Stay for lunch. I hope you like breaded ham.'

For Brabinger and Ned it was a silent journey back from the village post office. Brabinger sat in the passenger seat of the Rolls while Ned drove. It was only natural that he should resent this arrangement, particularly as Ned did not drive with the respect the car deserved. Particularly as he was driving very fast and erratically along the main road. Particularly as he knew that Ned was trying to frighten him, and to make him utter an oath or two which might have been the first words the two had exchanged for years. What did these two have against each other, to fuel this longstanding feud? Everybody knew. Everybody that is, except the man on the police motorcycle, now overtaking them with his siren blaring. Constable Peaslake waved them down and they pulled in at the side of the road. The police constable dismounted, took off his helmet and went to the driver's window.

'Right, Brabinger – I've got you now,' he sneered. His face fell when he saw Ned – his own father – looking at him from the driving seat.

'Oh –' he said, '– just to say I might be late home tonight, dad.' He put his crash helmet on again and went round to Brabinger's side of the car.

'One of these days, Mr Brabinger, one of these days. Remember '47.'

Deprived of a breaded ham, DeVere and Mrs Polouvička made do with a steak lunch from the deep freeze, served by Linda Cartwright. It was a silent meal in the sense that there was no conversation, though much talking was going on. DeVere did not stop for lunch but often brought his pocket dictaphone to the table and carried on dictating letters throughout the meal. In retaliation, his mother insisted on having a 'family hour' after lunch, but as this usually meant her sprawling out on the sofa and sleeping, the arrangement suited him as he could carry on working.

But occasionally, the need to talk asserted itself at the lunch table, and today was one of those days.

'This one is to Dr Yoshiaki Tanaguci – House of Perpetual Serenity and Moral Fibre, Dock Street, Osaka,' DeVere was saying into his machine as he rounded the meal off with biscuits and cheese. 'So, if you're ready, Hilda – Dear Dr Yoshiaki, thank you for your confirmation of the Cavendish order of...'

'Bedrich,' said the old lady.

'Ssh, thank you for your confirmation...'

'Bedrich.'

'Oh, do be quiet – not you Hilda,' he said to the machine, 'don't write that. Thank you for your confirmation...'

'Bedrich.'

'Mother, please.'

'Sorry I spoke. Pardon me for living,' sulked the old lady.

'Excuse me, Hilda,' he said switching his recorder off.

'Now, what is it, Mother?'

'I was just thinking you haven't seen Audrey lately.'

'As a matter of fact, I saw her this morning.'

'I hope you were civil to her.'

'Exemplary – I gave her a lift.'

'She knows a lot of useful people, that girl – be nice to her.'

'You don't have to tell me.'

'Did you ask her to come and advise you about the estate?'

'How could I? She's turned me down once. Anyway, I don't need her help.'

'Bedrich.'

'All right, I could do with it, but if she wants to play hard to get – that's up to her. I'm not going down on my knees.'

'You could ask her to help you in little ways, gently – coax a little, a little service rendered here, a little kindness there, and before you know where she is, she is running the estate without knowing it. Out of little acorns do great oaks grow.'

'No.'

'Why not?'

'Because.'

'Ah – I see – so she frightens you.'

'She does not.'

'She ruffles you.'

'No.'

'But she distracts you a little.'

'Certainly not.'

'Then why are you buttering your recording machine?'

'I'm not.'

'Then what's that on there, Bedrich?' she said pointing to the mouthpiece.

'Cheese.'

DeVere threw down his napkin, 'And my name's Richard,' he snapped, and stalked out of the dining room into the privacy of the study. There was no sanctuary there; for a start that was where mother and son returned for the statutory 'family hour'. Secondly, that was where the building work was currently in progress.

The old lady followed him into the room, which was once Marton's old study.

'Did I say something . . . Richard?' she said.

DeVere smiled to hear his mother use his adopted name.

'Oh, you're right as usual,' he grumbled.

Thus vindicated, the old lady swaddled herself in a tartan blanket and spread herself out on the sofa to sleep. DeVere went to his desk and began flicking through the pages of *Horse and Hound*.

He was still reading when two workmen returned from their lunch break. They were halfway through the job of knocking out the old fireplace to make room for a safe. The fireplace was an ugly piece of Victoriana and small, considering the size of the room, but effective enough to throw a generous heat the length and breadth of the grate. It was a simple installation job, but the banging, scraping, prising, crumbling, splintering and the nerve-tingling screech of heavy metal being dragged across stone, amplified by the hollow of the safe, could be heard from the old lodge. But not, it seemed, by old Mrs Polouvička, who could not be wrested from her slumbers, nor her son from *Horse and Hound*. When the workmen finally disappeared through the french window to park the old fireplace on the terrace, admitting a gust of air which dispersed the dust-clouds, the old lady opened an eye.

'Ah – I do so like the country,' she said. 'It's so quiet!'

A Postillion Struck by Lightning

Dirk Bogarde

The early years of Dirk Bogarde's life were spent in a
dreamy Sussex village where with his sister, Elizabeth, and
nanny, Lally, he passed a memorable summer in 1927...

We were almost halfway down the gully when my sister screamed and called
out, 'I've found him!'

But she hadn't: it was just an old rusty can gleaming wet in the dew among
the leaves. It wasn't George by any stretch of the imagination: I'd know
George anywhere and he wouldn't be down the gully, of that I was pretty
sure. He'd be up top, in the Great Meadow where the grass was fresh and
tender, and there were hosts of dandelions which he liked.

Not in the gully, which was deep, and dry, usually, and lined with great
ash and oak, and chalky along the edges full of warrens and, down at the
bottom by the road, old cans and bedsteads and stoves which people dumped
among the nettles. George was the kind of tortoise who thought for himself,
and he would never have thought to wander so far from the house when the
Great Meadow was bung full of food and surrounded the place in which he
usually lived. He wasn't a complete fool.

I struggled up the side of the gully and broke through the nettles and elder
bushes into the field. I was soaking with dew. Down below in the valley the
first chimneys were smoking and the meadow lay still in silver light, a good
hundred acres of it. It was going to be a bit of a job to find George among all
that grass.

My sister was behind me, having scrambled painfully through the elder
branches, whimpering from time to time. I didn't take any notice. If you said
anything the least bit kind or helpful, or sympathetic, they started to snivel,
and after that cry. And you might as well have said nothing, because then
they only did a whimper or two and, seeing you didn't care much, stopped.

So I didn't say a thing to her. She rubbed her stung knees with a dock leaf and pushed her hair from her eyes.

'Why did we have to get up at dawn to look for him?'

'Because.'

'But because why?'

'Because it's the best time to find them. That's why.'

'To find tortoises!' she scoffed, rubbing away at her wretched knees. 'You'd think you'd been hunting them all your life.'

I started to hum and sing a bit.

'And you haven't,' she continued, 'because they come from Africa and you've never been there.'

I left her and started walking down the long slope to the valley, peering at molehills and under tussocks of ragwort, and generally trying to seem as if I had a pattern. Pretty soon she'd get windy left up there by the dark old gully and she'd come trolling and skittering down to join me.

I found a large rabbit hole, and stooped to search it. Once, a month ago, he'd got out and stuck himself in a rabbit hole in the orchard.

She wasn't far behind me now, singing a bit, and brushing the long wet grasses with her skinny brown hands. She grabbed some sorrel leaves and chewed them.

'If he gets stuck in a hole again, we'll never find him, there must be five hundred million in this field. There must be.'

I got up and dusted my hands and walked on singing my bit of humming-song. She was right, but I wasn't going to let her know that.

'We'll just have to search every single one.'

'Well I won't!' She stopped some paces behind me, waving her arms like a windmill. I walked on, looking and kicking about the big grass clumps.

'It's not my tortoise. And I'm soaking wet. My sandals are all slimy. You'll be sorry!' she screeched.

Patiently I turned and looked up at her against the morning.

'It's half yours,' I said politely, but coldly. 'Uncle Salmon gave it to us *both*. So it stands to reason that it's *ours*. Not just mine.'

She shrugged, but was silent. I stared at her. She suddenly bent and started to unbuckle her sandal. 'Well, I don't want my half of it. You've got the part with the head. That's the best part.' She sat down in the wet shaking her old brown sandal. I could see her knickers, but I didn't bother to tell her. She was so rotten.

'Well, go on home and I'll look for him alone. And when I find him

I'll have both halves and you'll have to lump it.' I turned and ran away down the hill ... in case she tried to follow. She didn't, but she screeched again.

'The head part is the most interesting part. You said so. I don't like the tail part. And if I go home alone Aleford's stallion could get me.'

I reached the edge of the meadow and threw myself on to the grass under the ash tree and lay there looking at the sky and puffing a bit. It was quite a long run down from the top.

It was only yesterday evening that I had carefully washed his shell, and then put a little olive oil on it so that it shone and gleamed like a great golden brown pebble on the beach at Birling Gap. Only yesterday that he'd had the very innermost heart of a lettuce. The pale, yellowish-whitish bit. And only yesterday that Reg Fluke told me to put a little hole in her end of the shell and fix a bit of string to it. 'Then he won't wander,' he said.

But I didn't, and here we were in the dawn, searching for him, in vain it seemed.

There was a thumping in the earth under my back, and I could hear her running. Her feet thumping along in the grass. She slithered down beside me clutching her soaking sandals and peered at me. Her long hair hung over her face, and brushed my cheek. She looked like a hideous witch-thing: she crossed her eyes at me.

'Don't!' I said in alarm. 'You'll stay like it.'

'Not that you'd care. You left me up there and the stallion might be anywhere. You just don't mind about me. I won't help you look.' She leapt to her feet and ran barefoot through the field jumping over molehills, waving her skirts about, and singing very loudly indeed. This was not to impress me, but to frighten away Aleford's stallion, which we had never actually seen, but which we'd been told about in great detail by Reg Fluke and a boy from Woods, the butchers in the village.

And the telling was bad enough. I wasn't exactly anxious to see it myself. But I lay on, listening to her singing away in puffs and gasps as she ran furiously uphill.

The sun had been up only a little while and beside me, close to my face, so that it was actually all blurry and looked like an eagle, was a burnet-moth on a bit of grass, feeling the sun, and waiting for the dusk to come. I rolled over on my stomach and looked up the hill. She looked quite small now, leaping over the grasses, and jumping about with her long legs and the sandals held high, as if a great dog was running beside her trying to grab them.

A blackbird was singing in the ash tree and I was just wondering if there was a nest nearby when I heard her: it was rather frightening actually. She let out a terrible shriek, and then another and another as if someone was stabbing her.

I jumped up and stared. She was standing quite still, staring at the ground and holding her sandals close to her heart. Shrieking.

It must be George, and of course, he must be dead. Horribly, by the way she was yelling ... I started to walk up the hill towards her.

'What is it? What's happened?' I called.

'Come quickly ... come quickly ... it's ghastly! Hurry! God's honour, it's the biggest one ... it's the biggest! Quick.'

I ran. The wet grasses stinging my legs, and the tussocks and molehills tripping me. The yelling stopped but she was staring at me with great beseeching eyes.

'Come quickly!'

'This is as quick as I can. Is it a snake?' That was it, of course. An adder. And we'd both be bitten. 'If it's a snake,' I said, stopping immediately, 'come away. Don't stand there gawping, come away. It'll kill us. Just run.'

'It isn't a snake ... it isn't a snake ... it's terrible!' she hadn't moved, so I went on, rather reluctantly, but cheered that it was nothing too beastly ... obviously not George mangled by a fox or something, otherwise she'd be snivelling. But now she was crouching in the grasses, staring at it like a mad rabbit.

Then I was beside her, my shirt had come out of the top of my shorts, and my shoes were soaking too.

'What is it? What is it then?'

When she spoke her voice was sort of roughish and very low with wonder. 'Look,' she said, and very gently parted the grasses before her. 'Look, it's the biggest mushroom in the world. Look!'

And it was. It must have been about as round as a dinner plate, quite. And it sat in a little hollow with some others around it; but they were smaller, this was a giant.

'Gosh!'

'Isn't it *huge*? It's the biggest in the world.'

'It might be a toadstool, or something.'

'Well, let's pick it and take it home and they'll tell us.'

Very gingerly I reached out and pulled the great shiny brown top ... it smelt like a million mushrooms. It was golden brown in the sun and underneath it was pink and white, and damp. We smelt it carefully and she opened her skirt like an apron for it, and we walked breathlessly up to the house.

'It's like a beautiful parasol,' she said.

In the kitchen there was a breakfast smell. The kettle was steaming away on the Primus stove and Lally, plump in a print dress and tennis shoes, was sitting at the table buttering toast.

We stood on the brick floor looking at her, willing her to look up at us, but she went on scraping off the burnt bits and singing a song to herself. My sister deliberately dropped one sandal and then the other. Lally stopped singing and said: 'Go-and-wash-your-hands-why-haven't-you-got-your-shoes-on?' all in one breath, but still not looking up, although she must have seen us.

My sister said in her Old Maid's voice: 'We have something rather strange to show you.'

Lally looked briefly at her bulging skirt and said: 'If it's living throw it out and if it's dead likewise. Kettle's boiling.'

'It's alive and dead at the same time, sort of,' I said.

'Well, we don't want it in here, do we?' said Lally, stacking up some toast and cutting off the crusts all round. 'And I'd be pleased if you hurry up before the Prince of Wales is here.'

'It's a mushroom,' said my sister, moving across the floor with the bundle and laying it on the table among the crusts and the butter crock. 'And it's possibly the biggest in the world . . . or anyway in Sussex.' And she carefully opened her skirt and showed it.

Lally took a look and then was interested. 'Jerusalem!' she said. She always did when she couldn't think of anything else, or if you had surprised her, or if she was quite pleased but-not-going-to-show-it, or if she didn't understand clearly. And she didn't understand this. For a moment we all looked at it in dead silence.

'Well, it's big I grant you, probably wormy too. What do you want me to do with it?'

My sister removed it very gently from the cloth of her skirt and, wiping her hands together, she said: 'We could all have it for breakfast, couldn't we?'

'Fried,' I said.

'With bacon sort of,' said my sister.

'Be tough, I shouldn't doubt, you'd better ask your mother: it might be poisonous and then where should I be? Never get another job, not having poisoned a whole family. It's very large,' she said. 'Give it a good wash and we'll see.'

Well, you could tell she was impressed because she forgot to remind us to wash ourselves, and taking down the big iron frying-pan she started singing her song again.

Carefully we washed it at the big sink and smelled the fresh damp smell of it and admired the pink underneath part, and there were no worms.

It was about the best thing I've ever eaten. Cut in strips, like bacon, and fried in butter with tomatoes and a bit of ham and soft toast.

'Where did you find it then?' Lally asked.

'We were looking for George in Great Meadow and she found it.' I indicated my sister with a flick of jealousy.

'It was sort of in a little hollow place, right in the middle,' she said.

'It's a wonder Aleford's stallion wasn't about,' said Lally, wiping round her plate with a bit of bread: she said this was all right to do ever since she came to France the first time with us. Anything the French did was all right by her, which shows just how ignorant she was. 'That stallion could kick you to death with a look: there was a boy lived up at Teddington when I was your age, got kicked in the head by one. He was loopy all his life.' She cleaned the edge of her knife against the plate and stuck it in the butter. 'Any cows in the meadow?'

'Some,' I said. 'Right down the bottom.'

'Well, you need cows and horses in the same field for mushrooms,' said Lally. 'If you don't have it that way you can't get mushrooms.'

'Why?' asked my sister.

Lally was spreading damson jam all over her toast. 'Because when you get cow dung and horse dung in the same field you get mushrooms, that's why,' she said and bit into the jam.

My sister looked white but a little scornful. 'Dung,' she said.

'DUNG, dung,' said Lally. 'You ask anyone, anyone you like. Ask Aleford or Beattie Fluke down the bottom, or the Prince of Wales. They'll all say the same thing. Dung.'

For a little time we were silent, except for the clink and scrape of knives and forks and the kettle lid plopping up and down. Sunlight streamed through the windows, across the table and the bumpy whitewashed walls.

'Do the French eat them?' I asked.

'Wee,' said Lally, nodding her head.

'Well, it must be all right for us to, I mean if they do it must be,' I said.

'They're the best cooks in the world, aren't they?' said my sister. 'So they'd be bound to know if it was all right or not.'

Lally eased up from the table and started stacking the plates. 'Can't all be right at the same time,' she said, going across to the sink and dumping them into some water. 'Can't be right all the time. Even the French. Remember one thing,' she said, taking the soap up from the shelf. 'The French eat snails too.'

We helped with the drying-up in a thoughtful silence.

We lay on our backs under the ash tree by the top of the gully and watched the crows wheeling and gliding in the wind. All around my head sorrel, buttercup and long bendy plantains shimmered and nodded. I crumbled a little empty snail shell, transparent and silvery. My sister had her eyes closed, her hands folded on her chest like a dead Plantagenet. She had the same kind of nose, poky and long; her hair was scattered with pollen.

I leant up on one elbow and sprinkled the snail shell all over her face.

She screamed and hit me with her fist.

I fell back into the grass and lay still, staring at the crows. She was mumbling and brushing her chin.

'Stupid fool,' she said.

'I merely wondered if you were feeling sick yet. That's all.'

'Well I'm not.' She lay back. 'Are you?'

'No. Not sick. Full.'

'I think Lally is a liar anyway.'

'I know she is,' I said. 'Look at the Prince of Wales.'

'What about him?'

'Well, you know: she's always saying he's coming, or she met him at the pictures, or Victoria Station. And she's always talking to him on the telephone. She says.'

'Well, that doesn't say she's a liar,' said my sister, rolling on to her stomach and squinting at the sun. 'Not like Betty Engels. She's a liar properly.'

'Why ... I mean how do you know she is properly?'

'Because,' said my sister patiently, 'because she said her father was a millionaire and I know it's a lie.' She knelt up and picked some grass.

'How?'

'Because I saw him actually riding a bicycle.'

'Well I should think Lally is just as much of a liar as Betty Engels ... I bet she's never seen the Prince of Wales. And not at Victoria Station.'

'Why not Victoria Station?'

'Because to go to Sunningdale you have to leave from Waterloo.'

We lay still for a while, comforted by our proof and by the fact that we did not feel sick. After a little while I sat up and tucked my shirt into my shorts. Away across the meadow the Downs were smudged with the morning sun and a little red Post Office van went bundling along the lower road and got lost in the trees. You could just see it shining red here and there in the gaps and then it turned right up to Peachy Corner and disappeared. I got up. 'I'm going to have another look for George. Coming?'

She groaned. 'All right, coming,' she said. 'And then we'll go down to Bakers and get a bottle of Tizer, I've got threepence.' I pulled her up and we ran howling and laughing down the meadow: a linnet shot up at our feet, spiralling into the sky like a singing leaf, and as we whooped and leapt over the tussocks I could see the river sequinned with sunlight. I gave a great big shout of happiness ... we weren't going to be sick and it was going to be a beautiful morning.

Rumpole and the Case of Identity

John Mortimer

Horace Rumpole, an endearing barrister, is a colourful
figure in the law courts. He never prosecutes, his court
scenes are proverbial and his life is ruled by She Who Must
Be Obeyed – Mrs Horace Rumpole.

*'Was this the face that launched a thousand ships
And did the stabbing in the Wandsworth Off-Licence?'*

These lines passed through my mind as I sat working late in Chambers. My
wife Mrs Hilda Rumpole, known to me as She Who Must Be Obeyed, had
joined some dubious club called the Bar Choral Society and was out in the
evenings at this time, indulging her fantasies in rehearsing Handel's *Messiah*
as Christmas was growing remorselessly near. On my desk was a police
identikit photograph of a long-faced young man with bristling sideburns
wearing, just in case no one noticed him, a loudly checked red-and-yellow
tartan cap. This was the face, unreliably created from snatches of memory
and a police artist's pencil, of the man who entered an off-licence in
Wandsworth and stabbed the licensee, a small Irishman named Tosher
O'Neil, in the face and arm, making it necessary for repair work to be carried
out to the tune of twenty-seven stitches. Also on my desk was a photograph of
my client, a young man in his twenties named David Anstey, a driver in the
well-known South London mini-cab firm 'Allbright's Cars'. Friends and
fellow drivers had told the police that David's sartorial taste ran to an
unfortunate red-and-yellow tartan cap (I wondered how many thousand
lunatics went to football matches each weekend in such headgear). If the
prosecution could prove that this was the face Tosher remembered behind
the descending knife, then David was due for a substantial visit to Her
Majesty for Grievous Bodily Harm: which would be a pity as he had an
excellent work record, was just married to a young wife, and his previous

slips ran to driving off other people's Ford Cortinas, so that knifing his fellow citizens would seem to be something of a new departure.

I was also wondering, as I read the papers in R. *v.* Anstey, how many seconds Tosher had really had to see his attacker's face; and I was brooding on the horrible difficulty, and total unreliability, of trials decided on identification evidence. Do all the middle-aged ladies who write to 'Any Answers' calling for the return of hanging understand that the fallibility of human memory would ensure that we hanged at least a few of the wrong people, or is that a risk we are bound to take in the pursuit of their favourite sport? I was thinking of all these things, and of the greater difficulty in our case: Tosher O'Neil had picked David Anstey out at an identification parade when my unfortunate client wasn't wearing a cap at all. As I turned back to compare the identikit picture with the undoubted face of the said Anstey there was a brisk knock at my door and the anxious face of Claude Erskine-Brown peered into my room.

'Rumpole ... you're burning the midnight oil?'

'Ah, Erskine-Brown, Claude.' I decided to use him as a test of man's power of identification. 'How would you describe me, exactly?'

'You? Why on earth...?'

'Let's say I'm getting unsure of my own identity. Describe Rumpole as you saw him go into Chambers this morning. Are you sure you *did* see me go into Chambers this morning? Can you swear you're not mistaken?'

'Of course I saw you coming into Chambers. Look, Rumpole...'

'Yes, but how *did* you know it was me?' I pressed him.

'Well, it looked like you,' he answered rudely, 'short and fat.'

'You mean well filled out. Generously proportioned. Comfortable?'

'No. Fat. Look. There's something going on down the passage and I don't like the look of it...' He moved closer to me in a conspiratorial fashion.

'Are you *sure* it was me?' I returned to the subject which was starting to become an obsession.

'Of course it was you. It had your muffler. And your dreadful old hat on!'

'My old hat on! Exactly. You recognized the hat!' I felt that I had hit on a vital clue to David Anstey's defence.

'Rumpole. Will you come and look at this? It's a question of Chambers security!'

Erskine-Brown had become so insistent that I had to humour him. So off we set to the room of our learned Head of Chambers, Guthrie Featherstone, Q.C., M.P. There was a light on, showing a bright streak under the door, so that it seemed that he too was burning the midnight oil. However, Claude Erskine-Brown assured me, the door was locked, and by way of evidence he turned the handle and failed to gain admittance. There did seem to be a small sound, only a whisper like the intake of breath, or perhaps my old ears deceived me and it was the sigh of some building sinking into the ground or the distant thunder of traffic on the Embankment.

'Well, what's wrong?' I asked him, for some reason we both seemed to be whispering. 'Featherstone always locks his door. He's afraid people'll come in and read his "All England Reports", and pinch his paper clips.'

At which I thought I heard another sound from behind the door, less a distant whisper than a suppressed giggle.

'What on earth's that?' Erskine-Brown looked seriously alarmed.

'Mice!' I reassured him. 'These old places are overrun by mice.'

'It was a sound ... more like giggling.'

'Even mice – can enjoy a joke occasionally.' I put a comforting hand on Claude's shoulder. 'You're working too hard.'

'I have been snowed under lately,' the distraught man admitted.

'Pack it in, Erskine-Brown. Abandon the affidavits ... Come and have a nightcap at Pommeroy's Wine Bar.' I steered him away down the passage. 'You ought to watch out you know. A man's got to be very careful when he starts to hear mice giggling in the night.'

It was some weeks prior to this night of adventure that a second typist had joined our clerk's room staff, a fairly personable brown-haired young lady named Angela who wore jeans and an American combat shirt of the sort that might have been bought second-hand from some Vietnam veteran. I can't imagine that this apparition would have produced in old C. H. Wystan (my late father-in-law and our one-time Head of Chambers) any result less dramatic than a heart attack, but Guthrie Featherstone made no protest, Henry appeared to tolerate her and Uncle Tom seemed positively charmed by her; although I did catch in Erskine-Brown's eye, when he noticed her, the gleam of an early New England settler who's brought face to face with a young, attractive and particularly burnable witch. I came into the clerk's room one lunch-time, the jury at London Sessions having convicted three cannabis dealers of mine, and told the bad news to Henry. My clients had got three years a piece.

'I suppose the judge went off and drank his large whisky and soda!' Angela spoke indignantly from behind her typewriter.

'Yes. I suppose he did.' The judge had in fact been old Bullingham, so the young lady's instinct was undoubtedly correct.

'Still, it wasn't your fault. You did your best. You were defending, weren't you?' She gave me a warm smile of approval, at which point Erskine-Brown came in with some document and asked Angela to type it. She ran a quick eye over the pleading and gave us a quotation. '"The Plaintiffs, the Gargantua Trust Property Company Ltd, are landlords of the said premises."'

'Brilliant! You *can* read it,' Erskine-Brown said with more than a hint of irony.

'"And the defendant, Mrs Parfitt, is in default of rent to the extent of £208.13. Notice to quit having been given."' Angela read with considerable disapproval, and then exploded, 'Whose side are we on?'

'We are on the side, Angela, that sends us the work,' Erskine-Brown told her coldly.

'She got notice to quit. For a measly £208.13! Gargantua Trust Property Company Ltd! Well, I don't imagine they're short of a bob or two...'

I was observing this scene, which I was starting to enjoy as Erskine-Brown became irate.

'Angela! You're not required to judge the case. That can be left in the safe hands of the judge of the Marylebone County Court.'

'I bet Mrs Parfitt's an elderly widow,' said Angela with some considerable satisfaction.

'Of course. With twenty-three starving children. It doesn't matter what she is, Angela. Just you type it out.'

I had thought nothing of the mysterious incident of the light in the locked room (it's easy enough to forget to switch the light off when you lock a door) but I was a little worried, at this time, by the appearance and behaviour of our Head of Chambers, Guthrie Featherstone, G.C., M.P. He came into Chambers very late, he looked pale and somewhat seedy, and he showed a marked lack of enthusiasm for his practice at the Bar. I put all this down to the burden of governing England, seeing us through inflation, settling Rhodesia etc. which he had assumed; but, as I sat over an early evening claret with him and Erskine-Brown in Pommeroy's Wine Bar I couldn't help feeling that Claude's incessant complaints were adding considerably to the burdens of office. When the matter of the petty cash and Dianne's salary had been brought up the Head of Chambers gave a world-weary sigh.

'All-night sitting,' he said. 'I don't know how long the old frame'll stand it.'

'Really. What great affair of State were you discussing?' I asked.

'Some earth-shaking measure for the protection of cod in Scottish waters...' Guthrie told us.

'I want to raise the matter of security in Chambers.' Poor Featherstone groaned slightly. Erskine-Brown went on remorselessly. 'The other night there were lights left on. After you'd locked up...'

'I must have forgotten...'

'And we distinctly heard a sound. Coming from your room!'

'How extraordinarily odd!' Featherstone seemed puzzled.

'Rumpole thought it might have been mice.'

'Oh, really?' The Q.C., M.P. looked at me, I thought, gratefully.

'And there's another matter I wanted to raise.'

'Another?' Here was a camel I felt, whose back was about to be broken.

'That new girl, Angela. The one who does the typing now...'

'Henry says she's a bit of an asset. I know nothing about her, of course.' Featherstone sounded casual. 'But it seems that Dianne just couldn't cope single-handed...'

'The girl objects to typing a landlord's statement of claim. She only wants to type on behalf of the tenant. It really adds a new horror to life at the Bar, if one is going to have all one's cases decided in the typing pool.' Erskine-Brown completed the indictment and Featherstone gave him another uneasy smile.

'I really don't see how you can dignify those two girls, Dianne and "Angela", did you say her name was? with the title of "typing pool". Anyway, Henry tells me she's extremely good. It seems she's pretty well indispensable. But perhaps you'll head a small committee, Claude, to deal with the question of mice in Chambers.'

Shortly after this Erskine-Brown went off to some musical evening with Miss Phillida Trant, and Henry called in for a quick Cinzano Bianco and a complaint to his Head of Chambers.

'It's that new girl, Angela, Mr Featherstone. Quite frankly she's getting on my wick.'

At which I was amazed to hear Guthrie Featherstone say, 'Really, Henry? Mr Erskine-Brown was just saying what an enormous help she is, typing his pleadings.'

Henry turned to me for support.

'She wants to turn our clerk's room into a co-operative, sir. She thinks the girls should chip in to my percentage of Chambers' fees.'

'Workers' participation, Henry,' Featherstone closed his eyes wearily, 'it's bound to come.'

At which Henry gave me a look which said more clearly than words, 'not in these Chambers it bloody isn't,' and I was left to brood on the strange duplicity of Guthrie Featherstone, Q.C., M.P.

'Would I wear me cap, Squire? Would I? Not if I was going to cut up some geezer in an off-licence. That'd be like leaving me visiting card.' I was with my client, young David Anstey, and Jennifer, a pleasant and hard-working solicitor's clerk, in the interview room at Brixton Prison.

'Mr Anstey,' I told him. 'If I ever get you out of this hotel, you might consider reading for the Bar. Because, old darling, you have put your finger on the bull point of the defence! Why would anyone wear a comical cap when out on an errand of mayhem and malicious wounding? Unless...'

'Unless they wanted to be recognized!' Jennifer suggested.

'Unless they wanted *someone* to be recognized...' I lit a small cigar. Outside the glass box of the interview room I could see other barristers interviewing other clients in other glass boxes, until the series ended in the screws' office, with its pleasant collection of cacti in pots. Outside in the yard other screws were exercising malignant Airedales.

'I'm not worried, Squire,' Dave Anstey sounded unhealthily optimistic. 'I'm just not worried at all. I'm in the clear.'

'No one in Brixton's in the clear, old darling,' I told him. 'Not till they hear the magical words "Not Guilty".' I sat down, for the purpose of reading my brief. 'Now, this little alibi of yours ... It entirely depends on the evidence of your guv'nor?'

'He's very good to me, Mr Rumpole. And to the wife, since we got married. He bought all our home for us. Very generous-minded individual. "Freddy Allbright will see you right." That's his motto. Biggest mini-cab owner in London.'

'You were with him all the evening of Tuesday, March the fourth?' The stabbing in the off-licence had taken place at about a quarter to nine.

'I come back from a trip to Wembley at 8. Then Freddy took me for a curry. We was together until 10.30. Then I went home to the wife.'

Alibis always sound so delightfully healthy, but they crack up dreadfully easily. I asked Dave how this kindly employer could possibly fix the date of one out of a long line of curries.

'It was the evening before his wife's birthday. He'd got Mrs Allbright a gift.'

'What exactly?'

'It was an evening bag. Highly tasteful. For his Ladies' Night down at the Masons. He even showed it to me. Look, Mr Rumpole, it's cast iron, my alibi.'

Whatever the truth about his defence, Dave Anstey it seemed had total faith in it. As for me, I'm not sure that I like cast iron alibis. They're the sort that sink quickest, to the bottom of the sea.

To wash away the sour taste of Brixton nick I went for a glass of Chateau Fleet Street (as a matter of fact the metallic flavour of this particular claret gives it a slight prison flavour, as if the grape had been grown on the sunless side of Wormwood Scrubs: I exaggerate, of course; this is a libel on Pommeroy's Wine Bar, whose budget Bordeaux has elevated my evenings and kept me astonishingly regular for years). As I arrived in the bar I was greeted by Erskine-Brown who was waving a crumpled copy of *The Times* newspaper, and by Miss Phillida Trant, who had been booked as junior to 'Soapy Joe' Truscott of Treasury Counsel, to appear on behalf of Her Majesty the Queen in the case of David Anstey. No sooner had I drawn up a stool and ordered a bottle of the cooking claret and three glasses than Erskine-Brown shoved his newspaper under my nose, open at the uninspiring account of yesterday's debates in Parliament.

'Just take a look at the end. I've marked it in red.' Erskine-Brown was almost too excited for coherent speech.

'After the defeat of the motion to Preserve the Ancient Grasslands, the House rose at 10.30,' I read aloud. 'Earth-shattering news, is it, Claude? What, am I meant to flee the country? Put myself out to pasture in some newly preserved grasslands?'

'Guthrie Featherstone clearly told me that last night he was at an *all-night sitting* on the Cod Fisheries (Scotland) Bill.' Erskine-Brown had apparently reached the punch-line.

'Well, I don't see what's peculiar about that...' I gave him a blankish look.

'It sounds to me like the collapse of an alibi.' Miss Trant, our Portia, seemed to have sniffed a *prima facie* case.

'Exactly!' Erskine-Brown chimed in. I did my best to give their excitement a douche of cold water.

'Not at all. My God, I can see where you're headed, Miss Trant. The Portia of the Prosecution! Suspicious of everyone.' The claret arrived, I gave them each a glass and some soothing words. 'It's perfectly natural for Q.C., M.P.s to forget which day it is. Poor devils, they must be constantly under the delusion that they've been discussing cod in Scotland until the small hours. If you take my advice, Miss Trant, you'll keep your mind on the off-licence stabbing. I was meaning to ask the prosecution. Who owns that off-licence, by the way?' I was looking for a motive for the Wandsworth stabbing, so I casually asked the question which was almost fatal to the defence.

'Who *owns* it?' Miss Trant frowned. 'I don't know. I could find out for you.'

'Oh, do do that, Miss Trant. It might be so much more important than the busy life of our learned Head of Chambers.'

That evening an event of unearthly, not to say spooky significance occurred in Casa Rumpole, 25B Froxbury Court in the Gloucester Road. I was sitting by the electric fire, reading the depositions in a promising little indecent assault and taking a bedtime bracer of the old and Tawney, when the house was riven by the sound of a rich contralto voice raised in what seemed to be some devout ditty.

'The Lord God Omnipotent...
The Lord God Omnipotent...
The Lord God Omnipotent...

sang what I first took for the ghost of some member of the Bach Choir, justifiably murdered long ago in Froxbury Court. Then I remembered that my wife was in the kitchen, the apparent source of the sound. Had She Who Must Be Obeyed taken leave of her senses?

'*Hilda!* What on *earth's* going on?'

'I'm doing the *Messiah*,' Hilda said enigmatically, making a non-singing entrance with two cups of steaming Nescafé.

'What the hell for?'

'The Bar Choral Society.' She put down the coffee as though I should have known all about it. 'Marigold Featherstone rang me up and asked if I'd be interested. They take on wives.'

'An assembly of barristers' wives. Giving tongue. How perfectly ghastly!' I lapped up port, this was no moment for coffee.

'In praise of God, Rumpole. It is going to be Christmas.' Hilda installed herself on the other side of the electric fire.

'Sometimes I wonder if God enjoys Christmas all that much.'

At which Hilda put down her cup and saucer and leant forward to say, extremely seriously, 'Marigold Featherstone's not a happy woman.'

'Perhaps it's the *Messiah* getting her down. It's been known to have that effect on people.'

'It's Guthrie Featherstone.' Hilda shook her head softly. 'If you ask my opinion, that marriage is dying for lack of attention.'

'Hilda! You shock me. You don't stand there at choir practice when you should be giving praise to the Lord, gossiping away about Featherstone's marriage?'

'It's not gossip, Rumpole. I told you. She's not a happy woman. Of course, it's enormously difficult being married to a politician...'

Or a part-time contralto ... That was what I felt like saying. Actually I remained mute of malice.

'Their marriage is cracking up, Rumpole. And it's all *your fault*.'

'My fault?' I was astonished. I had only met Marigold Featherstone occasionally at a Chambers 'do'. An ex-nurse who had once played tennis for Roedean, she was not exactly Rumpole's bottle of claret.

'Guthrie's out late. Of course he has all-night sittings. But even when he hasn't ... it seems you keep him in Pommeroy's Wine Bar for hours. Boozing.'

'I do?' I only rarely took a glass with Guthrie, and, whenever I did, he was in and out of the bar like a rabbit in a hurry.

'Marigold asks him where he's been and he says, "Old Rumpole kept me talking about Chambers business in Pommeroy's. I simply couldn't get away from him."'

'*Old* Rumpole? Is that what he calls me?' If our learned Head of Chambers was going to use me as an alibi he might at least have been polite about me.

'I suppose that's what you were getting up to tonight.'

I had, it was true, whiled away a couple of hours in Pommeroy's, a place notable for the absence of Guthrie Featherstone, Q.C., M.P.

'Well, there wouldn't have been much point in coming back here, would there? Not while you were hitting high notes with Marigold Featherstone.'

'You want to be very careful, Rumpole. You want to be careful you don't break up *two* marriages.' On which line She returned to the kitchen to keep an urgent appointment with the washing-up. As the plates clattered I heard her, over again, carolling:

> 'The Lord God Omnipotent...
> The Lord God Omnipotent...
> The Lord God Omnipotent... e ... e ... e... ent
> *Reigneth!*'

Oh well, I thought, thank God He's doing something at last.

In due course we assembled, myself, 'Soapy Joe' leading for the prosecution, Miss Trant, junior for the prosecution, Dave Anstey and Jennifer my solicitor's managing clerk, before Mr Justice Vosper, a pale and sarcastic judge who has never learnt to sit quietly, but always wants to take part in the proceedings, usually as a super-leader for the prosecution. Tosher O'Neil, scarred down one side of his face, a living piece of evidence for the sympathetic jury, was in the witness-box, concluding his examination-in-chief by Miss Trant.

'Can you describe the man who attacked you?'

'He had this red cap on...'

'Apart from the red cap?'

'Yes. Apart from the red cap. Come on, Portia,' I muttered at her. It didn't put her off.

'Well, he was tall. Big-built.' The witness gave the man in the dock a meaningful look.

'Like about twenty million others,' I muttered, and found the judge staring in my direction, with some distaste.

'Did you say something, Mr Rumpole?' his Lordship asked.

'Nothing at all, my Lord.'

'What about his hair? What you could see of it.' Miss Trant asked.

'He had long sideburns. Sort of brown colour. What I could see of it.'

Miss Trant whispered to her leader to check she had asked all the relevant questions, and I heaved myself to my hind legs to cross-examine.

'If you look at my client, Mr O'Neil, you can see quite clearly. He has no sideburns at all.'

'No. No, he hasn't.'

'Mr Rumpole. I'm sure you don't need reminding. We live in the age of the electric razor.' Mr Justice Vosper was really the worst sort of judge; the judge who makes jokes.

'My Lord?'

'Sideburns can be shaved off. If it's convenient to do so.' Vosper J. didn't actually wink at the jury, but they gave him a conspiratorial smile.

I re-attacked the witness O'Neil.

'You told us his sideburns were sort of brown. Sort of ginger-brown? Greyish-brown? Blackish-brown? Or just brown-brown?'

Tosher didn't answer, so I pressed on.

'You know, we have heard the evidence of Mr Smith who was waiting for a bus outside the off-licence. He told us about a man with a red tartan cap and *black* sideburns.'

'I ... didn't have a lot of time to notice him. It was that quick.'

'That quick! You only saw him, didn't you, for a matter of seconds?'

'Yes.'

'So my client stands on trial for a couple of seconds...'

'It will no doubt be considerably longer, by the time *you're* finished, Mr Rumpole.' Vosper could never resist that sort of remark; the jury gave an obedient titter, and I said, 'if your Lordship pleases' as coldly as possible, then I asked the witness,

'You've never met Dave Anstey?'

'Never in my life.'

'So far as you knew he had absolutely no motive for attacking you?'

'Not as far as I know.'

'Mr Rumpole. As you know perfectly well, motive is quite irrelevant in a criminal prosecution.' Mr Justice Vosper was giving me a rough ride. I began to long for a 'Not Guilty' verdict, if only to see his Lordship's look of bemused disappointment.

Outside the Court, when we broke for lunch, a large man smelling of Havana cigars, wearing a camel-hair overcoat and several obtrusive rings came up to me smiling cheerfully. He was accompanied by a blonde and extremely personable young woman, lapped in an expensive fur coat.

'How're we doing, Mr Rumpole?' the man asked, and the lady announced herself as 'Dave's wife. Betty Anstey.'

'Betty's only been married to Dave six months,' the man said. 'Lovely girl, isn't she, Mr Rumpole? Particularly lovely girl...'

'You are...?'

'Freddie Allbright. "Allbright will see you right." That's my motto, Mr Rumpole. In mini-cars as in everything else.'

'Our alibi witness?' I asked Jennifer.

'I've got the alibi ready, Mr Rumpole. Ready to go whenever you want it.' Freddie Allbright smiled, ready, it seemed, to see us right at any time.

'Can't talk to witnesses, you know.' It silenced him. 'I expect we'll call you on Monday.' I asked Mrs Anstey if she'd been in Court. She shook her head tearfully.

'I can't go in there, Mr Rumpole. I really can't. Not to have everyone staring at me because of David. Dave's all right, is he?'

'As well as can be expected,' I told her. 'I'm sure he'd appreciate a visit, down the cells.'

'I promised the young lady a lunch, Mr Rumpole,' Freddie told me. 'Better get our skates on, Betty love. Don't want some lawyer snitching our table at the Savoy, do we, Mr Rumpole?'

'No. No, I'm sure you don't.'

I watched Betty put her arm in Freddie's and they walked away. I was trying to think of the implications of this vision when Miss Trant came alongside with some rather odd news.

'I've got that information for you,' she said helpfully. 'The landlord of the off-licence. It's a company called "Allbright Motors".'

'Thank you, Miss Trant.' I wished I hadn't asked.

I didn't myself have lunch in the Savoy that day. In fact I didn't even have a slice of cold pie in the pub opposite. I went straight down to the cells with Jennifer and voiced my anxieties to our client Dave Anstey.

'If an alibi comes unstuck, everything comes unstuck.' I looked at him thoughtfully and lit a small cigar. 'They may not believe *you*, just because they don't believe your alibi...'

'They'll believe Freddie, Squire. Freddie's got no axe to grind.' Dave seemed imperturbably cheerful.

'Hasn't he?'

'Has he, Mr Rumpole?' Jennifer frowned.

'Freddie Allbright owns the off-licence where Tosher was cut.'

'Never!' Dave seemed genuinely surprised to hear it.

'You didn't know that?'

'Straight up, Squire, I didn't ... Does it make any difference?'

'I don't know. Tosher picked you out at the ID parade. You'd never seen him before.'

'Never in my life. Straight up.'

'*Someone* must have told him ... about you and your remarkable head-gear. You trust Freddie Allbright?' Dave's answer was so enthusiastic that I almost began to doubt my own doubts.

'You must be joking. The things the Guvnor's done for me! Big bonus when we married. Canteen of cutlery, must have cost him two hundred nicker...'

'And a fur coat?' I asked him. But Dave Anstey didn't know anything about his wife's fur coat. And Jennifer seemed worried at my apparent distrust of our case on the alibi.

'If we don't call the alibi evidence,' she wondered, 'won't the prosecution comment? They've got Mr Allbright's statement.' She's a thoughtful girl Jennifer, with more sense of a trial than her employers who were no doubt lunching in the West End at length, setting up laundrettes and discos: I gave her the benefit of my learned opinion.

'Let Soapy Joe comment till he's blue in the face. He'll be left with a weak case of identification.'

However, any thought of giving our alibi a miss was clearly repugnant to our client.

'I want the Guvnor called,' he said. 'Freddie's been like a father to me.'

'Think about it, Dave. Then I'll need your written instructions before I call Mr Freddie Allbright.' I moved to the door. Dave looked up at me, he was frowning:

'What sort of coat exactly?'

'God knows! No doubt some rare animal gave up its life for it.'

'My Betty works, don't she? She saved up for it.' Dave had apparently convinced himself. 'You got to call the Guvnor, Mr Rumpole.'

'Please. Think about it, Dave.'

I was also thinking about it; and I was starting to get a glimmer of what later turned out to be the truth about the Anstey case as I called into Chambers the next morning to collect my brief, and a fresh supply of small cigars, on my way to the Bailey. When I got into my room I sniffed a female perfume and saw a familiar well-turned-out figure sitting in my client's chair. Although familiar I couldn't place my visitor at first, but the look of a rather attractive horse matched with the brisk tone of a ward sister left me in no doubt.

'I'm Marigold Featherstone. You remember me?'

'Of course. I'm just on my way down to the Bailey,' I dived for the brief and cheroots. 'Guthrie's room's along the passage.'

'He's not in. Whenever I ring up Chambers he's not in.'

'Perhaps, if I could give him some sort of message . . .' I went to the door in a meaningful manner. At which point Marigold, wife of our Head of Chambers, dropped her bombshell.

'Mr Rumpole. Do you handle divorce?'

'Only rarely. And with a strong pair of tongs. Look, I must rush, I'm . . .'

'I want you to act for me. If it should come to that.'

'Come to what, Mrs . . . Marigold?' I paused, somewhat weakly.

'Divorce! Guthrie's behaving extremely oddly. He's never there.'

I could see that the woman was outraged, and I tried to cheer her up.

'Well, that can be an advantage, I suppose. In married life. Speaking for myself, I'm married to someone who's always there. Now, if you'll excuse me . . .'

However, Mrs Marigold Featherstone wouldn't let me go until she had given evidence.

'I saw Guthrie in Sloane Square. I saw him from the top of a bus. He was arm-in-arm with a girl. They were looking into Peter Jones' window. When I tackled him, he denied it.'

'Well now. How can you be sure it was Guthrie?' Instinctively I started to test the evidence. 'I mean from a bus what did you see? The top of his head . . . For how long . . . a couple of seconds?'

'I'm *sure* it was Guthrie.' The witness was almost too positive. 'He had his black jacket on, and striped trousers.'

I renewed the cross-examination. 'Ah, Mrs Feather . . . Ah, Marigold. Now that's where mistakes are so easily made. You see, just *because* he had a black jacket on, you thought it was your husband! It's so easy to put a black jacket on, isn't it, or a red-and-yellow tartan cap. Do I make myself clear?'

'Not in the least.' Marigold frowned.

'Anyway. I'm a friend of Guthrie's. We stay out together late, boozing in Pommeroy's Wine Bar. That's where he is, a lot of the time.' I was beginning to feel anxious for the fate of the wretched Q.C., M.P.

'So he tells me.' Marigold did not sound friendly.

'And I'm in his Chambers. So I couldn't possibly act for you if it comes to divorce. It'd be extremely embarrassing,' I assured her.

Marigold's answer sounded like a brisk rebuke to a probationer nurse on the subject of bed-pans.

'If it comes to a divorce, Mr Rumpole,' she said, 'I want it to be as embarrassing as possible.'

Marigold's fell purpose was not, I was later to discover, the only trouble into which our Head of Chambers had been getting himself. It appeared that he had reached the stage of life when men are said to get hot flushes (I can't remember going through it myself) and suffer from the delusion that they embody the least admirable qualities of Don Juan and the late Rudolf Valentino. I heard that when Miss Phillida Trant, who is in fact, beneath a business-like exterior, extremely personable, went into Featherstone's room to borrow a book he invited her to lunch in Soho. When she told him, as was the case, that she was going out with Erskine-Brown (a contemporary phrase which I take to mean 'staying in' with Erskine-Brown) the rogue Guthrie said that Erskine-Brown never took her anywhere interesting, and asked if she had, in fact, ever been taken to 'Fridays', a dark cellar off Covent Garden where he said the B.P.s (Featherstone's appalling phrase, apparently it means Beautiful People) met nightly to jig about to loud music in the dark. This painful interview ended by Guthrie trying to remove Miss Trant's spectacles, in the way he said James Stewart always did, to reveal the full beauty of girl librarians in the films of the thirties.

It is a matter of history that, one night after a prolonged experience of *Rigoletto* at the Royal Opera House, Miss Trant did persuade her escort Erskine-Brown to take her down the inky entrance of 'Fridays'. There they saw, or thought they saw a disturbing spectacle which was only described to me later. At that time I had no thoughts in my head except for those concerning the defence of Dave Anstey, and the perils we might face when we tried to prove his alibi.

When I got down to the Old Bailey I saw Betty Anstey, proudly wrapped in the fur in which I was beginning to suspect she slept, waiting outside our

Court. I drew the usher aside and asked him as a particular favour to call her into Court when I tipped him the wink, and on no account give her the chance of taking off her coat. I then went into the ring and, having had firm instructions from Dave to do so, breathed a silent prayer, fastened my seat belt, and called Freddie Allbright Esq. in support of our alibi. Freddie walked confidently into the witness-box, large and neat in a blue suit, with a spotted blue tie and matching handkerchief, and smiled towards the dock (which smile was returned by Dave with a simple faith in good things to come).

At first we were rolling fairly smoothly. I established a curry dinner sometime in March, and then I asked an apparently helpful Freddie Allbright about the time.

'8.45. 'Course I was with Dave at 8.45. I took him for a meal at 8, and we was together till 9.30.' So far so good, I moved stealthily towards the clincher.

'Now, can you fix the date?'

''Course I can. My wife's birthday . . .' Well, nothing to worry about as yet.

'What's the date of that?'

'March the fifth. Same every year. I'd got her an evening bag, and I told Dave about it when I met him the next day.' Freddie was still smiling as he said it, but I felt as if I'd stepped into a lift-shaft some moments after the lift had gone. Was there a chance that we misunderstood each other?

'The *next* day?' I asked, apparently unconcerned.

'Right. The next day when we went for the curry.' There was no chance. Dave was looking stricken and incredulous – and the judge was making a careful note. He looked up, and asked with casual pleasure.

'That would be March the sixth?'

'That's right, my Lord.' Freddie agreed eagerly.

'I wanted to ask you about the day *before* your wife's birthday.' I felt like a surgeon trying to sew up an ever-expanding wound.

'March the fourth? Oh, I don't know what Dave was doing then. No. I tell a lie.'

'Do you, Mr Allbright?' I asked him. I hoped I sounded dangerous. Freddie only asked me an innocent question.

'Was that the Tuesday, March the fourth?'

'Yes.'

'Then Dave had *that* night off.' Freddie hammered the last nail in our coffin. 'I remember he'd been off a couple of nights before we went for the curry.'

Dave seemed about to shout from the dock. Wise Jennifer ssshed him. The judge leant forward to emphasize the hopelessness of our position. He addressed our broken reed of a witness.

'So you don't know what Mr Anstey was doing on the night of the fourth?'

'Haven't a clue, my Lord.' Freddie smiled charmingly.

The judge turned to me and put the boot in, gently but with deadly accuracy.

'You may like to remind the jury, Mr Rumpole, that the stabbing in the off-licence took place on the fourth of March.'

'I leave that to you, old darling. You're obviously loving it,' was what I thought of saying. Instead I asked the usher to present Mr Allbright (of 'Allbright's will see you right', not in Court they won't) with his signed statement in support of our alibi.

'Mr Allbright!' I put it to him. 'Did you not sign that document making it clear that you were with Mr Anstey on the evening of the *fourth* of March?'

'I may have done. Yes.'

At which Soapy Joe arose, his hands clasped together, his voice humble and low, and made a typically Soapy interjection.

'My Lord, is my learned friend entitled to cross-question his own witness?'

'If the witness is hostile. Yes.' I argued the law.

'Does my learned friend suggest that the witness is hostile to *him*?' said his Soapiness.

'No. I suggest that the witness is hostile to the *truth*!' I looked at the jury who were beginning to sense a Scene in Court and stirred with modified excitement.

'If the witness has signed a previous inconsistent statement you may cross-examine him,' said Vosper J. judicially and added I thought maliciously, 'if you think that's a *wise* course, Mr Rumpole.' The jury smiled at what they felt might have been a joke. Soapy Joe subsided, and I said I was obliged to his Lordship and began to attack the traitor in the witness-box. The time for half-measures was over. Now it was all or nothing.

'Mr Allbright. Is your company the landlord of the off-licence where Tosher was stabbed?'

'It might be.' My first shot had ruffled the Allbright feathers a little.

'What do you mean by that? Is your business empire so vast you can't be sure where your boundaries lie?'

'We've got the lease on the off-licence. Yes.'

'So Tosher was working for *you*.'

'He might have been.'

'And what was he doing? Putting his hand in the till. Not paying his dues? Did you have to send someone to teach him a lesson?'

Now the jury was interested. Freddie played a safe delaying shot. He looked puzzled.

'Someone?'

'Who are you suggesting *someone* might be, Mr Rumpole?' Mr Justice Vosper was weighing in on behalf of the witness. I ignored him and spoke directly to Allbright.

'Someone you sent in a cap like that worn by my client Dave Anstey.'

Even Vosper J. was quiet at that. I saw Dave looking lost in the dock and Freddie Allbright attempting a disarming smile.

'Now why would I do a thing like that, Mr Rumpole?'

I didn't answer him straight away. I was whispering a word of instruction to the usher who left the Court. I then turned again to the witness.

'Mr Allbright. Are you friendly with my client's wife, Betty?'

'I'm like a father to both of them. Yes.' Freddie smiled at the jury. They didn't smile back.

'While my client's been in custody, have you been seeing Betty regularly?'

'I've tried to take her out of herself, yes,' Freddie admitted after a helpful pause.

'Has taking her out of herself included buying her an expensive fur coat? The one she's wearing now?'

The usher opened the door. Betty came in, nestling in her slaughtered article of wild life. Dave looked at her from the dock. She avoided his eye. Freddie improved the effect of this scene on the jury by saying:

'I may have lent her a bob or two, to tide her over.'

'Yes. Thank you, Mrs Anstey.' I let Betty go with the bob or two of fur on her back, and some nasty looks from the ladies in the jury following her. When the Court was quiet again I unloosened the broadside.

'Mr Allbright,' I thundered. 'Has your object in this case always been to have Dave Anstey convicted?'

Freddie gave another answer which, from his point of view, could only be described as a bad error of judgement. 'No. I wanted to help Dave.'

'Is that why you've gone back on your alibi statement? Because you wanted to *help* him?'

'Or have you gone back on it because you are trying to tell us the truth?' The judge was doing his best in a tricky situation.

'Look. I put March the fourth first because Dave asked me to,' Freddie explained.

'*Mr Anstey* asked you to?' the judge was delighted.

'He said that was the date of the stabbing, like. Look, I'm sorry I can't help you, Mr Rumpole...'

'I'm sorry I can't help *you*, Allbright. In your attempt to get your mistress's husband put inside for a long period of years...'

'Mr Rumpole. Is there any basis for that suggestion?' Justice Vosper was losing what I believe is known nowadays as 'his cool'.

'If there isn't perhaps my learned friend will call the lady to rebut it. She's still outside Court.' I let the jury notice the lack of enthusiasm from Soapy Joe and went on. 'You sent your hireling, wearing that entirely recognizable cap, to teach Tosher a lesson. So Tosher identified him...'

'May I remind you, Mr Rumpole,' the judge sighed wearily, 'when your client was picked out at the identification parade, he wasn't wearing a cap.'

'Of course not, my Lord.' I turned on the witness.

'Perhaps you'd care to tell us, Allbright ... who was it gave Tosher his instructions?'

Freddie looked in silence at the unsympathetic jury. I went on, more in sorrow than in anger, to pry into this wretched conspiracy.

'Didn't Tosher know who you wanted fitted up with this little enterprise in the off-licence?'

'"Fitted up" is hardly a legal term, Mr Rumpole,' the judge tried the flippant approach. 'It makes it sound like a cupboard.'

I thought I'd teach Vosper J. to make jokes in Court.

'Then shall we say "framed", Allbright?' I said. 'It sounds like a picture. In this case the wrong picture entirely!'

The cross-examination of a hostile Allbright was, of course, only the beginning of a long and hot struggle with the judge which ended after two more days, with Rumpole suggesting to the jury that they had the alternative explanation of the events in the off-licence and they could not be certain that the case put forward by Soapy Joe on behalf of Her Majesty was certain to be correct.

'If you find Dave Anstey guilty,' I told them, 'the other man, the other man in the tartan cap sent by Freddie Allbright to enforce his dominion over the garages and off-licences of his part of Wandsworth, that "other man" will not go away or disappear, but he will return to haunt our dreams with the terrible possibility of injustice . . . It is your choice, members of the jury. Your choice entirely.'

After a nerve-wracking absence of five hours, and by a majority of ten to two, the jury opted for unhaunted dreams and decided to give Dave the benefit of the doubt and spring him from the dock. When I said 'goodbye' to him he was looking lost.

'Where do I go now, Mr Rumpole?'

'Not to Brixton at least.'

'I got no marriage, Squire. I got no job. I can't believe in anyone no more.'

'You'll get a job, Dave. You'll find another girl.'

'Not in Wandsworth I won't. Freddie'll see to that. He's got Wandsworth sewn up, has Fred Allbright. He's highly respected in this area.'

I was surprised by the tone in which he still spoke of his former employer.

'Cheer up, Dave. There is a world outside Wandsworth.'

Mr Anstey shook his head and went away looking as if he rather doubted that. I knew what I needed then, and went to find it in Pommeroy's Wine Bar, where I also saw the members of our clerk's room, Henry, Dianne and Angela in a corner and, at the bar, Erskine-Brown and Miss Trant. My former prosecutor gave me a smile of congratulation.

'We thought we had you chained up, padlocked in a tin trunk and sunk in the bottom of the sea,' she said. 'But with one leap Houdini was free.'

'Out five hours. It was a damned-close-run thing.'

'It was a smashing cross-examination, a lesson to us all,' Miss Trant told her *fiancé*.

'It's high time,' said Erskine-Brown, 'that a little justice was done to you, Rumpole.'

'Justice?'

'It's a rotten shame. You should have been Head of Chambers long ago. It was yours as the senior man. Everybody thought so.'

It was true that there had been a time when I was expected to be Head of Chambers; but Guthrie Featherstone, the newly arrived Q.C., M.P., put in for knee breeches and a pair of silk stockings and so got the blessing of my old Dad-in-law C. H. Wystan as the most desirable successor.

'I can't remember you voting for me at the time, Erskine-Brown,' I reminded him.

'Well, Guthrie Featherstone arrived. And he took silk and . . .'

'Popped in betwixt the election and my hopes.'

'It was a rotten shame, actually!' Miss Trant agreed.

'Of course, in those days ... we didn't know the truth about Guthrie Featherstone...' Erskine-Brown said darkly.

'Oh, no? And what is the truth about Guthrie Featherstone, Q.C., M.P.' I challenged him.

'Claude quite honestly thinks he's lost his marbles.' Miss Trant shook her head sadly.

'He made a pass at Philly!' Erskine-Brown sounded incredulous.

'Well, actually, he simply asked me out to lunch.'

But Erskine-Brown looked darkly across the room at Angela and almost whispered. 'And he's quite simply having it off with that female Communist in the typing pool.'

'Young Angela? You astonish me!' I raised an unbelieving eyebrow.

'We must have a reliable Head of Chambers,' Erskine-Brown insisted. 'Not someone who's about to be involved in an unsavoury scandal!' I wondered what a savoury scandal would be: a scandal fried on toast, perhaps, with an anchovy and a dash of Worcester Sauce?

'Everyone's noticed things about Guthrie,' Miss Trant said.

'Things?'

'Definite signs of unreliability. The point is ... We'll ask Guthrie Featherstone to resign and make way for *you*, Rumpole, as Head of Chambers.' Erskine-Brown the kingmaker was, it seemed, about to make me a definite offer.

'I do think you'd make an absolutely super Head!' Miss Trant seconded the motion with flattering enthusiasm. At which moment Featherstone looked into the bar, waved at us and left immediately for an unknown destination. When he had gone I gave my learned friend Erskine-Brown a warning.

'Guthrie Featherstone, Q.C., M.P. isn't an experienced Labour-Conservative M.P. for nothing. He hogs the middle of the road just in case anyone's trying to pass him. Perhaps he's not the resigning kind.'

'Then we simply move out from under him. To one of the new sets of Chambers in Lincoln's Inn,' Erskine-Brown smiled. 'I've sounded out Henry ... and Hoskins, and Owen Glendour-Jones.'

'Tell me, Erskine-Brown. Have you had any time for your practice with all this sounding?'

'No one's going to work with a Head of Chambers who's having it off with a revolutionary from the typing pool.'

At which point Miss Angela Trotsky got up and left the bar. Was it at a signal from our Head of Chambers?

'I'd just like to know *why* you're making this extraordinary allegation?' I asked Erskine-Brown for further and better particulars.

'Claude and I saw Guthrie Featherstone dancing. In "Fridays",' Miss Trant came out with a surprising piece of news.

'The Q.C., M.P. dancing? What's your evidence for that?'

'The evidence of my own eyes!' Erskine-Brown said proudly.

'The evidence of people's own eyes can, as Miss Trant knows, be extremely unconvincing. Did you see his face? What about the sideburns?'

'We didn't see his face exactly...' Miss Trant said.

'He had his back to us. But *she* was there!' said Erskine-Brown.

'The Communist menace of the clerk's room?'

'And Guthrie was wearing some sort of multi-coloured green-and-yellow shirt. With flowers on it.' Erskine-Brown brought out the full horror of the offence.

'Then it couldn't have been Guthrie Featherstone!' I assured him.

'Of course it was!'

'Mistaken identity. Guthrie Featherstone simply doesn't wear multi-coloured shirts with flowers on them.' I drained the blushing beaker of Chateau Fleet Street. 'As for the other matter. I'll think about it.' At which point I left Counsel for the prosecution of Guthrie Featherstone.

After Court the next evening I was in Guthrie Featherstone's room, awaiting an interview with our Head of Chambers. A cupboard door was squeaking, swinging open. I got up to shut it and looked into the cupboard. All I saw was Guthrie Featherstone Q.C.'S gear hanging on hangers. On another hanger I blinked at the sight of a ghastly green-and-yellow shirt, with a floral pattern. I shut the cupboard door quickly as Featherstone entered the presence.

'Henry said you wanted to see me...' he started.

'Don't you want to see *me*?'

'Not particularly.' He looked extremely tired.

'I would say, you need a little help.'

'I'm perfectly all right. Thank you, Rumpole.'

'Are you? They're closing in! Your wife Marigold wants to start a divorce. She consulted me.'

'*You!* Whatever did she consult *you* for?' Featherstone sounded shaken.

'No doubt to cause the maximum havoc. Young Erskine-Brown alleges he saw you dancing.'

The extraordinary thing was that Featherstone then smiled, apparently delighted with the accusation.

'With Angela?'

'Claude Erskine-Brown suspects you of having a Red in the bed, so far as I can gather.'

The accused Featherstone went to sit at his desk. He seemed perfectly relaxed as he made a full verbal confession.

'All right. It's all true. It's all perfectly true, Rumpole.'

'You plead guilty?' I must say I was surprised.

'As a matter of fact it's all terribly innocent,' he rambled on. 'Jumping about in "Fridays" till two o'clock in the morning. Then back for an hour or two in Angela's ridiculously narrow bed in Oakley Street. Then off to breakfast in the House of Commons.'

'That must be the worst part about it!'

'What?'

'Breakfast in the House of Commons.' I gave him a critical look-over. 'You're obviously not cut out for that type of existence.'

'The physical strain *is* exhausting.' Guthrie sighed.

'I imagine so. It must come as a terrible shock to a man only used to somnolent parliamentary debates and a little golf.'

'Golf! It happened when I was playing with Mr Justice Vosper. You know him?'

'Only in Court. Never on the green.'

'He was talking about the Death Penalty.'

'With nostalgia, I assume.'

'I sliced a drive into the rough,' Featherstone reminisced. 'I went behind a patch of low scrub and there were a boy and girl making love, not undressed, you understand. No great white bottoms waving in the air. Just kissing each other, and laughing. I felt there was an entire world I had totally missed. I told the judge I'd been taken ill, and left the course.'

'Taken ill? Of course you had.' I had no illusions about Guthrie's complaint.

'I spent the afternoon just wandering about Richmond. In search of adventure.'

'You drew a blank, I should imagine.'

'Next morning I came into Chambers and saw Angela. She's twenty-one, Rumpole, can you imagine it?'

'With difficulty. Tell me. What is that military uniform she affects?'

'An American combat shirt. It's a sort of joke. To show her pacifist convictions.'

'Most amusing! So you set out, quite deliberately, to destroy your position in Chambers?'

'Deliberately?'

'Of course. Locking yourself in this room. What on earth was that for?'

'We couldn't go back to Oakley Street. Her flatmate was entertaining a man from the BBC World Service...'

I remembered, with some humiliation, the night I'd played the unlovely role of eavesdropper with Erskine-Brown.

'Barristers' Chambers have been put to many uses, Featherstone, but only rarely as a setting for French farce! Oh, you were very determined, weren't you? Telling Marigold the most transparent lies. Carefully informing Miss Trant and therefore Erskine-Brown of the disco or Palais de Hop where you are apparently to be found nightly, tripping the light fantastic!' (I went to the cupboard and threw it open, dramatically displaying the incriminating evidence.) 'Keeping your dancing apparel in the cupboard.'

'Angela gave me that for my birthday,' Featherstone looked at the shirt with a tired affection. 'I couldn't take it home to Marigold.'

'What do you intend to do with it?' I asked with some contempt. 'Send Henry round to the launderette?'

'I don't know, Rumpole. What do you suggest?'

'I suggest you give it to the deserving poor. Look, Featherstone. My dear Guthrie.' I tried to bring some common sense to bear on the subject. 'You can't do it!'

'Do what, exactly?'

'Escape! You came to us as the ready-made figure of respectability. Q.C., M.P. Pipped me to the post as I remember it, for Head of Chambers – and remarkably gratified to get it. What are you going to do now? Abandon us, like a lot of ageing wives, leave us to rot on Bingo and National Assistance, while you go prancing off down Oakley Street in a remarkably lurid Paisley blouse! You can't do it. It's quite impossible. Out of the question!'

'Why *can't* I?' Featherstone was sitting behind his desk, smiling up at me.

'Because it was decided differently for you! When your mother gave proud birth to another Featherstone. When you became the youngest prefect at

Marlborough. When you humbly asked the Lord Chancellor for a pair of knee breeches and took Marigold's advice on a suspender belt for your silk stockings. And when you got yourself elected Head of Chambers! It's all mapped out for you, Guthrie! The tram-lines are leading to Solicitor General in the next middle-of-the-road Conservative-Labour government, and the High Court Bench, and death of Sir Guthrie Featherstone, a judge of courteous severity, and flags fluttering at half-mast over the Benchers' dining hall...'

'I don't *have* to do all that.' Guthrie stood up, defiant.

'What's the alternative? Hanging round the Pier Hotel, waiting for the man from the BBC to go on night duty. Scratching a living writing "Advice from a Barrister" in the Sunday papers. Come off it, that's someone else entirely. That's not our Guthrie Featherstone.'

He took all this quietly, and stood looking at me. Finally he made the most extraordinary counter-accusation.

'You're jealous!'

'Am I?' I was, I confess, puzzled.

'Just because *you* can't escape...'

'Can't I? Of course I can. I am a free soul.' I resented the accusation. 'A free soul entirely.'

'Just because you're tied hand and foot by the Income Tax and the VAT-man and when Henry's going to find you another brief, and "She Who Must Be Obeyed".'

'Featherstone! Is that any way to speak of Mrs Hilda Rumpole?'

'I don't know. You do.'

'That, sir, is a husband's privilege. Anyway. Why do you say I'm jealous?'

'I don't know. Is it because you want to be the only anarchist in Chambers?'

Featherstone moved away and lit a cigarette. I stood and looked at him, thoughtful, and if I'm honest I must say worried. Was there a certain truth in what he said? Had Guthrie Featherstone put his finger on the Achilles' Heel of Rumpole? Did I need *him* to make me feel a free, roving spirit. With Guthrie gone should I be reduced to a mere barrister, perhaps a deadly respectable Head of Chambers, calling meetings about the regrettable failure of learned friends to switch the light off in the loo, and their extravagance with the soap? I decided to deny his allegations.

'I don't need your sort of adventure to be a free soul, Featherstone. I can be bounded in the Temple and count myself a king of infinite space.' I went

to the door, using that moment to remind him of a case in which he was
prosecuting. 'Remember we've got a case on next week. Importation of
cannabis. You're against me.'

'Prosecuting?' He sounded doubtful.

'That is . . .' I looked at him accusingly, 'unless you've "Gone Dancing".'

I am not especially proud of what I did then, but the chance of Guthrie
Featherstone appearing as the Protector of Society against the insidious
attacks of the drug culture seemed too good to miss. Before the Q.C., M.P.
rose to open the prosecution, I had phoned Chambers and asked Harry to
send Angela straight down to the Old Bailey as I had urgent need of her
services as a shorthand note-taker. When I got to Court I was delighted to
see our Head of Chambers standing erect as a pillar of the Establishment,
saying exactly what I required him to say.

'In this case I appear with my learned friend Mr Owen Glendour-Jones to
prosecute and the defence is represented by my learned friend Mr Horace
Rumpole. Members of the jury, this case concerns the possession of a
dangerous drug – cannabis resin.' Guthrie began promisingly. At which
moment the glass door swung open to admit that girlish GI Angela. She
came to my side and I asked her to sit and take a note of Guthrie's opening
speech. Intent on his work he seemed not to have noticed her arrival. As he
carried on I could feel Angela's indignation glowing behind me.

'Cannabis, whatever you may have read in the papers, members of the
jury, is a dangerous drug. Prohibited by Parliament,' said Featherstone. 'Oh,
it may be very fashionable for young people to say that it does less harm than
a whisky and soda, or that smoking cannabis in some way makes you a
better, purer soul than squares like us, members of the jury, who may prefer
an honest pint, or in the case of the ladies of the jury, a small gin and tonic.
You will hear a lot in the case about the defendant feeling it his mission to
"turn us all on", as if we were electric lights. The fact remains, says the
prosecution, that the dealer in cannabis resin is merely a common criminal,
engaged in breaking the law for sordid commercial gain . . .'

The Court door banged. The outraged Angela, by now totally disillusioned with her swinging lover had gone. We never saw her round the
Temple or the Bailey again.

Christianity has no doubt brought great benefits to humanity, but in my opinion Christmas is not one of them. With a sickening of the heart I began to notice, as I went quietly about my life of crime, the dreadful signs of the outbreak of Christmas fever. My take-away claret from Pommeroy's was wrapped in paper decorated with reindeer and robins, Henry and Dianne began to put up holly in the clerk's room. Soon we should have to struggle down Oxford Street so that I could buy She the lavender water she never uses, and She could buy me the tie I never wear. Paper streamers went up in the list office at the Bailey, and there was plastic holly in the gate room at Brixton nick. In time more decorations were hung in Featherstone's room in Chambers, where was held our annual Christmas thrash (wives and girlfriends invited, warm gin and vermouth and Dianne traditionally far from steady on her pins before the end of the evening). I had gone through a drink or two at this gathering when I found myself in the centre of a group which consisted solely of Erskine-Brown and Miss Trant. I took the opportunity of telling them that I would take no part in a Chambers revolution; and that having looked carefully into the allegations against Guthrie Featherstone I found that the prosecution had not made out its case, indeed I believed the unfortunate Guthrie had this in common with Dave Anstey. They were both victims of cases of mistaken identity.

'What're you up to now, Houdini?' Miss Trant asked suspiciously.

'It may be. It may very well be,' I suggested, 'that there has been someone, a totally different someone, masquerading as Guthrie Featherstone!' I looked towards Featherstone, well-turned-out in a grey suit, who had arrived, escorting a smiling Marigold. 'All I can tell you for certain is,' I went on to the plotters, 'our respected Head of Chambers is clearly not the person you saw whooping it up in the disco. Look at him now, graciously escorting his lovely wife to our Christmas celebration. Look at him carefully, Erskine-Brown! Observe him closely, Miss Trant. Is that the man you saw? Certainly not! Do I make myself clear?'

'Not in the least, Rumpole,' Erskine-Brown grumbled and frowned displeased. I moved off. Marigold was enjoying a stimulating sherry. I came up to her. 'Mrs Featherstone. Marigold. I owe you an apology . . .'

'Mr Rumpole?'

'Keeping your husband out late boozing in Pommeroy's. Disgusting behaviour! I have put a complete stop to it.'

'So I've noticed.' Marigold smiled graciously. 'The all-night sittings seem to have dropped off lately, too. I get Guthrie for dinner nowadays.'

'How delicious!' I gave her a small bow and She Who Must Be Obeyed hove into view, clutching a large G and T.

'Rumpole!' She trumpeted.

'You know She ... you know my wife, of course.' I did my best to introduce her.

'Of course,' Marigold inclined her head. 'We sing together.'

'You're coming to the *Messiah*, Rumpole,' Hilda said.

'Oh, yes, Mr Rumpole,' Marigold added her pennyworth. 'Do come. We make a jolly brave stab at the "Hallelujah Chorus".'

'Do you really? How very sporting of you. I hate to miss it: but you see, the pressure of work in Chambers...'

'You *are* coming to the *Messiah*, Rumpole!' In She's mouth it was an announcement, not an invitation. Further conversation was precluded by Henry calling for silence for our Head of Chambers.

'I'm not going to make a speech...' Featherstone began to general applause. 'I just wanted to welcome you all ... Members and wives and girlfriends who are members also...' Here he raised his glass to our Portia, Miss Trant. 'To our annual Christmas "do". We have had a pretty good year, Henry tells me, in Chambers...' In fact Henry was wearing a new suit as a small tribute to his ten per cent. Featherstone boomed on, 'And we have managed to stick together throughout this year...'

'Except for one departure in the typing department,' I reminded him tactlessly.

Featherstone ignored this and continued, 'Glendour-Jones has joined us, since the departure of George Frobisher for the Circuit Court Bench. I only want to say...'

'"That he which hath no stomach to this fight"...' I felt it was time to put some force into this oration, so I almost shouted King Harry's call to battle.

'Did you want to say something, Horace?' Featherstone smiled and I cantered on, after draining my glass.

'Let him depart; his passport shall be made,
And crowns for convoy put into his purse:
We would not plead in that man's company
That fears his fellowship to plead with us.'

'What on earth's your husband talking about?' I heard Marigold whisper to She.

'It's Shakespeare. He does it all the time at home. I wish he wouldn't do it when we're out. So dreadfully embarrassing.'

'When people speak of a split in Chambers or of the possibility of any other head but our distinguished Q.C., M.P. ...' I turned my eyes on the subversive Erskine-Brown, 'they are making a grave error, and a terrible mistake ... Like the mistakes of identity which may do such terrible injustice in our Courts. My learned leader, Guthrie Featherstone, Q.C., M.P. is a man fashioned by nature to be Head of Chambers. He couldn't possibly be anything else. So we Old Bailey Hacks, we common soldiers at the Bar, will attack a New Year, under his leadership, crying together, "God for Guthrie, Henry and Dianne!"'

I moved to Featherstone, put a hand on his shoulder.

'Sorry, old darling,' I said quietly. 'You're lumbered with it!'

Diary of a Child Guerilla

Keith Waterhouse

Monday, March 1, St David's Day. Got up. Went to school. Came home. Had fish fingers. Went to bed. Started to count up to a billion but only got up to 7,643 for the reason that, my Father made me stop. He said that if he had to come up to my bedroom once more, that he would strangle me. This man is dangerous.

Tuesday, March 2, Got up. Had breakfast. Got ticked off by my Father for holding my Breath. People should not get ticked off for holding your breath, for the reasons that, it is a free country. Therefore I hate my Father. He thinks he is somebody but he is nobody. Also he have hair coming out of the end of his nose.

Wednesday, March 3, Ember Day. I am going to get my Father. He has been asking for it and now he is going to get it. Just because I was sucking bread. He go purple and bangs the table. If he was Run Over I would be glad. He look like a Jelly and also is Smelly.

Thurdsay, March 4, moon's first quarter 3.01am. Got up. Went school. Watched telly. Left roller skate on top of stairs, but, it did not work. This only works in comics such as Whizzer and Chips etc, therefore, comics are stupid. They, the people you are trying to get, do not step on the roller skate and go ker-bam-bam-bam-bam-bam-kkkklunk-splat-aaaargh. Instead of this, they just pick up the roller skate and say (This house getting more like a pig-sty every day.) He is Potty and also Grotty.

Friday, March 5, Today I said I was going to John's house but I did not, I went to the Pet Shop to buy a poisonous snake, but they did not have one. The copperhead, the Rattlesnake, the cobra and the Mamba are among the poisonous snakes to be found in the world. The man in the Pet Shop just laughed and tried to sell me a hamster. I am going to get him after I have got my Father.

Saturday, March 6, sun rises 7.35. I have got an Idea from watching

Telly. It is where they were in a certain foreign country and he, the Tall one, invents this special kind of warfare. It comes to pass that this Warfare is something nobody knows about, therefore he wins it. It is called (long word) warfare. (Long word) warfare is where, they do not fight with guns, tanks, also armoured cars, thus killing them, you fight a person's mind so therefore he will do what they tell them. It begins with the letter P. This I am going to do to my Father.

Sunday, March 7, 2nd in Lent, 1st day of Operation Stare. Operation Stare is where, you just look at your Father. You do not say anything, you just Look. This was when he was reading the paper, also when he was painting chest of drawers. He did not know I was there until, he saw me. I was just Staring at him. This is Operation Stare. It is (long word) warfare. It did not work, as he said (If you nothing to do you can tidy up your room). Another example of the poisonous snake is, the sea-snake. He has spots all on his neck. He is Spotty and also Potty.

Monday, March 8, On this important day I invented the art of making yourself cry. You have to pretend that you have a dog. This could be a Sheepdog or numerous others, it is called Zebadee. You have to pretend that it runs away in the park and, you come to this swamp and it rescues you and die. After you have gone into the swamp to get it out, the (dog). It dies and you are sorry. This can make you cry, but my Father just say, (Stop snivelling or I will give you something to snivel about).

Tuesday, March 9, Nothing happened. I am still going to get my Father. I will make him Crack.

Wednesday, March 10, birthday of Prince Edward. Today I got my Father to think that I could not move my left arm, also that I could not feel anything in it, it was Dead. I thought this would make him sorry and it did. He went all white and call me Son. He pinch my arm and asked if I could feel it, I replied that (I could not.) We had better see Dr Murray!!! he exclaimed, but just as he was helping me on with my coat to go Dr Murray, he sticks a pin in my arm accidentally on purpose. This hurt me so I said (Oh.) He went all purple and call me Lad.

Thursday, March 11, Got up. Decided to Lie Low.

Friday, March 12, full moon 3.34am. On this day Operation Blink came into being. You just blink your eyes all the time, it drive him Potty. Also, at the same time, you must screw your nose sideways and also make your mouth go down, while you are blinking your eyes. I did this all the time, until my Father Went Out.

Saturday, March 13, An unlucky day for my Father. On this, the 2nd day of the famous victorious Operation Blink, he take me to see (The Railway Children). I was sick on the bus going, also in the cinema. When we came out, he asked, (Are you feeling better now). I replied that I was, therefore, we went on the bus. I was sick. My Father does not know it, but, I did it on purpose. I have discovered the art of being Sick. It is my secret. I was Sick all over his shoes. The (Railway Children) is a good picture, it better than Rolf Harris. He is Cracking.

Sunday, March 14, 3rd in Lent. Operation Blink and Operation Sick are still in being. I said I was going to Get him and I have got him. If you keep sniffling, he does not say anything but you can tell he does not like it, this big Vein stands out in his forehead and sort of goes throb-throb. This is Operation Sniffle. This morning I heard him say to Mr Baker (Are they born like it or what, I don't know what I am going to do with him.) This means that I have won. He knew that I was holding my breath all through lunch time, but he does not say anything, he just Went Out. This also means, that I have won. Today I have started counting up to a billion and have got up to 10,500. I have got to get up to 25,000 before going to bed, or it will mean that I have lost the Battle. He has come back in and, he knows that I am counting up to a billion but, he is just staring at wall and drinking the whisky. It is 3.10pm on Sunday, March 14, the day of Victory. He has Cracked, and must sign my Terms.

Dear Electricity Board

Paul Jennings

Dear Electricity Board,

As you may know, our storage heater has failed. Well, perhaps you *don't know*, perhaps the girl who answered the three times I phoned you last week has left to get married, and forgot to tell you, in all the happy confusion of the office party, the presentation and so on. Anyway, as I haven't heard anything from you I thought I'd write.

There is something very wrong inside the heater itself. It isn't just the fuse. That was the first thing your girl asked me. As I told her, when I put a new fuse in and switch on, it emits a bright blue flash and a sound best spelt, I think, *kerspluck*.

A short, in short. Sorry about that; but it would be pointless for you to think you are dealing with a household where there is no technical knowledge of electricity at all. In these days of staff and other shortages I am sure you would not want to send a maintenance man on a round journey of 30 miles just to change a fuse.

However, I hope all your maintenance men have not left to get married as well, and that you will pass on to the one that eventually comes the contents of this letter. Then he will know what spare parts to bring.

It might also, perhaps be shown to your design department, because I have discovered a fault in your storage heaters which you perhaps do not know about and may wish to rectify in future models. It is this: your storage heaters are not mouse-proof.

I am not saying the mouse caused the short. We only got the short last week (the mouse was two months ago), when my younger son sat on the end of the heater to watch the television, as he often does when none of my daughters are sitting on it for the same purpose (and sometimes when they are, since he is stronger).

The reason the heater collapsed when my younger son sat on it was that my elder son (who is 21 and knows much more about electricity than even I do, as you will presently see) must have left out some purely mechanical part of the structure at one end when he re-assembled it after getting the mouse out, two months ago. When my younger son sat on it (last week) there was a sudden noise best spelt, I think, GAK, and this end (the end facing the television) was suddenly four inches lower than the other end. Some sort of leg or support had evidently not been properly secured.

Now you will doubtless say that my elder son had no business, however much he knows about electricity, dismantling one of your storage heaters. But I must point out that he only did this after you had sent no one in response to the calls I had made about the mouse.

In these calls, I told (I imagine) another girl who also left to get married and is probably back from the honeymoon by now, about the *smell*. Your heater, as I said, not being mouse-proof, a mouse had got into it. Arriving at a part no doubt warmer than the bit my children sit on to watch television, it had then, finding it *too* warm, discovered that it was easier to get in than out. And so it died, right in there.

Perhaps you do not realise how much smell a dead mouse can give off. Probably this smell is worse when the process of decomposition is speeded up by the surrounding heat.

You must remember that this was the most lived-in room in the house. The room with the TV in it, for Pete's sake, and the room we eat in. Even so, we had almost got used to it, as one does, when my elder son came home for a weekend from college, where he is doing science (I told you he knows all about electricity).

Coming straight from a fresher atmosphere, he found the smell intolerable. What finally decided him to have a go (and I am bound to tell you that my objection was by now very lukewarm) was that *another* mouse had got inside, that very day. We could hear it scuttling about. It must have known there was a dead comrade in there, but this did not seem to deter it. But then mice do not have our deductive minds, do they? Of course it may have been a heroic rescue mouse, or perhaps the loyal mate of the dead one; but this is mere speculation.

As I do not need to tell *you*, there is nothing very complicated electrically about a storage heater. Neither of us was very surprised, when we had finally lifted the casing off, to find just a lot of heavy concrete blocks, with grooves through which ran a long spiral element, and a great deal of stuff that looked to me like horsehair, although I don't doubt that in these scientific days, it is in fact some man-made material.

Our main trouble, as you will guess, was the purely mechanical one of getting the casing off. The four bottom screws at the sides were comparatively easy. It was the brackets fixing the blas ... – the heater to the wall. I have since rejected as fanciful the only explanation that seemed possible at the time – that *these* screws were put in by dwarfs or mannikins only two inches tall, but possessed of superhuman strength.

At any rate I shall be interested, when your man finally comes, to see what kind of tool can screw a screw so darn tight when the head of the screw is three inches away from a wall, at the bottom of a heavy and immovable object. The bracket itself is, as you know, apparently now a fixed part of the house.

We did get the casing off in the end, with what my son described as necessary and legitimate wrenching.

'It will go on again all right,' he said, and so it proved, some time after we had got the mouse out. This, as you may imagine was a laborious process, involving the removal of the concrete blocks layer by layer (I was quite right, they *do* get hotter as one gets lower) and keeping the yards of element untangled.

We found the dead mouse, and we could hear the live one scuttling about as we came nearer ground level, like harvesters pushing rabbits into an ever-decreasing circle of uncut corn.

We were waiting not with guns, of course, but with our cat. However, she took a minimal interest in the proceedings, and when we actually put her on what was left of the heater and told her to do her stuff she jumped away very angrily. We must be among the very few people who have ever actually seen a cat on hot bricks.

We are probably among the few, also, to have caught a mouse with a dustpan and brush, for this is what we used when it emerged from under the very last block and ran into a corner. We put it back in the garden, hoping against hope that it would tell the other mice to keep the hell out of it.

By the time we had cleared up the unbelievable mess of half-dried jam, half-eaten sweets, crumbs and crisps from that normally unreachable bit of floor (to a mouse it must have seemed like a marvellous Harrods' Food Hall where everything is free, as well as offering heated beds upstairs) and carefully reassembled the heater, it was time for my elder son to go back to college.

The casing, as he had predicted, did go on again all right, although one or two of the screws did not seem to be screwing *into* anything, and it rattled a bit if you hit it.

Most of all, it still *worked*. For two months, and without that smell. We put (and here is a free idea for your design department) a guard round the bottom, of chicken-wire. Well, mouse-wire I suppose you would call it really.

And now this. One end sort of collapsed, a dead short somewhere inside, muffled figures in blankets watching the television. A dead mouse we felt was in our province, but a dead short is surely in yours.

Do please send someone fairly quickly.

Yours faithfully,

Paul Jennings.

Talking Your Way to the Top

Harry Chance

It is no good expending time and effort on your personal appearance if at the end of it you are going to hide your glory behind a newspaper in a bus queue in Hendon. Once you are satisfied with the way you look, it is time to attack the citadels of society. The only way of doing this is by talking to people, preferably in places where drink is available. Public houses provide a reasonable starting ground for the tyro, but after a while it will become apparent that few of real power and influence frequent such places. Private parties are the only solution.

But how, I hear someone say, will I get asked to such parties?

An extraordinarily foolish question. You will not get asked. You will simply go.

But is this not gate-crashing?

Of course it is. There is nothing wrong with gate-crashing, except that you may find yourself being hurled into Belgrave Square by bouncers at 11 pm. The best way to get round this is to start with *cocktail parties*, which are very seldom guarded by bouncers. They can be found fairly easily. Simply roam the streets of the better parts of London, ears peeled for the roar of conversation and eyes alert for the parabolae of unwanted *canapés* from upper windows. Insinuate yourself, smiling broadly, and start talking. If anyone asks who you are, claim that Arthur brought you. If their name turns out to be Arthur point out another one. Maintain jauntiness until someone asks you to *their* cocktail party, next Tuesday. You should find that the thing snowballs rapidly after that; experts spend an average of one evening per year at home, if indeed they have a home at all. The only essentials are an excellent appearance, a flashing smile and remorseless flow of small talk. The most difficult part of small talk is beginning. Subjects like the weather, recent plays and important books are rapidly exhausted. The ensuing silence is normally filled with gossip, but if the gathering into which you have insinuated yourself consists of complete strangers, you are hardly going to have your finger on the pulse. Two techniques suggest themselves here. The first and best is to listen closely for the *dominant voice*. This will probably be female. A truly dominant voice rises above the general roar and does not pause for breath. Its conversational partners wear a glazed expression and will be only too happy to edge away as you approach. Once you set it going by asking it, for example, who is that man with the terrible squint, it will fill you in on the hopes, fears, aspirations and infidelities of everyone in the room before it gets round to trying to find out who you are, by which time you will in turn have edged away.

The second technique is the *Royal Insight*, in which a perfect stranger is bombarded with your observations on the inner workings of the Household. This works well with older women, who will form an exaggerated opinion of your connections and insist on introducing you to their daughters, who will probably be of an age to ask you to dinner parties.

Naturally one likes to get drunk at cocktail parties. A word of warning here: drunk is fine, but beastly drunk is not. It is difficult to appear in a good light when you are lying unconscious in a bath under a dozen Bollinger and a foot of crushed ice.

As you find your feet in society, conversation becomes more demanding. While the actual content of your remarks is not significant, correct language is. The conventions of your chosen group can be picked up rapidly – usages such as loo for toilet, sofa for settee, drawing room for lounge, should be carefully noted, as solecisms may actually be more damaging to your prospects than a fit of vomiting on the Aubusson. If in doubt, masquerade as a colonial of some kind. Colonials may be frightfully charlie and unaware of correct conduct at a cockers pee, as they are, well, such a *breath of fresh air*. Students requiring a closer knowledge of cocktail-party language are recommended to read the books of Evelyn Waugh and Nancy Mitford, as well as *Harpers and Queen*.

Cocktail parties lie at the foundations of social activity. There are other approaches which serve to impress listeners with the fact that you are a superior individual.

1 *Talking dirty* At its simplest, this takes the form of sprinkling your conversation with four-letter words, thereby suggesting that though well bred and educated you are still in touch with the masses and probably a born leader of men. More advanced dirty talkers eschew four-letter words,

however, preferring to attact attention with a fund of diverting yarns based
on the excretory and reproductive processes and a crisp insight into the
characteristics of the various races, particularly those from southern and
eastern nations. As I implied earlier, the cultivation of merriness during your
school career lays a firm foundation for such talk.

2 *Creative boringness* A valuable technique for those who find it difficult to
remember smutty stories, this depends for its effectiveness on the fact that all
the world loves an expert. The bore holds forth at length on the subject of his
choice, which should be unfamiliar to his listeners. Knowledge of this subject
is not important; what is vital is the acquisition of a store of *buzz words*. These
are words invented by cliques to make simple ideas sound large, mysterious
and daunting, or alternatively to make an unproven hypothesis sound like a
fait accompli, or alternatively, to mean nothing at all. Personally I am inclined
to subscribe to the latter type and have had great success with the Chance
Charts, which I now make available to you in truncated form.

HOW TO USE THE CHANCE CHARTS

Select a word from each column. String them together, puff out the chest and
force them across the teeth with an air of deep conviction. Best used after the
port.

Chance Charts: Buzz words

Military-industrial-agricultural (no. of possible combinations: 512)

hard	sin	surplus
soft	conversion	deficit
bloody	Russian	interface
liveweight	currency	situation
deadweight	response	index
pig	weapon	headache
North–South	trade	dialogue
overkill	destabilization	tendency

Arts (no. of possible combinations: 512)

beautiful	tension	disease
solid	whimsy	workshop

lapidary	reportage	theatre
terse	brushwork	inherency
incoherent	Weltschmertz	feats
seal-like	tennis shoe	relationship
gay	pride	obesity
foot	succumbed	quality

New technology (no. of possible combinations: 729)

program	program	program
software	debugging	facility
hardware	disc	capability
menu	search	data
RAM	accessing	drive
direct	input	enhancement
sodding	sales	man
mother	in	law
mainframe	terminal	key

Sporting landowners (no. of possible combinations: 6)

bloody	Russians
bloody	EEC
bloody	Americans
bloody	Hell
bloody	good port old boy
bloody	er, forgotten what I was goin' to say

PRONUNCIATION – A BRIEF NOTE

More has been written about correct pronunciation than about any other aspect of bounding. The original test, probably devised by Alexander Pope, consists of the repetition of the phrase: 'Thousands and thousands of Boy Scouts bounding around in brown trousers.' Meaningless, you may say; yet these syllables convey more about the speaker than several volumes of autobiography.

Those whose modes of speech were formed between the years 1945–68 should pronounce in the Churchillian manner, thus: 'Thowsands and

thowsands of Bory Scowts bownding arownd in browwn trowsers,' forming
the 'ow' sound by making a tight circle with the lips and keeping the tongue
stiff, but not tremulous.

Younger pronouncers, educated between 1968 and 1983, may prefer the
equally prestigious but somehow brisker: 'Thighsands and thighsands of Buy
Skites binding arinde in brine tryzers.' These sounds are accomplished with
a baring of clenched teeth, stretched but immobile lips, and a discreet
wagging of the tongue behind the ivory fence. It is a technique that has
recently gained popularity with Conservative back benchers, as it is always
extremely difficult to tell who is talking. And, of course, for such MPs, the
natural expression of the face in repose is the rictus described above.

The natural tendency of most of us is to say 'Theaousands and
theaousands of Boigh Skeaouts beaounding areaound in breaouwn treaous-
ers.' While this is to be discouraged, discreet interjection of such sounds into
the discourse can disorient and threaten the hearer. Salesmen seem to find it
a particularly useful gambit. In my view this fear is produced by an atavistic
race memory of the premiership of Edward Heath, a disorienting period in
human history if ever there was one.

There are few circumstances in which regional or working-class pronunci-
ations are permissible, though it is admittedly useful to have a reasonable
stock of them in the repertoire. They are most useful on the telephone when
financial restraint has made it necessary to dispense with the butler or other
intermediary. Milos Stugeron, of whom I have spoken before, carried
mimicry into the realms of high art, being able in times of stress to imitate
two crossed lines and a fault in the exchange, which made it possible for him
to terminate even the most delicate of calls in mid-sentence, attempts to
reconnect being met with his virtuoso imitation of the 'number unobtainable'
signal.

BIG TALK

A sound grasp of the principles of small talk should leave you with an air of
authority as visible as the fogs that cling to the shoulders of Mount Fuji, as
well as a reputation for charm and good nature. A talent for small talk is no
use in isolation, however; there will come a dread hour when reckonings have
to be paid, and deals closed. At this point you will have to make the
transition into *talking big*.

Much big talk is a matter for individual initiative. If, for instance, you are trying to convince shareholders that next year's performance will be an improvement on this year's £40 million operating loss, there is no sense in a pawky forecast of reduced losses. Let it be known that you confidently expect £100 million profit, to which end all directors' fees are being waived and you are actively considering takeover bids for Shell Petroleum, Barclays Bank and Trust House Forte. This will put a spring in the step of the assembled shareholders; any personal sacrifices in the way of directors' fees can be made up by creative accounting procedures.

NAME DROPPING

Probably the most efficient form of big talk is *name dropping*, a practice that has origins in far antiquity, when individuals invoked various deities in the hope that mention of self and deity in the same sentence would confer upon self the attributes of the deity. This seldom worked, but it instilled confidence in the invoker and any who happened to be listening.

Choosing a name

If you are trying to sell a car, the prospective buyer may be led to think more highly of the vehicle if you mention to him that Nicky Lauda dropped in last week and said he wished he had one of those.

When selecting a name to drop, ask yourself the following questions:
1 Will the target recognize this name?
2 Does the target know the droppee socially, and if so will he or she check up?
3 Is the droppee category-specific?

If the answer to questions 1 and 3 is 'yes' and question 2 'no', go ahead, and good luck to you.

There are three main techniques of name dropping, each excellent. They may be used singly or permed. The golden rule is to start simply, adding refinements and twists as your confidence increases. Those who find that they rely to a large extent on this technique may find it beneficial to keep a notebook in which one page is allotted per target. List names already dropped, and also names that for one reason or another should not be used.

1 *The simple drop with optional curriculum vitae* At its most basic this is the 'As I was saying to Carrington the other day, what the world needs at this point is a digital pop-up toaster.' This not only implies that you are on easy terms with Lord Carrington, but also that he is in the habit of asking your advice on matters of importance. It also flatters your listener by giving him the impression that were you, he and Lord Carrington in the same room together, you would certainly between you thrash out something pretty significant about the problems of the British electrical goods industry.

The optional curriculum vitae is used when your target may be unfamiliar with the droppee, or when you wish to give the target the impression that you have no great opinion of his intelligence; thus: 'As I was saying to Peter Carrington the other day, you may remember the chap, used to be Foreign Secretary, collects stamps, things are in a bit of a mess.'

NOTE: *Who's Who* is the name dropper's bible. Of course, I know almost everybody in the volume intimately, but even I admit that in early life I spent half an hour a day boning up a page, by rote. Never be without it.

2 *Story appropriation* A superficially simple gambit, but one requiring a fair degree of inventiveness. The dropper selects a well-known incident in the life of a famous name, and claims to have been present, narrating the anecdote from his own point of view. Thus: 'Yes, how well one recalls Tiger Marks. I remember the night they took him away, blood everywhere of course, but then – well, I'd better not tell you his name but suffice it to say he had concrete in his turnups when he came back. Yes, whenever I drive across the Hammersmith Flyover I shed a little tear for poor old Tig, as we used to call him. Had a wonderful baritone, did you know that?'

3 *The prime mover drop* In this well-loved technique, the dropper claims responsibility for starting a chain of events that rocked the world. Thus: 'Do you know a while back I was talking to Ronnie Reagan and he happened to say that he had never seen Mount Rushmore? Well, of course, I flew him right over and he was most impressed, and after that I caught him sneaking glimpses of his profile in the vanity mirror in the Cadillac and I thought, well, hell, you know actors. But then he turned to me and he said: "Harry," he said, "there's a big old lump of rock up yonder and it kind of reminds me of me." And I guess that was the start of it all.'

With time and application, a really good name dropper can acquire the reputation of being a man who knows everybody, advises the great, and has a tremendous fund of original ideas. There is a mystery to name dropping similar to that of Count Cagliostro, who always seemed to slip into the group photograph at the last moment, slipping away immediately afterwards. The cries of 'Who he?' swiftly changed to 'Ah, Cagliostro. Sound fellow.'

Sound fellows can get away with *anything*.

RUMOUR-MONGERING

Name dropping is a splendid way of building yourself up. There are times, however, when it is necessary to scupper those who do not see things your way. The quickest way is violence; but for those with instinctive shrinking from this a rumour is only slightly slower-acting and will probably be more effective in the long run. There are two main methods of mongering a rumour to the detriment of an opponent. The first is the saturation rumour, by which a slander is so widely repeated that the target is forced to throw up his job, grow a beard, change his name, acquire a false passport and leave the country. The second is the precision or pinpoint rumour, being a slander which may be of interest to only one other person besides the target, but which has a devastating effect.

1 *Saturation rumour-mongering* Most journalism is now saturation rumour-mongering, and the technique has achieved the status of an art form. Once you have invented a rumour, send anonymous letters to the press. The body will stick its foot in the target's door and commence speculating. Since the state education system has rendered a vast sector of the public incapable of rational thought, such speculations are soon accepted as gospel truth.

A fine example of saturation rumour-mongering is the spy fever that occasionally grips the populace. A putative ninth, tenth, or eleventh man can be publicly pilloried on the strength of a memo suggesting that he was once seen drinking vodka with a picture restorer who was known to have a conviction for soliciting in a gents in Peckham.

The old adage suggests that if you throw enough mud, some of it will stick. This method ensures that the mud arrives in a JCB bucket and does not so much stick as flatten.

2 *Precision rumour-mongering* This has long been a favourite technique with female bounders. Classically, the rumour is started by a bitch and an

accomplice, speaking in the hearing of (but not *to*) the target's spouse. The bitch makes an allegation concerning the blond hairs the dry cleaner noticed on target's coat collar, or the supposed resemblance of target's last child to the milkman. The mongerer will have been speaking in high, indignant tones, cutting herself off short on 'becoming aware' of target spouse's presence. Target and spouse can then be confidently expected to be living in separate accommodation within the month.

Your education is now complete.

The Seven Deadly Virtues

Jilly Cooper

I have long been fascinated by the Seven Deadly Sins: pride, envy, gluttony, anger, sloth, avarice and lust, a loathsome bunch stalking through medieval literature. I first encountered them when I did *The Faerie Queene* as a set book. Pride, I remember, was wonderfully beautiful and gazed permanently at herself in a mirror. Sloth dozed on a donkey carrying an unread prayerbook, Gluttony had a pot belly and waved a beer mug, and kept being sick on passers-by, Avarice, thin as a rake in threadbare clothes, was weighed down by bags of gold, Envy carried a toad in his mouth and spat out the poison, Anger waved a dagger and rode on a roaring lion, and Lechery was decked out in a clean green suit to hide his filthy body but was quite irresistible to women.

As I grew older though, I realized that these seven sins were only deadly in extreme form, that Sloth can be translated as the ability to relax, that Lechery within marriage becomes healthy passion (and we all know how that oils the matrimonial wheels), and that Pride if rightly channelled becomes healthy ambition. Put the word 'healthy' in fact in front of any vice, and it is promptly transformed into a virtue.

And as the world became less black and white, I learnt that virtues in extreme form can be just as deadly too. *Charity*, for example, would be my first deadly virtue – because it makes people so deadly boring. Personified, I see her as rather plump with her arms stretched out, and a soppy smile on her face, saying, 'I love everyone because I'm a people person.' She never says an unkind word about anybody, and is always sticking up for the most awful people. When you're in the full flood of vindictiveness about the atrocious behaviour of Aunt Gertrude, she will sweetly remind you that poor Gertrude is going through the change of life. When you're making up a real hate for the office crone because she's made you re-type a whole ten-page report because you spelt 'sillycone' wrong, she will remind you that Elinor (she always knows people's Christian names) has a bad back. Well she's got an even lousier front, too, you mutter, only to be gently reminded that poor Elinor's feeling sad this week because her parrot has died, and did you know she looks after a sick mother.

Charity always manages to talk for hours with shining eyes to the biggest bore in the room, crying, 'Water supplies, how fascinating! Do tell me more.' She has no social discrimination; she'll invite you to grisly tea parties to meet friends from the East and you never know if they're going to be East Enders or Chinamen. Her wretched husband suffers because every time he comes home battered by commuting, longing for a bit of peace and a large gin and tonic, the last of the gin is being poured down some snivelling lame duck undergoing some major crisis like the sack, or her television breaking down.

Browning once wrote a poem called 'My Last Duchess' about a beautiful woman who loved everything. Her looks went everywhere, goes the poem, and she liked what e'er she looked on. She showed the same joy at the sight of her donkey, the sunset, the branch of blossom some yokel picked for her in the orchard, and her husband, who with marriage had bestowed on her his nine-centuries-old title. In the end one can understand why he got so irritated by such blanket appreciation and did her in.

Oh I find it very hard to love my enemies, but it's even more irritating when someone else does.

'I met your husband's ex-wife,' Charity will say blithely. 'What a beautiful charming woman.' Or, 'Have you seen that girl who got that job you went for, what an absolute sweetie, and *so* young.' Or even worse: 'I do really *envy* you your mother-in-law.'

I suspect too that the charitable aren't really interested in people, or that their suppressed venom may come out in other ways.

One finds, conversely, that the more acerbic the writer, the more amiable they are in the flesh. Richard Ingrams, Clive James, Nigel Dempster and Bernard Levin are all the gentlest, most velvet-gloved company, because they've exhausted their vitriol and resentment on the page.

I have always liked people who have strong hates and loves, which brings me to my second deadly virtue, *Moderation*. I see Moderation with 34-in hips, sucking a boiled sweet to the end rather than biting it, and holding a hand over her glass saying, 'I've had enough, thank you,' because she's frightened of losing count.

If she's enjoying a book, she rations herself to reading a chapter a day, instead of galloping through it until four o'clock in the morning, or reading the end first like I do. She never has too hot a bath before a party so that she emerges scarlet in the face with swollen ankles. She never eats too much or between meals.

Jennifer is a natural weight-watcher, her friends say. If she puts on a couple of pounds she cuts out bread and potatoes for a week, unlike me, who can eat mindlessly through a whole box of chocolates or a packet of biscuits if I've had a row with my husband, or I can't think what to write.

Nor do I like moderation in men. Men who boast they've never had a hangover, or who put saccharine in their coffee or who won't make love to you on a Friday night in case it puts their eye out for cricket the next day. I don't like the kind of boss either who never takes three-hour drunken lunches, giving you the chance to scour Knightsbridge for a new dress; or men who never tell you they love you, in case they get compromised.

I admire the moderate, but they make me feel guilty; people who file and tidy their drawers every day, so they never disappear under a tidal wave of papers. One friend tidying up after nine months found a list headed: 'Ten Things I Must Do Today Or I Shall Get Sacked.' In fact he had done none of them, but after nine months they didn't matter any more.

My third deadly sin, first cousin to moderation, is *Respectability*. I can see her now. Her skin is good enough not to need any make-up, her short curly hair doesn't touch her collar, the top button of her shirt is done up, and underneath she wears a bra and a petticoat. When she bought her skirt she held it up to the light, not to test the colour, but to see if anyone could see through it. Respectability always writes her thank-you letters immediately, she never gossips with her charwoman, or even worse other people's charwomen, and when she undresses she always draws her curtains. She never looks at another man, never forgets the school run and she always claims she and her husband *never* quarrel. She never swears in front of her children, and never allows them to eat the fruit out of a Pimms glass in case they get 'tiddly' (a favourite word). If you ask her what she wants to drink she replies, 'Orange squash, I'm so thirsty.'

Respectability always dances concave at parties so no one can dance cheek to cheek with her, and if a man tries to kiss her she slaps his face – a sort of chastity belt. A wonderful wife and mother, a perfect secretary, a little homemaker, why do I want to kick her in the teeth (which are perfect, because she goes to the dentist every six months)?

I always find it sad, too, when very wild people suddenly become ultra respectable, like the little girl with a curl: when she was good she was very,

very good, but when she was bad she was much more amusing. One of the nastiest manifestations of respectability is that nothing must be allowed to rock the matrimonial boat. A married man will go on and on and on pestering a single girl until he seduces her, and she may then well fall in love with him; but then he may treat her appallingly – stand her up, not answer her letters, keep her waiting for hours in the cold – justifying such bad behaviour by telling himself that preserving his own marriage is the only thing that really matters.

I am always amused too by the hypocrisy that goes on in order to preserve a respectable front. I met a very glamorous peer, who is also an author, at a party, and he asked me out to lunch. I couldn't go that day so I rang up and, to my intense embarrassment, got his wife. 'I'm writing a book about the English class system,' I stammered. 'I wanted to pick his brain about what it's like being a lord.' His wife laughed: 'Oh,' she said, 'he told me he was writing a piece about newspapers, and wanted to pick your brain about being a lady journalist.'

Nor do I like the respectability that occasionally emerges in myself. Because we can't afford a holiday this year, I keep hearing myself chuntering disapprovingly about people who rush off and leave their children, and I can get very pompous over the wife-swappers rampaging through East Sheen. But at least I'm not such a horrible little prude as I was when I was engaged; one Sunday afternoon, my husband told me he'd once been to an orgy and, even worse, thoroughly enjoyed it. Tearing off my engagement ring, I threw it at him, and, crying great sobs, caught the first Green Line bus back home to Hampton Court, where I walked round the lake three times, realized I was over-reacting, and sent him a telegram saying, 'I have decided to forgive this dreadful thing I will marry you after all' and took the first Green Line bus back up to London again.

My fourth deadly virtue is *Cleanliness*. I can see her chasing me down the years, roaring Hoover in one rubber-gloved hand, in the other a flannel soaked in surgical spirit to clean my neck.

'I never have time to sit down,' she announces proudly, as her J-cloth whisks over the surfaces. Whites dancing on the clothes line excite her to a point of ecstasy, and the only thing she thinks about in the spring is cleaning.

I'm not attacking normal cleanliness, by which I mean bathing every day, and putting on clean pants (I think, too, I'd take off my make-up every night in my sleep). But I mean that obsessive cleanliness fostered by television commercials showing gleaming kitchens and permanently deodorized lavatories, which make women do far more housework than they need out of a sense of guilt.

Great battles used to go on at home, too, when we had a nanny looking after our children with a Lady Macbeth complex: she never stopped washing – herself or our clothes. Soon she had shrunk all my sweaters down to Action Man size. She used to get so irritated with my husband for taking down the washing line at weekends that she was always washing his dressing-gown, which took at least two days to dry, so that he was forced to scuttle round the landing with no clothes on, which was perhaps what she wanted all along. She even starched his jockstrap every week. The washing machine roared all day, the electricity bill for one quarter was £487, not to mention the vats of Daz, Flash and Finish which rocketed the household bills every week. Cleanliness may be next to Godliness, but it's very expensive.

What amazes me is that people regard cleanliness as such a virtue. Mohammed Ali at his retirement match boasted that he loved his latest girlfriend because she was 'clean and classy'. Then there was the wardrobe mistress who praised Audrey Hepburn for having the cleanest neck she'd ever seen. I suppose I am impressed by such a piece of information, but it does not endear me to Miss Hepburn. I met a man recently who said the most wonderful thing about his mother was that she always washed the kitchen floor every day. The most important thing about my mother was that she taught me that it was more important sometimes to read a book than do housework. Our house was always clean and sweet smelling (if not very tidy) but my abiding childhood memory of my mother is not of her sighing and scrubbing and banging pans, but of leaving the washing-up until later because she wanted to curl up on the sofa and finish her book. Likewise, my husband's aunt, who is a great writer, admits she only tidies up when she can't get to the bookshelves any more.

Anyway, dirty windows cast a far more flattering light, and dirty mirrors take at least ten years off one's age; and as I can never find a biro, dust is awfully useful to write in.

But even worse than excess cleanliness is the fifth deadly virtue: *Righteousness*, symbolized by all those do-gooders who keep trying to clean up people's lives, and by Mrs Whitehouse crying 'Filth' and 'Disgusting' every time the tip of a quarter frontal appears on telly.

The Righteous are those middle-class people who have enough influence to get their roads made private, so that all the through traffic spills into adjoining streets and working-class children get run over instead; and who take people away from their cosy slummy streets, and put them in high-rise blocks away from all their friends and family.

Among the righteous are all those idiotic women's libbers who keep on urging women to break up a marriage that's imperfect – what marriage isn't – so that they can become independent career women, forgetting to mention the appalling hassle and loneliness of running a job and children on one's own. But equally insidious are the women suffering from 'Mr Right'-eousness, who have found their man and got married, then become appallingly smug and try to force Mr Rights on all their girlfriends. Who has not suffered those ghastly candle-lit dinners, when the husband and wife smile on fondly, expecting you to get off with some sweaty, horn-rimmed spectacled horror they've specially provided for you, and then get livid if it doesn't work.

Another point about the righteous is that they are invariably trying to persuade people to do things they don't have to do themselves, like those demagogues at meetings who stir up the rabble to go out and get killed. They remind me of the woman in Saki, who 'inveighed eloquently against the evils of capitalism at drawing-room meetings and Fabian conferences, but was conscious of a comfortable feeling that the system with all its inequalities would probably last her time; it is one of the consolations of middle-aged reformers that the good they inculcate must live after them if it is to live at all'.

Finally, unlike the Bitchy and uncharitable who work off their spleen on the page or in a good gossip with a chum, the Righteous seem to exhaust their goodness on the public and often have little left for their own family. I know one woman who spends all week in London counselling unhappily married couples, leaving her poor husband in the country trying to cope with a job and four hopelessly disturbed children.

Another married acquaintance, a man who is always lobbying for private member's bills, met a woman at a political meeting and embarked on an affair with her (involving his own private member, no doubt). Being into honesty, however, he told his wife he had fallen in love with someone else and proudly announced to her that he was going straight out to dinner with the new mistress, whereupon his poor wife burst into tears.

'What on earth's the matter?' snapped her husband. 'You never minded when I was going out to meetings.'

Righteous he may have been, but he didn't suffer from unselfishness: our sixth deadly virtue. *Unselfishness* places herself behind the pillar at the theatre while her family on either side can see perfectly. She always sits in a draught, and gives the chicken breast to her husband, keeping the scrawniest, most sinewy wing for herself. She never says No to him in bed either, not because she likes sex, but because if he has pleasure it is enough for her. She wears her long mousy hair in a bun, because it would be wicked to waste money on the hairdressers that could be spent on the children.

'How beautiful,' she will cry when she sees you in a new dress, looking wistfully down at her ten-year-old mini, to which she has added an ingenious false hem to turn it into a midi; then she adds with a brave smile, 'But it's more important for Charles to have a new suit.'

She is Beth in *Little Women*, smiling through her tears. She's always bringing in windfalls, which go bad because one can't stand stewed apple, and riding round on a bicycle to save petrol, and running up sponge cakes for rugger teas, and manning the stall at the Bring and Buy when all her helpers have sloped off to the tea tent. 'I live for others,' she's fond of saying, and she always lets her husband watch what he wants on television. Some men infuriatingly seem to think she's wonderful, but then one man's meek is another man's poison.

The continually unselfish are irritating enough if they smile sweetly, but they're even worse if they're always sighing and looking martyred. How well I remember in my flat-sharing days coming back after a few days' riotous living to find my flat-mate tight-lipped and sighing like a furnace, having just spent forty-eight hours mucking out the communal bedroom. Or there are the mothers who are always reminding their children of the sacrifices they've made to send them to decent schools.

The unselfish are even worse in the office. They soldier in raging with temperatures, beads of sweat on their foreheads, devouring boxes of Kleenex and Beecham's Pills, and when you say, 'For God's sake, go home,' they start muttering about Someone Having To Keep the Show on the Road. I'm guilty of the same kind of martyrdom myself. Occasionally nannies who are supposed to be looking after my children and my house play hookey and fail to turn up on Sunday night. Instead of getting down to writing to meet some journalistic deadline on Monday morning, I start sulkily banging the iron over clothes that could easily be left twenty-four hours, praying in a perverted way that the nanny will turn up later and later, so that I can work up even more of a righteous rage at her not being there.

Finally we come to our last and socially deadliest virtue – *Honesty*. I see him standing with rosy cheeks, and clear truthful blue eyes, and a smug smile on his face, saying, 'May I be really frank with you?' Then he'll come out with some devastating home truth, such as, you're neglecting your children, or your house smells of cats, or surely your husband's car shouldn't be parked quite so often outside the house of the local temptress.

I do not like the truth. I do not like it when my husband comes home, treads on one marble, and says, 'This place is a shambles,' or tells me that it would be mutton dressed as lamb if I bought a pair of pink dungarees. Last week, a girlfriend told me I should cook more and brush my hair occasionally; another friend said I shouldn't gossip so much, and my husband must be a saint to put up with me. I smiled sweetly at them both, but inside I smarted. I shan't be asking *them* to dinner again for several months.

Burns in a fatuous mood contended that an honest man is the noblest work of God – maybe, but he isn't much fun to be married to. George Washington, never telling a lie, must have been a nightmare: 'That's not true, Mrs Washington, you were forty last birthday ... No, I don't love you at this moment, Mrs W, I think you're a great screeching old crow.... And this Thanksgiving dinner is not as good as last year' – he deserved to get pumpkin pie slapped in the kisser.

I'm always amazed too, that Jane Eyre accepted Mr Rochester's proposal – leading her into the garden and crying, 'You, poor and obscure, and small and plain as you are, I entreat you to accept me as a husband.'

I'd have slapped his craggy face.

Nor can I understand the logic of all those advertisements in which the girl is told her breath smells, or she suffers from BO, or her hair is dry and unmanageable, by her candid friend, and then actually turns round after she has hitched Prince Charming and thanks the candid friend for the advice. I'd go off and buy some Mum Roulette and then waltz off with the candid friend's boyfriend, raising two fingers as I went.

However, the opening I really shrink from is, 'I know with your sense of humour you'll really be amused by...' then *wham* comes some hideous revelation. When I first joined the *Sunday Times* I had lunch with a fellow journalist, who asked me whether I had heard the latest rumour, that I had got my job because I was having a rip-roaring affair with one of the Thomson Top Brass.

'But it's simply not true,' I wailed

So he went on to state the time and the name of the hotel we were allegedly supposed to meet at every week.

'But that's horrible,' I said, nearly in tears. 'I mean I've got my dear husband and a new baby.'

'Never mind, darling,' he said soothingly, 'you come out of it frightfully well. The Fleet Street *on dit* is that he can't get it up at all, but that you're always *frightfully* understanding about it.'

Finally, I remember my mother-in-law once saying to me: 'Women are either beautiful or good. Leo's first wife was beautiful.'

The truth docs grate, whether it prevails or not.

On Ilkley Moor b'aht Frog

John Wells

A French language 'survival kit' for the tourist who wants to travel, eat and shop in France has been introduced to Yorkshire schools, with the aim of overthrowing the present system of O-level exams. The teachers behind the scheme say that French O-level is a certificate of near incompetence and that, for most children, the exam course is boring and useless. The result is that schools are losing the battle against what has been called 'the obdurate non-lingualism of the British schoolboy.'

Right lads, let's be havin yer. Tek yer boots off desk, Scragley, pin yer lugholes back an yer might learn summat. Headmaster, Mr Postlethwaite, is in a right lather, and I fully understand his apoplexy, about standard of performance in French O Levels. They were bloody diabolical. Half of you seemed to be under impression Voltaire were a type of ventilation plant used in factories to keep temperature down, and Mr Postlethwaite tells me that when he mentioned Racine results he distinctly saw three members of this class pull out bettin slips. They may not, either of em, have had the advantage of bein born British, but they were both great Soccer players in their day and deserve to be remembered.

I personally attribute abysmal showing, though I wouldn't say it outside this classroom, to fact that teachin of French in this school has bin left in the twitchy and tremblin hands of Monsewer so-called Morris, a right shag in my opinion, with filthy personal habits, who might well learn a bit about gettin pickled onions an garlic off his breath before he starts teachin decent Yorkshire lads about how to talk foreign.

As your PT Instructor it has fallen to me to tell you that we have now changed all that. Monsewer Morris as I understand it is at this moment having his bones shaken to the marrow on hovercraft, on route, as they say down there, for eight weeks compulsory vacation in his country of origin, and we shall in future be equippin you with a brand new Survival Kit enablin any ordinary sensible lad with a tongue in his head to remain alive for up to seven days, assumin he has necessary protective clothin, water-purifying tablets and lurgi pills, even in an utter muckhole like Paris.

First off then, an I'll have that catapult if you please, Codrington, is to realise that Frog as a lingo is on its last legs. A dinosaur, waiting only for a sufficiently hard poke in ribs to crumble to dust. Quite apart from havin no satisfactory equivalent for such scientific terms as rog-wobble, scrintin baffle readjuster or Pontefract cake, Frog is hamstrung with countless archaic forms that effectively prevented it from ever draggin itself gruntin and gesticulatin out of twelfth century, let alone Middle Ages. *Lee* and *Lah*, to tek but one glarin example. Any form of communication that designates a hobnailed boot, *Lah Bott*, as feminine, or a brassiere, *Lee Soo-cha Gawj*, as masculine has clearly got its evolutionary knickers in a twist with disastrous results.

History has also bin against it. Had things turned out different history-wise, *Lah Bott* would no doubt be upon other foot, but as it is your speaker of Frog has got his back against wall and is lookin dead worried. Pockets of resistance there may be, notably among political extremists in Quebec, driven mad no doubt by havin to talk to other Canadians for a couple of hundred years, bits of Africa an odd desert islands dotted about where they still jabber a variety of Frog, albeit incomprehensible to man or beast on account of dinner plates stuck in their lips, but in point of fact what were once reckoned language of diplomacy is now entirely up spout.

Certainly Mainland Frog has taken a right poundin, what with pop records, telly an Scotch Soccer Hooligans swarmin all over em smashin place up, with result your ordinary Frog in Street has had to pull himself together an learn English like everybody else, if only for his own protection. The fact that those with a financial interest in keepin em prattling away in Frog – book writers, makers of spare parts with instructions on in Frog they can't flog off to anyone else etcetera – have had laws passed saying anyone as gets nabbed usin English words can be strung up by thumbs or for persistent offences burned at stake, only indicates cracks as are appearin in this whole superannuated edifice. It is through these cracks, lads, you will be well advised to direct the spearhead of your attack.

Examinin the form in front of you entitled *University of York Survival Kit*, and stop doin that Arkenshaw or you will have even greater difficulty in decipherin small print, you will see:

Exercise One: 'Askin Way and Understanding Directions.' Askin is one thing, understandin is another. However the followin basic plan should serve.

SURVIVAL SQUADDY: Eiffel Tower.

ALIEN: Jabber jabber jabber, waves arms about, rolls eyes etc.

SS: EI-FFEL TOW-ER.

A: Jabber jabber, points.

SS: Right, why didn't you bloody say so in the first place.

Exercise Two: 'Shoppin for Food, Souvenirs, Post Cards, Stamps Etc.' This has been made easier by almost complete penetration of Frog market by Yank brand-names but SS will be required to show some familiarity with Frog manners an a lynx-eyed interest in cash register at end of transaction.

SS: *See-voo Play*. I would like a Jumbo Packet of Frosticles, a bottle of milk, Mannekin Pis bottle opener, one Greetings from Paris with two ladies twangin each others' knicker elastic, and one o' them. Licks thumb and presses down on corner of postcard.

A: Jabber jabber.

SS: An I'll have that writ out in figures unless you're lookin for a knuckle sandwich.

Exercise Three: 'Go to a Caff or Restaurant.' No problem. They are all called Self-Service or Drugstore and Frog has largely bin eliminated from vocabulary. However to avoid bein stung, observin *Bong-shaw* on enterin will ensure you are taken for a local.

Exercise Four: 'Travel by Rail or Road.' Motorin, the Frog expression *Murd*, pronounced on windin down the car window, may be of some assistance. Goin by train, remember that unlike England many place names in France do not sound the same as they look. E.g.

SS: Rheims. There an back.

A: Speaking indistinctly through little amplifier in hatch, Jabber jabber.

SS: Rheims Froggichops an stop muckin about I've got a train to catch.

A: Jabber jabber jabber. Hangs label over little hatch saying *Ferm*.

SS: Sod that for a lark. Moves label sayin *Ferm*, reaches through little hatch, takes felt-tip pen an writes Rheims on ticket desk. There, pointing to place name, an Back, pointing to station entrance.

A: Produces ticket.

SS: *Mur-see.*

Exercise Five: 'Stay in a Hotel, Youth Hostel, Campsite or a French Home.'
Trick question, this. Correct answer is, unless you're after terminal
diarrhoea, fleas the size of a man-eating crab or a nasty dose of t'other, *don't.*
Keep movin, sleep when you get back to Wetherby. Frog thieves have been
known to strip sleepin visitors down to skellintons.

Summin up, you're goin into battle, lads. In recent years, your Frog has
forced us to scrap half-crown, bob and tanner, threatened to wipe out pounds
an ounces, and now has effrontery to try an massacre your inches feet yards
an miles, 'for convenience of visitors from abroad'. A hysterical, last ditch
counter-attack, comparable to Battle of Bulge, noted Ardennes Offensive,
when Krauts also knew in their heart of hearts that they were done for. Frog,
as a language, make no mistake about it, will soon collapse entirely, 'for the
convenience of visitors from abroad'. You, lads, will be forefront of that
assault. God bless you all, and in with *Lah Bott.*

Not My Day

An annoying start. My Teasmade, set to go off as per usual at 7am, turned
out to be minus the teapot part. As a result, on the stroke of seven, the light
came on, the buzzer went off, and the bloody thing poured scalding hot water
all over my new marquetry top bedside table from Heal's, absolutely soaking
my foam rubber posture pillow, and ruining my newly laundered Rear
Admiral brushed nylon pyjamas. I was hopping mad, I don't mind
admitting.

To crown it all, Bob Carr chose precisely that moment to come barging
straight in to my holy of holies, as I refer to my tastefully decorated bachelor
suite at Number Ten – with its nautical blue ceiling designed by Madge
Thrower, its Hokusai Shimbun multi-output loudspeaker equipment, and
the *Quaint Moments in Old London* series of art repro copper engravings by
Melvyn Pymm – saying he had to see me on urgent business.

He seemed, however, hugely amused by the Teasmade having gone
wrong, and said, 'Ha ha. I always said you'd get into hot water one of these
days, living alone like this.'

I said, 'Shut up, you bloody fool. Get a mop and start swabbing up.' He
then replied: 'It's no good, Fatty, it is your own fault for not getting a proper

gentleman's gentleman to boil your water in the mornings, thus dramatically reducing unemployment on Tyneside and elsewhere at a stroke. As it is, on your own head be it.'

I refused to be stung by this, and said, 'Nonsense. I already have Mrs Behr once a day.' I then pointed to the Teasmade and added: 'If you are incapable of absorbing the inevitable redundancies occasioned by the introduction of more complex technology, I for one am not surprised that people throw rotten cabbages whenever you show your silly bloody face in public. But come to the point. What is it you wish to see me about? I am a busy man.'

He said, 'Curly Barber and I dreamed up a little wheeze at Crockford's last night.'

'Very well,' I replied coldly. 'Leave it on the occasional table by the Elisabeth Frink and get out.' With this, I turned angrily on my heel and flounced out into the bathroom to do my Egyptian Air Force exercises.

While performing the 'Stand on Your Own Foot' exercise, I unfortunately fell over, banging my head on the Sèvres bidet presented to me last year by Monsieur Pompadour. I also had to get out of the bath on several occasions, first to turn off the *Today* programme, which seemed to be concerned exclusively with destruction in Ulster, and subsequently to adjust the manual control on my Banzai Shinto turntable, which repeatedly became stuck in Arturo Blitzkrieg's *sostenuto* during the famous fiddling scene from *Il Inflammazione de Nero*.

After perusing the contents of my Red Boxes, which contained over a hundred old restaurant bills submitted by Reggie Maudling for expenses, a 'saucy' postcard from Ian Smith and a curious ticking parcel which, unwrapped appeared to be some sort of home-made wireless set, I breakfasted as usual off one slice of starch-reduced Slimmawheet with a scrape of Blue Band and a cup of unsweetened black Kardomah coffee, and went down to the Cabinet Room to look at oilskins in the new catalogue from Simpson's

As I watched my colleagues coming into the Cabinet Room (at present being treated again for dry rot by white-overalled workmen from the Ministry of the Environment, some of whom speak fluent Russian) I was overwhelmed, as I always am, by a sense of my own superiority. They are a shabby lot, and it is a source of pride to me that I have risen above them. To pass the time until they settled down, I cast my eye over the note left by Bob Carr. It was written, rather unsteadily, on the back of a ticket for somewhere called the Nudes-a-Gogo Club, and bore the words 'Final Solution'.

I asked Barber what they meant by this when he and Carr came in, and they explained that the ideal population of the United Kingdom, in the interests of efficiency and the satisfactory running of service industries to maintain a reasonable standard of living for the nation's supertax-payers, was ten million. The remaining surplus which could be statistically broken down into Communist agitators, scroungers, immigrants, children, lunatics and old people, should be 'shaken out'.

Gavin Pine, our PR adviser, had apparently come up with some cliff-hanger scheme of the type used at Brussels and in Salisbury, whereby the general public is to be kept in suspense over the eventual cost to the taxpayer of the 'shaking out' plant, to be supplied by Porton Down, until such time as the necessary legislation is passed. I said the plan sounded perfectly fair to me, and the Cabinet dispersed.

I just had time for a cheese salad and a glass of water for lunch, prepared by Mrs Behr, before dashing off to catch the 1.43 to Broadstairs, leaving Alec to deal with Question Time.

After an extremely disagreeable trip down in the train, throughout which I was pestered by a plump matron in her mid-forties with pebble spectacles who kept asking me whether I wanted to play doctors and nurses, I arrived home to find that Dad had fallen off the roof trying to attach a pro Common Market banner to the television aerial, and broken several ribs. This was a nuisance as it made me late for sailing.

However, as I said to Captain Marryat, the horny-handed old salt who works, or should I say worked, the steering thing at the back end of *Morning Cloud*, watching the lights of Broadstairs disappear into the dusk, it's the little mishaps in life that really make one laugh in the long run. I was, in fact, just having a good laugh, when the main upright thing began vibrating, came loose from its socket, and fell over, unfortunately killing him. This delayed me for a further forty-five minutes, and I was not in my suspended bed, off Cherbourg, for the start of the Millionaires' Handicap, until 10pm. As I said to begin with, it was not my day.

Mrs Parkinson's Law

C. Northcote Parkinson

This chapter is specifically intended for the married woman whose children are of school age; the woman for whom life often becomes too much. This does not mean, however, that her husband should omit this chapter, for he needs, surely, to know what her problems are. Central to them is the periodic impact of the day of crisis, the moment of grief, the hour when the world seems about to end. Black disaster threatens on every side and you (the housewife) do not know whether to scream, to pray or to put your head in the gas oven. In studying this situation, let us see it, first of all, from the outside. Suppose in the first instance, that it is someone else who is in trouble; an acquaintance and neighbour, a woman known to you as respectable and harmless, one who lives a little way down the street on the opposite side. Suppose, further, that she is called (say) Yardley, the wife of a bank executive. Looking casually out of your front window, you realise that something has gone wrong.

Yes, there is something amiss in the Yardley's home and the goldfish-bowl nature of the modern suburb allows you to share in it. With picture windows and open plan, with flimsy walls and grass surround, our modern houses hold few secrets from each other. When the Robinsons at 34 are giving a party, the fact is apparent to all who were not invited. When the Jamesons at 31 are having a quarrel the cause of the dispute becomes instantly known to all within a hundred yards. In the present instance there is no family dispute and none expected – for the Yardleys are an amicable couple – but Gwen is clearly upset. Her voice is raised, and so, on a higher pitch, is that of her only child (Tommy, aged four). There is a man at her front door and you recognise him as the pollster who called yesterday on you. He is distributing some questionnaire in which opinions are canvassed about nuclear warfare – 'Ma-m-may I approach you,' he began, 'as a leader of op-op-opinion in this neighbourhood. . . .' Gwen has flung open the door and is listening to what

must be his standard opening. Even at this distance you can appreciate that
she is registering a sense of suppressed fury. You are not one to pry into your
neighbour's troubles (heaven knows you have other things to do), but
something of tension in the scene keeps you glued to the window. The little
man is explaining, no doubt, that the world – without Gwen's intervention –
is doomed. Gwen's hostility projects itself successfully the length of the block.
Suddenly there comes an explosion of almost nuclear violence. The words,
'GET OUT!!!' are all you actually hear, but Gwen's torrent of screamed
abuse is easily imaginable. The questionnaire is being torn into shreds. The
terrified pollster is stumbling down the path. He has tripped and fallen on
the pavement, scattering 'literature' as he runs towards his car, and a minute
later he and it have vanished and Gwen stops shaking her fist. Her glass-
topped door slams and there is the sound of broken glass. More faintly comes
the slam of an inner door, Tommy's wail and the crash of disintegrating
china. For Gwen, poor girl, it is evidently one of those days when *everything
goes wrong*.

Do you yourself have such days of disaster? You do? How do they begin,
then, and what is the sequence of events? Are they avoidable? You may have
concluded that they are a feature of an ill-planned universe and that there is
nothing you can do about it. In this you may well be mistaken. As diagnosis
comes before treatment, our first step must be to reconstruct the crisis. This
we have often seen done by television detectives.

'Put the furniture back where it was, open the window, switch off the
standard light. Sit in the armchair, Watson. Now, I will enter by the door as
the murderer must have done. . . . What do I see? Nothing. Why not? Because
the room is in pitch darkness!'

'Holmes, this is marvellous!'

The same technique can be applied to our own less melodramatic affairs.
Let us begin, then, with an imaginary situation of which you might well be
the victim. Your husband and children have gone respectively to office and
school and the day, we shall suppose, is cold, foggy and wet. With the post
comes a letter from the high-street department store, regretting that the
dressing-table you wanted, an antique, has been sold cheaply to someone
else. You learn by telephone that your plan for holidays has fallen through,
the hotel having been wrecked by an avalanche. The agent assures you that it
is now too late to book accommodation elsewhere. Martin's school report
arrives, and you tear it open, glimpsing the words 'untidy' and 'idle'. The
toaster jams, filling the kitchen with black smoke. The coffee saucepan boils

over on the hotplate. You break a decorative and valuable piece of china, the Royal Worcester plate on which you serve biscuits. Everything, but *everything* is against you. All evidence points to the existence of a conspiracy, which might be defined in scientific terms as the inveterate malignancy of inanimate objects. You relieve your feelings by cancelling a hair appointment and complaining by telephone about your neighbour's dog. You end with a minor car accident and a parking ticket.

Why does all this have to happen to us? Why this sequence of dilemma, disaster and dismay? Under emotional stress, we ask these questions of an unresponsive heaven, being unable to provide the answers for ourselves.

But *now*, as you read this, you are cool and collected and can realise that your sequence of events is not a sequence at all. The successive tragedies are unrelated and fall, in any case, into two separate groups. The bargain is lost, the holiday plan spoilt and the school report received; all these incidents are *external* and beyond your control. The toaster, the saucepan and the china dish are *internal* disasters and strictly your own doing. Study the apparent sequence afresh. The loss of the bargain is bad luck and there is nothing you can do about it – save to note that you have some extra money for the re-planned holiday. You might say that the hotel cancellation is purely disastrous; but is it? After all, the avalanche might have happened while you were there; and even while you were in the bath. You are well out of it in that sense. Now, look at the report again. How does it go? 'Although Martin is sometimes rather untidy, he is never ill-behaved or idle and his work shows definite signs of improvement.' Not so bad, really, and better anyway than the last.

The other disasters were all (let's face it) your own doing. The toaster and coffee went wrong because you were thinking about the dressing-table, not about the task in hand. But the breaking of the china dish represents something more complex. Women express their annoyance in the first place by rattling dishes and slamming doors. Dishes are apt to break when rattled. Broken to fragments and slammed into the dust bin, they also serve as a protest against the unfairness of the world. The odd plate or saucer would mean no more than that, but the breaking of Wedgwood or Spode is something different. It reveals that you are behaving childishly, that you *know* your behaviour is childish, that you are punishing yourself like a child and using a childish form of punishment. But your annoyance does not stop there. Why should it, and indeed how can it? You can go on to punish yourself and others until such time as you recover. It is only then, hours (or days) later, that you study the situation afresh and find that it is not so serious after all. Until that moment of calm you will continue to exemplify the *Second Law of Thermodynamics*; the law that heat energy is always transferred from a body with a higher temperature to one with a lower temperature. There can be no such transfer, however, unless there is another body there to receive it. In this instance your heat energy was distributed between the hairdresser and the neighbour's dog, which was fortunate for the latter, who might otherwise have been killed outright.

It is obvious that your generated and transferable heat is potentially dangerous and may lead to results which escalate (a good contemporary expression) from slander to assault and from divorce to murder. To lessen this danger, as we plainly must, we have to decide (i) how the heat generates and whether it need be generated at all, and (ii) if it has to generate, how it can be dispersed harmlessly before any real mischief has been done? The clue to (i) lies in the *First Law of Thermodynamics*: the law that heat is absorbed in proportion to the work done under pressure; a given quantity of work producing a definite equivalent of heat. This law applies to the emotional as well as to the physical temperature. Household work is apt to be done under pressure because it fluctuates, rising to a peak (for example) when packing the children off to school, and rising to another peak as the guests are due to arrive in the evening. The heat is apt to remain after its immediate causes have gone, building up at successive peaks until the explosion occurs – a nuclear accelerator works in somewhat the same way. But *why* does the heat build up? Why is it not dissipated between the periods of domestic crisis? After years of experiment, at the cost of millions (£247.3.9 in crockery alone), we have finally solved this apparently insoluble problem. And here in twelve words is the answer: *Because you have nobody else to whom your heat can be transferred.*

It all goes back to a song entitled *Tea for Two* which included the following significant lines:

> Tea for two and two for tea
> Me for you and you for me....
> Don't you see how happy we will be?

Reading between the lines, we conclude from this that the couple are to be alone together; which you may think normal. This plan is peculiar however to the twentieth century and peculiar to the West. In any previous century

and in almost any part of the world, your household could have been
organised on very different lines. The old-fashioned or oriental family
comprised relatives, children, servants and friends. In a Muslim household you might have three other wives, each one subject to replacement.
In Imperial Rome there would have been adherents and parasites,
eunuchs and concubines, bodyguards, astrologers, slave-girls and slaves.
Even in relatively modern India the seventh Grand Nizam of Hyderabad
had 1,000 servants to staff his principal palace, with 3,000 guardsmen and
4,000 more employees on other estates. In other words, there were other
people around. Given the day of apparent disaster you would have
someone to blame, someone who would sympathise and someone again
who would probably laugh. Your heat would then transfer itself to cooler
minds and, the initial disasters being forgotten, the later disasters would
not have occurred. All we ever had, by contrast was tea for two and two
for tea. With your husband at the office, you are alone in the house: with
the telephone your only hope. That instrument is your 'earth' in the
electrical sense, the lightning conductor which will convey some of your
emotions out of the house. This accounts for your fury when the number
is engaged or when nobody replies. Solitude, in short, has its drawbacks.
And the rhetorical question, 'Don't you see how happy we will be?' may
suggest the answer. 'Well, actually, I *don't*.'

Research has now established the fact that the day of domestic disaster is
due to stress caused by a heat for which there is no sufficient outlet. More
than that, we can put this into precise and scientific language. Mrs
Parkinson's Law, as it is called, applying to the married woman of the
Western world, runs thus:

*Heat produced by domestic pressure expands to fill the mind available from which it can
pass only to a cooler mind.*

This discovery, momentous as it is, must fail of its maximum impact if not
also stated in mathematical terms. For this purpose the first tentative
formula was submitted to the world's greatest authority on domestic
thermodynamics, Professor Darcy C. Coyle of the Rensselaer Polytechnic
Institute of Connecticut, Inc, a copy of whose first tentative reply was
accidently enclosed in some mail addressed to that Institute's Bureau of
Research. This Bureau took automatic action as a result of which copies in
quintuplicate were passed to ten Federal agencies in Washington, D.C.
Rather to his surprise (for he had made no application) Professor Coyle

promptly received a grant of $166,276, including $151,116 for overheads and paperwork. Thus encouraged, he made a series of field surveys for empirical data and several emergency visits to the hospitals of Connecticut. All results were then fed into an IBM 360 Computer, which then produced the following equation:

$$T_D = \cdot 052 \ (W \sqrt{S \times N} - W \sqrt{s+n})$$

where T_D = the emotional temperature differential,

W = the weight of the housewife in pounds,

S = her speed in mph, and

N = number of crises encountered by the housewife within the past six hours.

Of course, w, s, and n stand for the weight speed and crises involving another person encountered by the housewife while in orbit.*

Commenting upon these calculations, Professor Darcy Coyle states his opinion that any differential greater than plus or minus 5 is dangerous. He adds, however, that substantial testing of a very destructive type would be necessary to determine this safety range between two sigma limits of certainty. He suggests that there may be a far more dangerous point where T_D = o, but W and w are equally great and S and s are equally fast. This could be a point of destruction in both directions and a formula, in effect, for a nuclear explosion. Without further experiment (and probable casualties) there can, of course, be no certainty about this. Granted the desirability of research on these lines, there seems no point in any secrecy about the result so far obtained. In all its grand simplicity, the first mathematical statement of Mrs Parkinson's Law is now offered to the world.

This first result, impressive as it is, was thought, however, to be insufficiently complex and the same data were fed into a more expensive computer. The new result, a definite advance, reads thus:

$$T_d = \cdot 37 \ (WS - ws) + 2 \ (N-n) - \frac{45}{1+N-n}$$

where W is the housewife's weight in pounds, S is her speed in miles per hour, N is the number of disasters occurring to her, and w, s and n are weight, speed and number of crises occurring to another person just prior to contacting her. T_d is the emotional temperature differential; as long as it is positive, our

* It should be noted, incidentally, that the emotional temperature of any human is now contained in the formula: $T_H = \cdot 52 \ WS + N$.

heroine will tend to explode at the other person, but when it becomes negative, her own health may suffer.

If we translate this into the figures which might relate to a specific case, allowing the housewife a weight of 133.24lb and a crisis-free speed of 2mph, her emotional temperature under ideal conditions would read as follows:

$$T_{\mathrm{H}} = \cdot 37\ (133 \cdot 24 \times 2) = 98 \cdot 57°\mathrm{F}\ [\text{practically normal}]$$

If we assume, however, that she speeds up to 3mph and has one crisis just before she contacts another person who weighs 130lbs who is going 2½ mph without any problems, then we have:

$$T_{\mathrm{d}} = \cdot 37\ (133 \cdot 24 \times 3 - 130 \times 2\tfrac{1}{2})$$
$$+ 2\ (1 - 0) - \frac{45}{1 + 1 - 0}$$
$$= \cdot 37\ (399 \cdot 72 - 325) + 2 - 22.5$$
$$= 27 \cdot 65 + 2 - 22 \cdot 5$$
$$= 7 \cdot 15$$

Again, if the housewife weighs exactly 134·08 pounds and moves at 2mph without any crisis, we have

$$T_{\mathrm{H}} = \cdot 52\ (134 \cdot 08)\ \sqrt{2} = 98 \cdot 601°\mathrm{F},$$

only a bit over normal. However, at this same weight, but moving at 5·25mph after 4 crises her emotional temperature becomes

$$T_{\mathrm{H}} = \cdot 52\ (134 \cdot 08)\ \sqrt{5 \cdot 25} + 4 = 212 \cdot 050°\mathrm{F},$$

somewhat over the boiling point. On the other hand, men of passionate nature should avoid women weighing less than 102·56 pounds who move at a speed under ·36mph because: $T_{\mathrm{H}} = \cdot 52\ (102 \cdot 56\ \sqrt{\cdot 36} = 32 \cdot 000°\mathrm{F}$, or freezing, and this can be extremely dangerous regardless of T_{D}, the emotional temperature differential.

At this point the research fund was exhausted. While it may be true that further work at a higher cost would yield a more elaborate equation, the present result would seem quite sufficient for all practical purposes. Until superseded the present formula can be inscribed on granite in letters of gold.

We know now the process by which our heat is generated. We also know the circumstances in which it fails to disperse, building up to the point of explosion. This brings us to the two practical questions: How can we stop the process of generation? Failing that, how can we disperse the heat we have generated? Towards checking the rise in temperature the first step is to know

Mrs Parkinson's Law and realise that you are subject to it. The second step is to recognise the symptoms of stress and apply the following rules: First, never look at the incoming post until you have time to read it at leisure. A quick glance will often leave you with the wrong impression, worrying about some problem which may not even exist. Remember, therefore, that there is no special urgency about a piece of paper. It can wait and it probably should. Your better policy is to concentrate on what you are doing. Second, never answer the telephone if you are in the middle of something more important. Let it ring. If the caller has any message of consequence she will ring again. Third, when disaster strikes, the result of your own agitation, stop work, switch off, sit down, collect your thoughts and pull yourself together. Do nothing more until your temperature is normal.

Are these three rules sufficient? For the more emotional they are probably not. So there is a fourth rule which runs as follows: In the last resort take a cold bath or shower and emerge in a cooler frame of mind, your agitation having gone down the waste pipe. It is true that physical and emotional temperatures are not exactly the same thing. They are, however, closely related, and few moods of panic will actually survive a bucket of cold water emptied over the head. The point of this drastic measure, were it practicable, would be to lower the temperature and at the same time break the sequence of disaster. With something else to think about, the cold shock, the effort of drying herself, the housewife would eventually return to her work in a different mood. Once she has realised that the root of the trouble is in herself, not in a conspiracy of people and things, she is on the way to recovery. It would be wrong, incidentally, to conclude that men never yield to panic and ill-temper when things go wrong. They do so more rarely when at work, for few of them work entirely alone, but they are not invulnerable when at home. Given some task like mowing the lawn, papering the bathroom or pruning the roses (while the wife is out shopping), the husband can equally fall a victim to Mrs Parkinson's Law. He too can feel that everything is against him, that disasters have befallen and that a still worse disaster is probably on its way. The rules to obey in such a situation are exactly the same as laid down for the housewife, with the single addition that he should afterwards light his pipe. Stop work, switch off, sit down and, if necessary, take a cold shower.

Sound as far as they go, these rules which should be infallible so far as the husband is concerned may be insufficient to save the housewife. She is more vulnerable, perhaps, more prone to moods of despair. Events can happen too quickly, moreover, each calamity overtaking the last. Despite all our efforts, the situation can get out of hand. You find yourself disobeying rules (1) and (3). Let us suppose, in fact, that the sequence of events is very much that described earlier in this chapter and that heat remains *after* the incident on the doorstep. Your favourite piece of china is in fragments. You have burnt your best frock with the iron. You are all a-tremble, wondering what fresh catastrophe will follow. You seem to be on a collision course with Destiny. Were you ignorant of Mrs Parkinson's Law – as you were until a few minutes ago – your instinct would be to call your husband at the office. Grabbing the telephone and getting his extension, you would begin to babble your grief with emotional incoherence. 'It's-terrible-darling-I-only-wanted-him-to-go-away-but-there-he-was-stunned-and-the-ambulance-came-and-everything-my - best - frock - ruined - and - the - china - broken - if- only - everything - didn't-happen-at-once-I-could-cope-but-its-utter-hell-and-what-shall-I-do?' A message of this urgency will normally find your husband in one of two situations. He may be in conference, fighting for dear life against some idiotic scheme which threatens to wreck his whole career. He may, alternatively, be working quietly at his desk. In the one case his reply may be almost as agitated as your appeal for help: 'For-pete's-sake-I'm-in-conference-it's-all-I-can-do-to-hold-my-own-the-stupid-ideas-some-people-have-My-God-and-now-you-have-to-start-screaming-about-broken-china. Ring-off-like-a-good-girl-and-take-a-couple-of-aspirins-I'll-get-home-early-if-I-can-G'bye.' In the other event he will be perfectly and maddeningly sensible. 'Don't you think, darling, that you should tell me, in simple words, what you want me to *do*? Why don't I call you back in ten minutes so that you can decide by then what help you want? Ring off, love, and calm down. Then tell me how I can help. G'bye for now.'

Of these two possible types of response the second is the more fatal. The first admittedly gets you nowhere but it suggests that you are not alone: he too has his troubles. The second lacks even that crumb of comfort. What you are seeking is an 'earth' into which your heat can discharge itself. While cool enough for that purpose, your husband refuses to co-operate. Instead of listening to your incoherent drivel, he cuts through it and comes to the point – 'What do you *want*?' He doesn't understand, poor fish, that your need *is* to talk drivel and have someone who will listen to it. The question of what *action* he is to take is unimportant and you haven't given it a thought, and why should you? Slamming down the receiver you feel that your marriage is at an end. Your husband has deserted you, probably for another woman. He is almost certainly with her at this moment, laughing at your distress. You *must* tell your story to someone! Yes, Madge would be the friend you need – not ten minutes away in the car. Fuming at your husband's stupidity – it was all *his* fault, really, from the beginning – you jump into the car. Expressing your rage with abrupt acceleration, wide turns and violent braking, you set off to find Madge. Five minutes later the car is wrapped round a street lamp and you on the way to the hospital or mortuary.

Ringing your husband was a mistake. What should you have done? The correct action is as follows: Take a sedative. Then telephone Madge and ask *her* to come over to you for coffee, not immediately but in half-an-hour's time. Then sit down (very important, this) and write a brief report of the events which have disturbed you. Don't attempt to make any decisions. Decide, rather, not to decide for the present. Wait until you have further information or advice, putting problems out of your mind until you have time to deal with them. By the time your friend arrives you will have begun to cool. By the time you have told her the story, you should be back to normal. Having told your story and received some sympathy, and having shelved the practical problems until tomorrow, do the minimum of what has to be done and then settle down with an extremely unexciting book. What book? Why, this one, of course. And which chapter? The chapter you have just finished.

Happy Christmas and Merry New Year

P. G. Wodehouse

With the advent of each Christmas a new spirit seems to steal over the community, a spirit of cheerfulness and goodwill. Minor employees of hotels, restaurants, and the like smile at our approach. Our relatives in the country write us long, newsy letters and speculate round the fireside on how much we are good for. Our friends greet us with a merry 'Well, Christmas will soon be here!' registering the while a mental vow that, until they know what sort of a present we are going to give them, they are going to be pretty careful.

Everywhere you see it, this genial, Dickensy, peace-and-goodwill spirit.

In these circumstances, it behoves us to be prepared. It is useless to imagine, as every one has done in his more optimistic moments, that people will accept regrets and stories of parcels gone wrong in the post. You worked that, if you remember, in 1925, and it is not a thing that goes well twice.

No, presents must be bought, and the only thing is to try to get off as lightly as possible.

The first rule in buying Christmas presents is to select something shiny. If the chosen object is of leather, the leather must look as if it had been well greased; if of silver, it must gleam with the light that never was on sea or land. This is because the wariest person will often mistake shininess for expensiveness. A shiny pocket-book will get by where a duller gift of twice its value would have been received with sneers.

Books are very popular for this reason. There are very few things which can look so shiny as a Collected Works of Longfellow, Tennyson, or Wordsworth. Longfellow particularly. I have seen a common house-fly alight on the back of a Christmas Longfellow and slide the whole length of the volume, eventually shooting off with extraordinary velocity and stunning itself against the wall. For this reason a Collected Works will always be a welcome gift. They can be left about the drawing-room in lieu of fly-paper. They may also be used as mirrors.

Intelligence should be the sheet anchor of the Christmas-present buyer. This and a consideration for others. He should always bear in mind the fact that the recipient will be wanting to pass it on later to somebody as a wedding present. Much misery has been caused in a great number of homes by a want of thought in this matter.

I, myself, am not blameless. I recollect giving as a Christmas present to a friend a rather repellent claret-jug which had been given to me on my birthday by my aunt Charlotte, and which, unknown to me, bore the inscription 'With fondest love from C.B.H.'. Naturally, this friend gave it to another friend as a wedding present, and the discovery of it among the gifts and the bridegroom's total inability to explain who the fondly-loving C.B.H. was gave the bride an advantage from which he never recovered, and it was only when, a year later, the courts separated the happy pair that he found himself once more in possession of a latch-key.

How different a present was that Smoker's Ideal Comrade which I received on Christmas Day, 1922. It was given me by one of my uncles, and it had everything, including a brass cigar-cutter, which makes smoking disasteful to the right-thinking man. I hesitate, for I am not quite sure of my facts, to make such an accusation, but I rather think the thing included a velvet smoking-cap.

I gave it away in the autumn of 1923 to an old school friend as a wedding present, and thought no more of it. What was my surprise, on Christmas morning, 1924, to receive it back from a distant cousin. I gave it away once again, Christmas 1925, only to unpack it in my home on the twenty-fourth of December, 1930 – this time as the gift of the very uncle who had first given it to me in 1922. The thing had completed full circle, and looked as good as new, though it contained no smoking-cap. It may be that it never had contained a smoking-cap, or possibly the passage of time had wrought more heavily on the velvet than on the brass.

I confess to a not unmanly wave of sentiment when I beheld it once more and thought of all the good men whom it had enabled to give a handsome Christmas present without expense. In a month from now it will be starting out on its travels again, but on a different route, for I am sending it to a friend in Australia, whither, I feel sure, it has never yet penetrated.

In this instance we have watched the career of a Christmas present from start to – I hope – finish. But this is but one of millions. The question of what becomes of Christmas presents must still continue to vex thinking men. Every year a tidal wave of incredibly useless matter bursts upon the country, yet somehow or other it is disposed of long before the first mosquito steps from the West Indian pier into the crate of bananas which is to take it to the Old Country. A proportion of this, no doubt, is kept working after the manner of my Smoker's Ideal Comrade: but the vast majority of Christmas presents simply disappear. My own theory is that they are sold back to the shops, whence they emerge next year in another incarnation.

It is probably true, as I have heard said, that every large London shop retains a special staff of skilled workmen whose duty it is to transform old Christmas presents into new Christmas presents of a different nature. They receive the combined pocket-book, cigar-case, and handy manicure set and with a few deft touches transform it into Milady's vanity-case. They take the slightly soiled Longfellow and give it a new coat of varnish. The too bright scarf of yesteryear becomes a sweater for the Pekingese.

If I had only known in time of the existence of these men, I could, no doubt, for a small consideration, have got them to make over my aunt's claret-jug into a pair of slippers or a presentation set of the works of Robert Browning.

For that they do exist, I am now convinced. On no other theory is the total disappearance of last year's Christmas presents to be explained. Matter cannot be destroyed. It can only be transformed.

The burden of Christmas-present giving has of late years been sadly increased by the growing sophistication of the modern child. In the brave old days it was possible to give a child almost anything, and to receive in return a very warm gratitude. I can still recall thanking with genuine sincerity a relative whose annual Christmas gift to me consisted of an orange.

In fact, the thought of what the average child expects from you nowadays at Christmas is so saddening that I hurry to skip a week and get into the new year.

It was when I took down my *Encyclopædia Britannica* in order to obtain material for a few thoughtful pages on New Year's Day and its customs that I noticed, not for the first time, a very annoying habit of that great work of reference. I allude to its habit of leaving off just at the point where it has got the reader all agog and excited.

Take, for example, its description of New Year's Day in medieval England.

In those times, it says, it was the practice for the King to 'extort gifts from his subjects', adding that in the year 1533 Henry the Eighth collected many thousands of pounds in this manner – being laid a stymie in only one instance, when Bishop Latimer, a man with a good business head, handed him in lieu of cash a copy of the New Testament with the leaf turned down at Hebrews xiii. 4.

So far, so good. Most interesting. But then, having mentioned that on another occasion the bluff monarch got into the ribs of Cardinal Wolsey to the tune of one hundred and seventeen pounds, seventeen shillings and sixpence, it signs off without a word of explanation, leaving the reader completely mystified. Why one-one-seven, seventeen and six? Why the seventeen bob? Why the sixpence?

I have heard two theories advanced. The first, that the King met the Cardinal in a dark alley on his way back from the bank and stood him on his head and lifted the contents of his pockets, does not satisfy me. If Cardinal Wolsey drew a cheque to Self, it would have been for some less eccentric figure, and, knowing that it was New Year's Day and Henry was about, he would certainly not have gone to the bank without an armed escort. It is far more likely that the money changed hands at the conclusion of a merry party in the small hours of the morning. The waiter came round with the bill, and King Henry, after the usual unconvincing fumbling, told him to take it on to the clerical gentleman in the paper cap.

This would explain everything. The bill came to exactly a hundred and seventeen pounds, fifteen shillings. Two bob for the waiter and sixpence for the hat-check girl, and there you are. One can always reason these things out if one tries, but my point is that the *Encyclopædia Britannica* ought not to throw the burden of the brainwork on its readers. Making these silly mysteries is mere verbal horse-play, unworthy of its great reputation.

Another result of consulting the *Encyclopædia* is that my opinion of the ancient Persians has been considerably lowered. I had always looked on them as a sober, responsible people, by no means the kind you would suspect of a distorted sense of humour. And yet, we read, it was their custom to go round on New Year's morning making presents of eggs to their friends – the one day when one simply can't look at an egg. I shall never feel quite the same about the ancient Persians again.

How much more fitting was the attitude of the early Christians. Christians, in the early days of the Church, were, we are told, 'expected to spend New Year's Day in quiet meditation'. It is a custom which after nearly two thousand years still persists. Visit any of your friends on the morning of January the First, if you are in a condition to do so, and see for yourself. The odds are a hundred to one that you will find him in bed with a vinegar-soaked bandage round his head and the bromo-seltzer bottle by his side, quietly meditating.

Oddly enough, there has always been a great deal of confusion in the public mind as to when exactly New Year's Day really is. What reason have we to suppose that the year begins on January the First? One only, that the ancient Romans said it did. Yes, but what ancient Romans? Probably Horace or somebody at a moment when he was well into his second bottle of Falernian. One can picture the scene...

HORACE. Well, boys, Happy New Year, boys.

LUCULLUS (*looking up from the grape which he is cracking with the nutcrackers*). How do you mean, Happy New Year?

HORACE. It's New Year's Day to-morrow. We celebrate it with masquerades, the making of sacrifices to Janus, and feasting, Yessir!

MAECENAS. Feasting?

HORACE. Feasting was what I said.

MAECENAS (*thoughtfully*). I believe he's right.

LUCULLUS. I'm sure he's right. Happy New Year.

MAECENAS. Happy New Year.

HORACE. Happy New Year.

VIRGIL. All the same, I could have sworn it came at the time of the autumnal equinox, on September the twenty-first.

That was because Virgil had been brought up in the school of thought of the ancient Egyptians, Phoenicians, and Persians. In Egypt, Phoenicia and Persia the sale of squeakers and rattles and paper caps was brisk all through September, culminating on the twenty-first. The medieval Christians, on the other hand, held their celebrations on the twenty-fifth of March. The Greeks were broad-minded. Some of them thought New Year's Day came on December the twenty-first, while others voted for the twenty-first of June. This was good for the restaurateurs, who could count on two big nights in the year, but confusing for the Income Tax authorities, who never knew when to send in their demands.

One can readily see that this sort of conflict of ideas is not only bewildering but decidedly inconvenient. It makes it difficult for a conscientious man to do the right thing. He starts out simply and straightforwardly enough by taking a reserved table for the last night in December, prepared to dance on it should the occasion arise, and there, one would suppose, the matter would rest.

But mark the sequel. As March approaches, doubts begin to assail him. 'Was I right?' he begins to ask himself. 'Those medieval Christians were shrewd fellows. Who knows whether they may not have had the correct idea?' The only way he can square his conscience is by going out and lowering himself to the level of the beasts of the field on the night of March the twenty-fourth. And scarcely has the doctor left his bedside next morning with the statement that all he needs is a diet of arrowroot for a week or two, when he starts to brood on the fact that the ancient Phoenicians, who were no fools, were convinced that September the twenty-first was New Year's Day.

By this time he is so uncertain that he feels the only safe course is to hunt up all the data and celebrate every New Year that any nation or collection of people ever invented, with the result that he has only just time to get discharged from the nursing-home by December the thirty-first, the now fashionable date, and join his unthinking friends in their revels. Many a young man, in the springtime of life, has developed cyrrhosis of the liver simply through reading the New Year article in the *Encyclopædia*. My own perusal of it has left me with grave doubts, and I had better be closely watched on the eve of June the twenty-first, as I am beginning to come round to the Greek view.

I have little more to add. If any word of mine enables my readers to approach New Year's Eve in a more thoughtful frame of mind, I shall be amply repaid. If, when throwing celluloid balls at some perfect stranger while endeavouring to sing Auld Lang Syne, you pause for a moment to say to yourself 'Even so did the ancient Egyptians do!' or 'I bet Henry the Eighth was a whale at this sort of thing!' and, as you break the last remains of the crockery and glassware, you feel a passing pang for the days that are no more, my labours will not have been in vain. I thank you.

The Stake

Saki (H. H. Munro)

'Ronnie is a great trial to me,' said Mrs Attray plaintively. 'Only eighteen years old last February and already a confirmed gambler. I am sure I don't know where he inherits it from; his father never touched cards, and you know how little I play – a game of bridge on Wednesday afternoons in the winter, for threepence a hundred, and even that I shouldn't do if it wasn't that Edith always wants a fourth and would be certain to ask that detestable Jenkinham woman if she couldn't get me. I would much rather sit and talk any day than play bridge; cards are such a waste of time, I think. But as to Ronnie, bridge and baccarat and poker-patience are positively all that he thinks about. Of course I've done my best to stop it; I've asked the Norridrums not to let him play cards when he's over there, but you might as well ask the Atlantic Ocean to keep quiet for a crossing as expect them to bother about a mother's natural anxieties.'

'Why do you let him go there?' asked Eleanor Saxelby.

'My dear,' said Mrs Attray, 'I don't want to offend them. After all, they are my landlords and I have to look to them for anything I want done about the place; they were accommodating about the new roof for the orchid house. And they lend me one of their cars when mine is out of order; you know how often it gets out of order.'

'I don't know how often,' said Eleanor, 'but it must happen very frequently. When I want you to take me anywhere in your car I am always told that there is something wrong with it, or else that the chauffeur has got neuralgia and you don't like to ask him to go out.'

'He suffers quite a lot from neuralgia,' said Mrs Attray hastily. 'Anyhow,' she continued, 'you can understand that I don't want to offend the Norridrums. Their household is the most rackety one in the county, and I believe no one ever knows to an hour or two when any particular meal will appear on the table or what it will consist of when it does appear.'

Eleanor Saxelby shuddered. She liked her meals to be of regular occurrence and assured proportions.

'Still,' pursued Mrs Attray, 'whatever their own home life may be, as landlords and neighbours they are considerate and obliging, so I don't want to quarrel with them. Besides, if Ronnie didn't play cards there he'd be playing somewhere else.'

'Not if you were firm with him,' said Eleanor; 'I believe in being firm.'

'Firm? I am firm,' exclaimed Mrs Attray; 'I am more than firm – I am farseeing. I've done everything I can think of to prevent Ronnie from playing for money. I've stopped his allowance for the rest of the year, so he can't even gamble on credit, and I've subscribed a lump sum to the church offertory in his name instead of giving him instalments of small silver to put in the bag on Sundays. I wouldn't even let him have the money to tip the hunt servants with, but sent it by postal order. He was furiously sulky about it, but I reminded him of what happened to the ten shillings that I gave him for the Young Men's Endeavour League "Self-Denial Week".'

'What did happen to it?' asked Eleanor.

'Well, Ronnie did some preliminary endeavouring with it, on his own account, in connection with the Grand National. If it had come off, as he expressed it, he would have given the League twenty-five shillings and netted a comfortable commission for himself; as it was, that ten shillings was one of the things the League had to deny itself. Since then I've been careful not to let him have a penny piece in his hands.'

'He'll get round that in some way,' said Eleanor with quiet conviction; 'he'll sell things.'

'My dear, he's done all that is to be done in that direction already. He's got rid of his wrist-watch and his hunting flask and both his cigarette cases, and I shouldn't be surprised if he's wearing imitation gold sleeve links instead of those his Aunt Rhoda gave him on his seventeenth birthday. He can't sell his clothes, of course, except his winter overcoat, and I've locked that up in the camphor cupboard on the pretext of preserving it from moth. I really don't see what else he can raise money on. I consider that I've been both firm and farseeing.'

'Has he been at the Norridrums lately?' asked Eleanor.

'He was there yesterday afternoon and stayed to dinner,' said Mrs. Attray. 'I don't quite know when he came home, but I fancy it was late.'

'Then depend on it he was gambling,' said Eleanor, with the assured air of one who has few ideas and makes the most of them. 'Late hours in the country always mean gambling.'

'He can't gamble if he has no money and no chance of getting any,' argued Mrs Attray; 'even if one plays for small stakes one must have a decent prospect of paying one's losses.'

'He may have sold some of the Amherst pheasant chicks,' suggested Eleanor; 'they would fetch about ten or twelve shillings each, I dare say.'

'Ronnie wouldn't do such a thing,' said Mrs Attray; 'and anyhow I went and counted them this morning and they're all there. No,' she continued, with the quiet satisfaction that comes from a sense of painstaking and merited achievement, 'I fancy that Ronnie had to content himself with the rôle of on-looker last night, as far as the card-table was concerned.'

'Is that clock right?' asked Eleanor, whose eyes had been straying restlessly towards the mantelpiece for some little time; 'lunch is usually so punctual in your establishment.'

'Three minutes past the half-hour,' exclaimed Mrs Attray; 'cook must be preparing something unusually sumptuous in your honour. I am not in the secret; I've been out all the morning, you know.'

Eleanor smiled forgivingly. A special effort by Mrs Attray's cook was worth waiting a few minutes for.

As a matter of fact, the luncheon fare, when it made its tardy appearance, was distinctly unworthy of the reputation which the justly treasured cook had built up for herself. The soup alone would have sufficed to cast a gloom over any meal that it had inaugurated, and it was not redeemed by anything that followed. Eleanor said little, but when she spoke there was a hint of tears in her voice that was far more eloquent than outspoken denunciation would have been, and even the insouciant Ronald showed traces of depression when he tasted the rognons Saltikoff.

'Not quite the best luncheon I've enjoyed in your house,' said Eleanor at last, when her final hope had flickered out with the savoury.

'My dear, it's the worst meal I've sat down to for years,' said her hostess; 'that last dish tasted principally of red pepper and wet toast. I'm awfully sorry. Is anything the matter in the kitchen, Pellin?' she asked of the attendant maid.

'Well, ma'am, the new cook hadn't hardly time to see to things properly, coming in so sudden–' commenced Pellin by way of explanation.

'The *new* cook!' screamed Mrs Attray.

'Colonel Norridrum's cook, ma'am,' said Pellin.

'What on earth do you mean? What is Colonel Norridrum's cook doing in my kitchen – and where is *my* cook?'

'Perhaps I can explain better than Pellin can,' said Ronald hurriedly; 'the fact is, I was dining at the Norridrum's yesterday, and they were wishing they had a swell cook like yours, just for today and tomorrow, while they've got some gourmet staying with them; their own cook is no earthly good – well, you've seen what she turns out when she's at all flurried. So I thought it would be rather sporting to play them at baccarat for the loan of our cook against a money stake, and I lost, that's all. I have had rotten luck at baccarat all this year.'

The remainder of his explanation, of how he had assured the cooks that the temporary transfer had his mother's sanction, and had smuggled the one out and the other in during the maternal absence, was drowned in the outcry of scandalized upbraiding.

'If I had sold the woman into slavery there couldn't have been a bigger fuss about it,' he confided afterwards to Bertie Norridrum, 'and Eleanor Saxelby raged and ramped the louder of the two. I tell you what, I'll bet you two of the Amherst pheasants to five shillings that she refuses to have me as a partner at the croquet tournament. We're drawn together, you know.'

This time he won his bet.

Ear, Nose and Throat

Cornelia Otis Skinner

I have the greatest admiration for throat specialists. I am fond of them and patronize them far more than I care to say, but I do resent their methods. Just why the physicians who deal exclusively with ear, nose and throat (there's a scientific name for them, but it sounds confusingly like the term for a bird lover) should consider themselves privileged to treat their patients as if they were a bunch of Washington petitioners is as bewildering as why their clientele are saps enough to put up with it.

Make an appointment with a dentist and he sees you at the stated time with a punctuality by which you may set your watch. Make an appointment with a throat specialist and you are in luck if he sees you within an hour of it. You may have a day full of vital engagements, a train to catch, or a business that's going to pieces in your absence. He doesn't care – you have to bide your turn. And there's a catch to your turn, too: it isn't all yours. Most of these pampered physicians have their offices divided into two or three cubicles, like booths at a hairdresser's. Having put you in the chair and pinned you down with a bib, your man skips off to another cubicle, leaving you with so much cotton, argyrol, and oddments stuffed into your head that you feel like something left at the taxidermist's. But I'm getting ahead of my story; we're not anywhere near that chair yet.

The throat specialist's waiting-room is a menace to health and soul. Having phoned for a special appointment, you arrive on the dot only to find the place overflowing with others who have made appointments for the same or an earlier dot. As you enter they glare at you and indicate their animosity with a barrage of coughs, sneezes, and blowings. The young lady who acts as nurse and secretary is absent from the room. You stand at her deserted desk, hoping she will be back directly. After five minutes this becomes awkward and you decide to find a chair near the door that opens on the inner office. This is sheer optimistic insanity. There is no unoccupied chair near the door;

moreover, there is no unoccupied chair anywhere else in the room. All that is left is a settee, in front of the window, that serves also as a radiator cover. There is no alternative but to settle there, after you have selected a magazine from the table.

The patients ahead of you have already grabbed all the current periodicals and you are left with a choice of a four-month-old *Atlantic Monthly*, the *Annual Report of the American Medical Society*, and a *National Geographic* entirely devoted to fish. Shyly lurking beneath these is a mangled copy of *Screen Romances*, doubtless left behind by some less intellectual client. Ignoring the probability that this much-thumbed periodical is teeming with germs, you take it to the radiator seat. This proves to feel the way the hot-dish counter of a cafeteria looks, but you endure it, soothed by the hope that the young lady of the appointment desk will appear any minute and 'slip you in' as she has promised. Eventually she appears, all right, but she just sticks her head across the threshold for a swift glance around the room, which gives a spurious impression of efficiency. The occupants look up with expectancy. Some try to attract her attention by coughing pitifully. Others smile in a hideously friendly manner. But she's not to be lured. She looks back over her shoulder into the forbidden chamber, says, 'Yes, Doctor' (although no-one is heard to address any remarks to her), and vanishes as suddenly as she appeared.

These waiting-rooms are hatcheries of hatred as well as germs. There is usually some nasty little woman standing guard near the doctor's door with the defiant attitude of a goalkeeper. The air teems with mistrust. The waiting-room crowd suggests early squatters getting set for the rush into the River Cimarron. This unpleasant atmosphere strikes you as outrageous until some newcomer enters. Then you immediately join the ranks of the aggressively suspicious.

You wait amid churchly silence broken only by the conscientious coughers, who seem to feel that in the interests of the doctor's practice they must do a little intermittent bacteria spraying. The door of the inner office might be the door to a tomb were it not for the occasional noises that give evidence of life behind it. After countless hours of experience, you learn to gauge the progress of a consultation by these sounds. The procedure is almost invariably the same. After the patient has passed through the portal, the door closes and you hear a distant murmur of voices. Although the words are indistinguishable, this is presumably the doctor inquiring into the patient's symptoms and the patient replying. As the conversation continues

for an unreasonably long time, you come to the bitter conclusion that they
have switched from the larynx to the European question. The rumble of
voices stops at last and there is a pause. Then comes the sound of a gag,
followed by a distant 'Ah'. Then comes a second and rather violent gag,
followed by a silence so ominously prolonged that you wonder if you hadn't
better notify the police. Eventually there is the whirr of an electric motor and
the hiss of a spray. At the sound of spraying, hope revives. Then there's a
final gag and a few strangling effects thrown in for an encore, and you can
count on the door's opening and yourself moving up a notch. Finally, with
the slowness and sureness of a glacier's flow, your turn arrives and the young
lady beckons you in.

The cutting remarks you've been rehearsing, to the effect that the doctor
may think he's busy but there are other busy people in the world too, vanish
at sight of his bland smile and his white coat bristling with instruments. He
furthermore forestalls you by saying that he's sorry to have kept you waiting
but he's had to do a tonsillectomy (which means he's been taking out some
poor devil's tonsils). You are weak enough to murmur that it's all right,
happy to reach the chair at last.

A Visit to London

Frank Sullivan

We arrived in London in a fog. The great sprawling metropolis was completely enveloped in a pea-soup mist which, we were told, had descended a month and a half previously. We didn't mind, because somehow it seemed right that we should have our first sight of the great sprawling metropolis in a fog. Nell's only regret was that on account of the fog we could only get a dim view of the famous old Waterloo Station which we heard had been built on the cricket fields of Eton.

Nell wanted to put up at one of the fashionable caravansaries in Tooting Bec, but I vetoed that. I told her that as long as we were in London we ought to try to get the flavour of the great sprawling metropolis (which I shall refer to from now on as London) by stopping at one of those cosy old inns replete with historical interest and devoid of modern plumbing. Nell then suggested we go to the 'Cheshire Cheese', but I demurred again. I wanted to stop at the famous old inn frequented by Dr Samuel Johnson and those other noted Regency bucks, but for the life of me I couldn't think of the name of the place, so to the 'Cheshire Cheese' we went.

It proved utterly charming, exactly as we had pictured an old English inn – mullioned windows, mullioned waiters, ceilings with broad beams, barmaids with broader beams, etcetera. There was a room where Queen Elizabeth hid from Essex and his army, and another room where she hid with Essex and his army, and a third room where Essex and his army later hid from her.

There was a room where Shakespeare had been arrested for poaching and a room where Charles I hid from the Parliament while the Parliament was hiding from him in the room next door, which was the same room where Titus Oates hatched his plot. It was called the Plot Hatching Room on account of the fact that Guy Fawkes had also hatched his plot there.

Off the kitchen was a room where King Alfred let the cakes burn. And the tapster looked exactly like Sam Weller. Nell and I were delighted at our good fortune in finding such a really mellow old place.

We hired the Plot Hatching Room and proceeded to make ourselves comfortable. Both Nell and I had been looking forward with considerable interest to tasting British food and we were disappointed, for we dined excellently; a typical English meal of clotted Devonshire cream, roast beef, port wine, and plum pudding. Afterward we took a tram (short for perambulator) to His Majesty's Theatre in Ludgate Circus and there saw a play by Noel Coward.

Next morning we were awakened bright and early by the cries of the hawksters, tipsters, drapers, mercers, etcetera, vending their wares in the streets below. (London newsboys are not permitted to shout their headlines. They come up and whisper the news in your ear. This often tickles your ear, particularly if the whispered headline contains a lot sibilants, such as 'Lady Susan Sursingham Shoots Sire, Sir Seth Sursingham'.)

There was a dense fog out. It was much denser than the pea-soup fog that had greeted our arrival. It was more the consistency of creamed cauliflower soup. You could scarcely see Windsor Castle.

A rosy-cheeked serving-wench who reminded Nell of Sam Weller came in and laid a fire of sea coals and we breakfasted cosily by it. Typical English breakfast of clotted Devonshire cream, kedgeree, roast beef, Yorkshire pudding, mulled ale, crumpets, sack, and port. The girl was curious about America and wanted to know if the Indians still used bows and arrows in attacking Manhattan. Then she asked if we would give her an Indian yell, so Nell and I obliged with the old Ojibway war cry:

> 'Cornell I yell yell yell Cornell!
> Team Team Team!!!!'

She was quite impressed, even a bit terrified.

We spent the day sightseeing and went in the evening to His Majesty's Theatre to see a play. It was by Noel Coward.

What a fog next morning! I thought it was like *potage à la reine*, but Nell said it reminded her more of borsch. And those fascinating London noises, coming at you out of the mysterious fog. Nell and I are greatly interested in the noises characteristic of the various cities we visit. In Paris her favourite sound was the scrunch of the French burying the family sock, full of gold, in the backyard. Mine was the low hum of models posing for artists in the nude. Her favourite London noise was the click of pearl buttons dropping from costers' weskits, but I preferred the throaty drawl of duchesses snubbing persons in trade.

Nothing daunted by the fog, we sallied forth on our sightseeing, first taking the precaution of donning our raincoats, or waterproofs, as the English call them.

The English have the most peculiar words for things. Our subway, for instance, is their tube. I believe they have no word for our tube. They call baggage luggage; a cracker a lift, and an elevator a biscuit. Their meat is our poison and our drink is theirs. They call a spade a spade. In telephoning they say, 'Are you there?' where we say 'Hello, Hello, Hello, Operator, Operator. Yes, they do answer. There's always somebody there. Ring them again.'

The English are a great people for clipping their words, for making one syllable do the work of two or three. For instance, if an American were dining with a British lady of quality and he wanted the Worcestershire sauce he would say, 'Lady Ursula, could I trouble you for the Worcestershire sauce?' but an Englishman would say, 'Lady Ursula, pass the Woosh.'

On the other hand, they sometimes go to the other extreme. When they wish to express scepticism or incredulity they say, 'Oh, I say now, not really, you know what?' when we achieve the same effect by saying, 'Nuts!' A London society woman says, 'Too perfectly divayne,' where a New York society woman says, 'Too poifectly divine'. And when the British want to express disapproval of conduct they consider unsportsmanlike or unethical they say, 'That's not cricket,' where we say, 'That's probably wrestling.'

One soon gets used to these little strangenesses. By the time we had been in London a week, nobody would have dreamed we were Americans had it not been for our tortoise-shell glasses, Nell's habit of chewing tobacco and saying, 'Waal now, I reckon,' and of course the large American flags she and I always carried.

The following day was Thursday and there was a really superb fog, like lobster bisque with toast Melba, I thought, but Nell said she saw it as cream of asparagus. She read in 'The Old Lady of Threadneedle Street', as the British call the London *Times*, that a debate on the Boston Tea Party was the order of the day in the House of Lords, so we gulped a typical English breakfast of fish and chips, jugged hare, and gin and bitters, and hurried over to the Houses of Parliament. But the debate was not very exciting and there was such a dense fog in House of Lords that we couldn't see anything anyhow, so we went over to the Commons in the hopes of hearing Lady Astor, the American-born peeress, in action.

They were debating the oakum situation in Woking (or it may have been the woking situation in Oakum), and the Prime Minister was being interrogated by the Opposition, Mr Winston Churchill.

Next morning there was a glorious fog, just like oyster gumbo. I wanted to go over to Rotten Row to see the Regatta, but Nell had her heart set on going down to Trafalgar Square to see the famous statue of Lord Nelson. This is the statue which according to the old story (see any high-school textbook in English history) tips its hat every time a virgin passes. We no sooner reached the Square than Lord Nelson tipped his hat to Nell. Not only tipped his hat to her but told her in a low but quite audible whisper that she reminded him of Sam Weller. Nell was furious, on both counts, and strode off muttering, 'It's a fake. It's a fake!'

Nell went shopping the next day but flopped badly. The shopkeepers wouldn't sell her anything because she had never been formerly introduced to them. British shopkeepers are very strict about this. Nell came home angry and desperate.

'I need a new tooth-brush,' she wailed, 'and I don't know a single druggist in London socially. What am I going to do?'

'Well for one thing don't say druggist,' I warned her. In England a druggist is a chemist. A public school is a private school. The left side of the road is the right side, and gasoline is petrol. And 'My Country 'tis of Thee' is 'God Save the King'.

That night we thought we'd go to Soho, the Italian or Bohemian quarter of London, as we had heard there were some very good Italian restaurants there. We found a very good one and dined magnificently for two and thruppence hapenny on clotted Devonshire cream, roast beef, bubble and squeak, ale and ravioli.

Passing through Upper Tooting on the way home, I was interested in seeing the offices of the famous humorous weekly, *Punch*, or 'The Thunderer', as the English affectionately call it. Once a week the staff of *Punch* lunch together and then, over the port, decide on the cover for the next week.

Nell and I liked the London cops or bobbies very much. They are a highly efficient body of men who wear chin straps and never allow a murderer to escape. Murder is rare in England and an unsolved murder is rarer. The low rate of homicide is due to the fact that the British never get well enough acquainted to kill each other. Once in a while a foreigner kills an Englishman for being too reticent, but if you see an Englishman murdering another Englishman you can be pretty sure the victim is either a blood relative or a friend of long standing.

The suicides in London are mainly foreigners driven to despair by attempts to understand the difference between the city with a small c and the City with a capital C. It seems that the City is part of the city, but the City is not all of the city. You can be in the city and not be in the City, but you cannot be in the City without being in the city. Nell spent two days trying to figure this out and then I had to take her to a nursing home where she spent the week in a dense fog.

Our stay in London ended rather unexpectedly. After she returned from the nursing home Nell did not seem her usual self. Irritable and upset. One morning when I passed her the clotted Devonshire cream she glared at me and hissed, 'I don't want any clotted Devonshire cream. See?'

And a moment later she added:

'Nor any clotted Yorkshire pudding either. See?'

I thought this rather odd. Nell generally has a good appetite and cleans her plate.

I looked out of my window after we had finished breakfast.

'My, there is a magnificent fog out, Nell,' I said, to make a conversation. 'Just like mulligatawny soup.'

'It's not like mulligatawny soup at all,' she snapped. 'It's like clam chowder.'

For some time past she had been growing more unreasonable on the subject of fogs. It seemed to me she had an uncanny faculty for picking the wrong soup to fit a fog, and while much of the happiness of our life together has been based on mutual respect for each other's opinions, I considered this a plain question of fact on which it was my duty to set Nell right. The fog was certainly mulligatawny, not clam chowder. I told her so.

'The other day', I added, 'when it really was clam chowder you said it was like Philadelphia pepper pot.'

She flew into a rage, told me that it was I who had been quoting the wrong soups all along; that she was sick of it, sick of the fogs, and sick of me. With that she packed her bag and left for Cannes.

I dined alone at a pub that night and later went to a play. But somehow I could not enjoy it. Something was missing. Suddenly I realized what it was. The play was not by Noel Coward. I went home restless and uneasy.

Another day went by and then, feeling very blue indeed, I was on the point of sending Nell a wire telling her she could name her own fogs if she would only come back, when a message arrived from her. It read as follows:

'Sorry I dusted off in such a huff. Lovely cream of tomato soup down here. Do come on down before it's all gone. Love. Nell.'

I took the next train for Cannes.

How to Swat a Fly

Will Cuppy

Being as sound in mind and body as I am ever likely to be, I have decided to release my notes on Fly-swatting made from time to time during many years of active service at my Long Island beach cottage, Chez Cuppy. (It's the same old place I used to call Tobacco Road, but I think the new name sort of lends a tone – and, besides, it's a change.) In the belief that Fly-swatting is here to stay for a while, DDT and other squirts to the contrary notwithstanding, I am passing on the torch in Ten Easy Lessons, as follows:

1. Get set. Be sure you're not going to fall off your chair backwards in the act of swatting. Here as elsewhere, style is everything.

2. Still, don't take too much time with the preliminaries. The Fly won't wait there forever. He has other things to do with his time.

3. Try to ascertain in some unobtrusive way whether the object you're after is actually a Fly or a nail head. Don't go poking at the thing to see which it is. When in doubt swat.

Little situations like this are bound to occur in every swatter's routine. For instance, there is a small black spot on the ceiling of my bedroom that has embarrassed me dozens of times, it looks so exactly like a Fly of some large and vicious species. If I have crept up on it once – Oh, well! Stalking an imperfection in the paint and swinging one's heart out at a nail head are not things one likes to remember, but perhaps they have their place in the give and take of daily living. We can't be heroes to ourselves every instant.

4. In any case, never flirt your swatter back and forth past a fly before swatting, expecting to get him your next time around. When you finally make up your mind to hit him, he will not be there. The Fly who hesitates is lost. He knows this and acts accordingly.

5. Take aim quickly but carefully. A complete miss is not good for morale, either yours or the Fly's.

6. If possible, fix him with the first swat. Failure to do so may be serious.

For one thing, you didn't get him. That alone is bad. Secondly, conditions will never be quite the same again, since you are now dealing with an alert and disillusioned Fly. He is never going to trust you as he did before. He will avoid you in future.

That was one the many faults of my dear Aunt Etta's swatting. She never hit her Fly the first time and she seldom came anywhere near him on repeated attempts, partly because she employed that worst of all swatting techniques, the folded newspaper, or slow motion method. She would lunge at the Fly again and yet again with her antiquated weapon in a free-for-all that left her exhausted and the Fly in the best of health and spirits. A folded newspaper is only about 17 per cent efficient in anybody's hands, and Aunt Etta's form was nothing to boast of. Her batting average must have been something incredible. I'm glad to state that she often thought she had won. Her eyesight wasn't so good, either.

I assure you that Aunt Etta was one of the kindest persons I have ever known, though not so soft about Flies as my Uncle Toby, who did so much in his day to encourage the spread of typhoid fever and other diseases. There was certainly no sadistic urge in her swatting activities. She never engaged a Fly in hand-to-hand combat until after she and we children had staged a ceremonious Fly-drive with kitchen aprons and dish towels, then a second and often a third to chase the last one out the open screen door. It was only the Fly or Flies who failed to respect these rites that she tackled, and it always amazed me that there would be any such. If we thought Aunt Etta had one of her headaches, or felt a nap coming on, or couldn't stand such a racket – in which case she would tell us so in no uncertain terms – we disappeared. We vanished utterly, with the usual gift of cookies. But Flies are not brought up that way, apparently. They cannot take a hint.

The family would want me to add that Aunt Etta's house was no more Fly-ridden than any other home of the period. In fact, it was less so than most, as it was thoroughly screened. Which reminds me that she never did, to my knowledge, solve the riddle of how they got in. She was always saying there wasn't a crack where they could squeeze through. All right, then, how did the Mouse get in?

7. Don't mind a little incidental breakage around the house. Aunt Etta was much too careful of her bric-à-brac. She wouldn't strike within yards of her whatnot when a Fly took sanctuary there. For the cause I would smash anything in Chez Cuppy to smithereens, except possibly my shaving mirror. I'm not having seven years of bad luck for any Fly.

8. Cultivate patience. It is a beautiful thing in itself, and when you are after a Fly who will not light, you will need it. Eventually that Fly will light, and ten to one it will be in some dark inaccessible corner, down behind the stove.

The Fly who absolutely refuses to settle is a problem for advanced swatters, and not an easy one. Talk about a watched pot! Do not stalk such a Fly too openly, but try to act as though you were interested in something else altogether. This involves looking wall-eyed at the Fly while gazing fixedly in the other direction, but it can be done, with practice. It is my opinion that a Fly will not settle while you are looking straight at him with a swatter in your fist. At any rate, he won't while you are following him around the room, making passes at him. Believe me, he knows what you are up to.

I would not go so far as to say that a Fly knows the exact moment when you start looking for a swatter, if you should be caught without one. Edge yourself ever so casually in the general direction of a swatter, and notice what happens. Other persons who may be present will simply wonder why you are hitching your chair along in that insane fashion or tiptoeing across the room with one groping hand outstretched and haunted look in your eyes. They won't have the faintest notions of what goes on, but the Fly will. He has already figured out his first five moves and several of yours.

This does not necessarily prove that the Fly is more intelligent than you are. If such things could be measured – and they will be, some day – I have little doubt that you, gentle swatter, would be found to have a higher IQ than the average Fly. You may be slow on the uptake, while the Fly is unbelievably fast. His sheer brilliance in planning and executing manoeuvres of every sort on the ground and in the air amounts to genius, and you have all you can do to keep from falling over your feet. You cannot make quick decisions, or, if you do, you are generally dead wrong, as everybody at the office knows but yourself. The Fly's decisions are mostly right. They have to be.

Yet on the whole, taking it by and large, and allowing for individual exceptions, you are smarter than the Fly. You know more than he does about more things. Above all, you possess the power of abstract reasoning, a faculty which distinguishes mankind from the merely brute creation, such as Flies. You can listen to the radio, look at television, and go to the movies. You can read mystery stories and try to guess who done it. Keep your chin up and always remember that if you are not the Fly's superior in every single respect one might mention, you are at least his equal, mentally. Since you are fighting on practically even terms, then, when you are after a Fly who will not light you must seek for a flaw in his intellectual equipment if you hope to regain the initiative, and I can help you there. The key is his imperfect memory. You can remember as far back as yesterday. The Fly cannot. He forgets. The particular Fly of whom we are speaking will be out of his dark corner in a few brief moments, and you can begin the whole show all over again.

9. Check up on yourself occasionally. Ask yourself, 'Am I a better swatter than I was last year?' The correct answer is No.

10. Don't be discouraged at a few failures. I don't always get them myself, but I give them pause. It makes 'em think.

Sporting Life in America: Dozing

Robert Benchley

We Americans are a hardy race, and hardy races need a lot of sleep. 'Sleep, that knits up the ravell'd sleave of care,' Shakespeare has called it, and, except for the fact that it doesn't mean much, it is a pretty good simile. I often think of it myself just as I am dropping off into a light doze: 'Sleep, that sleeves up the raveled care of . . . knit, that sleeps up the shaveled neeve of pfor – pff – prpf – orpfff (*trailing off into a low whistle*).'

One of the most charming manifestations of sleep which we, as a nation, indulge in as a pastime is the Doze. By the Doze I mean those little snatches of sleep which are caught now and then during the day, usually with the collar on and choking slightly, with the head inclined coyly to one side, during which there is a semiconscious attempt to appear as if we were really awake. It is in this department of sleep that we are really at our best.

Of course, there is one form of doze which, to the casual observer or tourist gives the appearance of legitimate sleep. This is the short doze, or 'quickie', which is taken just after the main awakening in the morning. The alarm rings, or the Lord High Chamberlain taps us on the shoulder (in the absence of a chamberlain a relative will do. And right here I would like to offer for examination that type of sadistic relative who takes actual delight in awakening people. They hover about with ghoulish anticipation until the minute arrives when they may legitimately begin their dirty work, and then, leering unpleasantly, they shake the sleeper roughly with a 'Come, come! Time to get up!' and wait right there until he is actually out on the cold floor in his bare feet. There is something radically wrong with such people, and the sooner they are exposed as pathological cases the better it will be for the world.) I'm sorry, I didn't mean to be nasty about it.

At any rate, we are awakened and look at the clock. There are five minutes before it is absolutely necessary to get out of bed. If we leave shaving until night, there might even be fifteen minutes. If we leave dressing until we get to the office, snatching our clothes from the chair and carrying them downtown on our arm, there might even be half an hour more for a good health-giving nap. Who knows? Perhaps those few minutes of extra sleep might make us just ten times as efficient during the day! That is what we must think of – efficiency. We must sacrifice our petty opinions on the matter and think of the rest of the day and our efficiency. There is no doubt that fifteen minutes' more sleep would do wonders for us, no matter how little we really want to take it.

By the time we have finished this line of argument we are out pretty fairly cold again, but not so cold that we are not conscious of anyone entering the room. We feel that they are going to say: 'Come, come, don't go back to sleep again!' and we forestall this warning with a brisk 'I know! I know! I'm just thinking!' This is said with one eye partially open and one tiny corner of the brain functioning. The rest of our powers add up to a total loss.

It is one of Nature's wonders how a man can carry on an argument with someone standing beside his bed and still be asleep to all intents and purposes. Not a very good argument, perhaps, and one in which many important words are missing or indistinct, but still an argument. It is an argument, however, which seldom wins, the state of justice in the world being what it is today.

Dozing before arising does not really come within the range of this treatise. What we are concerned with are those little lapses when we are fully dressed, when we fondly believe that no one notices. Riding on a train, for example.

There is the short-distance doze in a day coach, probably the most humiliating form of train sleeping. In this the elbow is rested on the window sill and the head placed in the hand in an attitude of thought. The glass feels very cool on the forehead and we rest it there, more to cool off than anything else. The next thing we know the forehead (carrying the entire head with it) has slid down the length of the slippery pane and we have received a rather nasty bang against the woodwork. They shouldn't keep their glass so slippery. A person is likely to get badly hurt that way.

However, back again goes the forehead against the pane in its original position, with the hand serving more or less as a buffer, until another skid occurs, this time resulting in an angry determination to give the whole thing up entirely and sit up straight in the seat. Some dozers will take four or five slides without whimpering, going back each time for more with apparently undiminished confidence in their ability to see the thing through.

It is a game that you can't beat, however and the sooner you sit up straight in your seat, the sooner you will stop banging your head.

Dozing in a Pullman chair is not so dangerous, as one does not have the risk of the sliding glass to cope with, but it is even less lovely in its appearance. Here the head is allowed to sink back against the antimacassar – just for a minute to see if the headrest is really as comfortable as it seems. It is then but the work of a minute for the mouth to open slightly and the head to tip roguishly to the right, and there you are – as pretty a picture as one would care to see. You are very lucky if, when you come to and look about, you do not find your neighbours smiling indulgently at some little vagaries of breathing or eccentricities of facial expression which you have been permitting yourself.

The game in all this public dozing is to act, on awakening, as if you had known all along what you were doing. If your neighbours are smiling, you should smile back, as if to say: 'Fooled you that time! You thought I was asleep, didn't you?'

If they are not quite so rude as to smile, but look quickly back at their reading on seeing your eyes open, you should assume a brisk, businesslike expression indicating that you have been thinking out some weighty business problem with your eyes closed, and, now that you have at last come on its solution, that it is snap-snap! back to work for you! If, after a furtive look around, you discover that no one has caught you at it, then it will do no harm to give it another try, this time until your collar chokes you into awakening with a strangling gasp.

The collar, however, is not always an impediment to public dozing. In the theatre, for example, a good, stiff dress collar and shirt bosom have been know to hold the sleeper in an upright position when otherwise he might have plunged forward and banged his head on the back of the seat in front.

In my professional capacity as play reviewer I had occasion to experiment in the various ways of sitting up straight and still snatching a few winks of health-giving sleep. I found that by far the safest is to keep one's heavy overcoat on, especially if it is made of some good, substantial material which will hold a sagging torso erect within its folds. With a good overcoat, reinforced by a stiff dress shirt and a high collar, one may even go beyond the dozing stage and sink into a deep, refreshing slumber, and still not be made conspicuous by continual lurchings and plungings. Of course, if you are an uneasy sleeper and given to thrashing about, you will find that even a heavy overcoat will let you down once in a while. But for the average man, who holds approximately the same position after he has gone to sleep, I don't think that this method can go wrong. Its only drawback is that you are likely to get a little warm along about the middle of the second act.

If you don't want to wear your overcoat in the theatre, the next best method is to fold the arms across the chest and brace the chin against the dress collar, exerting a slight upward pressure with the arms against the shirt front. This, however, can be used only for the lightest of dozes, as, once unconsciousness has set in, the pressure relaxes and over you go.

Dozing at a play, however refreshing, makes it a bit difficult to follow the argument on the stage, as occasionally the nap drags itself out into a couple of minutes and you awake to find a wholly fresh set of characters on the scene, or even a wholly fresh scene. This is confusing. It is therefore wise to have someone along with you who will alternate watches with you, dozing when you are awake and keeping more or less alert while you are dozing. In this way you can keep abreast of what has been happening.

This, unfortunately, is impossible in personal conversations. If you slip off into a quick coma late some evening when your *vis-à-vis* is telling you about South America or a new solvent process, it is usually pretty difficult to pick up the thread where you dropped it. You may remember that the last words he was saying were '... which is situated at the mouth of the Amazon,' but that isn't going to help you much if you come to just as he is asking you: 'What would *you* say are?' As in the personal-conversation doze the eyes very seldom completely close (it is more of a turning back of the eyeballs than a closing of the lids) you may escape detection if you have a ready answer for the emergency. I find that 'Well, I don't know,' said very slowly and deliberately, will fit any question that has been asked you. 'Yes' and 'No' should never be offered as they might make you sound even sillier than you look. If you say: 'Well, I – don't – know,' it will give you a chance to collect your wits (what few there are left) and may lead your questioner into answering the thing himself.

At any rate, it will serve as a stall. If there are other people present, some one of them is quite likely to come to your rescue and say something which will tip you off as to the general subject under discussion. From then on, you will have to fight your own battle. I can't help you.

The whole problem is one which calls for a great deal of thought. If we can develop some way in which a man can doze and still keep from making a monkey of himself, we have removed one of the big obstacles to human happiness in modern civilization. It goes without saying that we don't get enough sleep while we are in bed; so we have got to get a little now and then while we are at work or at play. If we can find some way to keep the head up straight, the mouth closed, and just enough of the brain working to answer questions, we have got the thing solved right there.

I am working on it right now, as a matter of fact, but I find it a little difficult to keep awake.

The Cricket Match

A. G. Macdonell

In the words of Michael Barsley, 'the description, in *England Their England* (from which the following extract is taken), of the cricket match between Mr Hodge's literary team and the villagers of Fordenden, is his masterpiece, the finest passage of sustained fun in modern English literature.' Archibald Gordon Macdonell died in 1941 at the age of forty-five.

The cricket field itself was a mass of daisies and buttercups and dandelions, tall grasses and purple vetches and thistle-down, and great clumps of dark-red sorrel, except, of course, for the oblong patch in the centre – mown, rolled, watered – a smooth, shining emerald of grass, the Pride of Fordenden, the Wicket.

The entire scene was perfect to the last detail. It was as if Mr Cochran had, with his spectacular genius, brought Ye Olde Englyshe Village straight down by special train from the London Pavilion, complete with synthetic cobwebs (from the Wigan factory), hand-made smocks for ye gaffers (called in the cabaret scenes and the North-West Mounted Police scenes, the Gentlemen of the Singing Ensemble), and aluminium Eezi-Milk stools for the dairymaids (or Ladies of the Dancing Ensemble). For there stood the Vicar, beaming absent-mindedly at everyone. There was the forge, with the blacksmith, his hammer discarded, tightening his snake-buckled belt for the fray and loosening his braces to enable his terrific bowling-arm to swing freely in its socket. There on a long bench outside the Three Horseshoes sat a row of elderly men, facing a row of pint tankards, and wearing either long beards or clean-shaven chins and long whiskers. Near them, holding pint tankards in their hands, was another group of men, clustered together and talking with intense animation. Donald thought that one or two of them seemed familiar, but it was not until he turned back to the char-à-banc to ask if he could help with the luggage that he realized that they were Mr Hodge and his team already sampling the proprietor's wares. (A notice above the door of the inn stated that the proprietor's name was A. Bason and that he was licensed to sell wines, spirits, beers and tobacco.)

All round the cricket field small parties of villagers were patiently waiting for the great match to begin – a match against gentlemen from London is an event in a village – and some of them looked as if they had been waiting for a good long time. But they were not impatient. Village folk are very seldom impatient. Those whose lives are occupied in combating the eccentricities of God regard as very small beer the eccentricities of Man.

Blue-and-green dragonflies played at hide-and-seek among the thistle-down and a pair of swans flew overhead. An ancient man leaned upon a scythe, his sharpening-stone sticking out of a pocket in his velveteen waistcoat. The parson shook hands with the squire. Doves cooed. The haze flickered. The world stood still.

At twenty to three Mr Hodge had completed his rather tricky negotiations with the Fordenden captain, and had arranged that two substitutes should be lent by Fordenden in order that the visitors should field eleven men, and that nine men on each side should bat. But just as the two men on the Fordenden side, who had been detailed for the unpleasant duty of fielding for both sides and batting for neither, had gone off home in high dudgeon, a motor-car arrived containing not only Mr Hodge's two defaulters but a third gentleman in flannels as well, who swore stoutly that he had been invited by Mr Hodge to play and affirmed that he was jolly well going to play. Whoever stood down, it wasn't going to be him. Negotiations therefore reopened, the pair of local Achilles had to be recalled, and at ten minutes to three the match began upon a twelve-a-side basis.

Mr Hodge, having won the toss by a system of his own founded upon the differential calculus and the Copernican theory, sent in his opening pair to bat. One was James Livingstone, a very sound club cricketer, and the other one was called, simply, Boone. Boone was a huge, awe-inspiring colossus of a man, weighing at least eighteen stone and wearing all the majestic trappings of a Cambridge Blue. Donald felt that it was hardly fair to loose such cracks upon the humble English village until he fortunately remembered that he, of all people, a foreigner, admitted by courtesy to the National Game, ought not to set himself up to be a judge of what is, and what is not, cricket.

The Fordenden team ranged themselves at the bidding of their captain, the Fordenden baker, in various spots of vantage amid the daisies, buttercups, dandelions, vetches, thistle-down, and clumps of dark-red sorrel; and the blacksmith having taken in, just for luck as it were, yet another reef in his snake-buckle belt, prepared to open the attack. It so happened that, at the end at which he was to bowl, the ground behind the wicket was level for a few yards and then sloped away rather abruptly, so that it was only during the last three or four intensive galvanic yards of his run that the blacksmith, who took a long run, was visible to the batsman or indeed to anyone on the field of play except the man stationed in the deep field behind him. This man saw nothing of the game except the blacksmith walking back dourly and the blacksmith running up ferociously, and occasionally a ball driven smartly over the brow of the hill in his direction.

The sound club player having taken guard, having twiddled his bat round several times in a nonchalant manner, and having stared arrogantly at each fieldsman in turn, was somewhat surprised to find that, although the field was ready, no bowler was visible. His doubts, however, were resolved a second or two later, when the blacksmith came up, breasting the slope like a mettlesome combination of Vulcan and Venus Anadyomene. The first ball which he delivered was a high full-pitch to leg, of appalling velocity. It must have lighted upon a bare patch among the long grass near long-leg, for it rocketed, first bounce, into the hedge and four byes were reluctantly signalled by the village umpire. The row of gaffers on the rustic bench shook their heads, agreed that it was many years since four byes had been signalled on that ground, and called for more pints of old-and-mild. The other members of Mr Hodge's team blanched visibly and called for more pints of bitter. The youngish professor of ballistics, who was in next, muttered something about muzzle velocities and started to do a sum on the back of an envelope.

The second ball went full-pitch into the wicket-keeper's stomach and there was a delay while the deputy wicket-keeper was invested with the pads and gloves of office. The third ball, making a noise like a partridge, would have hummed past Mr Lvingstone's left ear had he not dexterously struck it out of the ground for six, and the fourth took his leg bail with a bullet-like-pitch. Ten runs for one wicket, last man six. The professor got the fifth ball on the left ear and went back to the Three Horseshoes, while Mr Harcourt had the singular misfortune to hit his wicket before the sixth ball was even delivered. Ten runs for two wickets and one man retired hurt. A slow left-hand bowler was on at the other end, the local rate-collector, a man whose whole life was one of infinite patience and guile. Off his first ball the massive Cambridge Blue was easily stumped, having executed a movement that aroused the professional admiration of the Ancient who was leaning upon his scythe. Donald was puzzled that so famous a player should play so execrable a stroke until it transpired, later on, that a wrong impression had been created and that the portentous Boone had gained his Blue at Cambridge for rowing and not for cricket. Ten runs for three wickets and one man hurt.

The next player was a singular young man. He was small and quiet, and he wore perfectly creased white flannels, white silk socks, a pale-pink silk shirt, and a white cap. On the way down in the char-à-banc he had taken little part in the conversation and even less in the beer-drinking. There was a retiring modesty about him that made him conspicuous in that cricket eleven, and there was a gentleness, an almost finicky gentleness about his movements which hardly seemed virile and athletic. He looked as if a fast ball would knock the bat out of his hands. Donald asked someone what his name was, and was astonished to learn that he was the famous novelist, Robert Southcott himself.

Just as this celebrity, holding his bat as delicately as if it was a flute or a fan, was picking his way through the daisies and thistledown towards the wicket, Mr Hodge rushed anxiously, tankard in hand, from the Three Horeshoes and bellowed in a most unpoetical voice: 'Play carefully, Bobby. Keep your end up. Runs don't matter.'

'Very well, Bill,' replied Mr Southcott sedately. Donald was interested by this little exchange. It was the Team Spirit at work – the captain instructing his man to play a type of game that was demanded by the state of the team's fortunes, and the individual loyally suppressing his instincts to play a different type of game.

Mr Southcott took guard modestly, glanced furtively round the field as if it was an impertinence to suggest that he would survive long enough to make a study of the fieldsmen's positions worth while, and hit the rate-collector's first ball over the Three Horseshoes into a hayfield. The ball was retrieved by a mob of screaming urchins, handed back to the rate-collector, who scratched his head and then bowled his fast yorker, which Mr Southcott hit into the saloon bar of the Shoes, giving Mr Harcourt such a fright that he required several pints before he fully recovered his nerve. The next ball was very slow and crafty, endowed as it was with every iota of finger-spin and brain-power which a long-service rate-collector could muster. In addition, it was delivered at the extreme end of the crease so as to secure a background of dark laurels instead of a dazzling white screen, and it swung a little in the air; a few moments later the urchins, by this time delirious with ecstasy, were fishing it out of the squire's trout stream with a bamboo pole and an old bucket.

The rate-collector was bewildered. He had never known such a travesty of the game. It was not cricket. It was slogging; it was wild, unscientific bashing; and furthermore, his reputation was in grave danger. The instalments would be harder than ever to collect, and Heaven knew they were hard enough to collect as it was, what with bad times and all. His three famous deliveries had been treated with contempt – the leg-break, the fast yorker, and the slow, swinging off-break out of the laurel bushes. What on earth was he to try now? Another six and he would be laughed out of the parish. Fortunately the village umpire came out of a trance of consternation to the rescue. Thirty-eight years of umpiring for the Fordenden Cricket Club had taught him a thing or two and he called 'Over' firmly and marched off to square-leg. The rate-collector was glad to give way to a Free Forester, who had been specially imported for this match. He was only a moderate bowler, but it was felt that it was worth while giving him a trial, if only for the sake of the scarf round his waist and his cap. At the other end the fast bowler pounded away grimly until an unfortunate accident occurred. Mr Southcott had been treating with apologetic contempt those of his deliveries which came within reach, and the blacksmith's temper had been rising for some time. An urchin had shouted, 'Take him orf!' and the other urchins, for whom Mr Southcott was by now a firmly established deity, had screamed with delight. The captain had held one or two ominous consultations with the wicket-keeper and other advisers, and the blacksmith knew that his dismissal was at hand unless he produced a supreme effort.

It was the last ball of the over. He halted at the wicket before going back for his run, glared at Mr Harcourt, who had been driven out to umpire by his colleagues – greatly to the regret of Mr Bason, the landlord of the Shoes – glared at Mr Southcott, took another reef in his belt, shook out another inch in his braces, spat on his hand, swung his arm three or four times in a meditative sort of way, grasped the ball tightly in his colossal palm, and then turned smartly about and marched off like a Pomeranian grenadier and vanished over the brow of the hill. Mr Southcott, during these proceedings, leant elegantly upon his bat and admired the view. At last, after a long stillness, the ground shook, the grasses waved violently, small birds arose with shrill clamours, a loud puffing sound alarmed the butterflies, and the blacksmith, looking more like Venus Anadyomene than ever, came thundering over the crest. The world held its breath. Among the spectators conversation was suddenly hushed. Even the urchins, understanding somehow that they were assisting at a crisis in affairs, were silent for a moment as the mighty figure swept up to the crease. It was the charge of Von Bredow's Dragoons at Gravelotte over again.

But alas for human ambitions! Mr Harcourt, swaying slightly from leg to leg, had understood the menacing glare of the bowler, had marked the preparation for a titanic effort, and – for he was not a poet for nothing – knew exactly what was going on. And Mr Harcourt sober had a very pleasant sense of humour, but Mr Harcourt rather drunk was a perfect demon of impishness. Sober, he occasionally resisted a temptation to try to be funny. Rather drunk, never. As the giant whirlwind of vulcanic energy rushed past him to the crease, Mr Harcourt, quivering with excitement and internal laughter, and wobbling uncertainly upon his pins, took a deep breath and bellowed, 'No ball!'

It was too late for the unfortunate bowler to stop himself. The ball flew out of his hand like a bullet and hit third-slip, who was not looking, full pitch on the knee-cap. With a yell of agony third-slip began hopping about like a stork until he tripped over a tussock of grass and fell on his face in a bed of nettles, from which he sprang up again with another drum-splitting yell. The blacksmith himself was flung forward by his own irresistible momentum, startled out of his wits by Mr Harcourt's bellow in his ear, and thrown off his balance by his desperate effort to prevent himself from delivering the ball, and the result was that his gigantic feet got mixed up among each other and he fell heavily in the centre of the wicket, knocking up a cloud of dust and dandelion-seed and twisting his ankle. Rooks by hundreds arose in protest from the vicarage cedars. The urchins howled like intoxicated banshees. The gaffers gaped. Mr Southcott gazed modestly at the ground. Mr Harcourt gazed at the heavens. Mr Harcourt did not think the world had ever been, or could ever be again, quite such a capital place, even though he had laughed internally so much that he had got hiccups.

Mr Hodge, emerging at that moment from the Three Horseshoes, surveyed the scene and then the scoreboard with an imperial air. Then he roared in the same rustic voice as before:

'You needn't play safe any more, Bob. Play your own game.'

'Thank you, Bill,' replied Mr Southcott as sedately as ever, and, on the resumption of the game, he fell into a kind of cricketing trance, defending his wicket skilfully from straight balls, ignoring crooked ones, and scoring one more run in a quarter of an hour before he inadvertently allowed, for the first time during his innings, a ball to strike his person.

'Out!' shrieked the venerable umpire before anyone had time to appeal.

The score at this point was sixty-nine for six, last man fifty-two.

The only other incident in the innings was provided by an American journalist, by name Shakespeare Pollock – an intensely active, alert, on-the-spot young man. Mr Pollock had been roped in at the last moment to make up the eleven, and Mr Hodge and Mr Harcourt had spent quite a lot of time on the way down trying to teach him the fundamental principles of the game. Donald had listened attentively and had been surprised that they made no reference to the Team Spirit. He decided in the end that the reason must have been simply that everyone knows all about it already, and that it is therefore taken for granted.

Mr Pollock stepped up to the wicket in the lively manner of his native mustang, refused to take guard, on the ground that he wouldn't know what to do with it when he got it, and striking the first ball he received towards square leg, threw down his bat, and himself set off at a great rate in the direction of cover-point. There was a paralysed silence. The rustics on the bench rubbed their eyes. On the field no one moved. Mr Pollock stopped suddenly, looked round, and broke into a genial laugh.

'Darn me –' he began, and then he pulled himself up and went on in refined English, 'Well, well! I thought I was playing baseball.' He smiled disarmingly.

'Baseball is a kind of rounders, isn't it, sir?' said cover-point sympathetically.

Donald thought he had never seen an expression change so suddenly as Mr Pollock's did at this harmless, and true, statement. A look of concentrated, ferocious venom obliterated the disarming smile. Cover-point, simple soul, noticed nothing, however, and Mr Pollock walked back to the wicket in silence and was out next ball.

The next two batsmen, Major Hawker, the team's fast bowler, and Mr Hodge himself, did not score, and the innings closed at sixty-nine, Donald not-out nought. Opinion on the gaffers' bench, which corresponded in years and connoisseurship very closely with the Pavilion at Lord's, was sharply divided on the question whether sixty-nine was, or was not, a winning score.

After a suitable interval for refreshment, Mr Hodge led his men, except Mr Harcourt who was missing, out into the field and placed them at suitable positions in the hay.

The batsmen came in. The redoubtable Major Hawker, the fast bowler, thrust out his chin and prepared to bowl. In a quarter of an hour he had terrified seven batsmen, clean bowled six of them, and broken a stump. Eleven runs, six wickets, last man two.

After the fall of the sixth wicket there was a slight delay. The new batsman, the local rate-collector had arrived at the crease and was ready. But nothing happened. Suddenly the large publisher, who was acting as wicket-keeper, called out 'Hi! Where's Hawker?'

The words galvanized Mr Hodge into portentous activity.

'Quick!' he shouted. 'Hurry, run, for God's sake! Bob, George, Percy, to the Shoes!' and he set off at a sort of gallop towards the inn, followed at intervals by the rest of the side except the pretty youth in the blue jumper, who lay down; the wicket-keeper, who did not move; and Mr Shakespeare Pollock, who had shot off the mark and was well ahead of the field.

But they were all too late, even Mr Pollock. The gallant Major, admitted by Mr Bason through the back door, had already lowered a quart and a half of mild-and-bitter, and his subsequent bowling was perfectly innocuous, consisting, as it did, mainly of slow, gentle full-pitches to leg which the village baker and even, occasionally, the rate-collector hit hard and high into the long grass. The score mounted steadily.

Disaster followed disaster. Mr Pollock, presented with an easy chance of a run-out, instead of lobbing the ball back to the wicket-keeper, had another reversion to his college days and flung it with appalling velocity at the unfortunate rate-collector and hit him in the small of the back, shouting triumphantly as he did so. 'Rah, rah, rah!' Mr Livingstone, good club player, missed two easy catches off successive balls. Mr Hodge allowed another easy catch to fall at his feet without attempting to catch it, and explained afterwards that he had been all the time admiring a particularly fine specimen of oak in the squire's garden. He seemed to think that this was a complete justification of his failure to attempt, let alone bring off, the catch. A black spot happened to cross the eye of the ancient umpire just as the baker put all his feet and legs and pads in front of a perfectly straight ball, and, as he plaintively remarked over and over again, he had to give the batsman the benefit of the doubt, hadn't he? It wasn't as if it was his fault that a black spot had crossed his eye just at that moment. And the stout publisher seemed to be suffering from the delusion that the way to make a catch at the wicket was to raise both hands high in the air, uttering a piercing yell, and trust to an immense pair of pads to secure the ball. Repeated experiments proved that he was wrong.

The baker lashed away vigorously and the rate-collector dabbed the ball hither and thither until the score – having once been eleven runs for six wickets – was marked up on the board at fifty runs for six wickets. Things were desperate. Twenty to win and five wickets – assuming that the blacksmith's ankle and third-slip's knee-cap would stand the strain – to fall. If the lines on Mr Hodge's face were deep, the lines on the faces of his team when he put himself on to bowl were like plasticine models of the Colorado Canyon. Mr Southcott, without any orders from his captain discarded his silk sweater from the Rue de la Paix, and went away into the deep field, about a hundred and twenty yards from the wicket. His beautifully brushed head was hardly visible above the daisies. The professor of ballistics sighed deeply. Major Hawker grinned a colossal grin, right across his jolly red face, and edged off in the direction of the Shoes. Livingstone, loyal to his captain, crouched alertly. Mr Shakespeare Pollock rushed about enthusiastically. The remainder of the team dropped.

But the remainder of the team was wrong. For a wicket, a crucial wicket was secured off Mr Hodge's very first ball. It happened like this. Mr Hodge was a poet, and therefore a theorist, and an idealist. If he was to win a victory at anything, he preferred to win by brains and not by muscle. He would far sooner have his best leg-spinner miss the wicket by an eighth of an inch than dismiss a batsman with a fast, clumsy full-toss. Every ball that he had bowled had brain behind it, if not exactness of pitch. And it so happened that he had recently watched a county cricket match between Lancashire, a county that he detested in theory, and Worcestershire, a county that he adored in fact. On the one side were factories and the late Mr Jimmy White; on the other, English apples and Mr Stanley Baldwin. And at this particular match, a Worcestershire bowler, by name Root, a deliciously agricultural name, had outed the tough nuts of the County Palatine by placing all his fieldsmen on the leg-side and bowling what are technically known as 'in-swingers'.

Mr Hodge, at heart an agrarian, for all his book-learning and his cadences, was determined to do the same. The first part of the performance was easy. He placed all his men upon the leg-side. The second part – the bowling of the 'in-swingers' – was more complicated, and Mr Hodge's first ball was a slow long-hop on the off-side. The rate-collector, metaphorically rubbing his eyes, felt that this was too good to be true, and he struck the ball sharply into the untenanted off-side and ambled down the wicket with as near an approach to gaiety as a man can achieve who is cut off by the very nature of his profession

from the companionship and goodwill of his fellows. He had hardly gone a
yard or two when he was paralysed by a hideous yell from the long grass into
which the ball had vanished, and still more by the sight of Mr Harcourt,
who, aroused from a deep slumber amid a comfortable couch of grasses and
daisies, sprang to his feet and, pulling himself together with miraculous
rapidity after a lightning if somewhat bleary glance round the field, seized
the ball and unerringly threw down the wicket. Fifty for seven, last man
twenty-two. Twenty to win: four wickets to fall.

Mr Hodge's fifth ball was not a good one, due mainly to the fact that it
slipped out his hand before he was ready, and it went up and came down in a
slow-lazy parabola, about seven feet wide of the wicket on the leg-side. The
baker had plenty of time to make up his mind. He could leave it alone and let
it count one run as a wide; or he could spring upon it like a panther and, with
a terrific six, finish the match sensationally. He could play the part either of a
Quintus Fabius Maximus Cunctator, or of a sort of Tarzan. The baker
concealed beneath a modest and floury exterior a mounting ambition. Here
was his chance to show the village. He chose the sort of Tarzan, sprang like a
panther, whirled his bat cyclonically, and missed the ball by about a foot and
a half. The wicket-keeping publisher had also had time in which to think and
to move, and he also had covered the seven feet. True, his movements were
less like the spring of a panther than the sideways waddle of an aldermanic
penguin. But nevertheless he got there, and when the ball had passed the
flashing blade of the baker, he launched a might kick at it – stooping to grab
it was out of the question – and by an amazing fluke kicked it on to the
wicket. Even the ancient umpire had to give the baker out, for the baker was
still lying flat on his face outside the crease.

'I was bowling for that,' observed Mr Hodge modestly, strolling up the
pitch.

'I had plenty of time to use my hands,' remarked the wicket-keeper to the
world at large, 'but I preferred to kick it.'

Donald was impressed by the extraordinary subtlety of the game.

Six to win and three wickets to fall.

The next batsman was a schoolboy of about sixteen, an ingenuous youth
with pink cheeks and a nervous smile, who quickly fell a victim to Mr
Harcourt, now wideawake and beaming upon everyone. For Mr Harcourt,
poet that he was, understood exactly what the poor, pink child was feeling,
and he knew that if he played the ancient dodge and pretended to lose the
ball in the long grass, it was a hundred to one that the lad would lose his

head. The batsman at the other end played the fourth ball of Mr
Livingstone's next over hard in the direction of Mr Harcourt. Mr Harcourt
rushed towards the spot where it had vanished in the jungle. He groped
wildly for it, shouting as he did so, 'Come and help. It's lost.' The pink child
scuttered nimbly down the pitch. Six runs to win and two wickets to fall. Mr
Harcourt smiled demoniacally.

The crisis was now desperate. The fieldsmen drew nearer and nearer to the
batsmen, excepting the youth in the blue jumper. Livingstone balanced
himself on his toes. Mr Shakespeare Pollock hopped about almost on top of
the batsmen, and breathed excitedly and audibly. Even the imperturbable
Mr Southcott discarded the piece of grass which he had been chewing so
steadily. Mr Hodge took himself off and put on the Major, who had by now
somewhat lived down the quart and a half.

The batsmen crouched down upon their bats and defended stubbornly. A
snick through the slips brought a single. A ball which eluded the publisher's
gigantic pads brought a bye. A desperate sweep at a straight half-volley sent
the ball off the edge of the bat over third-man's head and in normal
circumstances would have certainly scored one, and possibly two. But Mr
Harcourt was on guard at third-man, and the batsmen, by nature cautious
men, one being old and the sexton, the other the postman and therefore a
Government official, were taking no risks. Then came another single off a
mis-hit, and then an interminable period in which no wicket fell and no run
was scored. It was broken at last disastrously, for the postman struck the ball
sharply at Mr Pollock, and Mr Pollock picked it up and, in an ecstasy of zeal,
flung it madly at the wicket. Two overthrows resulted.

The scores were level and there were two wickets to fall. Silence fell. The
gaffers, victims simultaneously of excitement and senility, could hardly raise
their pint pots – for it was six o'clock, and the front door of the Three
Horseshoes was now as wide open officially as the back door had been
unofficially all afternoon.

The Major, his red face redder than ever and his chin sticking out almost
as far as the Napoleonic Mr Ogilvy's, bowled a fast half-volley on the leg-
stump. The sexton, a man of iron muscle from much digging, hit it fair and
square in the middle of the bat, and it flashed like a thunderbolt, waist-high,
straight at the youth in the blue jumper. With a shrill scream the youth
sprang backwards out of its way and fell over on his back. Immediately
behind him, so close were the fieldsmen clustered, stood the mighty Boone.
There was no chance of escape for him. Even if he had possessed the figure

and the agility to perform back-somersaults, he would have lacked the time. He had been unsighted by the youth in the jumper. The thunderbolt struck him in the midriff like a red-hot cannon-ball upon a Spanish galleon, and with the sound of a drumstick upon an insufficiently stretched drum. With a fearful oath, Boone clapped his hands to his outraged stomach and found that the ball was in the way. He looked at it for a moment in astonishment and then threw it down angrily and started to massage the injured spot while the field rang with applause at the brilliance of the catch.

Donald walked up and shyly added his congratulations. Boone scowled at him.

'I didn't want to catch the bloody thing,' he said sourly, massaging away like mad.

'But it may save the side,' ventured Donald.

'Blast the bloody side,' said Boone.

Donald went back to his place.

The scores were level and there was one wicket to fall. The last man in was the blacksmith, leaning heavily upon the shoulder of the baker, who was going to run for him, and limping as if in great pain. He took guard and looked round savagely. He was clearly still in a great rage.

The first ball he received he lashed at wildly and hit straight up in the air to an enormous height. It went up and up and up, until it became difficult to focus it properly against the deep, cloudless blue of the sky, and it carried with it the hopes and fears of an English village. Up and up it went and then at the top it seemed to hang motionless in the air, poised like a hawk, fighting, as it were, a heroic but forlorn battle against the chief invention of Sir Isaac Newton, and then it began its slow descent.

In the meanwhile things were happening below, on the terrestrial sphere. Indeed, the situation was rapidly becoming what the French call *mouvementé*. In the first place, the blacksmith forgot his sprained ankle and set out at a capital rate for the other end, roaring in a great voice as he went, 'Come on, Joe!' The baker, who was running on behalf of the invalid, also set out, and he also roared 'Come on, Joe!' and side by side, like a pair of high-stepping hackneys, the pair cantered along. From the other end Joe set out on his mission, and he roared 'Come on, Bill!' So all three came on. And everything would have been all right, so far as the running was concerned, had it not been for the fact that Joe, very naturally ran with his head thrown back and his eyes goggling at the hawk-like cricket ball. And this in itself would not have mattered if it had not been for the fact that the blacksmith and the baker, also very naturally, ran with their heads turned not only upwards but also backwards as well, so that they too gazed at the ball, with an alarming sort of squint and truly terrific kink in their necks. Half-way down the pitch the three met with a magnificent clang, reminiscent of early, happy days in the tournament-ring at Ashby-de-la-Zouche, and the hopes of the village fell with the resounding fall of their three champions.

But what of the fielding side? Things were not so well with them. If there was doubt and confusion among the warriors of Fordenden, there was also uncertainty and disorganization among the ranks of the invaders. Their main trouble was the excessive concentration of their forces in the neighbourhood of the wicket. Napoleon laid it down that it was impossible to have too many men upon a battlefield, and he used to do everything in his power to call up every available man for a battle. Mr Hodge, after a swift glance at the ascending ball and a swift glance at the disposition of his troops, disagreed profoundly with the Emperor's dictum. He had too many men, far too many. And all except the youth in the blue silk jumper, and the mighty Boone, were moving towards strategical positions underneath the ball, and not one of them appeared to be aware that any of the others existed. Boone had not moved because he was more or less in the right place, but then Boone was not likely to bring off the catch, especially after the episode of the last ball. Major Hawker, shouting 'Mine, mine!' in a magnificently self-confident voice, was coming up from the bowler's end like a battle-cruiser. Mr Harcourt had obviously lost sight of the ball altogether, if indeed he had ever seen it, for he was running round and round Boone and giggling foolishly. Livingstone and Southcott, the two cracks, were approaching competently. Either of them would catch it easily. Mr Hodge had only to choose between them and, coming to a swift decision, he yelled above the din, 'Yours, Livingstone!' Southcott, disciplined cricketer, stopped dead. Then Mr Hodge made a fatal mistake. He remembered Livingstone's two missed sitters, and he reversed his decision and roared 'Yours, Bobby!' Mr Southcott obediently started again, while Livingstone, who had not heard the second order, went straight on. Captain Hodge had restored the *status quo*.

In the meantime the professor of ballistics had made a lightning calculation of angles, velocities, density of the air, barometer-readings and temperatures, and had arrived at the conclusion that the critical point, the spot which ought to be marked in the photographs with an X, was one yard to the north-east of Boone, and he proceeded to take up station there, colliding on the way with Donald and knocking him over. A moment later

Bobby Southcott came racing up and tripped over the recumbent Donald and was shot head first into the Abraham-like bosom of Boone. Boone stepped back a yard under the impact and came down with his spiked boot, surmounted by a good eighteen stone of flesh and blood, upon the professor's toe. Almost simultaneously the portly wicket-keeper, whose movements were a positive triumph of the spirit over the body, bumped the professor from behind. The learned man was thus neatly sandwiched between Tweedledum and Tweedledee, and the sandwich was instantly converted into a ragout by Livingstone, who made up for his lack of extra weight – for he was always in perfect training – by his extra momentum. And all the time Mr Shakespeare Pollock hovered alertly upon the outskirts like a Rugby scrum-half, screaming American University cries in a piercingly high tenor voice.

At last the ball came down. To Mr Hodge it seemed a long time before the invention of Sir Isaac Newton finally triumphed. And it was a striking testimony to the mathematical and ballistical skill of the professor that the ball landed with a sharp report upon the top of his head. Thence it leapt up into the air a foot or so, cannoned on to Boone's head, and then trickled slowly down the colossal expanse of the wicket-keeper's back, bouncing slightly as it reached the massive lower portions. It was only a foot from the ground when Mr Shakespeare Pollock sprang into the vortex with a last ear-splitting howl of victory and grabbed it off the seat of the wicket-keeper's trousers. The match was a tie. And hardly anyone on the field knew it except Mr Hodge, the youth in the blue jumper, and Mr Pollock himself. For the two batsmen and the runner, undaunted to the last, had picked themselves up and were bent on completing the single that was to give Fordenden the crown of victory. Unfortunately, dazed with their falls, with excitement, and with the noise, they all three ran for the same wicket, simultaneously realized their error, and all three turned and ran for the other – the blacksmith, ankle and all, in the centre, and leading by a yard, so that they looked like pictures of the Russian *troika*. But their effort was in vain, for Mr Pollock had grabbed the ball and the match was a tie.

And both teams spent the evening at The Three Horseshoes, and Mr Harcourt made a speech in Italian about the glories of England and afterwards fell asleep in the corner, and Donald got home to Royal Avenue at 1 o'clock in the morning feeling that he had not learnt very much about the English from his experience of their national game.

England Their England

Flying with Child

Art Buchwald

Travelling is a pleasure instead of an ordeal when you go by air with baby or junior. It is wise to notify your airline ahead of time, however, so they will have certain things aboard for baby's comfort....

If he is a little older, make a game out of acquainting him with the objects around him. By the time he leaves the ground he will feel quite at home. You might take along a favourite toy to keep him busy and add to his feeling of security.

Children love to fly. They enjoy the excitement of boarding the big plane and watching the clouds go by the window. It is an experience they'll remember always and cherish. And so will Mother, because of the time and effort it has saved her in travelling with small fry.

From a pamphlet distributed
by the Air Transport Association

I was reading this pamphlet on a flight across the Atlantic Ocean recently. Standing next to me on the seat, reading over my shoulder, was a two-and-a-half-year-old boy who happens to be related to me.

There are certain things I would like to call to the attention of the Air Transport Association at this time. I followed their instructions to a T and it's apparent that the person who wrote the pamphlet has never flown higher than a thirty-inch desk.

In the first place, it's not as easy to take along a child's favourite toy as the article would imply. In my case X Jr's favourite toy happened to be a three-and-one-half-foot red-and-yellow stuffed Teddy bear. Although Pan American wanted my child to feel secure they pointed out that all stuffed Teddy bears three feet or over took up as much space as a two-and-a-half-year-old child and were subject to the same fare. We had to leave the bear at home. As soon as he boarded the plane, X Jr's insecurity was apparent.

He refused to buckle his safety belt and tripped the stewardess as she was explaining how to use a life jacket properly. As an afterthought he howled through the whole demonstration and I'm quite sure that if the emergency ever arose there were very few people on the plane who would know what to do.

Once the plane was safely in the air and out of danger, X Jr decided to fasten his seat belt. It took his mother and his father and a stewardess to get it unfastened.

Children are usually fed first on a plane. In theory this is a good idea, but in practice it works like this. The child, having finished *his* meal and noticing other passengers just starting theirs, will wander down the aisle staring at the people while they eat. Few people can stare down a child, and before I got wind of what was happening X Jr had managed to procure three pieces of cake, a lamb chop and a cup of salad dressing.

Following the article's suggestion, I made a game out of acquainting X Jr with objects around him. If he pushed the light switch he got one point. If he pushed the buzzer for the stewardess he got three points. If he pulled out the ash tray he got five points, and if he hit the person in front of him he got fifteen points. When he received a total of fifty points, he got the spanking of his life.

When a child gets bored with 'watching the clouds go by the window' (it usually takes about thirty seconds), he will head for the water fountain. The water fountain to a child is by far the most interesting part of an aeroplane. Aeronautical engineers, realizing this, have designed the fountains so that the water buttons are out of reach of tiny hands. Few children are daunted by this measure. In X Jr's case he stole a woman's jewellery case and someone else's movie camera and a copy of *Andersonville*. By piling them up he not only managed to reach the water button, but was also successful in destroying a month's supply of Pan American's paper cups.

The question of whether a parent should let his child wander up and down the aisle during the night or keep him in his seat is something each person must work out in his own conscience.

If you let the child wander you can probably get some sleep – but nobody else on the plane can. At three o'clock in the morning X Jr was serving Life Savers and chewing gum to the other passengers, or so I was told the next morning by several blood-shot people.

There is no doubt that travelling with a child is a memorable experience that everyone would like to forget.

Lindbergh had the right idea. He flew the Atlantic alone.

Breaking the Ice at St Moritz

Art Buchwald

Every year millions of civilized people, young and old, tall and short, rich and poor, gather on the snowy slopes of their favourite country to engage in a perilous sport called skiing. The sport which dates back to Time Immemorial (Time Immemorial was a little town just outside of Copenhagen), is attracting more and more enthusiasts each year, tempting them with cool breezes, breathtaking speeds, ticklish thrills and self-satisfying broken legs. The mould out of which good skiers are cast is usually made of plaster of Paris, and should be placed between the knee and the ankle, depending on the seriousness of the injury. There are some people who say skiing accidents are unavoidable, and it's true. But before the accident comes, before the enthusiast finds his leg hanging from a hospital pulley, I believe he can get more out of the sport than he's getting now. Having won the uphill slalom at St Moritz, and a fox-trot contest at Zermatt, I feel I am in a position to advise the fledgling as well as the expert on this sport of sports, this maker of men, this waylayer of women, this child of nature which we call skiing.

Winter sports being what they are, and winter-sports enthusiasts being what they are, it's very hard for a person who doesn't ski to turn up at a ski resort. On the other hand, statistics prove that for every person who comes to a resort to ski, there are two and three-quarter persons who don't. (The other fraction represents a person who gives no quarter). What do these people do? Where can they turn? What is their future?

In St Moritz, the heart of the broken-limb country, where a man must prove himself first on skis and then on a stretcher, I found the answer. This resort has made it easy on non-skiers. In place of skiing you can go down on the bobsled or the Cresta – one on the seat of your pants and the other on the flat of your stomach. By reaching speeds of sixty or seventy miles an hour, you get the same feeling as if you were on skis, and instead of running the risk of breaking your leg, the only thing you can possibly break on the bobsled or

Cresta is your neck.

But for those who, like me, want the glory without the danger, there are ways of getting around doing anything. If you follow instructions, the only risk you'll take is burning your tongue on the hot chocolate which everyone drinks at a ski resort when the long day is over.

It's all a question of looking good. The first place to look good is on the ski train. When leaving for a ski resort the non-skier should be completely dressed in ski pants, ski boots and goggles. The non-skier must remember that clothes make the skier, the skier doesn't make the clothes.

You don't have to carry any skis, but you should have two ski sticks with you. If you want to look good before the train starts, you can practise low crouches, jump turns, parallel swings, Christiania stems on the train platform. This will impress everyone on the station and you'll be a legend before you even get on the train.

Once aboard you can either wax your ski sticks or study snow bulletins. It's all right to strike up conversations about skiing with other passengers provided they are not going to the same resort. When walking to the dining car you can either use the 'alternate step' or you can do 'stakning.' The alternate step needs no explanation – you just put one foot after another. But stakning is more difficult. You have to keep your feet parallel and close together and slide along with the help of your ski sticks. This is very difficult to do without skis, but if the non-skier waxes the bottoms of his ski boots he'll get a nice effect.

When he arrives at the ski resort the non-skier has to be very careful. If there is snow on the ground he may be in trouble. One method of solving the problem would be jump off the train from the top step and then scream, 'My ankle, my ankle, I think I broke it!'

As soon as you reach the hotel, strap up one of your ankles with adhesive tape and for the rest of the time limp around. You never have to explain at a ski resort why you're limping. It's taken for granted, and you can even get people to buy you free drinks if you look as if you're in enough pain.

Once you're free of skiing you can stay up all night, drinking and having a ball, and sleep in the daytime. If you feel up to it, you can also collect ski medals in your spare afternoons.

Most ski medals can be bought in souvenir shops and others can be picked up accidentally. I was sitting in the lobby of the Palace Hotel one afternoon when Andreas Badrutt, the owner, walked by. He gave me a medal for skiing down Piz Nair, one of the highest and most frightening ski slopes in

Switzerland. Another time I had lunch at the Corviglia Club, and while I was ordering a dozen snails and a bottle of Rhine wine someone sewed the club's insignia on my ski jacket. It's these little things that make skiing fun for non-skiers.

A person may raise the question of boredom. 'If I don't ski, won't I be bored?' The answer is no. Ski resorts have ping-pong tables, bowling alleys, juke boxes and deck chairs. They also have beautiful women. Most beautiful women don't like to go skiing because they're afraid of breaking their beautiful legs. This leaves unlimited possibilities for the non-skier. Although women admire the athletic prowess of a skiing man, there is an old St Moritz saying that 'A bird in the lobby of a hotel is worth two on a ski lift.' For some reason the saying holds true all over the world.

For those who are not content with bending over the bar and are bent on hitting the slope (it usually hits back), here are some idle remarks about the sport. Skiing is the method of gliding on snow with the aid of two pieces of wood (or aluminium) fastened to the feet. By manipulating these pieces of wood, the skier can steer himself between rocks, trees and over other skiers. The expression 'over my dead body' originally was used by someone who had just had a skiing spill. Later it was adopted by Mr Casey Stengel of baseball fame, and he used the expression so many times that it has now become common usage in the English language.

There is no one too young or too old to engage in skiing. In some Scandinavian countries three-month-old babies are tied to the tops of cigar boxes and shoved down mountains before they are able to talk. In Switzerland, wheel chairs are equipped with skis and old men and women are encouraged to compete in jumping contests in wheel chairs.

In discussing the art of skiing let us take up some of the things that are required of one who wishes to participate in the sport. The first thing, of course, is equipment. Without the right equipment the skier is immediately handicapped if not ostracized by everyone in the sporting world.

The main items of clothing necessary are – a pair of peg-top trousers which are worn inside the boot. As far as socks go there are two schools of thought on the subject. One school believes you should wear your socks *outside* the boot. It makes a much better colour combination for that part of the leg where colour is always needed. The other school thinks it's better to wear the sock *inside* the boot and also believes that the trouser should be held in place by an elastic band. I am a member of the first school (Class of '48). Since most skiers are going to spend more time in bars and hotel lobbies than they are on the ski course, appearance counts much more than safety, and a pair of bright woollen socks over well-polished boots can make all the difference in the world in the fast-moving social circles that skiing has become so much a part of.

Boots should be chosen with a great deal of care. They should have rubber soles so you can't slip on dance floors and enough room in them to store a sandwich or two in case you get hungry during the day. Many people make the mistake of buying boots that fit. When the inevitable accident occurs the boot then has to be cut off the swollen foot and a good fifteen or twenty bucks is thrown down the drain. If the farsighted skier purchases ski boots several sizes too big, he will not have to have the ski boot cut off his foot and he will be able to continue skiing even if the foot swells up to twice its normal size. This is worth keeping in mind.

The next item of clothing to be considered is the ski sweater. The best ski sweaters should have elks on them. Men should purchase sweaters with one large elk, and women, sweaters with two little elks looking at each other over a great divide. The elks should be alert and their horns should protrude up towards the neck. Incidentally, turtle necks may be warmer, but at the moment they're out of fashion and a good skier would cut his throat before being caught with one on.

Gloves should also have elks on them. The faces of the elks should face inward and their horns should be part of the finger design. In the case of mittens the elks do not necessarily have to face each other.

Goggles and ear muffs are optional. If you're going skiing with your wife the ear muffs are not optional but a necessity. Sun glasses should be worn at all times, as they make the rankest amateur skier look like the rankest professional.

That's all the equipment one needs, except if one wants to carry a pistol. The law about shooting skiers with broken legs has never been clearly defined. In the only case that has ever come to court, Oscar Heppleworth was acquitted of shooting his wife with his famous defence line, 'They shoot horses, don't they?'

Now the question of choosing skis comes up. The length of the ski depends on the height of the person. A ski should reach the palm of the skier's hand just touching the nose of the embroidered elk. Longer skis are too difficult to manipulate and much heavier to carry on one's shoulder. The only advantage is that you can clear a very large path for yourself when climbing with them up the hill.

Hickory and ash are the two best woods that skis are made of. Hickory, a nut-bearing tree, is solid, thick and hard grained, and its elasticity and pliability have been tested time and time again in schoolrooms all over the world. Ash is the most suitable wood that grows in Europe. It is not as good as hickory, but it's better than plywood, which is something in its favour.

The wood used for making skis should not contain knots. If your ski contains a knot, do 'not' buy it. Once you have chosen the ski, then you must choose the binding. The binding should be strong enough to hold the shoe in place and at the same time flexible enough in case you want to leave the ski suddenly.

Ski sticks should be about six inches above the waist line and made of metal. They can be used to prevent you from falling and for roasting marshmallows in front of an open fireplace.

Having dealt with the question of equipment we are now faced with the problem of how to ski.

The best way of learning to ski is to hire an instructor. A ski instructor is probably the most patient man in the world and since he gets paid by the hour he doesn't care how much time you spend in the snow. The favourite phrase of the ski instructor is 'If you fall you have to get up yourself. It's the only way you'll learn.' If it looks as though you can't make it in a reasonable length of time, the instructor will bring you food and water, and a blanket if night is falling. But under no condition will he help you to get on your feet. If you don't suffer from frostbite, this is a lesson you'll remember for the rest of your skiing life.

The first thing every skier must master is the 'involuntary fall.' This means to be able to fall when you don't want to. It usually takes about five minutes to learn this, and once you have it down pat you can fall anywhere in the snow without the help of the instructor. Having learned the rudiments of falling, one should then try to pick up a few of the rudiments of staying up on the skis.

The easiest way to start off is to sit on the skis facing forward. In this way you can always grab on to the shoe-laces of one of the better skiers if you feel you're getting into trouble.

When you feel you've built up confidence in a sitting position, try kneeling. The bindings on your knees may at first bother you but after a while you will get used to them. In the kneeling position you can always grab on to someone's leg if you lose control of yourself.

After you have mastered the kneeling position, you are then in line to try the run standing up. When you are in position, throw your arms tightly around the neck of the ski instructor, who should have his back toward you. Then give him a slight push. Both of you will go tumbling down the hill and for the first time you'll feel the thrill that comes to all skiers who have conquered one of God's most fearful elements – snow.

If your ski instructor becomes angry, fire him on the spot. Don't take any back talk from him, and remind him there are a lot of ski instructors who would be happy to earn the money he's earning, and could do a much better job of teaching you how to ski. This should end the argument on the spot. If not, you have two ski poles and by now you'll know what to do with them.

Following your first ride down the hill standing up you are now ready to practise some of the more intricate turns. The stem Christiania, the snow plough and the jump turn are all easy to learn and should not take more than five years with daily practice.

After learning the turns you can then go in for jumping. Keep your feet together when jumping and your crouch low. The sticks shouldn't be placed too near the feet, and the hands and arms should be at shoulder level. Jump forward and not straight up into the air. Keep your knees on your chest, your heels up and your toes down, and whatever else you do, let your knees absorb the shock.

And above all, watch out for avalanches. An avalanche can always spoil a good jump. If you jump into an avalanche, find a shelter quick. That's all there is to jumping. From here on out you're on your own.

Before signing off this instructive article on skiing, I'd like to add a list of don'ts that the skier must pay attention to if he expects to be well informed on the sport.

First, don't admit to people in bars that you are an amateur and have never skied before. If you're dressed properly you can look as good as the next fellow, and if you buy the drinks they'll believe anything you tell them.

Secondly, don't use bad language when you fall. If you must be profane, be profane towards the ski instructor and not towards the skis.

Don't ski near children. They will in all probability only laugh at you.

If you are a woman, do not wear sweaters that will cause other skiers to forget where they're going.

Don't try to stop yourself by crashing into a tree. It may be somebody's mother.

Don't spend more than $3,000 for your first ski outfit.

Don't flirt with girls in your ski class. You may wind up paying for their lessons.

Don't eat at the ski club. It's very expensive and when they find out you are not a member they'll throw you out in the snow.

Don't shoot polar bears from a moving ski lift. It's considered poor sportsmanship, even for beginners.

Well, it looks as if I've covered the subject pretty well and there isn't any more advice I can give. From now on it's up to each individual to get out there and join the winter madness. Remember, class, for each pair of skis on a snowy hill there is a pair of crutches waiting for you at the local hospital. The question is, how soon will you earn yours?

I was sitting in the lobby of the Palace Hotel sipping tea and chewing on an old ski boot when I was approached by a large, good-looking man who introduced himself as Serge Oestesky. Serge asked if I liked skiing, and I said I didn't because it was too much work.

'I thought so,' he said. 'Let me introduce you to a sport that requires no work at all. All you have to do is lie on a sled and go down a hill called the Cresta. There are no ski-lift fees to pay, no chance of falling into the snow and no ski instructors to scream that you're doing everything wrong.'

'It sounds interesting,' I said, 'but everyone says it's very dangerous. There are vicious rumours that a man can do eighty-five miles an hour on the course. People say that you can get killed on the run. They say you're not a skeleton rider unless you've broken at least one leg or both arms.'

'Poppycock,' said Serge. 'Come down tomorrow morning and we'll fix you up. You'll never regret it.' As an incentive he added, 'Gregory Peck is going down tomorrow – probably right after you.'

That sold me, and the next morning I showed up at nine o'clock. Serge took me into a nice warm hut and started throwing things at me. First he threw some thick knee pads, then elbow pads, then a pair of boots with steel rakes jutting out of the toes. When I put those on he gave me a football helmet and two metal shields for my hands. I started to break into a sweat.

'W-w-w-where's Gr-gr-gregory P-p-p-peck?' I asked Serge.

'Don't worry, he's coming,' Serge said. 'Come on down the run. I'll show you the skeleton.'

'Th-th-the wh-wh-wh-what?'

'Skeleton. That's the sled. It's made of two rigid round steel runners which are welded to steel braces and a steel plate. There's a sliding seat to lie on. There's no danger at all.'

'Bb-bb-bbut w-w-wh-what in th-th-th-the h-hhh-hhell do you steer w-with?'

'With your body. It's very simple. Now come on and unwrap your arms and legs from that post.'

He pulled me out into the crisp Swiss morning air and took me down to the starting line, where I was introduced to a man named McCarthy, who is secretary of the Cresta Club and official timer and starter. He made me fill out a card for next of kin. The Cresta run was nothing but solid ice. I started to walk away but they caught me and carried me back.

'Wh-wh-wh-where's Gr-gr-gr-gr-gregory Peck?' I cried.

'He's coming,' said Serge. 'Now lie down on the sled. Hold on to the runners with both hands and keep your elbows in. Use the steel rakes on your feet to brake with. Look straight ahead and hold on tight. Go as fast as you want to. The ideal, of course, would be to crash the sound barrier, but if you don't do it on your first run, don't worry about it. Any questions?'

'Wh-wh-wh-where's Gr-gr-gregory P-p-peck?'

McCarthy rang the bell, Serge gave me a fast push and I was off. The skeleton started down at what is called Stream Corner at what I calculated to be three hundred miles an hour. I dug my rakes into the ice. Nothing happened. For two hundred yards straight down I hugged the sled thinking of absolutely nothing. I went under a road bridge and suddenly veered to the right on a sharp turn called Bullpetts. I straightened out, went under a railway bridge and then smashed hard against Scylla and was thrown over to a turn called Charybdis. Up until that time I was too frightened to think of anything, but just after Charybdis I had time to ask myself, 'Wh-wh-what in the h-h-h-hell are you d-d-d-doing here?'

After Charybdis the bottom dropped out and I whipped down Cresta Leap, which felt like a gentle 90-degree grade, on to the side of an ice mountain. As I gasped for air the skeleton returned to earth and the ride was over.

It took three men to pry my hands loose from the runners. I staggered back to the starting line. Serge was surprised to see me alive. But he wasn't discouraged.

'You did it in forty seconds. Now you have to do it *without* braking at all. Keep your feet off the ice.'

Skeleton riding is a Swiss version of Russian roulette. I went down again, and then (a good psychiatrist could probably explain it), I went down a third time.

The next afternoon I was sitting in the lobby of the Palace again. Serge came in. But he ignored me this time and went over to a man who was just checking in at the hotel. All I could hear of the conversation was 'Cresta Run,' 'safer than skiing' and 'Gregory Peck is coming tomorrow morning.'

The Pleasure Cruise, and How to Survive It

James Thurber

It has occurred to me that there may be persons here and there, young and inexperienced in the ways of the world, who might profit from my own personal TRAVEL HINTS compiled after looking back on thirty-odd years of knocking about, or being knocked about, the globe. I don't mean the whole globe, of course. I have never been south of Trinidad, north of Quebec, east of Italy, or west of San Francisco, but within these rather roomy limits, I have been knocked about quite a bit.

My first hint – to the gentleman traveller – is a simple one. Never go anywhere without your wife. If your wife won't go, because the concert or canning season is on, or something of the sort, take your sister or your mother or your cousin. The American woman is indispensable in getting the tickets and reservations, packing and unpacking, mixing Bromo-Seltzers, fending off beautiful ladies who are travelling alone, and making herself useful generally. Hers is also the only sex that can successfully close a wardrobe trunk. If a man closes a wardrobe trunk, there is always a sharp snapping sound, caused by the breaking of something that will not bend, such as the handle of a mirror, or the stem of a Dunhill pipe, or the stopper of a perfume bottle. If a woman is deprived of her Chanel No 5 during, say, a nineteen-day cruise, she will become irritable, and there is nothing more exasperating on a cruise, or anywhere else, than an irritable female companion.

Now that I have mentioned cruises, let us consider more closely the technique of the sea voyage. After the wife has closed the wardrobe trunk and called a taxi, it is only eight in the morning, and the ship doesn't sail till eleven. The husband will complain that it doesn't take three hours to get to a pier only eight blocks from their hotel. He will point out that they can get to Pier 58 in half an hour, with time to spare. He is right, it turns out, but it also turns out that he doesn't know where Pier 58 is. His wife has unfortunately left this one small detail up to him. He tells the taxi driver to take them to the foot of West 58th Street, but when they get there, it transpires that this is not the point of departure of their ship, the *Santa Maria*. It is the point of departure of the *J B Cathcart*, a coastwise fruit steamer bound for French Guiana. The taxi driver suggests that the *Santa Maria* probably sails from Brooklyn or Hoboken. The husband figures there is time to try both places, but his wife's sounder judgment prevails. She asks somebody – always an excellent idea – where Pier 58 is, and is told Pier 58 is at the foot of West 16th Street. It is too.

On the way to the right destination, with time to spare – just as the husband had promised – the taxi driver has a hunch that the *Santa Maria* sails at 11pm, on Tuesdays and not at 11am, on Thursdays. This throws his male passenger into a panic. The seasoned woman traveller pays no attention to all this unnecessary masculine excitement. She leans back in the cab, closes her eyes and wonders if she forgot to pack her white piqué evening dress. Once aboard the ship, the wife (Ellen) tells her husband (George) that she has to unpack her light things right away or they will crush, and she asks him, for heaven's sake, to get deck chairs on the sunny and windless side of the ship immediately, before they are all gone and also to make table reservations instantly, so they can have a table for two once in their lives, and not have to sit with a lot of strangers. George wanders away on these important errands and (1) runs into an old classmate from Dartmouth and (2) decides that they ought to find out where the bar is and what time it opens for business. When he returns to his stateroom, an hour later, Ellen is in excellent spirits – she has found the white piqué evening dress – but her amiable mood is not going to last very long. 'Did you reserve the chairs and the table?' she asks. 'Hm?' says George blankly. I will spare you the scene that follows. Suffice it to say that the Kendalls (their name is Kendall) have to settle for deck chairs on the sunless and windy side of the ship, and are put at a table for eight: two women buyers from Cleveland, an embalmer and his bride, a pair of giggling college girls and Mr and Mrs Kendall. She has the chair with the short right-rear leg.

My private tip here is that the wife should reserve the deck chairs and the table, let the dresses crush where they may, but I have never been able to sell the idea to any woman traveller.

The only woman who doesn't care whether her dresses crush or not is the seasick woman, but I wouldn't recommend seasickness as the way out of anything, not even the way out of sitting next to the embalmer at dinner. Speaking of seasickness, I am unlucky enough to have a stomach of platinum, and I haven't suffered from *mal der mer* since the eastward Atlantic crossing of the *USS Orizaba*, in November, 1918, but this was a transport that took nine days zigzagging from New York to St Nazaire in heavy weather, and there was honourable excuse for my condition. I say I am 'unlucky' enough to have a stomach of platinum, because the seasick turn to the unseasick on a ship for succour, sanctuary and salvation that are impossible to give. Once, on the Bermuda run – seventeen of us up and around on the second day, out of a passenger list of three hundred – I came upon a lone woman sprawled on a sofa in the library up forward, where rolling and pitching had flung her prostrate and forlorn. She lay on her hat and her right side; one shoe was off; her handbag was open on the floor, its contents scattered; her lipstick was smudged in such a way that she seemed to have bitten her own left cheek. I was appalled – sympathetic, gallant even, but appalled – and when I am appalled, my nervous system becomes an apparatus that, as the French say, *ne fonctionne pas*.

'Do something,' she said in a faint, awful voice.

'Madam,' I squeaked helplessly. I was unable to say anything, but I did something. I put her things back in her handbag and placed it on a table.

'I put your handbag on the table,' I finally managed to croak.

'Do something,' she said again, in the same voice. For a moment I considered putting her shoe back on, but like any other Ohio State man, I was restrained by the feeling that the act would be both insensitive and foolish. Then I suddenly decided to put the shoe on the table with the handbag.

'Do something,' she said, in a weaker tone. I staggered out of the library, hunted up a deck steward and told him about the lady and her extremity.

'Do something,' I begged him. He just shook his head sadly. I rolled on my way, and came to the elevator that ran from A Deck down to E Deck and back. There was a woman there, frantically pressing the bell button. She was standing, and she had both shoes on, but she looked just as ghastly as the lady in the library. She grabbed my arm as I tried to walk by.

'E Deck. Quick!' she gasped.

'The elevator will be up –' I began and caught myself, but not in time. Her face took on a saffron hue.

'I'm sorry,' I mumbled. She looked at me with the eyes of a stepped-on spaniel.

'E Deck,' she said again. 'Please.'

I had to do something. I brushed past her and began pushing the bell button wildly. Then I turned and ran. I have often wondered, in my own low and agonized moments, if she made it.

Just what hint to give to the unseasick passenger who may be faced, during an ocean voyage, with crises and suffering similar to my own that terrible day, I frankly do not know. There are certain tortures that we unseasick passengers simply have to endure, I guess. I would appreciate it, though, if you don't go around saying that, in the emergencies I have described, I just 'got the hell out.' I did what I could. There will, of course, always be two schools of thought about that shoe, the school that contends I should have put it back on, and the school that insists I should have let it lie where I found it. Apparently nobody in the world but me would have put it on the table with the handbag. I can only say that if I had it all to do over again, I would still put the shoe on the table with the handbag.

If you travel much on ships you are bound, sooner or later, to run into Mrs Abigail Pritchard, as I shall call her. She is not just one woman, but many; I have encountered at least fifteen of her. Mrs Pritchard may be forty-five, or she may be seventy, but her average age, I should say, is about fifty-seven. She comes from Boston, Hartford, Germantown, Syracuse, Toledo, Chicago, Louisville, St Louis, Denver, Sacramento, and both Portlands. She is a widow, fairly well off, whose children are happily married and the fathers, or mothers, of the prettiest and brightest youngsters in the world, and she has snapshots and anecdotes to prove it. She takes two Daiquiris before dinner and a highball afterwards, and smokes Players, on the ground that they are made of actual tobacco, whereas American cigarettes, in her opinion, are composed of rum, molasses, shredded cork, and factory sweepings. She prefers domestic Burgundies, however, because the so-called French vintages you find on ships are really only cheap Algerian wine that has been poured into genuine bottles labelled Pommard or Chablis. Mrs Pritchard is full of interesting little anecdotes about the late Sir Harry Oakes, the late Richard Halliburton ('that dear boy'), a Colonel Grosvenor in Penang, the gifted Courtney girls (whoever they are), John Barrymore ('poor old Jack') Heifetz, Houdini, Nell Brinkley, Anna Eva Fay, Percey Marmont, Maurice Costello ('the king of them all'), Kip Rhinelander, Mrs O. H. P. Belmont, Struthers Burt, Ky Laffoon and anybody else whose name you happen to mention. Mrs Pritchard is certain she saw Judge Crater in the Casino at Cannes in 1937, where he was known as Maltby or Goadby, or some such name. 'How do you do, Judge Crater?' she said to him firmly. He started – there could be no doubt of that. 'My name is Maltby (or Goadby), madam,' the man said, and hurried away.

Mrs Pritchard can invariably spot, aboard ship, professional gamblers, unmarried couples sharing the same stateroom, fugitives from justice, fingermen formerly in the employ of Al Capone, cocaine sniffers, bay-rum drinkers, professional men of dubious integrity, women who are mortally ill but don't know it, unhappy wives and gentlemen with phony foreign accents. It makes you nervous to talk to, or rather listen to, Mrs Pritchard. You twist restlessly in your chair, confident that she has figured you for an absconder, a black-marketeer, or a white-slave trader. Mrs Pritchard spends at least two months of every year on ships, but I often wonder why, since she suspects that there is skulduggery afoot from the chart room to the hold. If the ship is even half an hour late in shoving off, she whispers that 'Uncle Joe is behind this delay.' She never clears this up, though, but merely shakes her head wisely, if you ask her what she means. She is sure the ship is going to put to sea with broken pumps, insufficient lifeboats, and a typhoid carrier among the crew. Two days out, she tells you she doesn't like the look of the saxophone player's complexion – he has something contagious, mark her words. The third day out she declares that the chief steward is secreting fifteen thousand pounds of roast beef, which he intends to sell to a syndicate in Port-au-Prince. It costs ten thousand dollars a day to operate a ship, she read in the *Reader's Digest*, and this ridiculous amount is due to thefts of supplies by the stewards.

Even the captain of the ship is not above her suspicion. She is positive that he forgot to order all those automobiles in the hold lashed down, and she knows they will roll to one side if a storm comes up, causing the ship to list, like the *Vestris*, and sink. Mrs Pritchard loves to tell about the time the master of an ocean liner was seized with a heart attack while steering the boat – she still thinks he was an epileptic – and almost ran into an iceberg. But her favourite story is about the time she was on a West Indies cruise, and caught a glimpse of the captain one day. She recognized him instantly as a Major Quantrell (or Chantress, or some such name) wanted in Rangoon for the shooting of a missionary's daughter in a fashionable gambling house. Mrs Pritchard points out that a captain's cabin is the perfect hide-out for fugitives from justice, since nobody is allowed in the cabin except the officers, and they are probably no better than they ought to be, themselves.

The young traveller will naturally expect old, experienced me to advise

him how to avoid, or to deal with, Mrs Pritchard. Well, you can't avoid her.
Just dismiss that from your mind. She pops up from everywhere and out from
behind everything. Even if you hid in the engine room, she would search you
out. As for dealing with the old girl, I have invented a rather nasty game
called Back Her in the Corner, which works wonders.

'You know the Hotel l'Aiglon in Roquebrune, of course?' I say to her,
casually.

'To be sure,' she replies. 'That perfectly gorgeous view of the Bay of Monte
Carlo at night!'

We both look dreamy.

'Ah, yes,' I sigh, 'and those wonderful sardines grilled in triple-sec!'

'Yes, yes,' she sighs, 'those delicious sardines.'

You see, she has to keep up a show of having been every place I have been.
And here's where my game gets nasty.

'There isn't any Hotel l' Aiglon in Roquebrune,' I say coldly, 'and there
aren't any sardines grilled in triple-sec.'

She is furious. I have tricked her, and hell hath no fury like a woman
tricked. She gives me a wide berth after that, not even nodding or smiling
when I pass her on deck. I can get away with this little game because I am
fifty-six,* but such conduct on the part of the *young* traveller would seem
imprudent, disrespectful and ill-bred. You'll have to devise your own method
of dealing with Mrs Pritchard. You mustn't expect me to solve *all* your travel
problems. And please don't write and ask me what to do in the event that you
run into the gifted Courtney sisters. I simply do not know.

A few days out of New York (if you sailed from New York), printed copies of
the passenger list are usually distributed, containing such names as Jowes,
Qmith, Johnsob, Crazier, Aprker, Sommonx and Spider. It takes years of practice to decipher some passenger-list garbles. The letters of my own name have
assumed some twenty different permutations, but I am most often listed simply
as Jane Phurber, a winsome six-foot Ohio matron who affects men's clothes. My
wife, whose name is Helen Thurber, turned up on one ship under the alias of H.
Muriel. In some mysterious manner, our false names (I was Joseph Thacher on
this occasion) followed us ashore when we debarked at Naples. My wife indignantly showed our true passport names to one Italian official who had insisted
we were one J. Thacher and one H. Muriel. He saw his mistake.

'I am all of regret, *signorina*,' he said, in excellent English, 'and expressing
sorrows towards you and Signor Muriel.'

* Publishers note: He's fifty-eight if he's a day.

'Come on, H.,' I said, 'let's go.'

'OK, Joe,' she said, and we got out of there.

You will most likely have been at sea a week before you get around to reading the literature you picked up at your travel agency, or at the offices of the steamship line itself. This company gets out a pamphlet entitled *General Information*, and you should have read it before you got on the ship. It lists a number of things that should not be carried in a passenger's luggage: 'Dangerous articles, such as fireworks, matches, gunpowder, inflammable liquids, cartidges, inflammable motion-picture films.' If you have a supply of sky-rockets and Roman candles, it would be wise to dump them overboard some night when nobody is watching you. Skyrockets shot from decks accidentally or out of a misguided burst of patriotic spirit, are certain to be construed as signals of distress by other vessels, and this would vex the commander of your ship, to say the least. So leave your fireworks at home, in a safe, locked place, where the children can't get at them. I don't know why you keep fireworks in your house, anyway, but, of course, that is none of my business.

If you have gone on a cruise to relax, and you don't want to romp, run, race or wrestle, stay away from the sports director, a big, energetic blonde young man carrying a medicine ball. The female of this species, the sports directress, is active, alert, athletic, aggressive and capable of throwing your wife, or you, over her shoulder with her left hand. If you are not in training and under twenty-eight, don't monkey around with these two. They will run you ragged. They love squatting exercises, chinning themselves, holding their breath, standing on their hands, and touching the deck two thousand times with their finger tips, without bending their knees. Don't try to keep up with them. Refuse their challenges, ignore their taunts. You can't beat them at anything from squatting to ping-pong, unless you are young Mathias, the decathlon champion, and you probably aren't. The sports directors are supposed to organize group recreational activities. This is both a fact and a warning.

Speaking of ping-pong, I once entered a table-tennis tournament aboard the *SS President Garfield*, on a trip from New York through the Canal to Los Angeles. The sports director was determined to get me into the table-tennis tournament, probably because he wanted to see me humiliated in the finals. And he did. I lost two straight games to a pretty, attractive young lady, twenty years* my junior. The table was too short, the net was too high, the

* Publisher's note: Twenty-two years.

rackets were warped, the ship rocked, a small boy among the spectators
began riding me and I got something in my eye. I explained to my opponent
after the match that, on land and under fair and reasonable conditions, I
could have pinned her ears back, the best day she ever saw. She was honest
enough to admit this. A very pleasant girl, and the luckiest woman I have
ever met on sea or land.

The night before a ship makes home port at the end of a cruise, there is
usually a ship's concert, or programme of entertainment, in which the
Courtney sisters and other gifted passengers are invited to take part. If you
are a singer, violinist, bird caller, soft-shoe dancer, whistler, mimic,
monologist, contortionist, juggler, hypnotist, ventriloquist, swami, *diseuse* or
zither player, you are likely to be asked to join in the fun and do your act.
You may refuse, of course, and you should, if you plan to recite all of
Evengeline or *Hiawatha*. Your fellow-passengers will resent any act that lasts
longer than five minutes. Once, coming back from the West Indies on the
Conte Grande, I declined to appear on the concert programme, and then
suddenly, during a lull at midnight, I grabbed up a lighted megaphone and
sang *Who?* and *Bye, Bye Blackbird* with the orchestra. Well, not *with* it, exactly,
since in *Blackbird*, I was singing '*Oh, the hard-luck stories they all hand me*' while
the orchestra was playing *No one here can love or understand me*, but we were tied
at the finish, I am happy to say. The survivors of that concert will doubtless
remember my act, but they will not care to dwell on it any more than I do.

Since my performance that midnight, and possibly because of it, some of
the more cautious cruise ships have eliminated passenger participation and
turned the programme of the final night over to professionals. The last cruise
I was on, a few months ago, had no place for amateurs on the Big Night. The
entertainment department of WOR provided a soprano, a baritone (to
replace me), a prestidigitator, a couple of 'dance stylists,' an accordionist and
several other instrumentalists. Talented passengers who had counted on
imitating Tallulah Bankhead or playing Canadian Capers on a makeshift
xylophone composed of White Rock bottles were somewhat mollified when
they were given funny hats to wear, horns to blow, bells to ring, and rattles to
rattle at the Gala Farewell Dinner that preceded the Gala Farewell Revue. In
charge of these Galas, and such affairs as the Fancy Headdress Ball and
other intellectual goings on, are the cruise director and the cruise directress
(not to be confused with the sports director and the sports directress). When,
on my recent cruise, I returned to my stateroom after the Gala Farewell
Revue, I found a cheerful note from the cruise director. It read: 'Rise up in

the morning with the will that – smooth or rough – you'll grin!' I decided against this. You never know how a customs man may interpret a grin, especially a fixed grin.

Customs inspection is seldom as trying as you think it's going to be, unless you have a shoeful of diamonds or a trunk full of liqueurs. Just take your place under your proper letter (Q for Smith, E for Perkins, P for Thurber, and so forth) and see that you have assembled all your baggage. You will usually find that your typewriter case is missing and that you have a large grey suitcase that doesn't belong to you. The person who owns the grey suitcase may have your typewriter, and he may not. Don't get excited and rush around accusing people of stealing your Corona, just relax. You have all day, you know, and if you went to bed instead of to the bar after the Gala Revue, you will find yourself taking this ancient formality in your stride. It is important not to get mad at your inspector because he wants to go through your effects. That is his job. A Virginian I know, a man impatient of red tape and fiddle-faddle, as he describes all activities of the United States Government, once addressed a group of three customs inspectors as follows: 'Gentlemen, you are clearly insane.' He was the last man off the dock that day.

No travel hints would be complete without some word of caution about shipboard romances, engagements and marriages. The girl or young man you fell in love with on the ship when it was in Southern waters and the orchestra was playing 'Night and Day' is going to be subjected to a cruel and rigorous test standing there by a gloomy pile of baggage in a bleak and chilly ship shed. If the swan suddenly becomes a goose, or the knight a clodhopper, it is what is known as 'undergoing a land change.' If you were married aboard ship and the bride, or bridegroom, now appeals to you about as much as a piece of cold whole-wheat toast, you are in a rather serious jam. In America you cannot have a marriage annulled on the ground that it was contracted while you were under the influence of the Gulf Stream and Cole Porter. If you are a man, I suggest that you treat your inamorata with a gallantry tempered by caution during the voyage out and back, and refrain from proposing until you have caught her on the dock. If she is going to be met by her mother and father, her Aunt Louise and her Uncle Bert, you will want to get a look at them first too. During the cruise try to engage the girl of your dreams in discussions of books or politics if you find yourself with her on the promenade deck in the moonlight, while the band is playing 'I Told Every Little Star.' It won't work, but try it. All this, I suppose, is really no more concern of mine than why you keep fireworks in the house, so I will not pursue it further.

I hope that the foregoing helpful hints for a happy holiday will make your future sea voyages a little easier and merrier and safer. You need not, to be sure, take my advice or follow my example, in every situation and contretemps I have described hereinabove. If you want to put the shoe back on the sick lady's foot, or just leave it where you found it, feel free to do so. The reason I put the shoe on the table with the handbag was – but we have been all through that. I am beginning to repeat myself. Bon Voyage!

My Own Ten Rules for a Happy Marriage

James Thurber

Nobody, I hasten to announce, has asked me to formulate a set of rules for the perpetuation of marital bliss and the preservation of the tranquil American boudoir and inglenook. The idea just came to me one day, when I watched a couple in an apartment across the court from mine gesturing and banging tables and throwing *objets d'art* at each other. I couldn't hear what they were saying, but it was obvious, as the shot-put followed the hammer throw, that he and/or she (as the lawyers would put it) had deeply offended her and/or him.

Their apartment, before they began to take it apart, had been quietly and tastefully arranged, but it was a little hard to believe this now, as he stood there by the fireplace, using an andiron to bat back the Royal Doulton figurines she was curving at him from her strongly entrenched position behind the davenport. I wondered what had started the exciting but costly battle, and, brooding on the general subject of Husbands and Wives, I found myself compiling my own Ten Rules for a Happy Marriage.

I have avoided the timeworn admonitions, such as 'Praise her new hat,' 'Share his hobbies,' 'Be a sweet-heart as well as a wife,' and 'Don't keep a blonde in the guest room,' not only because they are threadbare from repetition, but also because they don't seem to have accomplished their purpose. Maybe what we need is a brand-new set of rules. Anyway, ready or not, here they come, the result of fifty years (I began as a little boy) spent in studying the nature and behaviour, mistakes and misunderstandings, of the American Male (*homo Americansis*) and his Mate.

RULE ONE: Neither party to a sacred union should run down, disparage or badmouth the other's former girls or beaux, as the case may be. The tendency to attack the character, looks, intelligence, capability, and achievements of one's mate's former friends of the opposite sex is a common cause of domestic discontent. Sweet-heart-slurring, as we will call this deplorable practice, is encouraged by a long spell of gloomy weather, too many highballs, hang-overs, and the suspicion that one's spouse is hiding, and finding, letters in a hollow tree, or is intercepting the postman, or putting in secret phone calls from the corner drugstore. These fears almost always turn out to be unfounded, but the unfounded fear, as we all know, is worse than the founded.

Aspersions, insinuations, reflections or just plain cracks about old boy friends and girl friends should be avoided at all times. Here are some of the expressions that should be especially eschewed: 'That waffle-fingered, minor-league third baseman you latched on to at Cornell'; 'You know the girl I mean – the one with the hips who couldn't read'; 'That old flame of yours with the vocabulary of a hoot owl'; and 'You remember her – that old bat who chewed gum and dressed like Daniel Boone.'

This kind of derogatory remark, if persisted in by one or both parties to a marriage, will surely lead to divorce or, at best, a blow on the head with a glass ash tray.

RULE TWO: A man should make an honest effort to get the names of his wife's friends right. This is not easy. The average wife who was graduated from college at any time during the past thirty years keeps in close touch with at least seven old classmates. These ladies, known as 'the girls,' are named, respectively: Mary, Marian, Melissa, Marjorie, Maribel, Madeleine, and Miriam; and all of them are called Myrtle by the careless husband we are talking about. Furthermore, he gets their nicknames wrong. This, to be sure, is understandable, since their nicknames are, respectively: Molly, Muffy, Missy, Midge, Mabby, Maddy and Mims. The careless husband, out of thoughtlessness or pure cussedness, calls them all Mugs, or, when he is feeling particularly brutal, Mucky.

All the girls are married, one of them to a Ben Tompkins, and as this is the only one he can remember, our hero calls all the husbands Ben, or Tompkins, adding to the general annoyance and confusion.

If you are married to a college graduate, then, try to get the names of her girl friends and their husbands straight. This will prevent some of those interminable arguments that begin after Midge and Harry (not Mucky and Ben) have said a stiff good-night and gone home.

RULE THREE: A husband should not insult his wife publicly, at parties. He should insult her in the privacy of the home. Thus, if a man thinks the soufflés his wife makes are as tough as an outfielder's glove, he should tell her so when they are at home, not when they are out at a formal dinner party where a perfect soufflé has just been served. The same rule applies to the wife. She should not regale his men friends, or women friends, with hilarious accounts of her husband's clumsiness, remarking that he dances like a 1907 Pope Hartford, or that he locked himself in the children's rabbit pen and couldn't get out. All parties must end finally, and the husband or wife who has revealed all may find that there is hell to pay in the taxi going home.

RULE FOUR: The wife who keeps saying, 'Isn't that just like a man?' and the husband who keeps saying, 'Oh, well, you know how women are,' are likely to grow farther and farther apart through the years. These famous generalizations have the effect of reducing an individual to the anonymous status of a mere unit in a mass. The wife who, just in time, comes upon her husband about to fry an egg in a dry skillet should not classify him with all other males but should give him the accolade of a special distinction. She might say, for example, 'George, no other man in the world would try to do a thing like that.' Similarly, a husband watching his wife labouring to start the car without turning on the ignition should not say to the gardener or a passer by, 'Oh, well, you know, etc.' Instead, he should remark to his wife, 'I've seen a lot of women in my life, Nellie, but I've never seen one who could touch you.'

Certain critics of this rule will point out that the specific comments I would substitute for the old familiar generalities do not solve the problem. They will maintain that the husband and wife will be sore and sulky for several days, no matter what is said. One wife, reading Rule Four over my shoulder, exclaimed, 'Isn't that just like a man?' This brings us right back where we started. Oh, well, you know how women are!

RULE FIVE: When a husband is reading aloud, a wife should sit quietly in her chair, relaxed but attentive. If he has decided to read the Republican platform, an article on elm blight, or a blow-by-blow account of a prize fight, it is not going to be easy, but she should at least pretend to be interested. She should not keep swinging one foot, start to wind her wrist watch, file her fingernails, or clap her hands in an effort to catch a mosquito. The good wife allows the mosquito to bite her when her husband is reading aloud.

She should not break in to correct her husband's pronunciation, or to tell him one of his socks is wrong side out. When the husband has finished, the wife should not lunge instantly into some irrelevant subject. It's wiser to exclaim, 'How interesting!' or, at the very least, 'Well, well!' She might even compliment him on his diction and his grasp of politics, elm blight or boxing. If he should ask some shrewd question to test her attention, she can cry, 'Good heavens!' leap up, and rush out to the kitchen on some urgent fictitious errand. This may fool him, or it may not. I hope, for her sake – and his – that it does.

RULE SIX: A husband should try to remember where things are around the house so that he does not have to wait for his wife to get home from the hairdresser's before he can put his hands on what he wants. Among the things a husband is usually unable to locate are the iodine, the aspirin, the nail file, the French vermouth, his cuff links, studs, black silk socks and evening shirts, the snapshots taken at Nantucket last summer, his favourite record of 'Kentucky Babe,' the borrowed copy of *My Cousin Rachel*, the garage key, his own towel, the last bill from Brooks Bros, his pipe cleaners, the poker chips, crackers, cheese, the whetstone, his new raincoat, and the screens for the upstairs windows.

I don't really know the solution to this problem, but one should be found. Perhaps every wife should draw for her husband a detailed map of the house, showing clearly the location of everything he might need. Trouble is, I suppose, he would lay the map down somewhere and not be able to find it until his wife got home.

RULE SEVEN: If a husband is not listening to what his wife is saying, he should not grunt, 'Okay' or 'Yeah, sure,' or make little affirmative noises. A husband lost in thought or worry is likely not to take in the sense of such a statement as this: 'We're going to the Gordons for dinner tonight, John, so I'm letting the servants off. Don't come home from the office first. Remember, we both have to be at the dentist's at five, and I'll pick you up there with the car.' Now, an 'Okay' or a 'Yeah, sure' at this point can raise havoc if the husband hasn't really been listening. As usual, he goes all the way out to his home in Glenville – thirteen miles from the dentist's office and seventeen miles from the Gordon's house – and he can't find his wife. He can't find the servants. His wife can't get him on the phone because all she gets is the busy buzz. John is calling everybody he can think of except, of course, in his characteristic way, the dentist and the Gordons. At last he hangs up, exhausted and enraged. Then the phone rings. It is his wife. And here let us leave them.

RULE EIGHT: If your husband ceases to call you 'Sugar-foot' or 'Candy Eyes' or 'Cutie Fudge Pie' during the first year of your marriage, it is not necessarily a sign that he has come to take you for granted or that he no longer cares. It is probably an indication that he has recovered his normal perspective. Many a young husband who once called his wife 'Tender Mittens' or 'Taffy Ears' or 'Rose Lips' has become austere or important, like a Common Pleas Judge, and he wouldn't want reports of his youthful frivolity to get around. If he doesn't call you Dagmar when your name is Daisy, you are sitting pretty.

RULE NINE:For those whose husbands insist on pitching for the Married Men against the Single Men at the Fourth-of-July picnic of the First M. E. Church, I have the following suggestion: don't sit on the sidelines and watch him. Get lost. George is sure to be struck out by a fourteen-year-old boy, pull up with a Charley horse running to first, and get his teeth knocked out by an easy grounder to the mound. When you see him after the game, tell him everybody knew the little boy was throwing illegal spitballs, everybody saw the first baseman spike George, and everybody said that grounder took such a nasty bounce even Phil Rizzuto couldn't have fielded it. Remember, most middle-aged husbands get to sleep at night by imagining they are striking out the entire batting order of the Yankees.

RULE TEN: A wife's dressing table should be inviolable. It is the one place in the house a husband should get away from and stay away from. And yet, the average husband is drawn to it as by a magnet, especially when he is carrying something wet, oily, greasy or sticky, such as a universal joint, a hub cap, or the blades of a lawn mower. His excuse for bringing these alien objects into his wife's bedroom in the first place is that he is looking for 'an old rag' with which to wipe them off. There are no old rags in a lady's boudoir, but husbands never seem to learn this. They search hampers, closets and bureau drawers, expecting to find a suitable piece of cloth, but first they set the greasy object on the dressing table. The aggrieved wife may be tempted, following this kind of vandalism, to lock her bedroom door and kick her husband out for good. I suggest, however, a less stringent punishment. Put a turtle in his bed. The wife who is afraid to pick up a turtle should ask Junior to help her. Junior will love it.

Now I realize, in glancing back over these rules, that some of my solutions to marital problems may seem a little untidy; that I have, indeed, left a number of loose ends here and there. For example, if the husbands are going to mislay their detailed maps of household objects, I have accomplished nothing except to add one item for the distraught gentleman to lose.

Then, there is that turtle. Captious critics will point out that a turtle in a husband's bed is not a valid solution to anything, but merely a further provocation. The outraged husband will deliberately trip his wife during their next mixed-doubles match. She will thereupon retaliate by putting salt in his breakfast coffee....

Let somebody else try to figure out what to do about the Running Feud in marriage. The Williamses are coming to dinner tonight, and I promised to put the white wine on the ice at three o'clock. It is now six-thirty. After all, I have my own problems.

Yoga Attempted

Cornelia Otis Skinner

An acquaintance of mine who hitherto has been in a state of chronic mental and physical collapse and has always seemed like something off the top shelf of Dr Caligari's cabinet, recently came to call, looking aggressively radiant and like a different person. She attributes it all to Yoga and in so insistently eloquent a manner that, were I not convinced of her integrity, I'd suspect her of being a scout for some Swami. Not only did she deliver a free and rather convincing talk on her newly discovered therapy, she illustrated it with a number of exercises that were pretty embarrassing but none the less impressive. Just what good it does body and soul, to say nothing of the state of mind of the domestics, to set down your drink and stand slowly on your head, I can't at present say. But it seemed a fine idea at the time and, to clinch the matter, the following day I chanced to see a book on Yoga in a shop window.

Purchasing books that deal with religion, health, or 'how to be happy though manic-depressive' shames me horribly. I always pretend I'm getting them for somebody else. After thumbing over 'Serenade' and 'The Hussy's Handbook' I bought the Yoga volume, laughing slyly as if it were meant as a joke, took it home, threw it in a suitcase, and never gave it another thought until I came across it several weeks later on a day I was by chance spending in a Cleveland hotel. Outside it was dank and cheerless. There was nothing to do but pay some back bills or go see Jane Withers in person. The time seemed perfect for trying out some Yoga, so I opened the book and skimmed a bit. It was illustrated with drawings of a sylph-like creature performing a lot of occult acrobatics. Disliking exercises in any form, I turned to the section dealing with meditation. What little I read was fascinating and I was all for starting for Nirvana in a big way. The author's warning that not only is Yoga for the few but that to do it properly requires not only months of practice but an experienced teacher, or *guru*, in no way discouraged me. After

all, you can't just pick up the classified phone directory and expect to find the
address of a first-class guru. As for the months of practice, what the hell – I'm
quick at languages, why not at Yoga?

I began under a definite handicap, for the book stated that the proceedings
should take place in a quiet room kept only for meditation and prayer. The
hotel had just housed a refrigerator's convention and I doubted if any of the
rooms had been devoted to spiritual communion. 'Yoga teachers recommend
flowers for your sanctuary and the burning of incense.' Here was a further
hurdle. I don't travel with incense and, besides, if you start burning it in the
bedroom of a commercial hotel there's no telling what it may lead to. As for
the flowers, all I had was a corsage of gardenias that had been kept so long
they'd turned into marigolds. The instructions that one must face either east
or north complicated things further, for murky clouds completely obscured
the position of the sun and I wasn't up on my Cleveland geography anyway.
I toyed with the idea of asking the operator or possibly the head porter which
way was east but was afraid of having to explain too much, so I muttered a
sort of 'eeny-meeny-miney-mo' and took a chance on it. For a mat, one is told
to fold a blanket then cover it with fur or silk. So I pulled a blanket off the bed
and spread over it a rather filmy slip that didn't look particularly occult.
Then, attired in what the poets might call my 'shift,' I set to work.

The book opened to the picture of a fantastic being sitting cross-legged in
lama-like pose. Running down its middle was a sort of X-ray view of brain
and spinal column, only in lieu of ordinary ganglia and vertebrae there
appeared at intervals a couple of lotuses, an elephant with seven trunks, a
goat, and a dragon. This seemed a trifle advanced for a beginner and I
decided to tackle the position before turning myself into a zoo. The creature
was seated in an attitude known as the 'Padmasana' or *lotus-seat*, which
looked as if it might be tough on the lotus but otherwise simple enough, being
chiefly a question of folding the legs. This to a trained Yogin may be just like
folding the arms, but to a novice it's a contortionist act worth booking in
vaudeville. Moreover, there's a saying in my family that the Skinners don't
bend (if there isn't such a saying there will be from now on). To place the
right ankle on the left thigh is bad enough, but then to bring the left ankle
over the right shin and get *it* somewhere up on the lap requires the strength
and cunning of the village blacksmith. I strained and panted, hissing
expletives that were hardly in the spirit. Twice my convulsive writhings
twisted off the silk slip and necessitated starting all over again. Finally with
super-human effort I managed to forge myself into a pattern that bore a

slight resemblance to the lotus-seat. I'm not up on lotuses and I've never deliberately sat on one but if they feel anything like my shin-bones I for one am going back to the old-fashioned morris-chair. The pain was excruciating. The book, however, assures one it's all a matter of rising above discomfort and I found solace in the thought that at least I hadn't reached the enlightened state of having to sit on nails. If this was the proper position for contemplation I was all for going the limit.

My ideas on how to set about contemplating were decidedly vague. The classic phrase concerning Buddha and what he contemplated recurred to me but I lack (thank God) the celestial rotundity that makes this practical. I fixed my eyes, instead, upon the fading gardenias and tried following the author's advice to start in by 'watching your thoughts.' This may be fine for anyone who has thoughts that are very pretty to watch but I find that mine aren't worth a penny in a slot machine marked 'For Adults Only.' Aside from the all-pervading sense of acute pain, my mind-stream turned out to be a jumble of irrelevant commonplaces connected only by the strains of 'I'm dancing and I can't be bothered now,' a tune that won't apparently find its way out of my head. This was hardly the state of serenity I had anticipated. I felt an unfortunate premonition that instead of a guru what I probably needed was a psychiatrist. However, I kept on watching those gardenias, hoping one moment to go into a trance and fearful the next lest I should. Would I come out of it by myself or would they have to send for the house physician? Stories of Hindu fakirs came to mind. I remembered reading a scientific report on the disturbing subject of levitation and wondered in the event that I floated out through the transom how I'd explain myself to the floor-clerk.

After a time the gardenias began to change shape and I waited hopefully for a vision. But what appeared was merely more gardenias; staring at them so long had made me go slightly cross-eyed. I attempted a few of the breathing exercises – long rhythmic in-takes followed by periods of breath-holding, and tried to picture that seven-trunked elephant cavorting happily about in my chest. The author warns that this may cause dizziness and he's quite right. Not only was I dizzy but my anatomy from the waist down felt like something unearthed at Angkor Vat. I kidded myself that this was the beginning of 'Pratyahara, or restraint of the senses,' but it proved to be my limbs going to sleep so soundly a bombardment wouldn't have disturbed them. This, at least, was better than pain, and for what seemed a very long time I sat on in a state of granite. This might have lasted for hours if the door which I'd neglected to bolt hadn't burst open to admit the colored chamber-maid who, at sight of me, screamed, dropped a set of towels, and fled.

I decided to call it a day and extricate myself. This in my state of atrophy was no easy matter. It was somewhat like untangling the Laocoön, and for a time it looked as if I'd have to stay that way. I finally managed to pry one foot free and found to my relief the other moved of its own accord. Stiff and aching, I limped to the bed and fell upon it exhausted. Perhaps the trouble lay in the fact that I may not have been facing the right way. Maybe instead of east or north I was battling away west-sou'west. Next time I shall have a compass with me.

Business Party

Cornelia Otis Skinner

There comes a moment in the life of the average New York woman when her
husband says to her, 'There's an important business man in town for the
week. He's here with his wife and we'll have to take them out for an evening.'
The fact that this announcement is uttered with the apologetic reluctance of
a surgeon breaking the news that an amputation is necessary merely makes
one brave. 'It's that Hoffman fellow with the big account. Sorry. It has to be
done.' With a baleful look and muttering clichés about 'selling your
birthright' and 'just another form of prostitution' you drag yourself to the
phone and call Mrs Hoffman at the Waldorf. You tell her who you are and
she says 'Oh, yes' in a tone which indicates that Mr Hoffman has been
working on her too. Why, yes, they'd simply love to dine and go to the play.
As for what they'd like to see ... oh, anything. You entertain a malicious
impulse to suggest 'Tobacco Road' but your husband's career hangs in the
balance and you offer the season's musical hit which you have already seen
three times. Mrs Hoffman says that will be lovely and you, contemplating the
probable cost of the tickets, almost retort that it had better be. You manage
to burble how glad you are they are in town and how nice it will be to see
them and other interesting entries for the note-book of the recording angel.
After which you arrange to meet for dinner at a restaurant whose prices are
in keeping with the style to which none of you are accustomed.

The appointed evening arrives and so do you ... fifteen minutes late. En
route in the taxi you and your husband have been discussing pretty heatedly
just whose fault this is and from the look of the waiting Hoffmans they, too,
have been giving each other their particular family brand of hell. The
greeting is consequently over-effusive. Mr Hoffman is large and rich and fifty
and looks like an elevated Elk. Mrs Hoffman is permanently waved both as
to hair and figure and is of an age the French would call 'certain.' Profuse
with apologies, you make your way to the bar where, as an anodyne for the

evening before you, you down twice your usual ration of cocktail. The
Hoffmans do the same. This takes quite some while and you arrive at your
table at the hour that you should be arriving at the theater. The menus are
written in French. As far as Hoffman is concerned, they might be written
shorthand in Chinese. The head waiter, realizing this, suggests grouse and
champagne. Mr Hoffman looks as if steak and onions were more in his line
and Mrs Hoffman gives the impression of being a fruit-salad-with-whipped
cream fancier; but the head waiter has the air of having a sawed-off machine-
gun in his hip pocket and you all submit. Conversation during dinner is
definitely impersonal. After a few polite generalities your husband goes into a
business huddle with Hoffman and you are left to make merry with Mrs. You
talk about the shops she has patronized, about how she likes New York. She
is the kind who refers to your apartment as your 'home.' The champagne
helps.

After dinner you rush to the theater in time to miss most of the first act.
During the intermission the men go out for a smoke and you again find
yourself stranded with Mrs Hoffman. By the end of the intermission you have
exhausted all apparent topics of conversation as well as each other and are
busily reading everything in the program from the credits to the familiar
admonition of John Dohrman, fire commissioner, who claims that 'this
theater can be emptied in 4 minutes.' He's a liar, because after the final
curtain it's a good fifteen before you find yourself on the pavement in the
ranks of taxi-seekers. The theater is far west on a west-bound street and
under ordinary circumstances you'd have walked to the corner to hail an
east-bound vehicle ... as indeed would the Hoffmans; but a ragged youth
who looks as if he were taking down names for the forthcoming revolution
opens the door of a waiting cab and your husband, after remunerating him,
meekly helps you in.

You have reserved a table at a popular night club. Its popularity is
manifest by the blast of stale air mingled with perfumed disinfectant that
greets you at the door, and by the bored look on the faces of a small mob
waiting for the lift. The place is a transformed garage and the elevator, built
to convey automobiles, is doctored up with red plush and some framed Ciro
menus, most of which have to do with children doing things childish. In a
discreet murmur you ask Mrs Hoffman if she'd care to powder her nose.
With alacrity but refinement she admits that she, too, is only human. The
room marked 'Ladies' is crowded with what appear to be anything else but.
Glittering creatures, they scowl at each newcomer, pointedly clutch their

purses to their brazen bosoms, and take up all available space before wash-basin, mirror and what-have-you. A leaky radiator lets forth a blast from Avenus and a noise like a peanut-wagon. Beside it sits an individual as wan as her Harlem complexion will allow, in a torn sweater and the throes of what sounds like bronchial pneumonia. She holds the faucets while you wash your hands with a sliver of soap resembling the top of a piano-key and doles out a towel as stiff, if not as clean, as a man's shirt-front; for which ministration she grudgingly accepts a quarter.

You rejoin the gentlemen who are standing unhappily behind a velvet rope looking into the dance-room like tourists at Sans-Souci. For ten minutes nothing happens. Then a head waiter rushes up like mad, flourishes a bit of card-board, and says 'Yes, sir.' Your husband states his name and the fact that he has made a reservation. The head waiter with an air of suppressed excitement, again says 'Yes, sir' and dashes off, making semaphore signals at another waiter. They both disappear and again nothing happens. After a time the second head waiter appears like an apparition in 'Macbeth,' looks intense, and says 'Yes, sir.' Your husband repeats his application for admission and this waiter, too, repeats a hectic 'Yes, sir.' Then he, too, scoots off, emitting curious smacking noises that in a less conventional person would sound like kisses. Again you are on the outside looking in. Mrs Hoffman gives Mr Hoffman a glance that clearly indicates what she thinks of his business acquaintances and your husband shows symptoms of imminent combustion. A third waiter (the place is run on a Triumvirate policy) races up to say 'Yes, sir.' This time your husband calls him 'captain' which has the same magical effect as calling a police sergeant 'officer.' He acknowledges the commission with a bow and announces, 'We have your table, sir.'

As a matter of fact, three bus-boys have it ... bringing it in from some hidden store-room. Two are bearing the legs and one is rolling along the top. They select a corner of the already over-populated dance-floor and proceed to set it up as if it were a hurdle to the passing couples and cover its kitchen nudity with a frayed felt pad and cloth. Squeezing through a maze of elbows, backs, evening-wraps, you make your way to this festive board, which has a distinct wobble, and distribute yourselves ... the Hoffmans facing the dancers 'so they can see' and you and your husband jutting out onto the floor, imperiled by every passing fanny. After champagne, grouse, and the theater you are all in condition of thirst equal to twenty-four waterless hours on the Sahara and you turn avidly to the waiters, all of whom have vanished into not any too thin air. In fact, the air itself has vanished, giving place to blue smoke. With parched lips you ask your husband to do something, and he claps his hands at a stray bus-boy who, taking this for a sign of inebriation, merely smiles indulgently and goes about his business. He tries hitting a glass with a fork, which confirms the original impression. He even attempts those kissing noises, which are grossly misinterpreted by a drunk at the next table. At length a perspiring menial appears, writes what looks like arabic on a card, and departs. He is followed by another and in turn by a third who both inquire if your order has been taken. It's been taken all right ... right over into Bergen County, and by the time some liquid arrives you are beginning to suffer from hallucinations.

Due to your proximity to the band, conversation is reduced to sign language. In fact, the din is so great you can't hear yourself think ... which is just as well, because what you're thinking isn't fit to be heard. Mr Hoffman signals an invitation to dance. Mr Hoffman's dancing has in it something of the Dalcroze method. His feet follow a four-four time while his left hand pumps an animated three-four, both of which are at utter variance with the music. Moreover, Mr Hoffman is prosperously adipose. You feel as if you were being clutched by a pillow. Eventually a fanfare from the traps proclaims the fact that the entertainment (so-called) is about to begin. This misnomer comprises a dance team with a name like 'Juan and Juanita.' To passionate music they slink forth stealthily into a blue spot-light that shines directly into your eyes and with expressions of considerable anguish, the man clutching the woman by the abdomen, goes into what one supposes is an adagio. This is followed by a tango equally passionate. As an encore they render a lively skipping bit meant to be ball-room comedy. This dubious divertissement is acclaimed by the spectators, most of whom haven't been watching. Some applaud, some thump with their spoons, and the drunk at the next table rouses from deep slumber to emit a shrill whistle of appreciation. The dance team is followed by a young society woman who, fired by success in the Junior League Follies, has turned crooner. As a blues singer she's about as authentic as Betty Boop might be as Isolde, but Mrs Hoffman thinks she's 'gorgeous' and Mr Hoffman in more honest vernacular calls her 'hot stuff'; so you applaud the inanities she croaks into a microphone, reflecting acidly that, given a similar figure, you could sing that well yourself.

Meanwhile the neighbouring drunk decides he wants to fight. Lacking Schmeling or a war, he picks on Mr Hoffman ... his provocation being that Hoffman has grazed him with his elbow. Wheeling about, he calls Mr

Hoffman an epithet acceptable only in the historical plays of Shakespeare, which Mr Hoffman, who is nothing if not legitimate, resents. The lady companion of the drunk, who is only one degree less boiled, comes to the rescue by tweaking the offender's ear and admonishing him to be a good boy. Mr Hoffman, his dignity and lineage restored, asks his wife to dance and you seize the opportunity to suggest that your husband demand the check. He has already done so and, when the Hoffmans return, your proposition that you all go home is met with the only enthusiasm left in anyone.

The taxis on the stand outside all look like contestants in the first Vanderbilt Cup Race. Praying that it will hold together, you enter one and drive home, dropping the Hoffmans on the way.

You fall into bed feeling terrible. Next morning you feel even more so. You call your husband at his office. He also has a head. You inquire if he has landed Hoffman's account. In weak triumph he states that he has ... then adds that after figuring his probable commission and the cost of last night his profit will be about 95 cents ... which, after all, is good for a couple of meals at Liggett's.

Mr Pumpenstempel's Orchestra

Eric Linklater

Mr Pumpenstempel, an eccentric millionaire, has a prized orchestra of many distinguished musicians. However, when he returns after an absence he finds that they have degenerated into a rather motley set. In this extract they are in the process of rehearsing with their conductor, Nikitin.

Mr Pumpenstempel's orchestra assembled for practice on Monday evenings, and as the Tantamount studio was generally busy with talking-sequences on a Monday, that was an easy day for Juan. His salary as a violinist was thirty dollars a month – how much more went into Nikitin's pocket he did not know – but Juan felt that he was well paid with what he got.

Mr Pumpenstempel's house in Pasadena was worthy of a man who owned an orchestra. It stood in large and elaborately gardened grounds where many varieties of palms, cacti, and other exotic plants grew with an air of unbending prosperity. The house was a vast building in the Spanish style of architecture. It had white stucco walls, curly red tiles, Castilian arches, Moorish grilles, balconies with bright awnings over them, casement windows, and heavily-hinged doors. Masses of brilliant flowers clustered against the pale walls that sometimes looked blue in shadow, and the lawns were kept bright green by dozens of water-sprays in which minute rainbows quivered. But within the walls was more splendour than anything without them could show, for the house was built round a courtyard conceived by someone who had distantly recollected the Alhambra. In the centre stood an alabaster fountain supported by marble lions, and all around were marble pillars and arches magnificently embellished with brightly coloured arabesques. The transition from external stucco to internal marble was perhaps a little strange, but Isadore Cohen, who accompanied Juan on his first attendance, saw nothing to weaken his admiration and Juan, who was no snob, agreed that the Pumpenstempel mansion was a remarkable building.

He was equally impressed by the members of the orchestra, some of whom had a pallid stucco look, while a few resembled statues of old stained marble. These were lifeless and dilapidated, like something left to the wind and the rain and the starlings that haunt a ruined house. Others again – the brasses particularly – had a hearty rococo appearance. Several of them wore curly moustaches, their hair was done in quiffs, they had red and bulbous noses, a sprinkling of warts, a squint or two, an eccentricity in their dress, and they talked loudly to their friends. One of the harpists looked like Herod the Tetrarch and the other seemed to be his ingle. Among the wood-winds were striking doubles of Philip IV of Spain, a Murillo peasant boy, and Leech's idea of James Pigge. It seemed to Juan indeed that he could recognize the models or subjects of several famous painters: one or two jaundiced lanternesque specimens who might have been used by El Greco, a desperate prison-hospital-looking fellow like a caricature of Goya's, two or three more out of *The Rake's Progress*, and a brace of second fiddles by Daumier. Half a dozen or so were decent-seeming men who supplemented their salaries from another source with this easy increment; all the rest were dregs, riff-raff, decadents, and failures who were glad to live in idleness on whatever Nikitin cared to give them.

The practice was soon over. The members of the orchestra arranged themselves in an orthodox manner while Nikitin stood at the far end of the concert hall and watched them. Then with a firm swaggering step he walked up, mounted the rostrum, and picking them off with a baton counted his troupe.

'Some of you were late in arriving,' he said gruffly. 'That will not do. You must come punctually to your practices or they are no good. Remember that, if you please. Now you can go.'

As the orchestra stumbled and fumbled, tottered and shuffled and scuffled away, Nikitin called to Juan and Isadore.

'Let us go to a restaurant,' he said, 'where we can sit and watch young ladies dancing.'

In the concert hall he found Nikitin talking to a group of strangers. There were ten or a dozen of them, and one who spoke louder than the others and seemed to have authority was a tall and burly man whose original fierceness of aspects was somewhat loosened and made fat by rich living. He had tremendous bushy eyebrows and choleric blue eyes, and he topped Nikitin by half a head. Elsewhere in the hall were thirty or forty other people, guests apparently of less importance, and half the orchestra were clustered like frightened sheep on the platform. The catastrophe which all this obviously portended was so great that Juan's private troubles were driven out of sight, and he stood for some minutes staring at the invaders with feelings comparable to those of Macbeth when the trees of Dunsinane came striding over the fields.

Nikitin, to Juan's surprise, showed no embarrassment as he faced his employer. When he had arrived and found Mr Pumpenstempel waiting for him he had trembled and felt weak as though his bowels were running out. Half its normal content of blood fled from his brain and he stared with white face at the man whom of all men in the world he least desired to see. But Mr Pumpenstempel was so busy explaining his unexpected arrival that he paid no attention to Nikitin's quandary.

'We are visiting friends in Kingston, Jamaica,' he said, 'and then my wife got an idea she'd like to see the Panama Canal. I didn't feel any special urge myself, but as she said, "What's the use of buying a yacht if you don't want to go places?" – That's the hell of a fine yacht I bought. You must come down and see it. – Well, everyone else was willing (we'd quite a party aboard) so we went through the Canal and turned north to have a look at Costa Rica and Nicaragua. I've got some business interests in Central America. Then Miss Comber here thought she'd like to see Mexico City, so we stopped off at Acapulco for a few days and took a trip there. And after that we didn't quite know what to do till old man Bostock – he's my wife's uncle – said there was mighty good salmon fishing in Vancouver Island, so my wife got a notion she'd like to go fishing and we decided to steam north, though it's a pretty long journey from Acapulco to Vancouver. Then as we were passing here I thought it would be kind of nice to stop in and have a look at the old home. It was just pure luck we arrived on your practice day, but now we are here I guess we might as well have a tune. What d'you say, my dear?'

Mrs Pumpenstempel emphatically wanted some music, and the other members of the yachting party said how fortunate they were to have an opportunity of hearing so famous an orchestra.

'That all right with you, Nikitin?' asked Mr Pumpenstempel. 'You got the boys all ready to do their stuff?'

'As soon as they are here they will be ready,' said Nikitin dully. During Mr Pumpenstempel's explanation he had recovered most of his composure and decided that, failing a miracle, he must philosophically admit defeat. Such luck as he had enjoyed could not last for ever, and he had saved enough money to keep him yet awhile from work. Ach, to be an old man and sit all day in a big chair, he thought. But *che sarà, sarà*. I will have the courage of a fatalist, he decided – and added a swift prayer for miracles.

'That's fine,' said Mr Pumpenstempel. 'Now suppose we have a bottle of champagne while Mrs Pumpenstempel telephones some of the neighbours to come in and listen to the concert? It's kind of selfish to keep good music all to ourselves, I guess, and there's a whole lot of folk round here just crazy about – hell, I can't remember those dago names. All your swell composers, I mean.'

Nikitin felt much better for the champagne, and after three glasses he was almost sure that a miracle of some description would occur. Meanwhile in twos and threes the orchestra arrived and Nikitin did his best to keep Mr Pumpenstempel from looking too closely at them. They appeared more disreputable than ever as, frightened by the unexpected visitors, they gathered in a furtive group at the back of the platform. Their clothes were shabby, they were blear-eyed, unclean, embossed with warts, shambling, lantern-jawed or pot-bellied fellows of whom Nikitin was thoroughly ashamed. – But God was good and he might by a miracle make them play as exquisitely as the original orchestra had done. – Isadore Cohen arrived. He was one of the dozen or so competent performers. Isadore could be relied on to do his best. But following him came the harpist who looked like Herod, his tittering ingle, a piccolo who would better grace a prison hospital, and three second fiddles white as candles, bare-bone wastrels hag-ridden with dope. Ugly though they were they had been profitable to Nikitin, for he paid them scarcely anything and according to the books they drew handsome salaries. – Well, we must take things as they come, he resolved, and meet catastrophe like men. – He swallowed a little more champagne. – But there is no need to despair just yet, he thought, for something unforeseen may still happen.

When Juan appeared Nikitin summoned him in a lordly way and presented him to the Pumpenstempels.

'Mr Juan Motley, the English violinist. Mr Motley is a newcomer to the orchestra and we were very lucky to get him.' –

Lucky to have someone I can show at close quarters, he meant as he saw that Juan's appearance favourably impressed the Pumpenstempels. They had already remarked on the droll look of the other musicians and Nikitin was greatly relieved by their occupation with Juan. They asked in what

orchestra he had previously played, and Juan kept the pot boiling with a
lavish use of famous names. But while he claimed acquaintance with Sir
Henry Wood, Coates, Toscanini, and Stokowski, he was wondering how the
devil Nikitin would manage to get himself out of the mess he was in.

'Well, what are we going to have?' asked Mr Pumpenstempel. The
orchestra was all present and a satisfactory number of guests had arrived.
'What are you going to give us, Nikitin?'

'Anything you like,' said Nikitin, 'it is all one to me.'

'You got the boys in pretty good trim, eh? Well, put a name to it,
somebody. I guess I got a mighty slick orchestra – they're not exactly
handsome but Nikitin tells me they know their onions – so it's up to you to
say what you want.'

The members of the yachting party raked their memories for the name of
some musical composition, and the guests invited from the neighbourhood
replied with a score of different suggestions.

'One at a time,' said Mr Pumpenstempel good-naturedly. 'Now, who
spoke first?'

Miss Comber seized the opportunity. She was a hungry-looking woman
with protruding eyes and teeth that took the air, and she had been watching
Juan with open admiration.

'I think we ought to have Strauss's *Don Juan* in honour of the orchestra's
latest recruit,' she said, and ogled the object of her flattery.

Juan bowed stiffly and Nikitin shrugged his shoulders. 'As you will,' he
said, 'everything is the same to me.'

'Atta boy,' said Mr Pumpenstempel heartily. 'We'll make a start with *Don
Juan* then.'

– And finish with it too, thought Juan as he went with Nikitin to the
library.

'What are you going to do about it?' he asked. 'We can't play this stuff and
you know we can't.'

'Pumpenstempel is ignorant of all music,' said Nikitin impatiently. 'He
won't know if you play it or not.'

'But other people will.'

'Perhaps something will happen. The house may go on fire, or there will be
an earthquake. You never know. Sometimes they have earthquakes here and
one may come tonight.' Nikitin refused to hear any further objections.

The library was in disorder and it took him some time to find *Don Juan*. He
puffed and blew as he searched along the shelves and peered into stacks of

manuscript. At last he found that he wanted, and loading Juan with a great pile told him to distribute it. Unfortunately among the Strauss music were some horn and other brass parts of *The Flying Dutchman* overture which Juan failed to observe.

The orchestra seated itself with an agonized scraping of chairs. Most of them were in a state of terror and their only comfort was that Nikitin must take the blame for whatever happened. Those who knew how to do it tuned their instruments, and those who did not furtively wiped sweaty hands on their trousers and looked with amazement at the music spread out before them.

Juan sat beside Isadore among the first violins and the little Jew, his eyes large with nervous anticipation, muttered, 'This is going to be pretty dull. It's going to be god-awful dull. Just you see!'

Nearby them a man was hiccupping with consternation, and the flautist who resembled Philip IV of Spain could not keep his teeth from chattering. The harpist who looked like Herod sat black-browed and unmoved by any excitement, but his ingle, alarmed by their prominent position on the right front of the stage, hardly restrained his tears. The leader of the orchestra, a sound musician made poor by a large family, watched with unhid dismay as Nikitin slowly walked to the front of the platform, bowed to polite applause, and turned to confront his men.

Nikitin's eyes were closed and soundlessly he gabbled a prayer for an earthquake. A large and immediate earthquake. But no earthquake came. He groaned, and then straightened his shoulders. If God withheld his miracles he must be a fatalist and take discomfiture like a man. He thought of his money in the bank – full forty thousand dollars – and tapping twice upon his desk raised his arms in a commanding gesture.

The wretched men before him brought their instruments into position, and still wondered if they were really meant to play. With dazed incredulous eyes they watched the impending baton . . .

The point descended.

Simultaneously the strings – or as many of them as could play; – began the opening theme of *Don Juan* and the brasses – the moustached, pot-bellied, pimple-studded, rococo fellows – blared forth the violent introductory chord of the *Flying Dutchman* overture.

Nikitin staggered as though he had been shot and almost fell off his perch. With a few squeaks and expiring grunts the noise before him died, while from behind him there came titters of laughter and Mr Pumpenstempel's angry voice demanding 'What the hell's the matter?'

Though badly shaken Nikitin ignored this interruption, and leaning forward with an expression of incredible ferocity hissed to the brasses, 'Keep quiet, you fools!' He was too flustered to guess what had happened and thought the mysterious hubbub another of fate's blows.

Then he started again, and while brasses maintained a puzzled silence – for the music before them clearly demanded action – the others again attacked *Don Juan*. Their music had a dismal sound, for half were out of time and a few among them who could not play at all but imitated the actions of their fellows sometimes allowed an untutored bow to scrape across the gut. Nevertheless a just recognisable statement of the three themes emerged.

But their succeeding contrapuntal interlacement was beyond the power of such a troop, and as Nikitin listened to the scraping he realised that it would not deceive even Mr Pumpenstempel, and an earthquake could do no more than blot out the memory of this infamy. He heard already the laughter and protests from the audience but because he could not screw his courage to the point of facing his employer and admitting his fraud he continued to conduct...

In a moment horns should sound. That meant more noise. Perhaps noise would conceal the awful holes in this tattered pattern of sound. Nikitin glared at the horns and mouthed an injunction to get ready. – These were the fools who had already upset his applecart. The brasses, seeing him grimace in their direction, stunned by their initial error and now utterly bewildered, glanced one to the other and muttered, 'Us? God knows what it's all about. But it's us he means!'

Their red cheeks were pale and their moustaches drooped, but obediently they looked to their music and licked their lips in readiness...

Nikitin's baton threatened them, and once more the opening fanfare of the *Flying Dutchman* overture drowned all other instruments with its brazen din.

Nikitin's hands dropped helplessly to his sides. For an instant he thought God's mercy of an earthquake had come, but then he recognized defeat. He listened to the awful note of the Dutchman's trumpeter, blown in the gale's despite to windward as his ghostly vessel heeled in the tempest, and shuddered at its doom. All other instruments were mute, but the indomitable horns continued.

Mr Pumpenstempel jumped from his seat and roared 'Stop that infernal row!'

The horns quavered into silence, but startled by the apparition of Mr

Pumpenstempel's scarlet face and bright blue eyes Herod's ingle clutched, as if for support, at the strings of his harp and drew from them an irreverent mocking tinkle and twang that further frightened him into tears.

While he wept Mr Pumpenstempel strode passionately on to the platform and shook his fist in Nikitin's face. The audience stopped its laughter to listen.

'You call this bunch of tin-gutted saps an orchestra?' he bellowed. 'You're an imposter, sir! A damned humbug, a quack and a rogue! By God, you'll suffer for insulting me and my guests in this way. By God you will! Think you could pull this on me, eh? I'll jail you all, you and your precious orchestra, for conspiracy, fraud, misappropriation of funds, and common swindling!'

Mr Pumpenstempel stamped with rage while the audience left their seats and crowded excitedly below the platform to urge him on. Nikitin sadly shook his head, and the sight of his red beard wagging was too much for the millionaire, who seized it in one hand and clenching the other fist punched Nikitin on the nose. Nikitin yelled with pain and would have fallen had not Mr Pumpenstempel retained a grip on his beard.

Juan alone among the musicians attempted to interfere as the millionaire prepared to repeat his blow. Quivering with fright the rest sat still, but Juan leapt forward and tried to pull Nikitin away. Mr Pumpenstempel swung out a mighty backhander that sent his new assailant sprawling. He fell among 'cellos. Now since the first blaring entry of the brasses Juan had been in trouble to keep his laughter out of sight, and he had joined the scrimmage for the relief of action as much as to defend Nikitin, and with a kind of hilarious wigs-on-the-green, free-for-all feeling. As he fell in a huddle of chairs, 'cellists, and music his spirits rose still higher and he looked about for a suitable weapon to express them ... and found behind him a double bass. He seized it in both hands and swinging its imponderous bulk aloft ran forward to smash it over Mr Pumpenstempel's head. It thundered like a drum and banged like gunfire as its back burst and swallowed the millionaire's skull in its huge interior. A frantic voice bellowed in its sounding womb and staggering to and fro, Mr Pumpenstempel fell over the edge into the arms of his friends.

Now like a panic-stricken sheep the orchestra broke its ranks and by the stairs at either side poured off the platform, leaving a wreckage of fluttering manuscript and overset music-stands. Nikitin headed the rout, puffing and blowing and working his elbows. The audience made a half-hearted attempt to stop them, but the musicians with their single impulse of escape were irresistible. Juan, momentarily startled by the havoc he had wrought, recovered his wits in time to join the tail of the stampede.

In the darkness outside he saw before him and on either side, black shapes of men who fled blindly from the wrath they had aroused. He could still hear the tumult of anger dominated by Mr Pumpenstempel's awe-inspiring voice. – the galloping shapes drew farther from him. He was sobbing with laughter so that he could not run, and presently he was all alone. He laughed till his belly hurt him, with the laughter that fills a small boy or a savage before the wild spectacle of farce at freedom. The night was dark and there was no one abroad in the tree-lined streets. The sky was round like a fool's bladder. There was no reason in the stars, and the world's gravity was a ninepin balanced upon ice. Touch it and it rolled. Turn solemnity over a fence to see the legs of lunacy, or catch pretence by the heels and watch mockery leap on to the stage like the devil in an old play...

'Lord; what a precarious thing is sobriety!' thought Juan, and strove to think reasonably of all that had happened.

Parlez-vous Franglais?

Richard Boston

Smellier even than the redoubtable Limberger is a cheese made in Lille which goes by the name of *le vieux puant* – the old stinker. So smelly is it that a bye-law in Lille forbids its carriage in taxis. This isn't really so much stranger than the Hansom Cab Act, still on the statute books, which obliges all London taxis to carry a bale of hay. So, at least, a taxi-driver once told me.

A still odder piece of legislation is the new French law forbidding the use of English or Franglais words in advertisements and certain other publications. Needless to say no one has taken a blind bit of notice. On a single page of *Le Figaro* this week I found *un best-seller, le footing, le trotting, un hold-up, correction-tape* and an advertisement for workers in the construction industry who are apparently called *bati-men*.

The French and the English have so much to contribute to one another, but so often it all goes wrong. In the past it did so tragically. Nowadays it usually takes the form of comedy. They take our words and make mincemeat of them. We take their culinary art and, I'm afraid, all too often make mincemeat of that. But the traffic in words and food goes both ways, as can be seen from the case of *sucre brûlé*. Instead of importing this as burnt sugar, which is what the words mean, we mistranslated *brûlé* as barley. The French must have thought we made quite a good job of this barley sugar, because they imported it back again with the literal translation of *sucre d'orge*. So it is that on both sides of the Channel a substance that contains no barley is called barley sugar.

In a small village in central France I once tried to buy some peanuts, the word for which is *cacahuètes*. This is not the easiest word to pronounce and I had to make several shots at it before the shopkeeper's face lightened with comprehension. It took her some minutes to find what she was looking for, but at last she returned bearing a packet of Quaker Oats, or cacker-o-ats as

she called them. It was doubtless a misunderstanding of just this kind that
started the Hundred Years' War.

I'm staying in that same village at the moment, my first real visit to France
for some years. Nothing much seems to have changed. M. Berger, who used
to stand swaying in the middle of the road, pissed out of his mind at ten
o'clock in the morning, has gone to an institution to be dried out. Madame
Baudouin looks just the same, round as an apple and with shining red
cheeks. I told her she looked very well. She agreed that she was, but added,
roaring with laughter, 'Except that I went off my rocker (*J'ai perdu les
pédales*).' She had been over-worried about her pension, but is now as
cheerful as ever again.

Otherwise everything is much the same. In the Bar-Tabac there is now a
pool table and Loustique has died. Loustique, whose breath was almost as
stong as *le vieux puant*, was a spaniel-like gundog who expressed pleasure not
in the normal canine manner of tail-wagging, but more confusingly by baring
his teeth and growling.

The Bar-café of a French village is about as different from an English pub
as is possible for establishments that serve not dissimilar functions. Whereas
the pub is a cosy refuge from the outside world, the French café is not only
open to the street but almost an extension of it. Or perhaps the street is an
extension of the café, for at the first sign of warm weather chairs and tables
begin to spill out on to the pavement.

The pub is made of natural materials. Benches, tables, dado and bar are
made of wood, and often there are also curtains and carpets to soften the
slow, quiet murmur of talk. The French café is made of glass and chromium
and hard glittering man-made substances that do not soothe the eye but
excite it, and that make every sound bounce round the room like the balls
round the billiard-table.

Steel chair-legs scraping on a marble floor – that is the distinctive sound of
the French café. That and the incessant noise of talking. God, how the
French talk. Yatter, yatter, yatter, all with a yellow cigarette drooping from
the corner of the mouth. Consuming a pint of beer is a slow reflective task
that gives pause to even the most talkative. A glass of wine or calvados can be
sunk with a swift movement in mid-sentence.

Not only do they talk all the time, and at top volume, but they also talk all
at once. What they talk about nobody knows, and is probably unimportant.
It is talk for talk's sake. It also provides an opportunity for arm waving. Arm-
waving comes high in a Frenchman's list of priorities. Eating and drinking

come first, but they are closely followed by arm-waving and talking. Next comes hand-shaking.

The French appetite for hand-shaking is insatiable. The amount of hand-shaking you get through in an hour in France could be eked out for five years in England. You go into the bar and shake hands with everyone. Every time someone else comes in, including total strangers, there is another full round of hand-shaking, often accompanied by semi-playful punches. Hardly have you recovered from this when a youth in a black jacket decides it's time to move on to another bar. He slaps a few coins on the counter and it's hand-shaking time again.

Certain occupations involve getting your hands dirty. This does not mean any diminution in hand-shaking. The hands of M. Doucet, the *garagiste*, are usually covered in engine oil. He greets you with a proffered wrist to shake. M. Davaigne, who has a wine-bottling business, offers his elbow.

Beyond talking and hand-shaking, two other passions rule a Frenchman's life. One is for pollarding trees, and the other is for building water-towers. Wherever you go in France evidence of both will be found. The water-towers cannot be explained by the flatness of the landscape, since you often see them on top of a hill. East Anglia, where you never see a water-tower, is much flatter than the Loire valley, where you are rarely out of sight of one. The only explanation I can think of is that the French like their shape which, like that of the pollard trees, is not only phallic but also reminiscent of certain kinds of mushroom.

The same is true of the conical towers they love to put on buildings, which have a distinct resemblance to the mushroom called *coprinus comatus*, the Shaggy Ink-cap. These shapes have a strong appeal to the eroto-gastric French. This theory will be expounded in more detail in my forthcoming volume on the subject to be entitled *Towards a fungo-sexual explanation of certain man-made features of the French landscape*.

(Subsequent correspondence proved me completely wrong about East Anglia. Apparently the area is crowded with water-towers.)

The She-Wolf

Saki (H. H. Munro)

Leonard Bilsiter was one of those people who have failed to find this world attractive or interesting, and who have sought compensation in an 'unseen world' of their own experience or imagination – or invention. Children do that sort of thing successfully, but children are content to convince themselves, and do not vulgarize their beliefs by trying to convince other people. Leonard Bilsiter's beliefs were for 'the few,' that is to say, any one who would listen to him.

His dabblings in the unseen might not have carried him beyond the customary platitudes of the drawing-room visionary if accident had not reinforced his stock-in-trade of mystical lore. In company with a friend, who was interested in a Ural mining concern, he had made a trip across Eastern Europe at a moment when the great Russian railway strike was developing from a threat to a reality; its outbreak caught him on the return journey, somewhere on the further side of Perm, and it was while waiting for a couple of days at a wayside station in a state of suspended locomotion that he made the acquaintance of a dealer in harness and metalware, who profitably whiled away the tedium of the long halt by initiating his English travelling companion in a fragmentary system of folk-lore that he had picked up from Trans-Baikal traders and natives. Leonard returned to his home circle garrulous about his Russian strike experiences, but oppressively reticent about certain dark mysteries, which he alluded to under the resounding title of Siberian Magic. The reticence wore off in a week or two under the influence of an entire lack of general curiosity, and Leonard began to make more detailed allusions to the enormous powers which this new esoteric force, to use his own description of it, conferred on the initiated few who knew how to wield it. His aunt, Cecilia Hoops, who loved sensation perhaps rather better than she loved the truth, gave him as clamorous an advertisement as any one could wish for by retailing an account of how he had turned a vegetable marrow into a wood-pigeon before her very eyes. As a manifestation of the possession of supernatural powers, the story was discounted in some quarters by the respect accorded to Mrs Hoops' powers of imagination.

However divided opinion might be on the question of Leonard's status as a wonder-worker or a charlatan, he certainly arrived at Mary Hampton's house-party with a reputation for pre-eminence in one or other of those professions, and he was not disposed to shun such publicity as might fall to his share. Esoteric forces and unusual powers figured largely in whatever conversation he or his aunt had a share in, and his own performances, past and potential, were the subject of mysterious hints and dark avowals.

'I wish you would turn me into a wolf, Mr Bilsiter,' said his hostess at luncheon the day after his arrival.

'My dear Mary,' said Colonel Hampton, 'I never knew you had a craving in that direction.'

'A she-wolf, of course,' continued Mrs Hampton; 'it would be too confusing to change one's sex as well as one's species at a moment's notice.'

'I don't think one should jest on these subjects,' said Leonard.

'I'm not jesting. I'm quite serious, I assure you. Only don't do it today; we have only eight available bridge players, and it would break up one of our tables. Tomorrow we shall be a larger party. Tomorrow night, after dinner—'

'In our present imperfect understanding of these hidden forces I think one should approach them with humbleness rather than mockery,' observed Leonard, with such severity that the subject was forthwith dropped.

Clovis Sangrail had sat unusually silent during the discussion on the possibilities of Siberian magic; after lunch he sidetracked Lord Pabham into the comparative seclusion of the billiard-room and delivered himself of a searching question.

'Have you such a thing as a she-wolf in your collection of wild animals? A she-wolf of moderately good temper?'

Lord Pabham considered. 'There is Louisa,' he said, 'a rather fine specimen of the timber-wolf. I got her two years ago in exchange for some Arctic foxes. Most of my animals get to be fairly tame before they've been with me very long; I think I can say Louisa has an angelic temper, as she-wolves go. Why do you ask?'

'I was wondering whether you would lend her to me for tomorrow night,' said Clovis, with a careless solicitude of one who borrows a collar stud or a tennis raquet.

'Tomorrow night?'

'Yes, wolves are nocturnal animals, so the late hours won't hurt her,' said Clovis, with the air of one who has taken everything into consideration; 'one of your men could bring her over from Pabham Park after dusk, and with a little help he ought to be able to smuggle her into the conservatory at the same moment that Mary Hampton makes an unobtrusive exit.'

Lord Pabham stared at Clovis for a moment in pardonable bewilderment; then his face broke into a wrinkled network of laughter.

'Oh, that's your game, is it? You are going to do a little Siberian magic on your own account. And is Mrs Hampton willing to be a fellow-conspirator?'

'Mary is pledged to see me through with it, if you will guarantee Louisa's temper.'

'I'll answer for Louisa,' said Lord Pabham.

By the following day the house-party had swollen to larger proportions, and Bilsiter's instinct for self-advertisement expanded duly under the stimulant of an increased audience. At dinner that evening he held forth at length on the subject of unseen forces and untested powers, and his flow of impressive eloquence continued unabated while coffee was being served in the drawing-room preparatory to a general migration to the card-room. His aunt ensured a respectful hearing for his utterances, but her sensation-loving soul hankered after something more dramatic than mere vocal demonstration.

'Won't you do something to *convince* them of your powers, Leonard?' she pleaded. 'Change something into another shape. He can, you know, if he only chooses to,' she informed the company.

'Oh, do,' said Mavis Pellington earnestly, and her request was echoed by nearly every one present. Even those who were not open to conviction were perfectly willing to be entertained by an exhibition of amateur conjuring.

Leonard felt that something tangible was expected of him.

'Has any one present,' he asked, 'got a three-penny bit or some small object of no particular value—?'

'You're surely not going to make coins disappear, or something primitive of that sort?' said Clovis contemptuously.

'I think it is very unkind of you not to carry out my suggestion of turning me into a wolf,' said Mary Hampton, as she crossed over to the conservatory to give her macaws their usual tribute from the dessert dishes.

'I have already warned you of the danger of treating these powers in a mocking spirit,' said Leonard solemnly.

'I don't believe you can do it,' laughed Mary provocatively from the conservatory; 'I dare you to do it if you can. I defy you to turn me into a wolf.'

As she said this she was lost to view behind a clump of azaleas.

'Mrs Hampton—' began Leonard with increased solemnity, but he got no further. A breath of chill air seemed to rush across the room, and at the same time the macaws broke forth into ear-splitting screams.

'What on earth is the matter with those confounded birds, Mary?' exclaimed Colonel Hampton; at the same moment an even more piercing scream from Mavis Pellington stampeded the entire company from their seats. In various attitudes of helpless horror or instinctive defence they confronted the evil-looking grey beast that was peering at them from amid a setting of fern and azalea.

Mrs Hoops was the first to recover from the general chaos of fright and bewilderment.

'Leonard!' she screamed shrilly to her nephew, 'turn it back into Mrs Hampton at once! It may fly at us at any moment. Turn it back!'

'I – I don't know how to,' faltered Leonard, who looked more scared and horrified than any one.

'What!' shouted Colonel Hampton, 'you've taken the abominable liberty of turning my wife into a wolf, and now you stand there calmly and say you can't turn her back again!'

To do strict justice to Leonard, calmness was not a distinguishing feature of his attitude at the moment.

'I assure you I didn't turn Mrs Hampton into a wolf; nothing was further from my intentions,' he protested.

'Then where is she, and how came that animal into the conservatory?' demanded the Colonel.

'Of course we must accept your assurance that you didn't turn Mrs Hampton into a wolf,' said Clovis politely, 'but you will agree that appearances are against you.'

'Are we to have all these recriminations with that beast standing there ready to tear us to pieces?' wailed Mavis indignantly.

'Lord Pabham, you know a great deal about wild beasts—' suggested Colonel Hampton.

'The wild beasts that I have been accustomed to,' said Lord Pabham, 'have come with proper credentials from well-known dealers, or have been bred in my own menagerie. I've never before been confronted with an animal that walks unconcernedly out of an azalea bush, leaving a charming and popular hostess unaccounted for. As far as one can judge from *outward* characteristics,' he continued, 'it has the appearance of a well-grown female of the North American timber-wolf, a variety of the common species *canis lupus*.'

'Oh, never mind its Latin name,' screamed Mavis, as the beast came a step or two further into the room; 'can't you entice it away with food, and shut it up where it can't do any harm?'

'If it is really Mrs Hampton, who has just had a very good dinner, I don't suppose food will appeal to it very strongly,' said Clovis.

'Leonard,' beseeched Mrs Hoops tearfully, 'even if this is none of your doing, can't you use your great powers to turn this dreadful beast into something harmless before it bites us all – a rabbit or something?'

'I don't suppose Colonel Hampton would care to have his wife turned into a succession of fancy animals as though we were playing a round game with her,' interposed Clovis.

'I absolutely forbid it,' thundered the Colonel.

'Most wolves that I've had anything to do with have been inordinately fond of sugar,' said Lord Pabham; 'if you like I'll try the effect on this one.'

He took a piece of sugar from the saucer of his coffee cup and flung it to the expectant Louisa, who snapped it in mid-air. There was a sigh of relief from the company; a wolf that ate sugar when it might at the least have been employed in tearing macaws to pieces had already shed some of its terrors. The sigh deepened to a gasp of thanksgiving when Lord Pabham decoyed the animal out of the room by a pretended largesse of further sugar. There was an instant rush to the vacated conservatory. There was no trace of Mrs Hampton except the plate containing the macaw's supper.

'The door is locked on the inside!' exclaimed Clovis, who had deftly turned the key as he affected to test it.

Every one turned towards Bilsiter.

'If you haven't turned my wife into a wolf,' said Colonel Hampton, 'will you kindly explain where she has disappeared to, since she obviously could not have gone through a locked door? I will not press you for an explanation of how a North American timber-wolf suddenly appeared in the conservatory, but I think I have some right to inquire what has become of Mrs Hampton.'

Bilsiter's reiterated disclaimer was met with a general murmur of impatient disbelief.

'I refuse to stay another hour under this roof,' declared Mavis Pellington.

'If our hostess has really vanished out of human form,' said Mrs Hoops, 'none of the ladies of the party can very well remain. I absolutely decline to be chaperoned by a wolf!'

'It's a she-wolf,' said Clovis soothingly.

The correct etiquette to be observed under the unusual circumstances received no further elucidation. The sudden entry of Mary Hampton deprived the discussion of its immediate interest.

'Some one has mesmerized me,' she exclaimed crossly; 'I found myself in the game larder, of all places, being fed with sugar by Lord Pabham. I hate being mesmerized, and the doctor has forbidden me to touch sugar.'

The situation was explained to her, as far as it permitted anything that could be called explanation.

'Then you *really* did turn me into a wolf, Mr Bilsiter?' she exclaimed excitedly.

But Leonard had burned the boat in which he might now have embarked on a sea of glory. He could only shake his head feebly.

'It was I who took that liberty,' said Clovis; 'you see, I happen to have lived for a couple of years in North-eastern Russia, and I have more than a tourist's acquaintance with the magic craft of that region. One does not care to speak about these strange powers, but once in a way, when one hears a lot of nonsense being talked about them, one is tempted to show what Siberian magic can accomplish in the hands of some one who really understands it. I yielded to that temptation. May I have some brandy? the effort has left me rather faint.'

If Leonard Bilsiter could at that moment have transformed Clovis into a cockroach and then have stepped on him he would gladly have performed both operations.

The Mouse

Saki (H. H. Munro)

Theodoric Voler had been brought up, from infancy to the confines of middle age, by a fond mother whose chief solicitude had been to keep him screened from what she called the coarser realities of life. When she died she left Theodoric alone in a world that was as real as ever, and a good deal coarser than he considered it had any need to be. To a man of his temperament and upbringing even a simple railway journey was crammed with petty annoyances and minor discords, and as he settled himself down in a second-class compartment one September morning he was conscious of ruffled feelings and general mental discomposure. He had been staying at a country vicarage, the inmates of which had been certainly neither brutal nor bacchanalian, but their supervision of the domestic establishment had been of that lax order which invites disaster. The pony carriage that was to take him to the station had never been properly ordered, and when the moment for his departure drew near, the handy-man who should have produced the required article was nowhere to be found. In this emergency Theodoric, to his mute but very intense disgust, found himself obliged to collaborate with the vicar's daughter in the task of harnessing the pony, which necessitated groping about in an ill-lighted outhouse called a stable, and smelling very like one – except in patches where it smelt of mice. Without being actually afraid of mice, Theodoric classed them among the coarser incidents of life, and considered that Providence, with a little exercise of moral courage, might long ago have recognized that they were not indispensable, and have withdrawn them from circulation. As the train glided out of the station Theodoric's nervous imagination accused himself of exhaling a weak odour of stableyard, and possibly of displaying a mouldy straw or two on his usually well-brushed garments. Fortunately the only other occupant of the compartment, a lady of about the same age as himself, seemed inclined for slumber rather than scrutiny; the train was not due to stop till the terminus was reached, in about an hour's time, and the carriage was of the old-fashioned sort, that held no communication with a corridor, therefore no further travelling companions were likely to intrude on Theodoric's semi-privacy. And yet the train had scarcely attained its normal speed before he became reluctantly but vividly aware that he was not alone with the slumbering lady; he was not even alone in his own clothes. A warm, creeping movement over his flesh betrayed the unwelcome and highly resented presence, unseen but poignant, of a strayed mouse, that had evidently dashed into its present retreat during the episode of the pony harnessing. Furtive stamps and shakes and wildly directed pinches failed to dislodge the intruder, whose motto, indeed, seemed to be Excelsior; and the lawful occupant of the clothes lay back against the cushions and endeavoured rapidly to evolve some means for putting an end to the dual ownership. It was unthinkable that he should continue for the space of a whole hour in the horrible position of a Rowton House for vagrant mice (already his imagination had at least doubled the numbers of the alien invasion). On the other hand, nothing less drastic than partial disrobing would ease him of his tormentor, and to undress in the presence of a lady, even for so laudable a purpose, was an idea that made his eartips tingle in a blush of abject shame. He had never been able to bring himself even to the mild exposure of open-work socks in the presence of the fair sex. And yet – the lady in this case was to all appearances soundly and securely asleep; the mouse, on the other hand, seemed to be trying to crowd a Wanderjahr into a few strenuous minutes. If there is any truth in the theory of transmigration, this particular mouse must certainly have been in a former state a member of the Alpine Club. Sometimes in its eagerness it lost its footing and slipped for half an inch or so; and then, in fright, or more probably temper, it bit. Theodoric was goaded into the most audacious undertaking of his life. Crimsoning to the hue of a beetroot and keeping an agonized watch on his slumbering fellow-traveller, he swiftly and noiselessly secured the ends of his railway-rug to the racks on either side of the carriage, so that a substantial curtain hung athwart the compartment. In the narrow dressing-room that he had thus improvised he proceeded with violent haste to extricate himself partially and the mouse entirely from the surrounding casings of tweed and half-wool. As the unravelled mouse gave a wild leap to the floor, the rug, slipping its fastening at either end, also came down with a heart-curdling flop, and almost simultaneously the awakened sleeper opened her eyes. With a movement almost quicker than the mouse's, Theodoric pounced on the rug, and hauled its ample folds chin-high over his dismantled person as he collapsed into the further corner of the carriage. The blood raced and beat in the veins of his neck and forehead, while he waited dumbly for the communication-cord to be pulled. The lady, however, contented herself with a silent stare at her strangely muffled companion. How much had she seen, Theodoric queried to himself, and in any case what on earth must she think of his present posture?

'I think I have caught a chill,' he ventured desperately.

'Really, I'm sorry,' she replied. 'I was just going to ask you if you would open this window.'

'I fancy it's malaria,' he added, his teeth chattering slightly, as much from fright as from a desire to support his theory.

'I've got some brandy in my hold-all, if you'll kindly reach it down for me,' said his companion.

'Not for worlds – I mean, I never take anything for it,' he assured her earnestly.

'I suppose you caught it in the Tropics?'

Theodoric, whose acquaintance with the Tropics was limited to an annual present of a chest of tea from an uncle in Ceylon, felt that even the malaria was slipping from him. Would it be possible, he wondered, to disclose the real state of affairs to her in small instalments?

'Are you afraid of mice?' he ventured, growing, if possible, more scarlet in the face.

'Not unless they came in quantities, like those that ate up Bishop Hatto. Why do you ask?'

'I had one crawling inside my clothes just now,' said Theodoric in a voice that hardly seemed his own. 'It was a most awkward situation.'

'It must have been, if you wear your clothes at all tight,' she observed; 'but mice have strange ideas of comfort.'

'I had to get rid of it while you were asleep,' he continued; then, with a gulp, he added, 'it was getting rid of it that brought me to – to this.'

'Surely leaving off one small mouse wouldn't bring on a chill,' she exclaimed, with a levity that Theodoric accounted abominable.

Evidently she had detected something of his predicament, and was enjoying his confusion. All the blood in his body seemed to have mobilized in one concentrated blush, and an agony of abasement, worse than a myriad mice, crept up and down over his soul. And then, as reflection began to assert itself, sheer terror took the place of humiliation. With every minute that passed the train was rushing nearer to the crowded and bustling terminus where dozens of prying eyes would be exchanged for the one paralysing pair that watched him from the further corner of the carriage. There was one slender despairing chance, which the next few minutes must decide. His fellow-traveller might relapse into a blessed slumber. But as the minutes throbbed by, that chance ebbed away. The furtive glance which Theodoric stole at her from time to time disclosed only an unwinking wakefulness.

'I think we must be getting near now,' she presently observed.

Theodoric had already noted with growing terror the recurring stacks of small, ugly dwellings that heralded the journey's end. The words acted as a signal. Like a hunted beast breaking cover and dashing madly towards some other haven of momentary safety he threw aside his rug, and struggled frantically into his dishevelled garments. He was conscious of dull suburban stations racing past the window, of a choking, hammering sensation in his throat and heart, and an icy silence in that corner towards which he dared not look. Then as he sank back in his seat, clothed and almost delirious, the train slowed down to a final crawl, and the woman spoke.

'Would you be so kind,' she asked, 'as to get me a porter to put me into a cab? It's a shame to trouble you when you're feeling unwell, but being blind makes one so helpless at a railway station.'

The Great French Duel

Mark Twain

Much as the modern French duel is ridiculed by certain smart people, it is in reality one of the most dangerous institutions of our day. Since it is always fought in the open air the combatants are nearly sure to catch cold. M. Paul de Cassagnac, the most inveterate of the French duellists, has suffered so often in this way that he is at last a confirmed invalid; and the best physician in Paris has expressed the opinion that if he goes on duelling for fifteen or twenty years more – unless he forms the habit of fighting in a comfortable room where damps and draughts cannot intrude – he will eventually endanger his life. This ought to moderate the talk of those people who are so stubborn in maintaining that the French duel is the most health-giving of recreations because of the open-air exercise it affords. And it ought also to moderate that foolish talk about French duellists and socialist-hated monarchs being the only people who are immortal.

But it is time to get to my subject. As soon as I heard of the late fiery outbreak between M. Gambetta and M. Fourtou in the French Assembly, I knew that trouble must follow. I knew it because a long personal friendship with M. Gambetta had revealed to me the desperate and implacable nature of the man. Vast as are his physical proportions, I knew that the thirst for revenge would penetrate to the remotest frontiers of his person.

I did not wait for him to call on me, but went at once to him. As I expected, I found the brave fellow steeped in a profound French calm. I say French calm, because French calmness and English calmness have points of difference. He was moving swiftly back and forth among the debris of his furniture, now and then staving chance fragments of it across the room with his foot; grinding a constant grist of curses through his set teeth; and halting every little while to deposit another handful of his hair on the pile which he had been building of it on the table.

He threw his arms around my neck, bent me over his stomach to his breast, kissed me on both cheeks, hugged me four or five times and then placed me in his own arm-chair. As soon as I got well again, we began business at once.

I said I supposed he would wish me to act as his second, and he said, 'Of course.' I said I must be allowed to act under a French name, so that I might be shielded from obloquy in my country, in case of fatal results. He winced here, probably at the suggestion that duelling was not regarded with respect in America. However, he agreed to my requirement. This accounts for the fact that in all newspaper reports M. Gambetta's second was apparently a Frenchman.

First, we drew up my principal's will. I insisted upon this, and stuck to my point. I said I never heard of a man in his right mind going out to fight a duel without first making his will. He said he had never heard of a man in his right mind doing anything of the kind. When he had finished his will, he wished to proceed to a choice of his 'last words'. He wanted to know how the following words, as a dying exclamation, struck me:

'I die for my God, for my country, for freedom of speech, for progress, and the universal brotherhood of man!'

I objected that this would require too lingering a death; it was a good speech for a consumptive, but not suited to the exigencies of the field of honour. We wrangled over a good many ante-mortem outbursts, but I finally got him to cut his obituary down to this, which he copied into his memorandum book purposing to get it by heart:

'I DIE THAT FRANCE MAY LIVE.'

I said that this remark seemed to lack relevancy; but he said relevancy was a matter of no consequence in last words – what you wanted was thrill.

The next thing in order was the choice of weapons. My principal said he was not feeling well, and would leave that and the other details of the proposed meeting to me. Therefore I wrote the following note and carried it to M. Fourtou's friend:

'Sir, – M. Gambetta accepts M. Fourtou's challenge, and authorises me to propose Plessis-Piquet as the place of meeting; tomorrow morning at daybreak as the time; and axes as the weapons. I am, sir, with great respect, MARK TWAIN.'

M. Fourtou's friend read this note, and shuddered.

Then he turned to me and said, with a suggestion of severity in his tone:

'Have you considered, sir, what would be the inevitable result of such a meeting as this?'

'Well, for instance, what *would* it be?'

'Bloodshed!'

'That's about the size of it,' I said. 'Now, if it is a fair question, what was your side proposing to shed?'

I had him there. He saw he had made a blunder, so he hastened to explain it away. He said he had spoken jestingly. Then he added that he and his principal would enjoy axes, and indeed prefer them, but such weapons were barred by the French code, and so I must change my proposal.

I walked the floor, turning the thing over in my mind, and finally it occurred to me that Gatling guns at fifteen paces would be a likely way to get a verdict on the field of honour. So I framed this idea into a proposition.

But it was not accepted. The code was in the way again. I proposed rifles; then double-barrelled shot-guns; then Colt's navy revolvers. These being all rejected, I reflected awhile and sarcastically suggested brick-bats at three-quarters of a mile. I always hate to fool away a humorous thing on a person who has no perception of humour; and it filled me with bitterness when this man went soberly away to submit this last proposition to his principal.

He came back presently and said his principal was charmed with the idea of brick-bats at three-quarters of a mile, but must decline on account of the danger to disinterested parties passing between. Then I said:

'Well, I am at the end of my string now. Perhaps *you* would be good enough to suggest a weapon. Perhaps you have even had one in your mind all the time?'

His countenance brightened, and he said with alacrity:

'Oh, without doubt, monsieur!'

So he fell to hunting in his pockets – pocket after pocket, and he had plenty of them – muttering all the while, 'Now, what could I have done with them?'

At last he was successful. He fished out of his vest pocket a couple of little things which I carried to the light and ascertained to be pistols. They were single-barrelled and silver-mounted, and very dainty and pretty. I was not able to speak for emotion. I silently hung one of them on my watchchain, and returned the other. My companion in crime now unrolled a postage stamp containing several cartridges, and gave me one of them. I asked if he meant to signify by this that our men were to be allowed but one shot apiece. He replied that the French code permitted no more. I then begged him to go on and suggest a distance, for my mind was growing weak and confused under the strain which had been put upon it. He named sixty-five yards. I nearly lost my patience. I said:

'Sixty-five yards, with these instruments? Squirt-guns would be deadlier at fifty. Consider, my friend, you and I are banded together to destroy life, not make it eternal.'

But with all my persuasions, all my arguments, I was only able to get him to reduce the distance to thirty-five yards; and even this concession he made with reluctance, and said with a sigh:

'I wash my hands of this slaughter; on your head be it.'

There was nothing for me but to go home to my old lion heart and tell my humiliating story. When I entered, M. Gambetta was laying his last lock of hair upon the altar. He sprang towards me, exclaiming:

'You have made the fatal arrangements – I see it in your eyes!'

'I have.'

His face paled a trifle, and he leaned upon the table for support. He breathed thick and heavily for a moment or two, so tumultuous were his feelings; then he hoarsely whispered:

'The weapon, the weapon! Quick! What is the weapon?'

'This!' and I displayed that silver-mounted thing. He cast but one glance at it, then swooned ponderously to the floor.

When he came to, he said mournfully:

'The unnatural calm to which I have subjected myself has told upon my nerves. But away with weakness! I will confront my fate like a man and a Frenchman.'

He rose to his feet, and assumed an attitude which for sublimity has never been approached by man, and has seldom been surpassed by statues. Then he said, in his deep bass tones:

'Behold, I am calm, I am ready, reveal to me the distance.'

'Thirty-five yards. . . .'

I could not lift him up, of course; but I rolled him over, and poured water down his back. He presently came to, and said:

'Thirty-five yards – without a rest? But why ask? Since murder was that man's intention, why should he palter with small details? But mark you one thing: in my fall the world shall see how the chivalry of France meets death.'

At half-past nine in the morning the procession approached the field of Plesis-Piquet in the following order: first came our carriage – nobody in it but M. Gambetta and myself; then a carriage containing M. Fourtou and his second; then a carriage containing two poet-orators who did not believe in God, and these had MS funeral orations projecting from their breast-pockets;

then a carriage containing the head surgeons and their cases of instruments; then eight private carriages containing consulting surgeons; then a hack containing a coroner; then two hearses; then a carriage containing the head undertakers; then a train of assistants and mutes on foot; and after these came plodding through the fog a long procession of camp followers, police, and citizens generally. It was a noble turn-out, and would have made a fine display if we had had thinner weather.

There was no conversation. I spoke several times to my principal, but I judge he was not aware of it, for he always referred to his notebook and muttered absently, 'I die that France may live.'

Arrived on the field, my fellow-second and I paced off the thirty-five yards, and then drew lots for choice of position. This latter was but an ornamental ceremony, for all choices were alike in such weather. These preliminaries being ended, I went to my principal and asked him if he was ready. He spread himself out to his full width, and said in a stern voice, 'Ready! Let the batteries be charged.'

The loading was done in the presence of duly constituted witnesses. We considered it best to perform this delicate service with the assistance of a lantern, on account of the state of the weather. We now placed our men.

At this point the police noticed that the public had massed themselves together on the right and left of the field; they therefore begged a delay, while they should put these poor people in a place of safety. The request was granted.

The police having ordered the two multitudes to take positions behind the duellists, we were once more ready. The weather growing still more opaque, it was agreed between myself and the other second that before giving the fatal signal we should each deliver a loud whoop to enable the combatants to ascertain each other's whereabouts.

I now returned to my principal, and was distressed to observe that he had lost a good deal of his spirit. I tried my best to hearten him. I said, 'Indeed, Sir, things are not as bad as they seem. Considering the character of the weapons, the limited number of shots allowed, the generous distance, the impenetrable solidity of the fog, and the added fact that one of the combatants is one-eyed and the other cross-eyed and near-sighted, it seems to me that this conflict need not necessarily be fatal. There are chances that both of you may survive. Therefore cheer up; do not be downhearted.'

This speech had so good an effect that my principal immediately stretched forth his hand and said, 'I am myself again; give me the weapon.'

I laid it, all lonely and forlorn, in the centre of the vast solitude of his palm. He gazed at it and shuddered. And still mournfully contemplating it he murmured, in a broken voice:

'Alas! it is not death I dread, but mutilation.'

I heartened him once more, and with such success that he presently said, 'Let the tragedy begin. Stand at my back; do not desert me in this solemn hour, my friend.'

I gave him my promise. I now assisted him to point his pistol towards the spot where I judged his adversary to be standing, and cautioned him to listen well and further guide himself by my fellow-second's whoop. Then I propped myself against M. Gambetta's back, and raised a rousing 'Whoop-ee!' This was answered from out the far distances of the fog, and I immediately shouted:

'One – two – three – *fire!*'

Two little sounds like *spit! spit!* broke upon my ear, and in the same instant I was crushed to the earth under a mountain of flesh. Bruised as I was, I was still able to catch a faint accent from above, to this effect:

'I die for ... for ... perdition take it, what *is* it I die for? ... oh, yes – FRANCE! I die that France may live!'

The surgeons swarmed around with their probes in their hands, and applied their microscopes to the whole area of M. Gambetta's person, with the happy result of finding nothing in the nature of a wound. Then a scene ensued which was in every way gratifying and inspiriting.

The two gladiators fell upon each other's necks, with floods of proud and happy tears; the other second embraced me; the surgeons, the orators, the undertakers, the police, everybody embraced, everybody congratulated, everybody cried, and the whole atmosphere was filled with praise and with joy unspeakable.

It seemed to me then that I would rather be a hero of a French duel than a crowned and sceptred monarch.

When the commotion had somewhat subsided, the body of surgeons held a consultation, and after a good deal of debate decided that with proper care and nursing there was reason to believe that I should survive my injuries. My internal hurts were deemed the most serious, since it was apparent that a broken rib had penetrated my left lung, and that many of my organs had been pressed out so far to one side or the other of where they belonged, that it was doubtful if they would ever learn to perform their functions in such remote and unaccustomed localities. They then set my arm in two places, pulled my right hip into its socket again, and re-elevated my nose. I was an object of great interest, and even admiration; and many sincere and warm-hearted persons had themselves introduced to me, and said they were proud to know the only man who had been hurt in a French duel in forty years.

I was placed in an ambulance at the very head of the procession; and thus with gratifying éclat I was marched into Paris, the most conspicuous figure in that great spectacle, and deposited at the hospital.

The Cross of the Legion of Honour has been conferred upon me. However, few escape that distinction.

Such is the true version of the most memorable private conflict of the age.

I have no complaints to make against anyone. I acted for myself, and I can stand the consequences. Without boasting, I think I can say I am not afraid to stand before a modern French duellist, but as long as I keep in my right mind I will never consent to stand behind one again.

Child-Holding

Robert Benchley

Fathers, god-fathers and uncles will be glad to learn that baby specialists have now decided that the child is given beneficial exercise by being shifted about from one position to another in the holder's arms. This will eliminate a great many dirty looks and much kidding at the male relative's expense.

No male relative, in his right mind, ever takes a baby to hold of his own free will. The very thought of dropping it, a thought which is always present, is enough to reduce all his vital organs to gelatin. Some female always suggests it. 'Let Joe hold him for a minute. Hold him, Joe!'

So, Joe, sweating profusely, picks the infant up and becomes a figure of fun. 'Look at how Joe's holding him, Bessie. Like he was a golf bag!' 'Poor kid – put him down, Joe!' 'Look out, Joe – you'll strangle him!' Lynching is in the air.

But now Joe can come back with the excuse that he is giving the baby exercise. 'You women hold him in that one position all the time, and his body doesn't develop symmetrically. Ask anyone who knows!'

For male relatives who find it necessary for one reason or another to hold a baby, the following positions are suggested as being most beneficial to the child's development and most conducive of apprehension on the mother's part.

If the child has to be lifted from its crib by the father or uncle, the old-fashioned way of reaching down and grabbing it under the arms should be discarded. The male relative should get into the crib with the child, and lie on his back (his own back), taking the child on his chest and rising to a sitting posture. Then call for someone else to come and lift both father and child from the crib at once.

In taking the baby from the arms of someone else, as at the christening or general family gathering, grasp one of the child's ankles firmly in the right hand and tell the other person to let go. The child will then swing, head down, from the other person and can be twirled in a semi-circle, in the manner of an adagio dancer, until the arc is completed, and the child lands across the uncle's shoulder, the latter, if possible, still holding firmly on to the ankle. This will develop the child's leg, and give it poise.

For just ordinary holding, a good bit of exercise can be worked into a method whereby the male relative holds the child by both wrists and lets it hang down in front of him, swinging slowly back and forth like a pendulum. It can then be tossed high into the air and caught, or not, as Fate will have it.

A still better way to develop the child is to have it hold the male relative.

Unhappy Meeting

Dennis Rooke

Driblingthorpe lowered himself into the chair next to mine and leant out of it at a confidential angle. 'Did I ever tell you the story about how I met my wife?' he inquired.

Being by profession an Astrological Consultant and Adviser on Health and Business, I am naturally interested in anything like this, and I put down *The Musical Times*, which I had in any case picked up in mistake for *The Paviors' and Cement-Mixers' Chronicle* (I make a point of reading *The Paviors' and Cement-Mixers' Chronicle* every week because I am very interested in Dowsing – the discovery of water and minerals by supernatural means – and as the editor has not so far printed an article on the subject or made any reference to it I do not wish to be caught out by a change of policy) and looked up.

'Tell Uncle all,' I said. (I am not of course Driblingthorpe's uncle really. His uncle is a garrulous slow-moving man who breeds a type of pig with big floppy ears in Gloucestershire. So far as I am aware this is the only uncle he has. I have an uncle who spears a type of salmon in Alberta, Canada, with a long walrus moustache.) And I lent him my— (I hope I am making myself clear. He spears them with a spear of course. And it is the uncle who has the walrus moustache, not the salmon. The salmon are clean-shaven.) And I lent him my ear (We've got back to Driblingthorpe now of course – I never lent my uncle anything in my life except, in my prep.-school days, a pencil constructed to explode with a loud report in the writer's hand. My uncle, however, kept his pencils behind his ear, which made him even more amused.)

'It happened in this way,' began Driblingthorpe. 'I had stepped into Pogson's in Piccadilly with a view to purchasing a pair of green pyjamas, and, while waiting for an assistant to come up and serve me, was glancing at some dressing-gowns and table-napkins – not taking much notice, you understand, of the other customers in the shop – when I suddenly saw, standing right beside me—'

'When were you born?' I inquired.

'August 19th, 1913.'

'Then your happiness is dependent upon your having married a Pisces child, or fish woman.'

'Oh, good – suddenly saw, standing right beside me—'

'I understand.'

I saw what had happened of course. Standing right beside him was a beautiful girl with fluttering eyelids and quivering nostrils, and the assistant had naturally assumed that they were together. One could guess the rest. The assistant asked Driblingthorpe if he were with the lady and Driblingthorpe replied, No, he was afraid not. The assistant then explained that he'd only asked because he knew the lady was being attended to and thought that, if Driblingthorpe were with her, he would doubtless have no further wishes or requirements.

This of course put ideas into Driblingthorpe's head, and before you could say 'knife' he was exchanging quips, pleasantries and telephone numbers with the girl in the most abandoned manner.

I could only hope she'd been born under the right auspices. Driblingthorpe didn't know a horoscope from an hour-glass and he might easily have fallen into an error, even a trap. If this girl were Sun in Gemini, conj. Neptune, opp. Uranus, square Saturn she would, married to Driblingthorpe, become overbearing, truculent, violent and destructive, making her difficult to live with. She would probably throw shoes and porcelain vases at him as he came into the house, and give him prunes and rice-pudding for dinner.

As I thought about it my heart bled for the poor fellow, and my clear penetrating eyes assumed a sympathetic, agonized expression. It was a tragedy that this unhappy fate – a fate which a little knowledge of the planets and their orbits could so easily have prevented – should have overtaken him.

'Driblingthorpe,' I said, laying a hand on his arm and choking back a sob, 'I'm sorry. Sorrier than I can say. It means a divorce of course. Too bad, old man, too bad. I'd have asked you to come and stay till the case was over but I've already got two aunts and a stepmother staying with me, to say nothing of my father, who thinks – rightly – that he owns the place, and I just don't see how ... Wait a minute, old boy, there may be a way out. I believe I've been working on the wrong date. Did you say you were born on the—'

'– suddenly saw, standing right beside me, a fellow I hadn't seen for years and—'

'Never mind about that,' I said, realizing that in his dull-witted slow-thinking way he'd only got to the part where he was in Pogson's buying some green pyjamas. 'A *what*?'

'A fellow I hadn't seen for years and—'

I looked at him keenly, suspicion and astonishment writ large on my brow. (There was a mirror behind him and I could see how large they were writ.) 'Driblingthorpe,' I said, 'you distinctly told me that this was a story about how you met your wife.'

He nodded deferentially. 'It *is*,' he said. 'I'd arranged to meet her outside Swan and Edgar's that afternoon, but owing to my getting into conversation with this fellow in Pogson's I was ten minutes late and—'

I rose from my chair, a stern unyielding expression on my entire face. 'Mr Driblingthorpe,' I said, 'I waste a great deal of time giving the wrong solutions to people's private and personal problems, but if there is one thing that absolutely gets my goat, or Capricorn, it is giving the wrong solution to the wrong problem. Next time you meet your wife outside Swan and Edgar's,' I concluded, giving way for an instant to a savage ferocity usually foreign to my nature, 'I hope the Sun's in Scorpio, conj. Mercury, opp. Venus, tr. Mars. Good day.'

Three Men on the Bummel

Jerome K. Jerome

George, Harris and the narrator decide to tour the Black
Forest by bicycle, and find the constraints of German law a
little more tricky than they had bargained for...

All three of us, by some means or another, managed, between Nuremberg
and the Black Forest, to get into trouble.

Harris led off at Stuttgart by insulting an official. Stuttgart is a charming
town, clean and bright, a smaller Dresden. It has the additional attraction of
containing little that one need to go out of one's way to see: a medium-sized
picture gallery, a small museum of antiquities, and half a palace, and you are
through with the entire thing and can enjoy yourself. Harris did not know it
was an official he was insulting. He took it for a fireman (it looked like a
fireman), and he called it a 'dummer Esel.'

In Germany you are not permitted to call an official a 'silly ass', but
undoubtedly this particular man was one. What had happened was this:
Harris in the Stadtgarten, anxious to get out, and seeing a gate open before
him, had stepped over a wire into the street. Harris maintains he never saw
it, but undoubtedly there was hanging to the wire a notice 'Durchgang
Verboten!' The man, who was standing near the gate, stopped Harris, and
pointed out to him this notice. Harris thanked him, and passed on. The man
came after him, and explained that treatment of the matter in such offhand
way could not be allowed; what was necessary to put the business right was
that Harris should step back over the wire into the garden. Harris pointed
out to the man that the notice said 'going through forbidden', and that,
therefore, by re-entering the garden that way he would be infringing the law
a second time. The man saw this for himself, and suggested that to get over
the difficulty Harris should go back into the garden by the proper entrance,
which was round the corner, and afterwards immediately come out again by

the same gate. Then it was that Harris called the man a silly ass. That delayed us a day, and cost Harris forty marks.

I followed suit at Carlsruhe, by stealing a bicycle. I did not mean to steal the bicycle; I was merely trying to be useful. The train was on the point of starting when I noticed, as I thought, Harris's bicycle still in the goods van. No one was about to help me. I jumped into the van and hauled it out, only just in time. Wheeling it down the platform in triumph, I came across Harris's bicycle, standing against a wall behind some milk-cans. The bicycle I had secured was not Harris's, but some other man's.

It was an awkward situation. In England, I should have gone to the station-master and explained my mistake. But in Germany they are not content with your explaining a little matter of this sort to one man: they take you round and get you to explain it to about half a dozen; and if any one of the half-dozen happens not to be handy, or not to have time just then to listen to you, they have a habit of leaving you over for the night to finish your explanation the next morning. I thought I would just put the thing out of sight, and then, without making any fuss or show, take a short walk. I found a woodshed, which seemed just the very place, and was wheeling the bicycle into it when, unfortunately, a red-hatted railway official, with the airs of a retired field-marshal, caught sight of me and came up. He said:

'What are you doing with that bicycle?'

I said: 'I am going to put it in this woodshed out of the way.' I tried to convey by my tone that I was performing a kind and thoughtful action, for which the railway officials ought to thank me; but he was unresponsive.

'Is it your bicycle?' he said.

'Well, not exactly,' I replied.

'Whose is it?' he asked quite sharply.

'I can't tell you,' I answered. 'I don't know whose bicycle it is.'

'Where did you get it from?' was his next question. There was a suspiciousness about his tone that was almost insulting.

'I got it,' I answered, with as much calm dignity as at the moment I could assume, 'out of the train. The fact is,' I continued frankly, 'I have made a mistake.'

He did not allow me time to finish. He merely said he thought so, too, and blew a whistle.

Recollection of the subsequent proceedings is not, so far as I am concerned, amusing. By a miracle of good luck – they say providence watches over certain of us – the incident happened in Carlsruhe, where I possess a

German friend, an official of some importance. Upon what would have been my fate had the station not been at Carlsruhe, or had my friend been from home, I do not care to dwell; as it was I got off, as the saying is, by the skin of my teeth. I should like to add that I left Carlsruhe without a stain upon my character, but that would not be the truth. My going scot free is regarded in police circles there to this day as a grave miscarriage of justice.

But all lesser sin sinks into insignificance beside the lawlessness of George. The bicycle incident had thrown us all into confusion, with the result that we lost George altogether. It transpired subsequently that he was waiting for us outside the police court; but this at the time we did not know. We thought, maybe, he had gone on to Baden by himself; and anxious to get away from Carlsruhe, and not, perhaps, thinking out things too clearly, we jumped into the next train that came up and proceeded thither. When George, tired of waiting, returned to the station, he found us gone and he found his luggage gone. Harris had his ticket; I was acting as banker to the party, so that he had in his pocket only some small change. Excusing himself upon these grounds, he thereupon commenced deliberately a career of crime that, reading it later, as set forth baldly in the official summons, made the hair of Harris and myself almost to stand on end.

German travelling, it may be explained, is somewhat complicated. You buy a ticket at the station you start from for the place you want to go to. You might think this would enable you to get there, but it does not. When your train comes up, you attempt to swarm into it; but the guard magnificently waves you away. Where are your credentials? You show him your ticket. He explains to you that by itself that is of no service whatever; you have only taken the first step towards travelling; you must go back to the booking-office and get in addition what is called a '*Schnellzug* ticket.' With this you return, thinking your troubles over. You are allowed to get in, so far so good. But you must not sit down anywhere, and you must not stand still, and you must not wander about. You must take another ticket, this time what is called a '*Platz* ticket,' which entitles you to a place for a certain distance.

What a man could do who persisted in taking nothing but the one ticket, I have often wondered. Would he be entitled to run behind the train on the six-foot way? Or could he stick a label on himself and get into the goods van? Again, what could be done with the man who, having taken his *Schnellzug* ticket, obstinately refused, or had not the money to take a *Platz* ticket: would they let him lie in the umbrella rack, or allow him to hang himself out of the window?

To return to George, he had just sufficient money to take a third-class slow train ticket to Baden, and that was all. To avoid the inquisitiveness of the guard, he waited till the train was moving, and then jumped in.

That was his first sin:

(a) Entering a train in motion;

(b) After being warned not to do so by an official.

Second sin:

(a) Travelling in train of superior class to that for which ticket was held.

(b) Refusing to pay difference when demanded by an official. (George says he did not 'refuse'; he simply told the man he had not got it.)

Third sin:

(a) Travelling in carriage of superior class to that for which ticket was held.

(b) Refusing to pay difference when demanded by an official. (Again George disputes the accuracy of the report. He turned his pockets out, and offered the man all he had, which was about eightpence in German money. He offered to go into a third class, but there was no third class. He offered to go into the goods van, but they would not hear of it.)

Fourth sin:

(a) Occupying seat, and not paying for same.

(b) Loitering about corridor. (As they would not let him sit down without paying, and as he could not pay, it was difficult to see what else he could do.)

But explanations are held as no excuse in Germany; and his journey from Carlsruhe to Baden was one of the most expensive perhaps on record.

Reflecting upon the ease and frequency with which one gets into trouble here in Germany, one is led to the conclusion that this country would come as a boon and a blessing to the average young Englishman. To the medical student, to the eater of dinners at the Temple, to the subaltern on leave, life in London is a wearisome proceeding. The healthy Briton takes his pleasure lawlessly, or it is no pleasure to him. Nothing that he may do affords to him any genuine satisfaction. To be in trouble of some sort is his only idea of bliss. Now, England affords him small opportunity in this respect; to get himself into a scrape requires a good deal of persistence on the part of the young Englishman.

I spoke on this subject one day with our senior churchwarden. It was the morning of the 10th of November, and we were both of us glancing, somewhat anxiously, through the police reports. The usual batch of young men had been summoned for creating the usual disturbance the night before at the Criterion. My friend the churchwarden has boys of his own, and a nephew of mine, upon whom I am keeping a fatherly eye, is by a fond mother supposed to be in London for the sole purpose of studying engineering. No names we knew happened, by fortunate chance, to be in the list of those detained in custody, and, relieved, we fell to moralizing upon the folly and depravity of youth.

'It is very remarkable,' said my friend the churchwarden, 'how the Criterion retains its position in this respect. It was just so when I was young; the evening always wound up with a row at the Criterion.'

'So meaningless,' I remarked.

'So monotonous,' he replied. 'You have no idea,' he continued, a dreamy expression stealing over his furrowed face, 'how unutterably tired one can become of the walk from Piccadilly Circus to the Vine Street Police Court. Yet, what else was there for us to do? Simply nothing. Sometimes we would put out a street lamp, and a man would come round and light it again. If one insulted a policeman, he simply took no notice. He did not even know he was being insulted; or, if he did, he seemed not to care. You could fight a Covent Garden porter, if you fancied yourself at that sort of thing. Generally speaking, the porter got the best of it; and when he did it cost you five shillings, and when he did not the price was half a sovereign. I could never see much excitement in that particular sport. I tried driving a hansom cab once. That has always been regarded as the acme of modern Tom and Jerryism. I stole it late one night from outside a public-house in Dean Street, and the first thing that happened to me was that I was hailed in Golden Square by an old lady surrounded by three children, two of them crying and the third one half asleep. Before I could get away she had shot the brats into the cab, taken my number, paid me, so she said, a shilling over the legal fare, and directed me to an address a little beyond what she called North Kensington. As a matter of fact, the place turned out to be the other side of Willesden. The horse was tired, and the journey took us well over two hours. It was the slowest lark I ever remember being concerned in. I tried once or twice to persuade the children to let me take them back to the old lady: but every time I opened the trap-door to speak to them the youngest one, a boy, started screaming; and when I offered other drivers to transfer the job to them most of them replied in the words of a song, popular about that period: "Oh, George, don't you think you're going just a bit too far?" One man offered to take home to my wife any last message I might be thinking of, whilst another promised to organize a party to come and dig me out in the spring. When I mounted the dickey I had imagined myself driving a peppery old colonel to some lonesome and cabless region, half a dozen miles from where he wanted to go, and there leaving him upon the kerbstone to swear. About that there might have been good sport or there might not, according to circumstances and the colonel. The idea of a trip to an outlying suburb in charge of a nursery full of helpless infants had never occurred to me. No, London,' concluded my friend the churchwarden with a sigh, 'affords but limited opportunity to the lover of the illegal.'

Now, in Germany, on the other hand, trouble is to be had for the asking. There are many things in Germany that you must not do that are quite easy to do. To any young Englishman yearning to get himself into a scrape, and finding himself hampered in his own country, I would advise a single ticket to Germany; a return, lasting as it does only a month, might prove a waste.

In the Police Guide to the Fatherland he will find set forth a list of the things the doing of which will bring to him interest and excitement. In Germany you must not hang your bed out of the window. He might begin with that. By waving his bed out of the window he could get into trouble before he had his breakfast. At home he might hang himself out of a window, and nobody would mind much, provided he did not obstruct anybody's ancient lights or break away and injure any passer underneath.

In Germany you must not wear fancy dress in the streets. A Highlander of my acquaintance who came to pass the winter in Dresden spent the first few days of his residence there in arguing this question with the Saxon Government. They asked him what he was doing in those clothes. He was not an amiable man. He answered, he was wearing them. They asked him why he was wearing them. He replied to keep himself warm. They told him frankly that they did not believe him, and sent him back to his lodgings in a closed landau. The personal testimony of the English minister was necessary to assure the authorities that the Highland garb was the customary dress of many respectable, law-abiding British subjects. They accepted the statement, as diplomatically bound, but retain their private opinion to this day. The English tourist they have grown accustomed to; but a Leicestershire gentleman, invited to hunt with some German officers, on appearing outside his hotel, was promptly marched off, horse and all, to explain his frivolity at the police court.

Another thing you must not do in the streets of German towns is to feed horses, mules, or donkeys, whether your own or those belonging to other people. If a passion seizes you to feed somebody else's horse, you must make an appointment with the animal, and the meal must take place in some properly authorized place. You must not break glass or china in the street, nor, in fact, in any public resort whatever; and if you do, you must pick up all the pieces. What you are to do with the pieces when you have gathered them together I cannot say. The only thing I know for certain is that you are not permitted to throw them anywhere, to leave them anywhere, or apparently to part with them in any way whatever. Presumably, you are expected to carry them about with you until you die, and then be buried with them; or, maybe, you are allowed to swallow them.

In German streets you must not shoot with a crossbow. The German law-maker does not content himself with the misdeeds of the average man – the crime one feels one wants to do, but must not: he worries himself imagining all the things a wandering maniac might do. In Germany there is no law against a man standing on his head in the middle of the road; the idea has not occurred to them. One of these days a German statesman, visiting a circus and seeing acrobats, will reflect upon this omission. Then he will straightway set to work and frame a clause forbidding people from standing on their heads in the middle of the road, and fixing a fine. This is the charm of German law: misdemeanour in Germany has its fixed price. You are not kept awake all night, as in England, wondering whether you will get off with a caution, be fined forty shillings, or, catching the magistrate in an unhappy moment for yourself, get seven days. You know exactly what your fun is going to cost you. You can spread out your money on the table, open your Police Guide, and plan out your holiday to a fifty pfennig piece. For a really cheap evening, I would recommend walking on the wrong side of the pavement after being cautioned not to do so. I calculate that by choosing your district and keeping to the quiet side-streets you could walk for a whole evening on the wrong side of the pavement at a cost of little over three marks.

In German towns you must not ramble about after dark 'in droves'. I am not quite sure how many constitute a 'drove', and no official to whom I have spoken on this subject has felt himself competent to fix the exact number. I once put it to a German friend who was starting for the theatre with his wife, his mother-in-law, five children of his own, his sister and her fiancé, and two nieces, if he did not think he was running a risk under this by-law. He did not take my suggestion as a joke. He cast an eye over the group.

'Oh, I don't think so,' he said; 'you see, we are all one family.'

'The paragraph says nothing about its being a family drove or not,' I replied; 'it simply says "drove". I do not mean it in any uncomplimentary sense, but, speaking etymologically, I am inclined personally to regard your collection as a "drove". Whether the police will take the same view or not remains to be seen. I am merely warning you.'

My friend himself was inclined to pooh-pooh my fears; but his wife thinking it better not to run any risk of having the party broken up by the police at the very beginning of the evening, they divided, arranging to come together again in the theatre lobby.

Another passion you must restrain in Germany is that prompting you to throw things out of window. Cats are no excuse. During the first week of my residence in Germany I was awakened incessantly by cats. One night I got mad. I collected a small arsenal – two or three pieces of coal, a few hard pears, a couple of candle ends, an old egg I found on the kitchen table, an empty soda-water bottle, and a few articles of that sort – and, opening the window, bombarded the spot from where the noise appeared to come. I do not suppose I hit anything; I never knew a man who did hit a cat, even when he could see it, except, maybe, by accident when aiming at something else. I have known crack shots, winners of Queen's prizes – those sort of men – shoot with shot-guns at cats fifty yards away, and never hit a hair. I have often thought that, instead of bull's-eyes, running deer, and that rubbish, the really superior marksman would be he who could boast that he had shot the cat.

But, anyhow, they moved off; maybe the egg annoyed them. I had noticed when I picked it up that it did not look a good egg; and I went back to bed again, thinking the incident closed. Ten minutes afterwards there came a violent ringing of the electric bell. I tried to ignore it, but it was too persistent, and, putting on my dressing-gown, I went down to the gate. A policeman was standing there. He had all the things I had been throwing out of the window in a little heap in front of him, all except the egg. He had evidently been collecting them. He said:

'Are these things yours?'

I said: 'They were mine, but personally I have done with them. Anybody can have them – you can have them.'

He ignored my offer. He said:

'You threw these things out of window.'

'You are right,' I admitted; 'I did.'

'Why did you throw them out of window?' he asked. A German policeman has his code of questions arranged for him; he never varies them, and he never omits one.

'I threw them out of the window at some cats,' I answered.

'What cats?' he asked.

It was the sort of question a German policeman would ask. I replied with as much sarcasm as I could put into my accent that I was ashamed to say I could not tell him what cats. I explained that, personally, they were strangers to me; but I offered, if the police would call all the cats in the district together, to come round and see if I could recognize them by their yawl.

The German policeman does not understand a joke, which is perhaps on the whole just as well, for I believe there is a heavy fine for joking with any German uniform; they call it 'treating an official with contumely'. He merely replied that it was not the duty of the police to help me recognize the cats; their duty was merely to fine me for throwing things out of window.

I asked what a man was supposed to do in Germany when woken up night after night by cats, and he explained that I could lodge an information against the owner of the cat, when the police would proceed to caution him, and, if necessary, order the cat to be destroyed. Who was going to destroy the cat, and what the cat would be doing during the process, he did not explain.

I asked him how he proposed I should discover the owner of the cat. He thought for a while, and then suggested that I might follow it home. I did not feel inclined to argue with him any more after that; I should only have said things that would have made the matter worse. As it was, that night's sport cost me twelve marks; and not a single one of the four German officials who interviewed me on the subject could see anything ridiculous in the proceedings from beginning to end.

But in Germany most human faults and follies sink into comparative insignificance beside the enormity of walking on the grass. Nowhere, and under no circumstances, may you at any time in Germany walk on the grass. Grass in Germany is quite a fetish. To put your foot on German grass would be as great a sacrilege as to dance a hornpipe on a Mohammedan's praying-mat. The very dogs respect German grass; no German dog would dream of putting a paw on it. If you see a dog scampering across the grass in Germany, you may know for certain that it is the dog of some unholy foreigner. In England, when we want to keep dogs out of places, we put up wire netting, six feet high supported by buttresses, and defended on the top by spikes. In Germany, they put a notice-board in the middle of the place, 'Hunden verboten', and a dog that has German blood in its veins looks at that notice-board and walks away. In a German park I have seen a gardener step gingerly with felt boots on to a grass-plot, and removing therefrom a beetle, place it gravely but firmly on the gravel; which done, he stood sternly watching the beetle, to see that it did not try to get back on the grass; and the beetle, looking utterly ashamed of itself, walked hurriedly down the gutter, and turned up the path marked 'Ausgang'.

In German parks separate roads are devoted to the different orders of the community, and no one person, at peril of liberty and fortune, may go upon another person's road. There are special paths for 'wheel-riders' and special paths for 'foot-goers', avenues for 'horse-riders', roads for people in light vehicles, and roads for people in heavy vehicles; ways for children and for 'alone ladies'. That no particular route has yet been set aside for bald-headed men or 'new women' has always struck me as an omission.

In the Grosse Garten in Dresden I once came across an old lady, standing, helpless and bewildered, in the centre of seven tracks. Each was guarded by a threatening notice, warning everybody off it but the person for whom it was intended.

'I am sorry to trouble you,' said the old lady, on learning I could speak English and read German, 'but would you mind telling me what I am and where I have to go?'

I inspected her carefully. I came to the conclusion that she was a 'grown-up' and a 'foot-goer', and pointed out her path. She looked at it, and seemed disappointed.

'But I don't want to go down there,' she said; 'mayn't I go this way?'

'Great heavens, no, madam!' I replied. 'That path is reserved for children.'

'But I wouldn't do them any harm,' said the old lady, with a smile. She did not look the sort of old lady who would have done them any harm.

'Madam,' I replied, 'if it rested with me, I would trust you down that path, though my own first-born were at the other end; but I can only inform you of the laws of this country. For you, a full-grown woman, to venture down that path is to go to certain fine, if not imprisonment. There is your path, marked plainly – "Nur für Fussgänger", and if you will follow my advice, you will hasten down it; you are not allowed to stand here and hesitate.'

'It doesn't lead a bit in the direction I want to go,' said the old lady.

'It leads in the direction you *ought* to want to go,' I replied, and we parted.

In the German parks there are special seats labelled, 'Only for grown-ups' ('Nur für Erwachsene'), and the German small boy, anxious to sit down and reading that notice, passes by, and hunts for a seat on which children are permitted to rest; and there he seats himself, careful not to touch the woodwork with his muddy boots. Imagine a seat in Regent's or St James's Park labelled 'Only for grown-ups'! Every child in five miles round would be trying to get on that seat, and hauling other children off who were on. As for any 'grown-up', he would never be able to get within half a mile of that seat for the crowd. The German small boy, who has accidentally sat down on such without noticing, rises with a start when his error is pointed out to him, and goes away with downcast head, blushing to the roots of his hair with shame and regret.

Not that the German child is neglected by a paternal Government. In German parks and public gardens special places (*Spielplätze*) are provided for him, each one supplied with a heap of sand. There he can play to his heart's content at making mud pies and building sand castles. To the German child a pie made of any other mud than this would appear an immoral pie. It would give to him no satisfaction: his soul would revolt against it.

'That pie,' he would say to himself, 'was not, as it should have been, made of Government mud specially set apart for the purpose; it was not manufactured in the place planned and maintained by the Government for the making of mud pies. It can bring no real blessing with it; it is a lawless pie.' And until his father had paid the proper fine, and he had received his proper licking, his conscience would continue to trouble him.

Another excellent piece of material for obtaining excitement in Germany is the simple domestic perambulator. What you may do with a *Kinderwagen*, as it is called, and what you may not, covers pages of German law; after the reading of which, you conclude that the man who can push a perambulator through a German town without breaking the law was meant for a diplomatist. You must not loiter with a perambulator, and you must not go too fast. You must not get in anybody's way with a perambulator, and if anybody gets in your way you must get out of their way. If you want to stop with a perambulator, you must go to a place specially appointed where perambulators may stop; and when you get there you *must* stop. You must not cross the road with a perambulator; if you and the baby happen to live on the other side, that is your fault. You must not leave your perambulator anywhere, and only in certain places can you take it with you. I should say that in Germany you could go out with a perambulator and get into enough trouble in half an hour to last you for a month. Any young Englishman anxious for a row with the police could not do better than come over to Germany and bring his perambulator with him.

In Germany you must not leave your front door unlocked after ten o'clock at night, and you must not play the piano in your own house after eleven. In England I have never felt I wanted to play the piano myself, or to hear anyone else play it, after eleven o'clock at night; but that is a very different thing to being told that you must not play it. Here, in Germany, I never feel that I really care for the piano until eleven o'clock, then I could sit and listen to the 'Maiden's Prayer', or the Overture to 'Zampa', with pleasure. To the law-loving German, on the other hand, music after eleven o'clock at night ceases to be music: it becomes sin, and as such gives him no satisfaction.

The only individual throughout Germany who ever dreams of taking liberties with the law is the German student, and he only to a certain well-defined point. By custom, certain privileges are permitted to him, but even these are strictly limited and clearly understood. For instance, the German student may get drunk and fall asleep in the gutter with no other penalty than that of having the next morning to tip the policeman who has found him and brought him home. But for this purpose he must choose the gutters of side-streets. The German student, conscious of the rapid approach of oblivion, uses all his remaining energy to get round the corner where he may collapse without anxiety. In certain districts he may ring bells. The rent of flats in these localities is lower than in other quarters of the town; while the difficulty is further met by each family preparing for itself a secret code of bell-ringing, by means of which it is known whether the summons is genuine or not. When visiting such a household late at night it is well to be acquainted with this code, or you may, if persistent, get a bucket of water thrown over you.

Also the German student is allowed to put out lights at night, but there is a prejudice against his putting out too many. The larky German student generally keeps count, contenting himself with half a dozen lights per night. Likewise, he may shout and sing as he walks home up till half past two; and at certain restaurants it is permitted to him to put his arm round the fraulein's waist. To prevent any suggestion of unseemliness, the waitresses at restaurants frequented by students are always carefully selected from among a staid and elderly class of women, by reason of which the German student can enjoy the delights of flirtation without fear and without reproach to anyone.

They are a law-abiding people, the Germans.

Advice to Beginners

Tim Brooke-Taylor

'Advice,' said the fourth Earl of Chesterfield, whose unfortunate natural son, Philip Stanhope, was no stranger to it, 'is seldom welcome; and those who want it the most always like it the least.'

British gentlemen have been handing down words of wisdom from generation to generation. At first only their families suffered. But as the demand for instruction increased, their pearls found their way into countless books, ranging from rough shooting to regulating the servants, whose authors set out to instruct their readers in the ways and mores of the true gentleman in these diverse fields. At the top of the list came personal conduct, everything from drinking to dying. This is what Lord Chesterfield himself had to say about displaying one's amusement:

> Having mentioned laughing, I must particularly warn you against it: and I could heartily wish that you may often be seen to smile, but never heard to laugh. Frequent and loud laughter is the characteristic of folly and ill manners: it is the manner in which the mob express their silly joy of silly things ... in my mind there is nothing so illiberal, and so ill-bred, as audible laughter.

I happen to think there is no greater joy than audible laughter. But I would agree wholeheartedly if Lord Chesterfield's indictment were to be applied to canned laughter.

Health was another field in which those who were least qualified to pontificate on the subject felt it their duty to lay down the law to young men in the prime of life. The 'Old Boy', quoted elsewhere, drew up six 'essentials to the preservation of health': pure air; wholesome diet; regular exercise; scrupulous cleanliness; proper clothing; regular hours. 'There is no nerve tonic like pure mountain air,' he confides:

It exhilarates like a draught of champagne, and leaves no headache behind. Climb as often as you can to the top of the highest hill within twenty miles of you, and expand your lungs with fresh, pure air. Indoors avoid close, stuffy rooms, especially close, stuffy bedrooms; and as far as possible avoid also rooms that are heated or lighted by gas, which exhausts the oxygen of the air with terrible rapidity.

No amount of pure air, however, can counteract bad breath, a problem which clearly concerned our great-grandfathers as much as it concerns the advertisers of present-day toothpastes. Again the *Dictionary of Daily Wants* had a ready answer to the problem:

There is nothing more annoying to a person of refined feeling, or disagreeable to all who approach him, than to be afflicted with an impure breath: and as the causes are so limited from which it proceeds, and the mode of treatment so simple and attainable by all, it becomes a great social dereliction in any one so afflicted not to immediately avail himself of a remedy.

He then proceeds to diagnose three causes of bad breath, providing a treatment for each. If an 'impure state of the stomach' happens to be your problem, the author prescribes 'wormwood or camomile tea . . . a spoonful of carbonate of soda in each dose with an aleotic or colocynth pill, twice a week.' 'By this means,' he assures, 'persisted in for a short time, the worst case of fetid breath may be conquered, when dependent on a depraved state of the digestive organs.' Ugh! He even gives a recipe for his own tooth powder 'to be used freely, and allowed to remain some minutes in the mouth and over the teeth before being washed away':

> Powdered cuttlefish – 2 drachms
> Powdered myrrh – ½ drachm
> Carbonate of soda – 1 drachm
> Charcoal powder – 1 ounce

Living as we do at a time when the country's youth are being exhorted to find themselves a job of some description, if only to save the government's face, it's refreshing to see that every generation has felt obliged to goad its juniors into employment. Not every generation has held the same priorities in terms of employment, though our 'Old Boy' drew up a very individualistic list in 1889, putting Medicine and Surgery at the top and the Stage at the bottom. His criteria for selection were, 'their operation on the man himself, their usefulness to mankind, and the prospect of success which they afford.' Why is it, do you suppose, that recently so many doctors have become actors?

Out of his list, 'Old Boy' chose twenty-three occupations and professions in which Education ranked second; Literature third; Commerce tenth; Banking fourteenth; the Law seventeenth; 'Clerkly work of all kinds' nineteenth; 'Manufacturers of luxuries and non-essentials' twentieth; and the Army twenty-second.

Certain openings offered a hundred years ago have closed now, of course. The Indian Civil Service, number six on the list and in the author's own words, 'a very admirable and honourable career', which 'gives scope for the exercise of the most heroic qualities', is obviously a non-starter today, and the call to future farmers to leave their homes for 'fresh fields and pastures new' in the colonies has never held the same attraction since the disastrous scheme to grow groundnuts in Africa thirty years ago.

On the question of trade, the author makes one very interesting observation, namely that 'it is genteel' to sell in bulk the same things that it is 'vulgar' to sell piecemeal. There was still a prejudice against 'trade' in his day, and apart from working in Harrods at Christmas for a laugh, few gentlemen even today willingly admit to being engaged in trade at the sharp end of the business. If they are, they call it management. They are, of course, all 'company directors'.

On the assumption that most gentlemen will try and avoid any activity that could be too easily classified as work, the choice of profession today is governed largely by its social acceptability. The Foreign Office has taken over the colonial role from the ICS and similar institutions dotted across those parts of the globe painted pink. Today the more exclusive merchant banks attract young gentlemen, and the traditional and historical associations of the bar, coupled with the fortunes it can offer, are proving very popular.

On a wider level, young gentlemen have never suffered from a shortage of advice on how to set the right example to their juniors and inferiors. 'Have courage, boys, to do the right!' reads the first line of the poem. 'Do the Right, Boys', published in the *Boys' Own Annual* of 1881, repeated at the beginning of every other of the five verses, as in the case of this third one:

> Have courage, boys, to do the right!
> Be bold, be brave, be strong!
> By doing right we get the might
> To overcome the wrong.
>
> 'Tis only those who evil do
> That need a coward fear,
> So let your lives be good and true,
> And keep your conscience clear.

The need to mark the dividing line between master and servant was given great emphasis, too. 'Employers should present to their servants an example of propriety of deportment and language,' advised *The Master and Mistress: or Hints to the heads of Families Relative to their servants*, adding:

> If a servant be addressed with the familiarity of an equal, or allowed to speak in a tone of familiarity to the master and mistress – especially if the heads of the family addict themselves to a low jesting manner of expression – all sense of distinction and propriety will soon be lost.

At the same time the employer of the future was warned against abusing his servants. The author of *Notes for Boys* cautioned against this in his section entitled 'Of Unselfishness' in which he provided this charming example of thoughtfulness towards domestic staff:

> You have set your mind on wearing a particular pair of boots, but you find that they are not cleaned, and that the servants are busy; and, rather than give needless trouble, you put on another pair: that is unselfishness.

Similar displays of self-denial include getting up in time for breakfast; not mentioning that you have a headache; running errands for a sister in the rain; and making life cheerier for your workmates 'by giving yourself a little extra trouble, or putting yourself to some inconvenience'. Would that the only advice needed today was so easy and straightforward.

Ambrose Bierce described 'advice' as 'the smallest current coin', but he
was an American. All Britishers offering advice on any subject like to see
themselves through Pope's idealized eyes:

> But where's the man, who counsel can bestow,
> Still pleased to teach, and yet not proud to know?
> Unbiass'd, or by favour, or by spite:
> Not dully prepossess'd, nor blindly right;
> Tho' learn'd, well-bred; and tho' well-bred, sincere;
> Modestly bold, and humanly severe:
> Who to a friend his faults can freely show,
> And gladly praise the merit of a foe?

But then most of them could do with a word in their ear.

1066 And All That

W. C. Sellar & R. J. Yeatman

Henry VIII was a strong King with a very strong sense of humour and VIII wives, memorable amongst whom were Katherine the Arrogant, Anne of Cloves, Lady Jane Austin and Anne Hathaway. His beard was, however, red.

In his youth Henry was fond of playing tennis and after his accession is believed never to have lost a set. He also invented a game called '*Bluff King Hal*' which he invited his ministers to play with him. The players were blindfolded and knelt down with their heads on a block of wood; they then guessed whom the King would marry next.

Cardinal Wolsey, the memorable homespun statesman and inventor of the Wolsack, played this game with Henry and won. But his successor, Cromwell (*not to be confused with Cromwell*), after winning on points, was disqualified by the King (who always acted as umpire), and lost.

In the opinion of Shakespeare (the memorable playwriter and Top Poet) his unexpected defeat was due to his failure to fling away ambition.

The Restoration

Henry wanted the Pope to give him a divorce from his first wife, Katherine. He wanted this because
  (a) she was Arrogant.
  (b) he had married her a very long time ago.
  (c) when she had a baby it turned out to be Broody Mary, and Henry wanted a boy.
  (d) he thought it would be a Good Thing.
The Pope, however, refused, and seceded with all his followers from the Church of England. This was called the Restoration.

Henry's Plan Fails

Curiously enough Henry had all the time had an idea about a new wife for himself called Anne, who, he thought, looked as if she would be sure to have a son. So when the Divorce was all over (or nearly) he married her; but he was wrong about Anne, because she had a girl too, in a way.

After this Henry was afraid his reign would not be long enough for any more divorces, so he gave them up and executed his wives instead.* He also got less interested in his wives and gave himself up to Diplomacy, spending a great deal of his time playing tennis, etc., with the young King of France in a field called the Field of the Crock of Gold.

End of Wolsey

Cardinal Wolsey, although (as is well known) he had not thought to shed a tear about all this, did ultimately shed a memorable one. Having thus fallen from grace (indeed he had already been discovered entertaining some Papal Bulls) Wolsey determined to make a Pilgrimage to Leicester Abbey, saying to himself: 'If I had served my God as I have served my King, I would have been a Good Thing.' Having thus acknowledged that he was a Bad Man, and being in due course arrived at the Abbey, Wolsey very pluckily expired after making a memorable speech to the Prior, beginning, 'Father Abbot, I come to lay my bones among you, Not to praise them...'

The Monasteries

One of the strongest things that Henry VIII did was about the Monasteries. It was pointed out to him that no one in the monasteries was married, as the Monks all thought it was still the Middle Ages. So Henry, who, of course, considered marrying a Good Thing, told Cromwell to pass a very strong Act saying that the Middle Ages were all over and the monasteries were all to be dissolved. This was called the Disillusion of the Monasteries.

Edward VI and Broody Mary

Edward VI and Broody Mary were the two small Tudors who came in between the two big ones, Henry VIII and Elizabeth. Edward VI was only a

---

*All except Anne of Cloves, whom he had on approval from Belgium and sent back on discovering that she was really not a queen at all but a 'fat mare with glanders'.

boy and consequently was not allowed to have his reign properly, but while he was sitting on the throne everyone in the land was forced to become Protestant, so that Broody Mary would be able to put them to death afterwards for not being Roman Catholics. A good many people protested ·against this treatment and thus it was proved that they were Protestants, but most of the people decanted and were all right. Broody Mary's reign was, however, a Bad Thing, since England is bound to be C. of E., so all the executions were wasted.

Cramber and Fatimer

It was about this time that a memorable Dumb Crammer and one of Henry VIII's wives called Fatimer, who had survived him, got burnt alive at Oxford, while trying to light a candle in the Martyr's memorial there: it was a new candle which they had invented and which they said could never be put out.

Shortly after this the cruel Queen died and a post-mortem examination revealed the word 'Callous' engraved on her heart.

Elizabeth

Although this memorable Queen was a man, she was constantly addressed by her courtiers by various affectionate female nicknames, such as Auroraborealis, Ruritania, Black Beauty (or Bête Noire) and Brown Bess. She also very graciously walked on Sir Walter Raleigh's overcoat whenever he dropped it in the mud and was, in fact, in every respect a good and romantic Queen.

One of the most romantic aspects of the Elizabethan age was the wave of beards which suddenly swept across History and settled upon all the great men of the period. The most memorable of these beards was the cause of the outstanding event of the reign, which occurred in the following way.

The Great Armadillo

The Spaniards complained that Captain F. Drake, the memorable bowlsman, had singed the King of Spain's beard (or Spanish Mane, as it was called) one day when it was in Cadiz Harbour. Drake replied that he was in his hammock at the time and a thousand miles away. The King of Spain, however, insisted that the beard had been spoilt and sent the Great Spanish Armadillo to ravish the shores of England.

The crisis was boldly faced in England, especially by Big Bess herself, who instantly put on an enormous quantity of clothing and rode to and fro on a white horse at Tilbury – a courageous act which was warmly applauded by the English sailors.

In this striking and romantic manner the English were once more victorious.

The Queen of Hearts

A great nuisance in this reign was the memorable Scottish queen, known as Mary Queen of Hearts on account of the large number of husbands which she obtained, e.g. Cardinale Ritzio, Boswell and the King of France: most of these she easily blew up at Holywood.

Unfortunately for Mary, Scotland was now suddenly overrun by a wave of Synods led by Sir John Nox, the memorable Scottish Saturday Knight. Unable to believe, on account of the number of her husbands, that Mary was a single person, the Knight accused her of being a 'monstrous regiment of women', and after making this brave remark had her imprisoned in Loch Lomond. Mary, however, escaped and fled to England, where Elizabeth immediately put her in quarantine on the top of an enormous Height called Wutheringay.

As Mary had already been Queen of France and Queen of Scotland many people thought that it would be unfair if she was not made Queen of England as well. Various plots, such as the Paddington Plot, the Threadneedle Conspiracy and the Adelfi Plot, were therefore hatched to bring this about. Elizabeth, however, learning that in addition to all this Mary was good-looking and could play on the virginals, recognized that Mary was too romantic not to be executed, and accordingly had that done.

'Tickets, Please!'

John Aye

There is perhaps no phase of railway life that so nearly approximates to warfare as the never ending conflict between the booking clerk and the ticket
collector on the one hand and that large section of the general public that
dislikes paying railway fares on the other. It is a game of attack and defence,
of thrust and counter thrust, with the odds largely in favour of the railway
company, since it is usually backed by the full force of the law. The nearest
thing to which it can be compared, perhaps, is the fight between the landowner and the poacher, with the ticket collector playing the rôle of gamekeeper, and in both cases the general sympathy appears to go to the person
who is 'ag'in the law'.

There are three ways of travelling without a ticket. Of these the first is to
journey under the seat, though that has the drawback of being a somewhat
dirty method and cannot be recommended to anyone who wishes to make a
good impression on arrival at his destination. A second is to leave the train
before it gets to the station and walk the remainder, but this is not always
possible, and where it is there is too great an element of danger. A third, and
certainly the most popular, is to say 'Season,' but even this magic word fails
sometimes to achieve its purpose, with results which are often disastrous.

As regards the first method an excellent story is told of a trick played upon
the great actor Toole by his almost equally well known brother actor Sothern.
The latter was an inveterate practical joker, and on one occasion, when the
two were travelling north together, while Toole was looking out of the
window, Sothern abstracted his ticket, which for safety Johnny had placed in
the band of his hat. As they slowed down prior to entering York Sothern
casually remarked, 'They inspect tickets here.' Toole, having searched everywhere in vain for his ticket, finally exclaimed, 'By George, I've lost mine.' 'Get
under the seat, man, quickly, it will be all right,' hurriedly advised Sothern.
Hardly had Toole stowed himself away when the ticket inspector entered and

was presented by Sothern with two tickets. 'But why do you give me two tickets?' said the mystified official. 'Oh, that's all right,' replied Sothern, 'but the other gentleman prefers to travel under the seat,' from which dusty refuge Toole had then to crawl.

As a variant to the three methods mentioned above, there is a good story told by a prominent lawyer of an incident that he witnessed in the eighties. He was travelling north, and at Crewe a woman and a small boy got into the carriage. Shortly afterwards there was an examination of tickets, and when the lawyer turned round from looking out of the window the boy had disappeared. The whole thing was most mysterious: a moment before the boy had been there, he had not gone out by the door, and yet he was no longer there. All the time the woman's face moved not a muscle. Then came the collection of tickets, and as the train moved out of the station the mystery became clear, for in response to a whispered, 'Come out, Johnnie,' the small boy reappeared from beneath his mother's petticoats. It is scarcely necessary to point out that at the present time such a trick would, for obvious reasons, be impossible.

The battle of the no-ticket commences with the 'under three years of age', and one cannot have but great hopes of the coming generation when one sees what stalwarts some of these children are. Generally, however, it is the child itself who gives away the deception. 'Is that child over three?' asked a ticket collector. 'Certainly not,' was the indignant reply. 'Oh, Daddy,' corrected the child, 'I was six last birthday. Don't you remember the presents?' Another section of the community labours under the idea that so long as a child is not occupying a seat no ticket need be taken. 'Have you a ticket for that child?' asked a collector of a lady on whose lap sat a sturdy boy of six or seven years of age. 'Certainly not,' was the indignant reply, 'it has nothing to do with the company. I'm carrying the child.'

There must be some look of conscious guilt about persons travelling without a ticket that enables the lynx-eyed collector to detect them at once, for, as a general rule, these gentlemen rarely make a mistake. One wonders what was the sequel to the following story, and whether the inspector carried the matter any farther. First flapper: 'The cheek of that inspector, he glared at me as if I hadn't a ticket.' Her companion: 'What did you do?' Flapper: 'Glared back at him as if I had.'

The old excuse of 'lost ticket' has now gone into the limbo of the past, since, to use a vulgarism, it cuts no ice with the powers that be, and is only met by a stern demand for the fare. In this connection one recalls that delightful picture that appeared many years ago in *Punch*. It represented a ticket collector demanding a ticket from a burly volunteer, whose duty in the cause of national defence consisted in beating the big drum, a duty which, on this occasion, had evidently led to a big thirst and the subsequent quenching thereof. 'Now then,' said the ticket collector, 'make haste, where's your ticket?' 'Aw've lost it,' was the reply of the drummer. 'Nonsense,' said the collector; 'feel in your pocket, you cannot have lost it.' 'Cannot 'ave losts it,' roared the indignant bandsman; 'why, mon, aw've lost the big drum.'

Although in the 'no-ticket' battle the railway company is almost always victorious, it happens occasionally that the fortune of war veers to the other side.

An old lady was much distressed by discovering that she had lost her ticket, but was very much comforted when a gentleman travelling to the same station gave her his, assuring her that it would be quite all right. He took the precaution, however, of putting his name on it, and writing down the number in his pocket book. The old lady was the first to pass through the barrier, and, having given up the ticket, proceeded on her way. She was shortly followed by the gentleman, who asserted that he had already given up his ticket, quoted the number, and at the same time pointed out to the collector that he would find it among those collected with his, the passenger's, name on it.

An even better story comes from Ireland. The scene was a train going down to Punchestown Races, and just as the train left Kingsbridge three sportsmen jumped in who had not had time to take tickets. 'There will be trouble about the tickets,' said one after a time; 'what shall we do?' 'Leave it to me,' said the second, 'I'll make it all right.' When the station at which the tickets were examined was reached No. 2 at once jumped out of the carriage, and in a few minutes returned with a ticket for himself and each of his companions. 'How did you manage it?' asked the other two. 'Simple enough,' was the reply. ''Twas as easy as falling off a log. I went into a carriage containing some Englishmen and said, "Tickets, please." '

Side by side with the 'no-ticket' war there goes on what might be called the battle of the half ticket, a battle older than Stephenson's 'Rocket', since it comes down to us from the old coaching days. How confused some children must become when on the one hand they hear their parents conclusively pointing out to the railway officials that they are only eleven and three-quarters, while on the following day they insist to the school attendance officer that the same child is over fourteen. We are all familiar with the small boy who asked for a half ticket, and on being interrogated as to his age replied, 'I'm thirteen at home, but I'm only ten on the railway.' It was of the old

Eastern Counties Railway that the tale was originally told of how a ticket collector who was expostulating that a strapping lad of sixteen could scarcely be entitled to travel at half rate was met by the crushing reply that he was under fourteen when the train started. It was of the same railway, by the way, that Thackeray wrote, 'Even a journey on the Eastern Counties must have an end at last.'

But usually in these encounters it is the railway official who wins, and here are two excellent examples. 'How much for this child?' said a gruff father, pointing to a lank elderly boy at his side. 'Half fare?' 'Well, no,' said the booking clerk; 'he looks as if he was kept on half fare at home and wants a change, so it will be full fare this time, please.'

A precocious youth, cigarette in mouth, lounged up to a booking office and rudely demanded, ''Arf a ticket to King's Cross.' 'It's a shameful thing to see a kid like you smoking,' said the booking clerk in mild rebuke.'Garn,' was the saucy reply, 'who's a kid? I'm fifteen.' 'Oh, are you?' said the clerk. 'Then it's full fare for you, my lad.'

In some respects, however, the youth of the present day requires little teaching, and he has no objection to turning to his own advantage the attempt of his father to save money. 'If you don't stop crying at once,' said a father to his son, 'I'll give you a severe thrashing.' 'And if you do,' replied the young hopeful, 'I'll tell the ticket collector I'm over twelve. Boo hoo.'

Lastly, we come to the type of passenger who will ride in a superior class to that for which he has paid, and here again may we quote an excellent story from *Punch*:

Ticket inspector: 'Hullo. You've no call to be in here. You haven't got a first class ticket.'

Rough looking customer: 'No, I hain't.'

Ticket inspector: 'Well, come out; this ain't a third class carriage.'

Rough looking customer: 'Hain't it? Lumme, well, I thought it was by the look of the passengers.'

If there is one class of railway servants with which we should have every sympathy it is that of the booking clerks, especially when we consider the thousand and one silly questions that are put to them, and these usually in the busiest hours of the day. Can we have anything but admiration for the clerk who figured in the following incident, and yet managed to keep his temper?

Old negro woman: 'Ise want a ticket foh Florence.'

Booking clerk (after vainly searching the racks and time tables): 'Where the dickens is Florence?'

Old negro woman: 'Setten over dar on de bench.'

Perhaps too it required more than the average amount of intelligence to grasp the desire of a foreigner who required a return ticket for himself and a single for his wife, and who framed his request thus: 'Gib me two dickets. Von for me to come back and von for my wife not to come back.'

Most annoying of all to the busy booking clerk is the passenger who holds up the queue with stupid and unnecessary questions, and the woman who commits a similar crime while she searches among some fifty articles in her handbag for the necessary change. A specimen of the first named class butted into a waiting queue at a northern ticket office the other day, and although the men whose place he had usurped glared at him, they said nothing. 'I want a ticket for Wigan,' said the interloper, throwing down sixpence with the air of one to whom money was nothing. 'You can't go to Wigan for sixpence,' said the clerk. 'Well, then,' said the imperious one, 'tell me where I can go for sixpence.' Whereupon each of the twelve men in the queue found his voice, and told him in no uncertain terms exactly where he could go.

Sometimes, when the questioner is of the fair sex, and the booking clerk is young and impressionable, his answer will delicately convey the information that he would like to improve their very limited acquaintanceship, and that supplementary questions would not be unwelcome. 'Do you go to Kew Gardens?' said a sweet young thing who was somewhat hazy about the line on which she proposed to travel. 'Sometimes on a Sunday, Miss, if it's a fine afternoon,' was the reply that she received, and another romance was started.

To many of us it sometimes seems that the booking clerks and ticket collectors are perhaps a little over zealous in exacting the company's legal dues, but if such is the case we can still congratulate ourselves that our railway officials are mildness itself compared to some of their colleagues abroad. Recently a man in Dresden having purchased his ticket collapsed and died just as he was about to enter the train. His relatives subsequently claimed repayment of the amount of the unused ticket, and after some correspondence this was allowed, with the exception of one penny for a platform ticket, the argument being that the man had used the platform while still alive.

Requests for payment, too, are usually more correctly and more diplomatically expressed in this country than in the following case. A tea planter with his wife and daughter arrived at the station at Colombo with only a second or two to spare, so they boarded the train without tickets, assuring the staff that they would pay the fares at the other end. To make certain that this was done, however, the native booking clerk wired to the station to which they were travelling as follows: 'Obtain fares three Europeans travelling first class sleeping compartment in night attire, one adult and two adultresses.'

There are few of us who at some time or other have not felt indignant when we have been aroused from sleep to show our tickets, and we have heartily cursed the curiosity of collectors and inspectors with regard to this piece of pasteboard, but we must remember that our fate would be much worse if we were in Germany. Here is the account of his trials in this respect given by Jerome K. Jerome in his *Diary of a Pilgrimage*:

'Every few minutes, so it seemed to me, though in reality the intervals may perhaps have been longer, a ghastly face would appear at the carriage window and ask to see our tickets.

'Whenever a German railway guard feels lonesome and does not know what to do with himself, he takes a walk round the train and gets the passengers to show him their tickets, after which he returns to his box cheered and refreshed. Some people rave about sunsets and mountains and old masters, but to the German railway guard the world can show nothing more satisfying, more inspiring, than the sight of a railway ticket.

'Nearly all the German railway officials have this same craving for tickets. If only they can get somebody to show them a railway ticket they are happy. It seemed a harmless weakness of theirs, and B. and I decided that it would be only kind to humour them in it during our stay.

'Accordingly, whenever we saw a German railway official standing about, looking sad or weary, we went up to him and showed him our tickets. The sight was like a ray of sunshine to him, all his care was immediately forgotten. If we had not a ticket with us at the time we went and bought one. A mere single third to the next station would gladden him sufficiently in most cases, but if the poor fellow appeared very woebegone, and as if he wanted more than ordinary cheering up, we got him a second class return.

'For the purpose of our journey we each carried with us a folio containing some ten or twelve first class tickets between different towns, covering in all a distance of some thousand miles, and one afternoon at Munich, seeing a railway official, a cloak-room keeper, who they told us had recently lost his aunt, and who looked exceptionally dejected, I proposed to B. that we should take this man into a quiet corner and both of us show him all our tickets at once – the whole twenty-four of them – and let him take them in his hand and look at them for as long as he liked. I wanted to comfort him.

'B., however, advised against the suggestion. He said that even if it did not turn the man's head (and it was more than probable that it would), so much jealousy would be created against him among the other railway people throughout Germany that his life would be made a misery to him.

'So we bought and showed him a first class ticket to the next station but one, and it was quite pathetic to see the poor fellow's face brighten up at the sight, and to see the faint smile creep back to the lips from which it had so long been absent.'

Before leaving the subject of tickets it may be pointed out that it is quite easy to travel on the Continent in a higher class than that for which you have paid if you will remember to profess entire ignorance of the language. If, for example, you are riding to Paris in a first class carriage (your correct place being, of course, second), and a demand is made for your ticket, the correct procedure is to smile blandly and say simply, 'Paree'. After much gesticulation and many words on the part of the collector you will apparently assume from the actions of the other passengers that your piece of pasteboard is required, whereupon you should hold it out with a smile of childish innocence and another bland 'Paree'. The collector will, no doubt, then grow very voluble, and when he at length stops for breath, you will reply with a cheery nod of affirmation, conveying if you can the idea that he is one of the best fellows in the world, and another 'Paree'. He will then call in the stationmaster, a gendarme, and a few odd porters, and after they have sung to you as a duet, trio, quartet and grand chorus, you will respond with a continuous kindly smile of $3\frac{1}{2}$ horse power, waving your ticket and still repeating the magic word 'Paree.' In the end, as the train cannot be delayed any longer, they will probably leave you to continue your journey in peace.

The Faux Pas

Denis Norden

'Doing it that way,' I said to Peter Scott, the naturalist, in the course of idle conversation, 'you can kill two birds with one stone.'

Robert Morley's request to sweep up some of my brick-dropping brought it home to me that, after what seems a lifetime in the service of *gaucherie* I've probably done for the art of social interaction what the film *Jaws* did for swimming.

'Hey, what happened to that skinny blonde your husband used to be married to?' I asked this nice lady at a party. After a pause, she said, 'I dyed my hair.'

It's at parties that the dull thud is most frequently heard. I was only formally introduced to Christiaan Barnard after I'd advised him what to do for his cold. At another gathering I casually asked Andy Stewart if he was doing anything on New Year's Eve. In the course of similar cocktail chat, 'Neither a borrower nor a lender be,' I quoted to a foreign gentleman who turned out to be distinguished banker. And, on the same collision course, I used the phrase 'stick to your guns', while trying to express to Canon Collins my wholehearted support for his ideals.

Shall I go on about the lady down the road who asked me to bring back something decorative from Geneva that she could give her son for his new offices? It was only after I'd handed her the cuckoo clock that I remembered he was a psychiatrist.

They say – and I suppose it is one of the purposes of this book – that we all profit from our mistakes. If there were any kind of truth in that, I would be one of the richest men in town.

On Remembering Names

Frank Muir

My problem, which at times approaches the speed of paranoia, is remembering names. Not difficult names, which are always poised on the tip of the tongue, but the easy, friendly, much loved names of friends and colleagues, the forgetting of which becomes a social gaffe of frightful proportions. This, to me, is what the French call – in an old Norman phrase which I have just invented – *'le brick-drop formidable'*.

I have in my time introduced the Director General of the BBC, to a group anxious to meet him, as the Chairman of the Independent Broadcasting Authority. I have introduced Miss Thora Hird, on television, as 'Miss Hannah Gordon'.

I *know* the name, but when the occasion arises the name simply evaporates. I am rapidly moving towards the terminal *'brick-drop formidable'* as suffered by the late Sir Malcolm Sargent. The story goes – and I pray it is true – that Sir Malcolm, who like Garrick, 'dearly loved a lord', once had a member of Scandinavian royalty present at one of his concerts. At the interval he rushed around to the Royal Box with his leading soloist and said proudly, 'Your Majesty, may I introduce Sergio Poliakoff? Sergio – the King of Norway!' The distinguished figure in the box shifted slightly and murmured, 'Sweden.'

The Big Yin and Tonic

Jasper Carrott

Billy Connolly and myself are often compared, although both of us are adamant that we don't approach comedy in the same way. But I can see that because we both come from the same grass-root folk club background, there are similarities in our styles.

It was an incident in an Edinburgh bar that once brought home to me the great differences that lie between Billy's and my approach.

I was up in Edinburgh at the time of the festival for a seminar which was part of a general meeting of the people running British television. They have this three-day conference, the mornings of which are spent in serious discussion about really important media issues: is television a good thing? Does 'Coronation Street' genuinely offer art to the masses? Can anything be done about the flavour of the crisps in the Television Centre canteen?

By about midday, everybody is nicely dropping off because they haven't got to bed until at least four o'clock in the morning. I always think that they ought to hold TV conferences at three a.m. in the hotel bar – they'd get a much better attendance.

I had been invited to speak at a seminar on light entertainment along with Bob Monkhouse, John Lloyd and Dudley Moore. It was strange to see how, after his great success in Hollywood, Dudley Moore was held in great awe by everyone – we were all hanging on his every word. He'd be wondering out loud where to put his coat and everyone would solemnly write down what he had said and how he said it.

I find that when television people get together, there is a lot of in-talking and gossip. You also begin to realize the amazing number of drunks in the business – very famous drunks. People on television are, in fact, just very famous drunks. They are permanently ratted. I think that's why they are so confident – when you're that ratted, you know no fear.

I soon fell into these ways quite comfortably.

So it was in this hotel bar one lunch time that I remember having a chat with Billy. Although he was not participating in the seminar, he was up in Edinburgh for the festival and had joined up with quite a large group of television people in the bar.

The place was packed. The seminars had just finished for the morning and, since they all worked in television, all these ratted people had raced round to the nearest bar as soon as they got out.

We'd been there for a while, jammed solid in this bar, when I offered to buy a round of drinks. Although I do struggle hard to keep up the traditional, mean comic image, I'd bought one in January and it was now September so I thought it was my turn again.

So I started to try to find my way through this mass of people to the bar to buy a round for about six people, including Billy.

In the distance, I could see the four barmen working away behind the bar. The head one was wearing standard hotel barman gear – he was bursting out of his shirt and his bow tie was all askew.

It appears to be a rule in hotels that they issue uniforms two sizes too small for overweight staff and three sizes too big for the skinny, anorexic ones. Hence the fat barmen are purple and bursting while the thin barmen seem, well, a bit draughty.

Since it was a very hot September, these barmen were spraying everyone with perspiration, running up and down behind the bar like bright red lawn sprinklers. As they went by, people were yelling out things like, 'Four Cinzanos with a twist of lemon and a Buck's Fizz,' because it's very important at these gatherings not to order anything ordinary. So they'll ask for one Jamaican Road Drill, a Tasmanian Lobe Squeezer and a Hawaiian Papa Doc Juice. They only ask for a gin and tonic if they can have something exotic in it like a paw paw or a sculpted yam.

These Scottish barmen, who were used to 'Four pints o' heavy and a triple scotch', were getting a bit uptight as they had to work out these ridiculous orders and find straws, frills and bits of exotic tropical fruit. By the time I had worked my way to the bar, which took about ten minutes, they were more than a little brassed off.

They were sweating away and pounding up and down the bar, banging down glasses everywhere, and the angrier the people waiting became, the more the barmen banged and stomped and sweated and pounded.

Meanwhile I'm going 'Ahem, ahem,' as they went by me with the speed of a ball at the Wimbledon final and it was obviously useless – they were never going to answer to a polite cough. So, summoning up a bit more bottle, I say, 'Two pints of bitter and one —' but no luck.

Five minutes later, and I'm still there waiting and by now people are getting served all around and over my head so I'm beginning to lose my temper a bit.

I don't know why I'm losing control because, in fact, this is quite a usual occurrence for me. I have the greatest difficulty in ever getting served at a bar.

It was once explained to me that there is a manual for barmen which contains a description and identikit picture of a potentially difficult customer and instructions as to how to detect and ignore him. Yes – I look like that person.

I had been trying the same order in a Scottish accent and holding two £5 notes in my hands but that didn't seem to be working either.

'Tae pints o'bitter and a wee scotch a'lemon,' I'd be saying, but it was still Borg to McEnroe, backhand return from McEnroe as they pounded up and down the bar in front of me.

So then I get more money out and I'm holding a bunch of £5 notes in each hand, shouting, 'Will *anybody* serve me tae pints o' bitter and a wee —' By the time I had got my American Express card, Barclaycard, Access card in one hand and £50 in the other, I'm beginning to get really annoyed and still the barmen are ignoring me as they rush up and down the bar.

Just then, I heard Billy's voice from about ten foot back from the bar. It's a voice that barmen notice.

'Hey, pal,' he was yelling. 'Hae ye got any change for the cigarette machine?'

All the barmen immediately stopped what they were doing and there was a mad scramble to the tills to see who could get the change first. McEnroe won.

Meanwhile I'm staring with disbelief at the disruption. I must have looked pathetic, clutching a handful of fivers and cards and with a mouthful of glacé cherries – well, you have to do something while you're waiting.

McEnroe stared at me. Now was my chance. Quickly I gabble my order, 'Two pints of bitter, a scotch, a dry martini and tonic, two glasses of red wine and a large Ruritanian mango.'

'Can you pass this change to the big fella at the back, Jimmy?'

And not wanting to lose the effect of the cards and the fivers, I say, 'Why, yes . . . yes, of course. Put it in my mouth and I'll transfer it back gladly.'

Somehow that sums up the difference between Billy and myself.

Straight Bat Department

J. B. Morton

'Cricket is not taken seriously enough by the players.'

(Evening paper)

(SCENE: The Oval)

UMPIRE: Out!
  BATSMAN: Oh, please! Not that!
  UMPIRE: Out, I said.
  BATSMAN: Have you thought what this means?

(A long pause)

Have you visualized the aftermath; the lonely walk to the pavilion, the jeers of one's mates, the comments in the press?

UMPIRE: I see no other course.
  BATSMAN: You yourself, umpire, have fans. You know what it is to run the gauntlet of hostile eyes, to be held up to ridicule. Little children, years hence, will tell the story of how I was given out, l.b.w., in this match, and will say, 'He was given out l.b.w. by Soames.'

UMPIRE: You only make it harder for me.
  BATSMAN *(quickly)*: But supposing I were not really out——
  UMPIRE: Would not matter. I have said you are out, and that is all that matters. After all, a man must be either in or out. Life is like that. Some are in, others are not.

BATSMAN *(with lowered head)*: Very well. You are but the victim of a system, and I bear you no ill will. Your training leads you to believe that I am out. You act according to your lights. Nevertheless *(with raised voice)*, I ream of a day when no batsman will ever be out, and when umpire and batsman will work hand in hand to build a better cricket field. Goodbye, umpire, oodbye!

(Exit to pavilion)

On Having a Cold

R. S. Hooper

I have a cold. Or rather my cold has begun. It is rather late this year, but three days ago it arrived. It invariably comes about this period of the winter, and stays for several months. This year it gave me quite a shock. The first of November dawned foggily on a snivelling world, and my cold was not there to greet me. As a rule, it turns up as regularly as clockwork in the last week of October. Naturally, I began to wonder what had happened to it. Something had obviously gone wrong, though where the hitch had occurred I knew not. It might have been the Gulf Stream or the Einstein theory, or perhaps a bit of both. I rather thought of ringing up my doctor and asking him what he advised me to do about it. Doctors realize full well the danger of any hiatus in the regular working of nature and mine, I knew, would have been rather upset by my obstinate condition. There was a lot of subdued influenza about, and here was I, after all these years, without a germ to my name or a handkerchief to my nose. By this time last year I was in the midst of an ever-rolling stream that bore all my friends away. The year before my nose became so rubicund, and at the same time so musical, that people used to ask me to play *O Ruddier than the Cherry* on my nasal guitarrh. The year before that I broke the family record for sneezing, spent Christmas in bed, and was turned out of a charity *matinée* for coughing. Previous winters bear the same record of continuous suffering manfully and stoically endured. Being but a poor creature of habit, you can quite understand my feeling of alarm which almost amounted to a disappointment. Another week without a sneeze and it would be a grievance. Pulling myself together, I determined not to telephone to the doctor. I would keep my troubles to myself. No one should know that beneath my smiling exterior there lurked the secret dread that all was not well. I felt like those ancient Greeks who loaded themselves with so much prosperity that the gods grew jealous and dispatched a thunderbolt, carriage forward, to cure them of their presumption. It was a drastic remedy, but it never failed to function. Supposing something like that happened to me? December would arrive without a sign of a sniff; the Christmas festivities would pass off without the vestige of a chill; February-fill-dyke would succeed January-blow-nose, and still I should be dry of eye and clear of lung. My chest would remain immune from the lingering aroma of goose grease; my throat would leave unperformed the symphony of the gargle, now *crescendo*, now *diminuendo*, and finally *andante con molto troppo*. My inside would forget the thrill of its slice of cinnamon melba and the pang of its first amalgamated puncture of quinine. March would come in like a lion and find me trembling with anticipation like a lamb. And then the thunderbolt would fall. The east winds would blow a million microbes into my system – the deadly nightshade, the deadlier night light, the *bacillus angostura*, and all those other bacilli that make the rents so high in Harley Street. By April the first I should be down with pulmonary arthritis on my Jupiter Pluvius. Lynx-eyed specialists, grave-eyed doctors, and wall-eyed sisters would hover round my bed with hot water bottles, s'deathoscopes, forceps, biceps, and all the grim impedimenta of a sick room. April would draw to an end and the spring would come. But I should not be Queen of the May. They would come and call me early, but I should not answer. Ah, no. Outside the birds would be singing their first vernal song, the croci would be opening their gaudy parasols to the sun, the wombat would be heard building his nest in the wistaria, while I . . . 'Lower the blinds, Parkinson. Your master has gone. Heigho!'

When I think what I have been spared – what Parkinson has been spared – you can imagine the first signs of deliverance did not come amiss. To tell the truth, I was beginning to feel rather out of it. All my friends had colds and I had none. 'How's your cold?' they would ask, blowing their noses heartily; and I would be forced to reply, feebly and uncomfortably, 'I haven't got one.' 'Haven't got a cold? Good heavens, man! Everybody's got a cold. Had mine for days. Can't get rid of it. Most extraordinary the sort of colds every one's wearing this year. Quite different from last . . .' and so on. By the time mine did arrive everybody else would have forgotten theirs weeks ago . . . No one would want to compare notes on our respective symptoms; no one would take any interest or sympathize. 'Fancy having a cold now!' people would say. 'I got rid of mine ages ago.' These callous brutes would regard me with none of that fellow feeling which borrows handkerchiefs and exchanges remedies.

No wonder then, three days ago, I awoke with a weight off my mind (which had transferred itself to my chest), and, sitting up in bed, cleared my throat and exclaimed with joy and thanksgiving, 'I hab a gold – in by head, in by

dose, on by jest. Alleluia!' By evening it was settling down nicely. But next
morning I had a terrible shock. I thought it had gone. In some way quite
unintentionally I must have offended it the night before. At any rate, when
I looked for it in the morning I couldn't find it. By breakfast there was no
sign of it. After lunch I got on the track of it by going out without a coat on;
by tea time I could feel it returning slowly but surely; and by bed time the
reconciliation was complete. Yesterday I had a few anxious moments, but
today its success is assured.

Tonight I am going through the same old ceremony that has become almost
a ritual. I shall eat as much as I can for dinner, pull the best armchair half
way into the fire, pile on the coal, close my eyes, and sink into a deep stertorous coma. I shall be a very old man – or rather a young man with a very
bad cold – my winter cold that is to last me well into the New Year. I shall
say goodbye to it just before Easter – not harshly, but more in sorrow than
in anger, for it is an old companion. I know its ways so well by now and it
knows mine. We become a little distant as the months wear on, and sometimes
it leaves me for a week or two, but always it comes back to find me ready
to make it up again and let bygones be bygones. Meanwhile, tonight the little
drama of welcoming the prodigal's return will go on. There is whisky, there
is sugar, and there is water, though I cannot guarantee the lemon. I shall sip
this nectar as I shiver in bed with a pain in my head and a sore throat that
makes 'gaspers' taste beastly – like real cigarettes. With the last mouthful I
shall swallow with difficulty two aspirins and sink into a heavy sleep. Being
wise and patient, I shall not cheat myself into thinking by doing all these
things to cure my cold. No one can cure a cold. Some people, but very few,
can prevent it coming by being careless and never wearing thick underclothes,
but to cure a cold when once it has come upon you – it is absurd. No. My
cold has come. I drink hot drinks, I swallow tabloids, I embrace hot water
bottles, not because I am fool enough to think I shall cure it. Rather because,
knowing that it will stay as long as it likes, I realize that old customs are old
customs, and must be honoured; not in the breach, but in the observance. My
cold expects it. It knows as well as I do that I shall be feeling no better in
the morning. But by Easter . . . Who nose?

The Double

E. V. Lucas

There must be few minor agonies more disturbing than the presence of a constant suspicion which no amount of investigation can ever confirm or disperse.

And when a matter of eighty Fishers is concerned, why, then . . .

On the assumption that everyone now bets on horses, I have latterly opened
all casual conversations in street and tram, office and bus, lift and cloakroom,
with the remark, 'I hope you backed so-and-so?' – or whatever outsider it was
that had most recently upset all the form and the prophets and won at long
odds – and in ninety-nine cases out of a hundred the answer indicated that,
although that most desirable proceeding was not indulged in, money had been
invested on one or more runners.

The honour of being the hundredth man fell to the old waiter at a certain
chop-house.

No, he said, he hadn't backed so-and-so or anyone else. Because he didn't
hold with betting. A mug's game. He'd never had but one bet, and that was
enough for him. Too much, in fact, for it had poisoned his life.

'Poisoned?' I repeated.

'Yes,' he said, 'poisoned. It was like this: I never took any interest in racing,
except now and then to be barged into and very nearly knocked down and
most likely killed by newspaper boys rushing about with the winner of the
three-thirty, till one day a customer here – a nice, affable gent too – when
the time came to pay hadn't a brown left for me, so he said, "I can't give
you any money, Robert, but I'll give you a tip of a better kind. Tomorrow
there's a double that's a cert – Pneumonia and Knightsbridge." You know
what a double is? Both horses have to win or you don't get anything; but if
both win you get a packet.

'As I knew nothing about racing I went to a pal who was going to the races
and handed him a sovereign, for, "If I am going to gamble," I said, "I'll do
it proper. Put that on Pneumonia and Knightsbridge for the double," I said.

"Righto," he said. "Don't forget," I said. "Not 'arf," he said, and then I went home to bed.

'But I couldn't sleep for thinking about those two horses. And all next day. I was like a maniac. Every time I heard a paper boy my heart turned right over. At lunch I got all the orders wrong. I served mulligatawny instead of custard, and if I broke one plate I broke twenty. My hand was like a shuttle. And then at last I got a paper with the first of my races in it, and found that Pneumonia had won at 10 to 1. I could hardly stand up.

'Half the double had come home, and all I had to do now was to win the other half and then I'd be a millionaire – a Solly Joel and Harry Lauder rolled into one – for that's what all that money would mean to me.

'Well, my second race wasn't till late, and how I got through that afternoon I don't know. And then when I had bought a paper I didn't dare to look at it. It cost me eighteenpence for brandy before I could bring my eyes to the print, and there, sure enough, Knightsbridge had won too, at 8 to 1. Just think of it, 10 to 1 and 8 to 1 – that was eighty-eight pounds to me, because they add the first quid on. No one knows how I felt. I was just like a baby – I laughed and cried both together. I thought of all the things I'd buy. I was mad with joy.'

He stopped and gulped.

'And then in walks my pal and hands me a sovereign. "I'm really very sorry," says he, "but I quite forgot to put it on for you."

'Well, I hope I'll never have another shock like that. In fact, I couldn't stand another. Another would do me in.

' "You forgot it?" I said, when I came to. "Yes," he said, "I'm very sorry. I forgot it."

'And to this day I don't know whether he did or not. That's what I mean by poisoning life. Whenever I meet him I look him in the eye and wonder and wonder. "Did you have eighty of the best off me, or didn't you?" I says to myself, staring at him X-ray like. But I shall never know. Is he my friend, or is he a wrong 'un? I shall never know. Isn't that poisoning life?'

Hot Potatoes

Arnold Bennett

I

It was considered by certain people to be a dramatic moment in the history of musical enterprise in the Five Towns when Mrs Swann opened the front door of her house at Bleakridge, in the early darkness of a November evening, and let forth her son Gilbert. Gilbert's age was nineteen, and he was wearing evening dress, a form of raiment that had not hitherto happened to him. Over the elegant suit was his winter overcoat, making him bulky, and round what may be called the rim of the overcoat was a white woollen scarf, and the sleeves of the overcoat were finished off with white woollen gloves. Under one arm he carried a vast inanimate form whose extremity just escaped the ground. This form was his violoncello, fragile as a pretty woman, ungainly as a navvy, and precious as honour. Mrs Swann looked down the street, which ended to the east in darkness and a marl-pit, and up the street, which ended to the west in Trafalgar Road and electric cars; and she shivered, though she had a shawl over her independent little shoulders. In the Five Towns, and probably elsewhere, when a woman puts her head out of her front door, she always looks first to right and then to left, like a scouting Iroquois, and if the air nips she shivers – not because she is cold, but merely to express herself.

'For goodness sake, keep your hands warm,' Mrs Swann enjoined her son.

'Oh!' said Gilbert, with scornful lightness, as though his playing had never suffered from cold hands, 'it's quite warm tonight!' Which it was not.

'And mind what you eat!' added his mother. 'There! I can hear the car.'

He hurried up the street. The electric tram slid in thunder down Trafalgar Road, and stopped for him with a jar, and he gingerly climbed into it, practising all precautions on behalf of his violoncello. The car slid away again towards Bursley, making blue sparks. Mrs Swann stared mechanically at the flickering gas in her lobby, and then closed her front door. He was gone! The boy was gone!

Now, the people who considered the boy's departure to be a dramatic
moment in the history of musical enterprise in the Five Towns were Mrs
Swann, chiefly, and the boy, secondarily.

II

And more than the moment – the day, nay, the whole week – was dramatic
in the history of local musical enterprise.

It had occurred to somebody in Hanbridge, about a year before, that since
York, Norwich, Hereford, Gloucester, Birmingham, and even Blackpool had
their musical festivals, the Five Towns too, ought to have its musical festival.
The Five Towns possessed a larger population than any of these centres save
Birmingham, and it was notorious for its love of music. Choirs from the Five
Towns had gone to all sorts of places – such as Brecknock, Aberystwyth, the
Crystal Palace, and even a place called Hull – and had come back with first
prizes – cups and banners – for the singing of choruses and part-songs. There
were three (or at least two and a half) rival choirs in Hanbridge alone. Then
also the brass band contests were famously attended. In the Five Towns the
number of cornet players is scarcely exceeded by the number of public houses.
Hence the feeling, born and fanned into lustiness at Hanbridge, that the Five
Towns owed it to its self-respect to have a Musical Festival like the rest of the
world! Men who had never heard of Wagner, men who could not have told
the difference between a sonata and a sonnet to save their souls, men who
spent all their lives in manufacturing teacups or china door knobs, were
invited to guarantee five pounds apiece against possible loss on the festival;
and they bravely and blindly did so. The conductor of the largest Hanbridge
choir, being appointed to conduct the preliminary rehearsals of the Festival
Chorus, had an acute attack of self-importance, which, by the way, almost
ended fatally a year later.

Double-crown posters appeared magically on all the hoardings announcing
that a Festival consisting of three evening and two morning concerts would
be held in the Alexandra Hall, at Hanbridge, on the 6th, 7th and 8th
November, and that the box-plan could be consulted at the principal sta-
tioners. The Alexandra Hall contained no boxes whatever, but 'box-plan' was
the phrase sacred to the occasion, and had to be used. And the Festival more
and more impregnated the air, and took the lion's share of the columns of the
Staffordshire Signal. Every few days the *Signal* reported progress, even to intimate biographical details of the singers engaged, and of the composers to be
performed, together with analyses of the latter's works. And at last the week

itself had dawned in exhilaration and excitement. And early on the day before the opening day John Merazzi, the renowned conductor, and Herbert Millwain, the renowned leader of the orchestra, and the renowned orchestra itself, all arrived from London. And finally sundry musical critics arrived from the offices of sundry London dailies. The presence of these latter convinced an awed population that its Festival was a real Festival, and not a local make-believe. And it also tranquillized in some degree the exasperating and disconcerting effect of a telegram from the capricious Countess of Chell (who had taken six balcony seats and was the official advertised high patroness of the Festival) announcing at the last moment that she could not attend.

III

Mrs Swann's justification for considering (as she in fact did consider) that her son was either the base or the apex of the splendid pyramid of the Festival lay in the following facts:

From earliest infancy Gilbert had been a musical prodigy, and the circle of his fame had constantly been extending. He could play the piano with his hands before his legs were long enough for him to play it with his feet. That is to say, before he could use the pedals. A spectacle formerly familiar to the delighted friends of the Swanns was Gilbert, in a pinafore and curls, seated on a high chair topped with a large Bible and a bound volume of the *Graphic*, playing *Home, Sweet Home* with Thalberg's variations, while his mother, standing by his side on her right foot, put the loud pedal on or off with her left foot according to the infant's whispered orders. He had been allowed to play from ear – playing from ear being deemed especially marvellous – until some expert told Mrs Swann that playing solely from ear was a practice to be avoided if she wished her son to fulfil the promise of his babyhood. Then he had lessons at Knype, until he began to teach his teacher. Then he said he would learn the fiddle, and he did learn the fiddle; also the viola. He did not pretend to play the flute, though he could. And at school the other boys would bring him their penny or even sixpenny whistles so that he might show them of what wonderful feats a common tin whistle is capable.

Mr Swann was secretary for the Toft End Brickworks and Colliery Company (Limited). Mr Swann had passed the whole of his career in the offices of the prosperous Toft End Company, and his imagination did not move freely beyond the company's premises. He had certainly intended that Gilbert should follow in his steps; perhaps he meant to establish a dynasty of Swanns, in which the secretaryship of the 20 per cent paying company should descend for ever from father to son. But Gilbert's astounding facility in music had shaken even this resolve, and Gilbert had been allowed at the age of fifteen to enter, as assistant, the shop of Mr James Otkinson, the piano and musical instrument dealer and music-seller, in Crown Square, Hanbridge. Here, of course, he found himself in a musical atmosphere. Here he had at once established a reputation for showing off the merits of a piano, a song, or a waltz to customers male and female. Here he had thirty pianos, seven harmoniums, and all the new and a lot of classical music to experiment with. He would play any 'piece' at sight for the benefit of any lady in search of a nice easy waltz or reverie. Unfortunately ladies would complain that the pieces proved much more difficult at home than they had seemed under the fingers of Gilbert in the shop. Here, too, he began to give lessons on the piano. And here he satisfied his secret ambition to learn the violoncello, Mr Otkinson having in stock a violoncello that had never found a proper customer. His progress with the 'cello had been such that the theatre people offered him an engagement, which his father and his own sense of the enormous respectability of the Swanns compelled him to refuse. But he always played in the band of the Five Towns Amateur Operatic Society, and was beloved by its conductor as being utterly reliable. His connection with choirs started through his merits as a rehearsal accompanist who could keep time and make his bass chords heard against a hundred and fifty voices. He had been appointed (*nem. con.*) rehearsal accompanist to the Festival Chorus. He knew the entire Festival music backwards and upside-down. And his modestly expressed desire to add his 'cello as one of the lcoal reinforcements of the London orchestra had been almost eagerly complied with by the Advisory Committee.

Nor was this all. He had been invited to dinner by Mrs Clayton Vernon, the social leader of Bursley. In the affair of the Festival Mrs Clayton Vernon loomed larger than even she really was. And this was due to an accident, to a sheer bit of luck on her part. She happened to be a cousin of Mr Herbert Millwain, the leader of the orchestra down from London. Mrs Clayton Vernon knew no more about music than she knew about the North Pole, and cared no more. But she was Mr Millwain's cousin, and Mr Millwain had naturally to stay at her house. And she came in her carriage to fetch him from the band rehearsals; and, in short, anyone might have thought from her self-satisfied demeanour (though she was a decent sort of woman at heart) that she had at least composed *Judas Maccabeus*. It was at a band rehearsal that she had graciously commanded Gilbert Swann to come and dine with her and Mr Millwain between the final rehearsal and the opening concert. This invitation was, as it were, the overflowing drop in Mrs Swann's cup. It was proof, to her, that Mr Millwain had instantly pronounced Gilbert to be the equal of London 'cellists, and perhaps their superior. It was proof, to her, that Mr Millwain relied on him particularly to maintain the honour of the band in the Festival.

Gilbert had dashed home from the final rehearsal, and his mother had helped him with the unfamiliarities of evening dress, while he gave her a list of all the places in the music where, as he said, the band was 'rocky', and especially the 'cellos, and a further list of all the smart musical things that the players from London had said to him and he had said to them. He simply knew everything from the inside. And not even the great Merazzi, the conductor, was more familiar with the music than he. And the ineffable Mrs Clayton Vernon had asked him to dinner with Mr Millwain! It was indubitable to Mrs Swann that all the Festival rested on her son's shoulders.

IV

'It's freezing, I think,' said Mr Swann, when he came home at six o'clock from his day's majestic work at Toft End. This was in the bedroom. Mrs Swann, a comely little thing of thirty-nine, was making herself resplendent for the inaugural solemnity of the Festival, which began at eight. The news of the frost disturbed her.

'How annoying!' she said.

'Annoying?' he questioned blandly. 'Why?'

'Now you needn't put on any of your airs, John!' she snapped. She had a curt way with her at critical times. 'You know as well as I do that I'm thinking of Gilbert's hands . . . No! you must wear your frock-coat, of course! . . . All that drive from the other end of the town right to Hanbridge in a carriage! Perhaps outside the carriage, because of the 'cello! There'll never be room for two of them and the 'cello and Mrs Clayton Vernon in her carriage! And he can't keep his hands in his pockets because of holding the 'cello. And he's bound to pretend he isn't cold. He's so silly. And yet he knows perfectly well he won't do himself justice if his hands are cold. Don't you remember last year at the Town Hall?'

'Well,' said Mr Swann, 'we can't do anything; anyway, we must hope for the best.'

'That's all very well,' said Mrs Swann. And it was.

Shortly afterwards, perfect in most details of her black silk, she left the bedroom, requesting her husband to be quick, as tea was ready. And she came into the little dining room where the youthful servant was poking up the fire.

'Jane,' she said, 'put two medium-sized potatoes in the oven to bake.'

'Potatoes, mum?'

'Yes, potatoes,' said Mrs Swann, tartly.

It was an idea of pure genius that had suddenly struck her; the genius of common sense.

She somewhat hurried the tea; then rang.

'Jane,' she inquired, 'are those potatoes ready?'

'Potatoes?' exclaimed Mr Swann.

'Yes, hot potatoes,' said Mrs Swann, tartly. 'I'm going to run up with them by car to Mrs Vernon's. I can slip them quietly over to Gil. They keep your hands warm better than anything. Don't I remember when I was a child! I shall leave Mrs Vernon's immediately, of course, but perhaps you'd better give me my ticket and I will meet you at the hall. Don't you think it's the best plan, John?'

'As you like,' said Mr Swann, with the force of habit.

He was supreme in most things, but in the practical details of their son's life and comfort she was supreme. Her decision in such matters had never been questioned. Mr Swann had a profound belief in his wife as a uniquely capable and energetic woman. He was tremendously loyal to her, and he sternly inculcated the same loyalty to her in Gilbert.

V

Just as the car had stopped at the end of the street for Gilbert and his violoncello, so – more than an hour later – it stopped for Mrs Swann and her hot potatoes.

They were hot potatoes – nay, very hot potatoes – of a medium size, because Mrs Swann's recollections of youth had informed her that if a potato is too large one cannot get one's fingers well around it, and if it is too small it cools somewhat rapidly. She had taken two, not in the hope that Gilbert would be able to use two at once, for one cannot properly nurse either a baby or a 'cello with two hands full of potatoes, but rather to provide against accident. Besides, the inventive boy might after all find a way of using both simultaneously, which would be all the better for his playing at the concert, and hence all the better for the success of the Musical Festival.

It never occurred to Mrs Swann that she was doing anything in the least unusual. There she was, in her best boots, and her best dress, and her best hat, and her sealskin mantle (not easily to be surpassed in the town), and her muff to match (nearly), and concealed in the muff were the two very hot potatoes. And it did not strike her that women of fashion like herself, wives of secretaries of flourishing companies, do not commonly go about with hot potatoes concealed on their persons. For she was a self-confident woman, and after a decision she did not reflect, nor did she heed minor consequences. She was always sure that what she was doing was the right and only think to do. And, to give her justice, it was; for her direct, abrupt common sense was indeed remarkable. The act of climbing up into the car warned her that she must be skilful in the control of these potatoes; one of them nearly fell out of the right end of her muff as she grasped the car rail with her right hand. She had to let go and save the potato, and begin again, while the car waited. The conductor took her for one of those hesitating, hysterical women who are the bane of car conductors. 'Now, missis!' he said, 'Up with ye!' But she did not care what manner of woman the conductor took her for.

The car was nearly full of people going home from their work, of people actually going in a direction contrary to the direction of the Musical Festival. She sat down among them, shocked by this indifference to the Musical Festival. At the back of her head had been an idea that all the cars for Hanbridge would be crammed to the step, and all the cars from Hanbridge forlorn and empty. She had vaguely imagined that the thoughts of a quarter of a million of people would that evening be centred on the unique Musical Festival. And she was shocked also by the conversation – not that it was in the slightest degree improper – but because it displayed no interest whatever in the Musical Festival. And yet there were several Festival advertisements adhering to the roof of the car. Travellers were discussing football, soap, the weather, rates, trade; travellers were dozing; travellers were reading about starting prices; but not one seemed to be occupied with the Musical Festival. 'Nevertheless,' she reflected, with consoling pride, 'if they knew that our Gilbert was playing 'cello in the orchestra and dining at this very moment with Mr Millwain, some of them would be fine and surprised, that they would!' No one would ever have suspected, from her calm, careless, proud face, that such vain and twopenny thoughts were passing through her head. But the thoughts that do pass through the heads of even the most common-sensed philosophers, men and women, are truly astonishing.

In four minutes she was at Bursley Town Hall, where she changed into another car – full of people equally indifferent to the Musical Festival – for the suburb of Hillport, where Mrs Clayton Vernon lived.

'Put me out opposite Mrs Clayton Vernon's, will you?' she said to the conductor, and added, 'You know the house?'

He nodded as if to say disdainfully in response to such a needless question: 'Do I know the house? Do I know my pocket?'

As she left the car she did catch two men discussing the Festival, but they appeared to have no intention of attending it. They were earthenware manufacturers. One of them raised his hat to her. And she said to herself: 'He at any rate knows how important my Gilbert is in the Festival!'

It was at the instant she pushed open Mrs Clayton Vernon's long and heavy garden gate, and crunched in the frosty darkness up the short winding drive, that the notion of the peculiarity of her errand first presented itself to her. Mrs Clayton Vernon was a relatively great lady, living in a relatively great house; one of the few exalted or peculiar ones who did not dine in the middle of the day like other folk. Mrs Clayton Vernon had the grand manner. Mrs Clayton Vernon instinctively and successfully patronized everybody. Mrs Clayton Vernon was a personage with whom people did not joke. And lo! Mrs Swann was about to invade her courtly and luxurious house, uninvited, unauthorized, with a couple of hot potatoes in her muff. What would Mrs Clayton Vernon think of hot potatoes in a muff? Of course, the Swanns were 'as good as anybody'. The Swanns knelt before nobody. The Swanns were of the cream of the town, combining commerce with art, and why should not Mrs Swann take practical measures to keep her son's hands warm in Mrs Clayton Vernon's cold carriage? Still, there was only one Mrs Clayton Vernon in Bursley, and it was impossible to deny that she inspired awe, even in the independent soul of Mrs Swann.

Mrs Swann rang the bell, reassuring herself. The next instant an electric light miraculously came into existence outside the door, illuminating her from head to foot. This startled her. But she said to herself that it must be the latest dodge, and that, at any rate, it was a very good dodge, and she began again the process of reassuring herself. The door opened, and a prim creature stiffly starched stood before Mrs Swann. 'My word!' reflected Mrs Swann, 'she must cost her mistress a pretty penny for getting up aprons!' And she said aloud curtly:

'Will you please tell Mr Gilbert Swann that some one wants to speak to him a minute at the door?'

'Yes,' said the servant, with pert civility. 'Will you please step in?'

She had not meant to step in. She had decidedly meant not to step in, for she had no wish to encounter Mrs Clayton Vernon; indeed, the reverse. But she immediately perceived that in asking to speak to a guest at the door she had socially erred. At Mrs Clayton Vernon's refined people did not speak to refined people at the door. So she stepped in, and the door was closed, prisoning her and her potatoes in the imposing hall.

'I only want to see Mr Gilbert Swann,' she insisted.

'Yes,' said the servant. 'Will you please step into the breakfast room? There's no one there. I will tell Mr Swann.'

VI

As Mrs Swann was being led like a sheep out of the hall into an apartment on the right, which the servant styled the breakfast room, another door opened, further up the hall, and Mrs Clayton Vernon appeared. Magnificent though Mrs Swann was, the ample Mrs Clayton Vernon, discreetly *décolletée*, was even more magnificent. Dressed as she meant to show herself at the concert, Mrs Clayton Vernon made a resplendent figure worthy to be the cousin of the leader of the orchestra – and worthy even to take the place of the missing Countess of Chell. Mrs Clayton Vernon had a *lorgnon* at the end of a shaft of tortoiseshell; otherwise, a pair of eyeglasses on a stick. She had the habit of the *lorgnon*; the *lorgnon* seldom left her, and whenever she was in any doubt or difficulty she would raise the *lorgnon* to her eyes and stare patronizingly. It was a gesture tremendously effective. She employed it now on Mrs Swann, as who should say, 'Who is this insignificant and scarcely visible creature that has got into my noble hall?' Mrs Swann stopped, struck into immobility by the basilisk glance. A courageous and even a defiant woman, Mrs Swann was taken aback. She could not possibly tell Mrs Clayton Vernon that she was the bearer of hot potatoes to her son. She scarcely knew Mrs Clayton Vernon, had only met her once at a bazaar! With a convulsive unconscious movement her right hand clenched nervously within her muff and crushed the rich mealy potato it held until the flesh of the potato was forced between the fingers of her glove. A horrible sticky mess! That is the worst of a high class potato, cooked, as the Five Towns phrase it, 'in it's jacket'. It will burst on the least provocation. There stood Mrs Swann, her right hand glued up with escaped potato, in the sober grandeur of Mrs Clayton Vernon's hall, and Mrs Clayton Vernon bearing down on her like a Dreadnought.

Steam actually began to emerge from her muff.

'Ah!' said Mrs Clayton Vernon, inspecting Mrs Swann. 'It's Mrs Swann! How do you do, Mrs Swann?'

She seemed politely astonished, as well she might be. By a happy chance she did not perceive the wisp of steam. She was not looking for steam. People do not expect steam from the interior of a visitor's muff.

'Oh!' said Mrs Swann, who was really in a pitiable state. 'I'm sorry to trouble you, Mrs Clayton Vernon. But I want to speak to Gilbert for one moment.'

She then saw that Mrs Clayton Vernon's hand was graciously extended. She could not take it with her right hand, which was fully engaged with the extremely heated sultriness of the ruined potato. She could not refuse it, or ignore it. She therefore offered her left hand, which Mrs Clayton Vernon pressed with a well-bred pretence that people always offered her their left hands.

'Nothing wrong, I do hope!' said she, gravely.

'Oh, no,' said Mrs Swann. Only just a little matter which has been forgotten. Only half a minute. I must hurry off at once as I have to meet my husband. If I could just see Gilbert——'

'Certainly,' said Mrs Clayton Vernon. 'Do come into the breakfast room, will you? We've just finished dinner. We had it very early, of course, for the concert. Mr Millwain – my cousin – hates to be hurried. Maria, be good enough to tell Mr Swann to come here. Tell him that his mother wishes to speak to him.'

In the breakfast room Mrs Swann was invited, nay commanded by Mrs Clayton Vernon to loosen her mantle. But she could not loosen her mantle. She could do nothing. In clutching the potato to prevent bits of it falling out of the muff, she of course effected the precise opposite of her purpose, and bits of the luscious and perfect potato began to descend the front of her mantle. The clock struck seven, and ages elapsed, during which Mrs Swann could not think of anything whatever to say, but the finger of the clock somehow stuck motionless at seven, though the pendulum plainly wagged.

'I'm not too warm,' she said at length, feebly but obstinately resisting Mrs Clayton Vernon's command. This, to speak bluntly, was an untruth. She was too warm.

'Are you sure that nothing is the matter?' urged Mrs Clayton Vernon, justifiably alarmed by the expression of her visitor's features. 'I beg you to confide in me if——'

'Not at all,' said Mrs Swann, trying to laugh. 'I'm only sorry to disturb you. I didn't mean to disturb you.'

'What on earth is that?' cried Mrs Clayton Vernon.

The other potato, escaping Mrs Swann's vigilance, had run out of the muff and come to the carpet with a dull thud. It rolled half under Mrs Swann's dress. Almost hysterically she put her foot on it, thus making pulp of the second potato.

'What?' she inquired innocently.

'Didn't you hear anything? I trust it isn't a mouse! We have had them once.'

Mrs Clayton Vernon thought how brave Mrs Swann was, not to be frightened by the word 'mouse'.

'I didn't hear anything,' said Mrs Swann. Another untruth.

'If you aren't too warm, won't you come a little nearer the fire?'

But not for a thousand pounds would Mrs Swann have exposed the mush of potato on the carpet under her feet. She could not conceive in what ignominy the dreadful affair would end, but she was the kind of woman that nails her colours to the mast.

'Dear me!' Mrs Clayton Vernon murmured. 'How delicious those potatoes do smell! I can smell them all over the house.'

This was the most staggering remark that Mrs Swann had ever heard.

'Potatoes?' very weakly.

'Yes,' said Mrs Clayton Vernon, smiling. 'I must tell you that Mr Millwain is very nervous about getting his hands cold in driving to Hanbridge. And he has asked me to have hot potatoes prepared. Isn't it amusing? It seems hot potatoes are constantly used for this purpose in winter by pupils of the Royal College of Music, and even by the professors. My cousin says that even a slight chilliness of the hands interferes with his playing. So I am having potatoes done for your son too. A delightful boy he is!'

'Really!' said Mrs Swann. 'How queer! But what a good idea!'

She might have confessed then. But you do not know her if you think she did. Gilbert came in, anxious and alarmed. Mrs Clayton Vernon left them together. The mother explained matters to the son, and in an instant of time the ruin of two magnificent potatoes was at the back of the fire. Then, without saluting Mrs Clayton Vernon, Mrs Swann fled.

On Being Mean

Peter Fleming

My friend's gamekeeper was inveighing against a man whose house, surrounded by a large garden, stood in the middle of the estate, and who was alleged to shoot any pheasants that strayed within range of his dining room window. 'There's one lucky thing, though,' said the gamekeeper philosophically. 'He's too mean to give his gardener any money to buy raisins with.' Raisins, as every single one of my readers will be well aware, are a lure as supposedly irresistible to pheasants as mink is to ladies.

The remark set me pondering, as I drove home that evening, on the whole question of stinginess. I suppose it would be no easier to find a man who knew he was mean than one who admitted that he had no sense of humour. The timid and the reckless, the choleric and the greedy, the absent-minded and the unpunctual – these are generally aware, in some degree, of their failings. The mean man is mercifully but rather unfairly protected from self-knowledge. He will confess, he may even boast, that he is prudent, thrifty, economical; the suspicion that he is mean never crosses his mind.

Perhaps it is partly for this reason – because he sees no cause to hide a fault which he does not acknowledge – that meanness is so readily discernible. Though normally betrayed only by small acts or small omissions, it almost always sticks out a mile. It is sometimes diagnosed where it may not in fact exist. When, for instance, I raised the question at the dinner-table that night, a man claimed that his elderly uncle was mean because he always travelled by bus to the City, where he is a person of great consequence: it was implied that he could, and should, have been transported in a car provided for the purpose by his firm or if necessary by himself.

But true meanness should surely have a victim. For all anybody knows this outwardly parsimonious tycoon *likes* travelling in buses, or takes pride in observing a long-established routine, or has some other good personal reason for doing what he does. The point is that nobody suffers, nobody is bilked or disappointed or given short measure, as a result of his austerity. It would be different if he took a taxi from the West End to the City every morning and consistently under-tipped the driver. Then you would say with certainty that he was mean.

After this conversation a slight feeling of uneasiness began to creep over me. I think of myself as a reasonably open-handed man, but is this conception valid? If mean men never know that they are mean, how do I know that I am not? Almost everybody is parsimonious about something. My grandmother, for instance, although generous by nature and extremely well off, used when she sent us a pound note on our birthdays to post this largesse in an envelope without a stamp on it. Someone had told her (I do not know if it is or was true) that an unstamped envelope left in its transit through the mails a spoor as clearly marked as a registered letter and if it went astray could be traced as easily as the more costly missive. By this stratagem she effected a small, superfluous saving.

She was also extremely economical with notepaper; having covered both sides of a sheet with her bold, exclamatory, scarcely legible script she would fill in the open space above the letter-head and any other virgin territory round the margins until the whole thing became a sort of calligraphic maze.

Here (now I come to think of it) I detect the baneful influence of heredity in my own habits at the escritoire. I am not mean over notepaper. My letters, however disagreeable or inelegant their content, present a straightforward, symmetrical appearance, the lines reading from left to right and never from north to south down the side of the page. My grandmother's letters gave you the impression that, possibly owing to her house being under some form of siege, she found herself obliged to husband her writing materials with the utmost care; mine do not do this.

But confront me with a blank sheet of foolscap and the hidden streak of avarice is revealed. I do not *want* to save paper by squeezing as many lines on to a page as I can. I know it is directly contrary to my interests to do this, for it leaves me insufficient room to make insertions and alterations in the deathless prose, and by the time the manuscript reaches my secretary's typewriter parts of it are barely decipherable. I used (whenever I remembered in time) to leave proper spaces between the lines when I began a fresh page, but as soon as I got under way the subconscious urge to pack the little strips of prose together as though they were sardines took control and the end-product was another overcrowded palimpsest.

Involuntary and atavistic though it may have been, this practice conformed to my definition of meanness because it had, in the person of my luckless secretary, a victim. I am happy to say I have overcome it. Like an uncertified lunatic ordering a straitjacket from the Army and Navy Stores (their Christmas catalogue advertises Easi-Kneeler Stools, Tele Fireside Chairs, Cosy Travelling Footmuffs and other artefacts which suggest that this great emporium could, if it wished to, claim to be the maniac's friend), I have procured a great mass of paper with lines ruled across it and a margin marked out in red. Since then, as old-fashioned advertisements used to say, I have used no other. The raw material produced by my pen, however banal, is tractable, convertible into a typescript. The snake of my meanness has at least been scotched.

But probably I, like everybody else, am mean in other unsuspected ways. Admittedly we are set a bad example by our rulers, to whichever faction they happen to belong. A minister may appear, fleetingly, to be generous when concessions are announced, subsidies increased, pension scales reviewed. But in fact all those in charge of public funds – and most of those in charge of other people's money in any form – keep a tight hold on the purse-strings, as is their duty. They often are, and they almost always think they are, generous; but even to the successful applicants for their bounties they appear to be mean. It was never their intention to appear so. Nor, if it comes to that, was it ours.

Whether he likes it or not, whether he knows it or not, *homo sapiens* has a streak of meanness in him.

The Mid-Atlantic Man

Tom Wolfe

Roger! Have you met George? Cyril! Have you met George? Keith! Have you met George? Brian! Have you met George? Tony! Have you met George! Nigel! Have you—

—oh god, he's doing a hell of a job of it, introducing everybody by their first names, first-naming the hell out of everybody, introducing them to George, who just arrived from New York: George is an American and the key man in the Fabrilex account. A hell of a job of introductions he is doing. He has everybody from the firm, plus a lot of other people, English and American, all calculated to impress and flatter American George, all piled into this sort of library-reception room upstairs at the —— Club amid the lyre-splat chairs, bullion-fringe curtains, old blacky Raeburn-style portraits, fabulously junky glass-and-ormolu chandeliers, paw-foot chiffoniers, teapoys, ingenious library steps leading resolutely up into thin air, a wonderful dark world of dark wood, dark rugs, candy-box covings, mouldings, flutings, pilasters, all red as table wine, brown as boots, made to look like it has been steeped a hundred years in expensive tobacco, roast beef, horseradish sauce and dim puddings.

The Americans really lap this Club stuff up, but that is not the point, the point is that – Christ, Americans are childish in many ways and about as subtle as a Wimpy bender: but in the long run it doesn't make any difference. They just turn on the power. They have the power, they just move in and take it, introducing people by their first names as they go, people they've never laid eyes on, *pals*, and who gives a damn. They didn't go to Cambridge and learn to envy people who belonged to the Pitt Club and commit the incredible gaffe of walking into the Pitt Club with a Cambridge scarf on. They just turn on the money or whatever it takes, and they take it, and the grinning first names shall inherit the earth, their lie-down crewcuts as firm and pure as Fabrilex – and –

—he has had a couple of highballs. Highballs! That is what they call whisky and sodas. And now he is exhilarated with the absolute *baldness* of putting on his glistening ceramic grin and introducing all of these faces to George by their first names, good old George, cleaned and pressed old George, big blucher shoed old George, popped out of the Fabrilex mould old George – the delicious baldness of it!

Karl! Have you met George? Alec! Have you met George? John! Have you met George? George, predictably, has a super-ingratiating and deferential grin on his face, shaking hands, pumping away, even with people who don't put their hands out at first – Mark! shake hands with George, he wants to say – and as George shakes hands he always lowers his head slightly and grins in panic and looks up from under his eyebrows, deferentially, this kind of unconscious deference because he . . . is meeting *Englishmen* . . .

Still! Why should George give a damn? He can throw away points like this right and left. That's the way Americans are. They can make the wrong gesture, make the most horrible malapropisms, use so many wrong forks it drives the waiter up the wall; demonstrate themselves to be, palpably, social hydrocephalics, total casualties of gaucherie and humiliation – and yet after-wards they don't give a damn. They are right back the next morning as if nothing had happened, smashing on, good-humored, hard-grabbing, win-ning, taking, clutching. George can scrape and bobble his eyeballs under his eyebrows all day and he will still make his £20,000 a year and buy and sell every bastard in this room –

Nicholas! Have you met George?

Harold! Have you met George?

Freddie! Have you met George?

'Pe-t-e-r . . .'

. . . Oh Christ . . . the second syllable of the name just dribbles off his lips.

With Peter – suddenly he can't go through with it. He can't do the first name thing with Peter, he can't hail him over and introduce him to this Amer-ican – Peter! – George! – as if of course they're pals, *pals*. Peter? A pal? Peter is on precisely his level in the hierarchy of the firm, the same age, 33, yet . . . in another hierarchy – class, to call it by its right name –

Peter's fine yet languid face, his casual yet inviolate wavy thatchy hair – that old, ancient thing, class, now has him and he can't introduce Peter by his first name. It is as if into the room has burst the policeman, the arresting officer, from . . . that world, the entire world of nannies, *cottages ornées* in Devonshire, honeysuckle iron balustrades, sailor suits, hoops and sticks, lolly Eton collars, deb parties, introductions to rich old men, clubs, cliques, horn-handled cigar cutters – in short, the ancient, ineradicable anxiety of class in England – and he knows already the look of patient, tolerant disgust that will begin to slide over Peter's face within the next half second as he looks at him and his American friends and his ceramic grin and his euphoria and his *high-balls*. In that instant, confronted by the power of the future on the one hand – George's eyeballs begin to bobble under the eyebrows – and the power of the past on the other – Peter's lips begin to curdle – he realizes what has happened to himself. He has become a Mid-Atlantic Man.

He meets them all the time in London now. They are Englishmen who have reversed the usual process and . . . gone American. The usual process has been that Americans have gone to England and . . . gone English. Woodrow Wilson appoints Walter Hines Page ambassador to the Court of St James's and tells him: 'Just one word of advice, don't become an Englishman.' Page says, 'Sure, OK,' but, of course, he does, he becomes so much an Englishman he can't see straight. The usual pattern is, he begins using his knife and fork continental style, holding the fork in the left hand. He goes to a tailor who puts that nice English belly into the lapels of his coat and builds up suits made of marvelous and arcane layers and layers of worsted, welts, darts, pleats, double-stitches, linings, buttons, pockets, incredible numbers of pockets, and so many buttons to button and unbutton, and he combs his hair into wings over the ears, and he puts a certain nice drag in his voice and learns to walk like he is recovering from a broken back. But one knows about all that. The American has always gone English in order to endow himself with the mystique of the English upper classes. The Englishman today goes American, becomes a Mid-Atlantic Man, to achieve the opposite. He wants to get out from under the domination of the English upper classes by . . . going classless. And he goes classless by taking on the style of life, or part of the style of life, of a foreigner who cannot be fitted into the English class system, the modern, successful, powerful American.

The most obvious example of the Mid-Atlantic Man is the young English show business figure, a singer, musician, manager, producer, impresario, who goes American in a big way. A singer, for example, sings American rhythm and blues songs, in an American accent, becomes a . . . *pal* of American entertainers, studs his conversation with American slang, like, I mean you know, man, that's where it's at, baby, and, finally, begins to talk with an American accent in an attempt to remove the curse of a working class accent. But the typical Mid-Atlantic Man is middle class and works in one of the newer industries, advertising, public relations, chemical engineering, consulting for this and that, television, credit cards, agentry, industrial design, commercial art, motion pictures, the whole world of brokerage, persuasion, savantry and shows that he has grown up beyond the ancient divisions of landowning, moneylending and the production of dry goods.

He is vaguely aware – he may try to keep it out of his mind – that his background is irrevocably middle class and that everybody in England is immediately aware of it and that this has held him back. This may even be why he has gravitated into one of the newer fields, but still the ancient drag of class in England drags him, drags him, drags him . . .

They happen to be watching television one night and some perfectly urbane and polished person like Kenneth Allsop comes on the screen and after three or four sentences somebody has to observe, poor Kenneth Allsop, listen to the way he says practically, he will never get the Midlands out of his voice, he breaks it all up, into practi-cally . . . and he laughs, but grimly, because he knows there must be at least fifty things like that to mark him as hopelessly middle class and he has none of Allsop's fame to take the curse off.

He first began to understand all this as far back as his first month at Cambridge. Cambridge! – which was supposed to turn him into one of those inviolate, superior persons who rule England and destiny. Cambridge was going to be a kind of finishing school. His parents had a very definite idea of it that way, a picture of him serving sherry to some smart friends in his chambers, wearing a jacket that seems to have worn and mellowed like a 90-year-old Persian rug. Even he himself had a vague notion of how Cambridge was going to transform him from a bright and mousy comprehensive schoolboy into one of those young men with spread collars and pale silk ties who just . . . *assumes* he is in control, at restaurants, in clubs, at parties, with women, in careers, in life, on rural weekends, and thereby is.

And then the very first month this thing happened with the Pitt Club and the Cambridge scarf. His first move on the road to having smart people over to his chambers for sherry, and Cuban tobacco – Cuban tobacco was also included in this vision – was to buy a Cambridge scarf, a nice long thing with confident colours that would wrap around the neck and the lower tip of his chin and flow in the wind. So he would put on his scarf and amble around the streets, by the colleges, peeking in at the Indian restaurants, which always seemed to be closed, and thinking, Well, here I am, a Cambridge man.

One day he came upon this place and a glow came from inside, red as wine, brown as boots, smart people, sherry-sherry, and so he stepped inside – and suddenly a lot of white faces turned his way, like a universe erupting with eggs

Benedict, faces in the foyer, faces from the dining tables farther in. A porter with chipped-beef jowls stepped up and looked him up and down once, dubious as hell, and said:

'Are you a member, sir?'

Such a voice! It was obvious that he knew immediately that he was not a member and the question was merely, witheringly, rhetorical and really said, Why does a hopeless little nit like you insist on wandering in where you don't belong, and all the eggs Benedict faces turned toward him were an echo of the same thing. They all knew immediately! And it was as if their eyes had fastened immediately upon his jugular vein – no! – upon the Cambridge scarf.

He mumbled and turned his head . . . there in the ancient woody brown of the place was a long coat rack, and hanging on it was every kind of undergraduate garment a *right* mind could think of, greatcoats, riding macs, cloaks, capes, gowns, mantles, even ponchos, mufflers, checked mufflers, Danish mufflers, camel-tan mufflers, ratty old aunt-knitty mufflers – everything and anything in the whole woofy English goddamn universe of cotton, wool, rubber and leather . . . except for a Cambridge scarf. This place turned out to be the Pitt Club, watering trough of the incomparables, the Cambridge elite. Wearing a Cambridge scarf in here was far, far worse than having no insignia at all. In a complex Cambridge hierarchy of colleges and clubs – if all one had was an insignia that said merely that one had been admitted to the university – that was as much as saying, well, he's here and that's all one can say about him, other than that he is a hopeless fool.

He did not throw the Cambridge scarf away, strangely enough. He folded it up into a square and tucked it way back in the bottom of his bottom drawer, along with the family Bible his grandfather had given him. From that day on he was possessed by the feeling that there were two worlds, the eggs Benedict faces and his, and never, in four years, did he invite a single smart person over for sherry. Or for Cuban tobacco. He smoked English cigarettes that stained his teeth.

Even years later, in fact, he held no tremendous hopes for the advertising business until one day he was in New York – one day! – with all Mid-Atlantic Men it seems to start one day in New York.

Practically always they have started flying to New York more and more on business. He started flying over on the Fabrilex account. Fabrilex was going to run a big campaign in England. So he began flying to New York and getting gradually into the New York advertising life, which turned out to be a strangely . . . *stimulating* – all Mid-Atlantic Men come back with that word for New York, stimulating . . . strangely stimulating aura of sheer money, drive, conniving, hard work, self-indulgence, glamour, childishness, cynicism.

Beginning with the reception room of the——Agency. It was decorated with the most incredible black leather sofas, quilted and stuffed to the gullet, with the leather gushing and heaving over the edge of the arms, the back and everywhere. There was wall to wall carpet, not like a Wilton but so thick one could break one's ankle in it, and quite vermilion, to go with the vermilion walls and all sorts of inexplicable polished brass objects set in niches, candelabra, busts, pastille burners, vases, etc., and a receptionist who seemed to be made of polished Fabrilex topped with spun brass back-combed hair. She didn't sit at a desk but at a delicate *secretaire* faced with exotic wood veneers, tulipwood, satinwood, harewood. She also operated a switchboard, which was made to look, however, like the keyboard of a harpsichord. There was one large painting, apparently by the last painter in Elizabeth, New Jersey, to copy Franz Kline. Three different members of the firm, Americans, told him the reception room looked like 'a San Francisco whorehouse.' Three of them used that same simile, a San Francisco whorehouse. This was not said in derision, however. They thought it was crazy but they were proud of it. New York!

One of them told him the reception room looked like a San Francisco whorehouse while having his shoes shined at his desk in his office. They were both sitting there talking, the usual, except that a Negro, about 50, was squatted down over a portable shoeshine stand shining the American's shoes. But he kept right on talking about the San Francisco whorehouse and Fabrilex as if all he had done was turn on an air conditioner. He also had an 'executive telephone'. This was some sort of amplified microphone and speaker connected to the telephone, so that he didn't have to actually pick up a telephone, none of that smalltime stuff. All he had to do was talk in the general direction of the desk. But of course! The delicious . . . *baldness* of it! Who gives a damn about subtlety? Just win, like, that's the name of the game, and the —— Agency had £70 million in accounts last year.

They always took him to lunch at places like the Four Seasons, and if it came to £16 for four people, for lunch, that was nothing. There are expensive places where businessmen each lunch in London, but they always have some kind of coy atmosphere, trattorias, chez this or that, or old places with swiney, pebbly English surnames, Craw's, Grouse's, Scob's, Clot's. But the Four Seasons! The place practically exudes an air conditioned sweat of pure huge expensive-account . . . *money*. Everybody sits there in this huge bald smooth slab Mies van der Rohe style black onyx executive suite atmosphere taking massive infusions of exotic American cocktails, Margaritas, Gibsons, Bloody Marys, Rob Roys, Screwdrivers, Pisco Sours, and French wines and French brandies, while the blood vessels dilate and the ego dilates and Leonard Lyons, the columnist, comes in to look around and see who is there, and everyone watches these ingenious copper chain curtains rippling over the plate glass, rippling up, up, it is an optical illusion but it looks like they are rippling, rippling, rippling, rippling up this cliff of plate glass like a waterfall gone into reverse.

And some guy at the table is letting everybody in on this deliciously child cynical American secret, namely, that a lot of the cigarette advertising currently is based on motivational research into people's reactions to the cancer scare. For example, the ones that always show blue grass and blue streams and blond, blue eyed young people with picnic baskets, and gallons of prime of life hormones gushing through their Diet-Rite loins, are actually aimed at hypochondriacs who need constant reassurance that they aren't dying of cancer. On the other hand, the ones that say 'I'd rather fight than switch' really mean 'I'd rather get cancer than give up smoking' – New York! – the copper curtains ripple up . . .

One interesting, rather nice thing he notices, however, is that they are tremendously anxious to please him. They are apparently impressed by him, even though he comes there very much as the beggar. They are the parent firm. Whatever they say about the Fabrilex campaign in England goes, in the long run. If they want to aim it at hypochondriac masochists who fear cancer of the skin, then that's it. Yet they treat him as a partner, no, as slightly superior. Then he gets it. It is because he is English. They keep staring at his suit, which is from Huntsman and has 12-inch side vents. They watch his table manners and then . . . glorious! *imitate* him. Old George! He used to say to waiters, '*Would* you please bring some water' or whatever it was, whereas he always said, '*Could* you bring the cheese now, please?' or whatever it was – the thing is, the Americans say *would*, which implies that the waiter is doing one a favour by granting this wish, whereas the Englishman – class! – says *could*, which assumes that since the waiter is a servant, he will if he can.

And old George got that distinction right off! That's it with these Americans. They're incurable children, they're incurable nouveaux, they spell *finesse* with a *ph* to give it more *tone* – but they sense the status distinctions. And so by the second time old George is saying 'Could you bring me some water, do you think?' and running do you think together into an upper class blur over the top of his sopping glottis just . . . like a real Englishman.

So all of a sudden *he* began to sense that he had it both ways. He had the American thing and the English thing. They emerge from the Four Seasons, out on to 52nd Street – kheew! – the sun blasts them in the eyes and there it is, wild, childish, bald, overpowering Park Avenue in the Fifties, huge cliffs of plate glass and steel frames, like a mountain of telephone booths. Hundreds of, jaysus, millions of dollars' worth of shimmering junk, with so many sheets of plate glass the buildings all reflect each other in marine greens and blues, like a 25 cent postcard from Sarasota, Florida – not a good building in the lot, but, jaysus, the sheer incredible yah! – we've got it money and power it represents. The Rome of the twentieth century – and because wealth and power are here, everything else follows, and it is useless for old England to continue to harp on form, because it is all based on the wealth and power England had 150 years ago. The platter of the world's goodie sweets tilts . . . to New York, girls, for one thing, all these young lithe girls with flamingo legs come pouring into New York and come popping up out of the armpit steaming sewer tunnels of the New York subways, out of those screeching sewers, dressed to the eyeballs, lathed, polished, linked, lacquered, coiffed with spun brass.

Ah, and *they* loved Englishmen, too. He found a brass topped beauty and he will never forget following her up the stairs to her flat that first night. The front door was worn and rickety but heavy and had an air hinge on it that made it close and lock immediately, automatically – against those ravenous, adrenal New York animals *out there*; even New York's criminals are more animal, basic savage, Roman, *criminal*–he never remembered a block of flats in London with an air hinge on the front door – and he followed her up the stairs, a few steps behind her, and watched the muscles in her calves contract and the hamstring ligaments spring out at the back of her knees, oh young taut healthy New York girl flamingo legs, and it was all so . . . tender and brave.

Precisely! Her walk up flat was so essentially dreary, way over in the East Eighties, an upper floor of somebody's old townhouse that had been cut up and jerry-built into flats just slightly better than a bedsitter, with the bedroom about the size of a good healthy wardrobe closet and a so-called Pullman kitchen in the living room, some fiercely, meanly efficient uni-unit, a little sink, refrigerator and stove all welded together behind shutters at one end, and a bathroom with no window, just some sort of air duct in there with the slits grimed and hanging, booga, with some sort of grey compost of lint, sludge, carbon particles and noxious gases. And the toilet barely worked, just a lazy spiral current of water down the hole after one pulled down that stubby little handle they have. The floor tilted slightly, but – brave and tender!

Somehow she had managed to make it all look beautiful, Japanese globe lamps made of balsa strips and paper, greenery, great lush fronds of some kind of plant, several prints on the wall, one an insanely erotic watercolour nude by Egon Schiele, various hangings, coverings, drapings of primitive textiles, monk's cloth, homespuns, a little vase full of violet paper flowers, a bookcase, painted white, full of heavyweight, or middleweight, paperback books, *The Lonely Crowd, The Confessions of Felix Krull, African Genesis* – brave and tender! – all of these lithe young girls living in dreadful walk up flats, alone, with a cat, and the faint odour of cat feces in the kitty litter, and an oily wooden salad bowl on the table, and a cockroach silhouetted on the rim of the salad bowl – and yet there was something touching about it, *haunting*, he wanted to say, the desperate fight to stay in New York amid the excitement of money and power, the Big Apple, and for days, if he is to be honest about it, he had the most inexplicably tender memory of – all right! – the poor sad way the water had lazed down in the toilet bowl. That poor, marvellous, erotic girl. At one point she had told him she had learned to put a diaphragm on in 15 seconds. She just said it, out of thin air. So bald.

Early the next morning he took a cab back to his hotel to change for the day and the driver tried to project the thing in manic bursts through the rush hour traffic, lurches of acceleration, sudden braking, skids, screeches, all the while shouting out the window, cursing and then demanding support from him 'Dja see that! Guy got his head up his ass. Am I right?' – and strangely, he found himself having a thoroughly American reaction, actually answering these stupid questions because he wanted to be approved of by this poor bastard trying to hurtle through the money and power traffic, answering a cab driver who said, 'Guy got his head up his ass, am I right?' – because suddenly he found himself close to the source, he understood this thing – the hell with scarves, Pitt Clubs and pale silk ties, and watch out England, you got your head up your ass, and here comes a Mid-Atlantic Man.

Slow Trains

John Aye

Slow trains have been a fruitful subject for humour with the comic press ever since the far off days when *Punch* wrote: 'On Wednesday last a respectably dressed young man was seen to go to the Shoreditch terminus of the Eastern Counties Railway and deliberately take a ticket for Cambridge. No motive has been ascribed for the rash act.' Somewhat of the same idea, although in this case the railway was different, must have been the schoolboy, who, being asked in a literature paper, 'What is the most pathetic line you know?' promptly wrote down, 'The South Eastern'.

We are all familiar with the alleged humorist who, when the train stops between stations, shouts to the guard for permission to get out and pick flowers, but one individual, realizing that this piece of humour was growing a little stale, carried the joke a step farther. To his request to descend the guard good humouredly pointed out that he would hardly find many flowers at that time of the year. 'Oh, that's all right,' replied the jovial one, 'there'll be heaps of time; I've brought a packet of seeds with me.' More practical, however, was the season ticket holder who, on being pulled up at the barrier because his season ticket had expired, retaliated with, 'Can you wonder? Look how late the train is!'

Much as one admires a spirit of esprit de corps and a pride in their job on the part of officials, it is not perhaps advisable for either income tax collectors or the guards of some of our slow suburban trains to show too much pride in their position. They should not forget that in the one case the tax payer, and in the other the passenger, may have a totally different outlook on the matter. 'I've been on this train seven years,' said the guard of a slow going Southern train proudly to a grumbling passenger. 'Is that so?' came the quiet reply. 'Where did you get on?'

There are two stories told in connection with slow trains which are too good to be left out of any book dealing with railway humour. The first concerns a line which was well known for the elasticity of its train schedule. Had one of its trains run to time there would have been consternation among the staff. One day, however, the miracle happened, and one of its morning trains rolled into the station exact to the second. Moved by this unusual circumstance a traveller waiting for the train went up to the engine to pay a personal tribute to the driver. 'Sir,' he said, 'I've been travelling on this line for many years, and this is the first time I have ever known this train to be on time. I tender you my heartiest congratulations. Have a cigar?' Regretfully and solemnly the driver gently pushed away the proffered gift. 'As a conscientious person and an honest man,' he said, 'I can't take it. The fact is, we were due at this time yesterday morning.'

The second story relates to a traveller who had made the long and weary journey from the hinterland of Kent to London. As the train reached Charing Cross he arose wearily and commenced to get together his baggage, at the same time muttering thankfully, 'Ah well, that's the worst of the journey over.' 'Are you going far?' asked the only other occupant of the carriage. 'China,' came the laconic but cheerful answer.

But perhaps these two stories are beaten by one told by the late Coley O'Connell. This related to a linesman, who, arriving at a West Clare station one evening on completion of his day's work on the permanent way, was asked by the stationmaster if there was any sign of the mail. 'She'll be here in a few minutes,' was the reply; 'I passed her in the cutting.'

Even an attempt on the part of the authorities to speed up their services does not always bring a chorus of unqualified approval from those they wish to benefit. A recent instruction of the Southern Railway to the effect that trains were in future only to remain twenty seconds in stations (other than the termini) brought forth an enquiry through the Press from a season ticket holder regarding certain rumours current among the travellers on that line. These rumours ran somewhat as follows:

1. Classes would be held by the company to instruct passengers how to enter or alight from trains on the command, 'Now, then, jump to it.'

2. Passengers who persisted in taking more than the scheduled time would, for the first offence, be fined the amount of the ticket in their possession. For the second offence they would, if season tickets holders, forfeit their season, or, if ordinary passengers, the privilege of travelling on the railway would be withdrawn for ever.

3. A casualty coach would be run on every train and, although the company could admit no liability for casualties, the bodies of the dead would

be conveyed to Brookwood free of charge, and their ashes interred in the
Garden of Sleep. Further, marble tombstones would be erected, suitably
inscribed in green lettering, 'Southern Railway, Casualty No. ..... A traveller
on the Sunshine Line who fell by the wayside.'

It must be admitted, however, that the slow train serves one purpose in the
great scheme of things, and that is, that it has been, and still is, one of the
jokes of the century. Let the conversation be as dull as it will, someone has
only to mention slow trains, whereupon everyone is ready either with a tale
or a personal experience. Eyes sparkle, broad smiles spread across faces till
then steeped in gloom, the conversation becomes at once bright and witty,
and where sadness once prevailed there is now nothing but animation and
laughter. Take away the slow trains of the 'go easy railway,' and the world
is robbed of one of those subjects that, working through the divine spirit of
humour, make the whole world kin. What can be more delightful than the
story of the angry passenger who, after a long wait on an Irish platform,
turned to the stationmaster and complained, 'What is the good of your time
tables if the trains are always late?' only to receive the unruffled reply, 'And
how would yez know the trains were late if we didn't give yez a time table?'
Or the story of the American who was bragging of the wonderful railways in
his country. 'Yes, sir,' he said, 'in God's own country we don't do things by
halves. You can travel all day, all night and part of the next day, and still
be in the same state.' 'Yes,' said the stolid Britisher, thinking of his daily journey to and fro, 'we've a few trains like that in this country, but we ain't over
proud of them.'

If trains on our railways were always to run to time, what a safety valve
for grumbles would be closed! One can imagine the rows of disconsolate season
ticket holders, sitting glaring at each other, with the one bond of union that
had held them together in the past, the common grumble, broken for ever.
Why, under such conditions, and with no legitimate outlet, the one time
grumbler would have to confine his complaints to the home, with the result
that many would be broken up, and wife (or in some cases husband) beating
would become a common practice. How much better is the present practice
where the traveller can get rid of that early morning feeling by a little 'morning hate' directed against the railway company. What can compensate for the
opportunity to blackguard the company when the train is held up for ten
minutes, or even in extreme cases the joy of writing to the papers about it?
No, let us keep our slow trains as a sort of Aunt Sally at which we can throw
bricks when the mood is upon us.

Besides, when one comes to look more deeply into the matter, the slow train has its advantages, one of which was discovered by the old lady who said that she preferred to travel by trains of this kind, as 'there was too much osculation about the expresses for her liking.' Does not also the slow or late train cater for that numerous class of the population who seem to find it an impossibility to get anywhere at the appointed time? Given that every train ran to time, these poor people would be condemned to remaining always in the same place. 'Do you mean to say she left on time?' demanded a would-be passenger who had just missed the train, of an Irish stationmaster. 'She did that,' was the reply. 'Shure, she's the punctuallest train in the country, and she's the cause of great inconvenience to the public.'

Many and varied have been the excuses put forward by railway officials to cover delay in their section of the line, but perhaps none so convincing as the one in the following story. A certain train on the Dublin and South Eastern Railway is much in favour with Dublin residents for taking the bodies of relatives and friends into the country for burial at their native village. Complaints were constantly being received at headquarters of the unpunctuality of this train, and letters to the stationmaster concerned effected no improvement. Ultimately a superintendent was sent down to investigate, when the following conversation took place. 'So the ten o'clock was twelve minutes late again this morning, in spite of all the warnings sent you.' 'True for yez, sir, but what was I to do? I was quite ready to start the train off to the minute when up walked another blooming corpse.'

From its earliest days *Punch* has been the severe critic of slow and late trains, but it reached the high water mark of sarcasm in 1922 when it produced the following priceless titbit. 'Edible snails from France are now brought to London by aeroplane. It will be remembered that in the old days, when the South Eastern Railway had no rival, it was found quicker to let them walk the final stage of the journey.'

Adam and Colonel Blount

Evelyn Waugh

At Aylesbury Adam got into a Ford taxi and asked to be taken to a house called Doubting.

'Doubting 'All?'

'Well I suppose so. Is it falling down?'

'Could do with a lick of paint,' said the driver, a spotty youth. 'Name of Blount.'

'That's it.'

'Long way from here Doubting 'All is. Cost you fifteen bob.'

'All right.'

'If you're a commercial, I can tell you straight it ain't no use going to 'im. Young feller asked me the way there this morning. Driving a Morris. Wanted to sell him a vacuum cleaner. Old boy 'ad answered an advertisement asking for a demonstration. When he got there the old boy wouldn't even look at it. Can you beat that?'

'No, I'm not trying to sell him anything – at least not exactly.'

'Personal visit, perhaps.'

'Yes.'

'Ah.'

Satisfied that his passenger was in earnest about the journey, the taxi-driver put on some coats – for it was raining – got out of his seat and cranked up the engine. Presently they started.

They drove for a mile or two past bungalows and villas and timbered public houses to a village in which every house seemed to be a garage and filling station. Here they left the main road and Adam's discomfort became acute.

At last they came to twin octagonal lodges and some heraldic gate posts and large wrought iron gates, behind which could be seen a broad sweep of ill kept drive.

'Doubting 'All,' said the driver.

He blew his horn once or twice, but no lodge keeper's wife, aproned and apple cheeked, appeared to bob them in. He got out and shook the gates reproachfully.

'Chained and locked,' he said. 'Try another way.'

They drove on for another mile; on the side of the Hall the road was bordered by dripping trees and a dilapidated stone wall; presently they reached some cottages and a white gate. This they opened and turned into a rough track, separated from the park by low iron railings. There were sheep grazing on either side. One of them had strayed into the drive. It fled before them in a frenzied trot, stopping and looking round over its dirty tail and then plunging on again until its agitation brought it to the side of the path, where they overtook it and passed it.

The track led to some stables, then behind rows of hot houses, among potting sheds and heaps of drenched leaves, past nondescript outbuildings that had once been laundry and bakery and brewhouse and a huge kennel where once someone had kept a bear, until suddenly it turned by a clump of holly and elms and laurel bushes into an open space that had once been laid with gravel. A lofty Palladian façade stretched before them and in front of it an equestrian statue pointed a baton imperiously down the main drive.

''Ere y'are,' said the driver.

Adam paid him and went up the steps to the front door. He rang the bell and waited. Nothing happened. Presently he rang again. At this moment the door opened.

'Don't ring twice,' said a very angry old man. 'What do you want?'

'Is Mr Blount in?'

'There's no Mr Blount here. This is Colonel Blount's house.'

'I'm sorry . . . I think the Colonel is expecting me to luncheon.'

'Nonsense. I'm Colonel Blount,' and he shut the door.

The Ford had disappeared. It was still raining hard. Adam rang again.

'Yes,' said Colonel Blount, appearing instantly.

'I wonder if you'd let me telephone to the station for a taxi?'

'Not on the telephone . . . It's raining. Why don't you come in? It's absurd to walk to the station in this. Have you come about the vacuum cleaner?'

'No.'

'Funny, I've been expecting a man all the morning to show me a vacuum cleaner. Come in, do. Won't you stay to luncheon?'

'I should love to.'

'Splendid. I get very little company nowadays. You must forgive me for opening the door to you myself. My butler is in bed today. He suffers terribly in his feet when it is wet. Both my footmen were killed in the war . . . Put your hat and coat here. I hope you haven't got wet . . . I'm sorry you didn't bring the vacuum cleaner . . . but never mind. How are you?' he said, suddenly holding out his hand.

They shook hands and Colonel Blount led the way down a long corridor, lined with marble busts on yellow marble pedestals, to a large room full of furniture, with a fire burning in a fine rococo fireplace. There was a large leather topped walnut writing table under a window opening on to a terrace. Colonel Blount picked up a telegram and read it.

'I'd quite forgotten,' he said in some confusion. 'I'm afraid you'll think me very discourteous, but it is, after all, impossible for me to ask you to luncheon. I have a guest coming on very intimate family business. You understand, don't you? . . . To tell you the truth, it's some young rascal who wants to marry my daughter. I must see him alone to discuss settlements.'

'Well, I want to marry your daughter, too,' said Adam.

'What an extraordinary coincidence. Are you sure you do?'

'Perhaps the telegram may be about me. What does it say?'

' "*Engaged to marry Adam Symes. Expect him luncheon. Nina*". Are you Adam Symes?'

'Yes.'

'My dear boy, why didn't you say so before, instead of going on about a vacuum cleaner? How are you?'

They shook hands again.

'If you don't mind,' said Colonel Blount, 'we will keep our business until after luncheon. I'm afraid everything is looking very bare at present. You must come down and see the gardens in the summer. We had some lovely hydrangeas last year. I don't think I shall live here another winter. Too big for an old man. I was looking at some of the houses they're putting up outside Aylesbury. Did you see them coming along? Nice little red houses. Bathroom and everything. Quite cheap, too, and near the cinematographs. I hope you are fond of the cinematograph too. The Rector and I go a great deal. I hope you'll like the Rector. Common little man rather. But he's got a motor car, useful that. How long are you staying?'

'I promised Nina I'd be back tonight.'

'That's a pity. They change the film at the Electra Palace. We might have gone.'

An elderly woman servant came in to announce luncheon. 'What is at the

Electra Palace, do you know, Mrs Florin?'

'Greta Garbo in *Venetian Kisses*, I think, sir.'

'I don't really think I like Greta Garbo. I've tried to,' said Colonel Blount, 'but I just don't.'

They went in to luncheon in a huge dining room dark with family portraits.

'If you don't mind,' said Colonel Blount, 'I prefer not to talk at meals.'

He propped a morocco-bound volume of *Punch* before his plate against a vast silver urn, from which grew a small castor oil plant.

'Give Mr Symes a book,' he said.

Mrs Florin put another volume of *Punch* beside Adam.

'If you come across anything really funny read it to me,' said Colonel Blount.

Then they had luncheon.

They were nearly an hour over luncheon. Course followed course in disconcerting abundance while Colonel Blount ate and ate, turning the leaves of his book and chuckling frequently. They ate hare soup and boiled turbot and stewed sweetbreads and black Bradenham ham with Madeira sauce and roast pheasant and a rum omelette and toasted cheese and fruit. First they drank sherry, then claret, then port. Then Colonel Blount shut his book with a broad sweep of his arm rather as the headmaster of Adam's private school used to shut the Bible after evening prayers, folded his napkin carefully and stuffed it into a massive silver ring, muttered some words of grace and finally stood up, saying:

'Well, I don't know about you, but I'm going to have a little nap,' and trotted out of the room.

'There's a fire in the library, sir,' said Mrs Florin. 'I'll bring you your coffee there. The Colonel doesn't have coffee, he finds it interferes with his afternoon sleep. What time would you like your afternoon tea, sir?'

I ought really to be getting back to London. How long will it be before the Colonel comes down, do you think?'

'Well, it all depends, sir. Not usually till about five or half past. Then he reads until dinner at seven and after dinner gets the Rector to drive him in to the pictures. A sedentary life, as you might say.'

She led Adam into the library and put a silver coffee pot at his elbow.

'I'll bring you tea at four,' she said.

Adam sat in front of the fire in a deep armchair. Outside, the rain beat on the double windows. There were several magazines in the library – mostly cheap weeklies devoted to the cinema. There was a stuffed owl and case of

early British remains, bone pins and bits of pottery and a skull, which had
been dug up in the park many years ago and catalogued by Nina's governess.
There was a cabinet containing the relics of Nina's various collecting fevers
– some butterflies and a beetle or two, some fossils and some birds' eggs and
a few postage stamps. There were some bookcases of superbly unreadable
books, a gun, a butterfly net, an alpenstock in the corner. There were catalogues of agricultural machines and acetylene plants, lawnmowers, 'sport
requisites'. There was a fire screen worked with a coat of arms. The chimney-
piece was hung with the embroidered saddle cloths of Colonel Blount's regiment of Lancers. There was an engraving of all the members of the Royal
Yacht Squadron, with a little plan in the corner, marked to show who was
who. There were many other things of equal interest besides, but before Adam
had noticed any more he was fast asleep.

Mrs Florin woke him at four. The coffee had disappeared and its place was
taken by a silver tray with a lace cloth on it. There was a silver teapot, and
a silver kettle with a little spirit lamp underneath, and a silver cream jug and
a covered silver dish full of muffins. There was also hot buttered toast and
honey and gentleman's relish and a chocolate cake, a cherry cake, a seed cake
and a fruit cake and some tomato sandwiches and pepper and salt and currant
bread and butter.

'Would you care for a lightly boiled egg, sir? The Colonel generally has one
if he's awake.'

'No, thank you,' said Adam. He felt a thousand times better for his rest.
When Nina and he were married, he thought, they would often come down
there for the day after a really serious party. For the first time he noticed an
obese liver and white spaniel, which was waking up, too, on the hearthrug.

'Please not to give her muffins,' said Mrs Florin, 'It's the one thing she's
not supposed to have, and the Colonel will give them to her. He loves that
dog,' she added with a burst of confidence. 'Takes her to the pictures with
him of an evening. Not that she can appreciate them really like a human can.'

Adam gave her – the spaniel, not Mrs Florin – a gentle prod with his foot
and a lump of sugar. She licked his shoe with evident cordiality. Adam was
not above feeling flattered by friendliness in dogs.

He had finished his tea and was filling his pipe when Colonel Blount came
into the library.

'Who the devil are you?' said his host.

'Adam Symes,' said Adam. 'I came about being married to Nina.'

'My dear boy, of course. How absurd of me. I've such a bad memory for names. It comes of seeing so few people. How are you?'

They shook hands again.

'So you're the young man who's engaged to Nina,' said the Colonel, eyeing him for the first time in the way prospective sons in law are supposed to be eyed. 'Now what in the world do you want to get married for? I shouldn't, you know, really I shouldn't. Are you rich?'

'No, not at present, I'm afraid, that's rather what I wanted to talk about.'

'How much money have you got?'

'Well, sir, actually at the moment I haven't got any at all.'

'When did you last have any?'

'I had a thousand pounds last night, but I gave it all to a drunk major.'

'Why did you do that?'

'Well, I hoped he'd put it on Indian Runner for the November Handicap.'

'Never heard of the horse. Didn't he?'

'I don't think he can have.'

'When will you next have some money?'

'When I've written some books.'

'How many books?'

'Twelve.'

'How much will you have then?'

'Probably fifty pounds advance on my thirteenth book.'

'And how long will it take you to write twelve books?'

'About a year.'

'How long would it take most people?'

'About twenty years. Of course, put like that I do see it sounds rather hopeless . . . but, you see, Nina and I hoped that you, that is, that perhaps for the next year until I get my twelve books written, that you might help us . . .'

'How could I help you? I've never written a book in my life.'

'No, we thought you might give us some money.'

'You thought that, did you?'

'Yes, that's what we thought . . .'

Colonel Blount looked at him gravely for some time. Then he said, 'I think that an admirable idea. I don't see any reason at all why I shouldn't. How much do you want?'

'That's really terribly good of you, sir . . . well, you know, just enough to live on quietly for a bit. I hardly know . . .'

'Well, would a thousand pounds be any help?'

'Yes, it would indeed. We shall both be terribly grateful.'

'Not at all, my dear boy. Not at all. What did you say your name was?'

'Adam Symes.'

Colonel Blount went to the table and wrote out a cheque. 'There you are,' he said. 'Now don't go giving that away to another drunk major.'

'Really, sir! I don't know how to thank you. Nina . . .'

'Not another word. Now I expect that you will want to be off to London again. We'll send Mrs Florin across to the Rectory and make the Rector drive you to the station. Useful having a neighbour with a motor car. They charge fivepence on the buses from here to Aylesbury. *Robbers*.'

Guards

John Aye

Of all railway servants who are brought into close contact with the travelling
public there is no class that is so generally popular as that of the guard.
Inspectors, collectors, porters, all may be indifferent, if not hostile, to the
traveller, but still he feels that he can always turn to the luggage van and find
there a constant friend.

The booking clerk is a man apart. Secure in his little room, and only to
be glimpsed by peeping through the little wicket, he is a sort of railway hermit,
but, sad to say, a hermit of little feeling, who only displays emotion – and that
of sombre satisfaction – when he is able to say that there are no cheap fares
to the place to which you wish to travel. Indeed, more likely than not, his
face will light up with an unholy joy when he can tell you that there was a
cheap ticket issued yesterday, but such a concession will not recur for another
six months. Poor man, it is not really his fault. He is the victim of circumstances. He, too, would fain spread his wings and voyage to distant lands, but
saddened and subdued he has perforce to remain, looking out continually on
a world that is ever travelling, while he, cribbed, cabined and confined,
remains pent in one small room, with passports to half the world on the shelves
around him.

Hostile also is the attitude of the ticket collector, whose outlook on life
would appear to be very similar to that of the traffic policeman who is 'looking
for a cop.' To him the world is peopled only by those who are trying to 'do'
him (for in this one case he identifies himself with the company), and he
intends by every means in his power to circumvent them. One can easily
imagine that in the course of time this will become second nature, and that
in his own home the married ticket inspector will keep more than a sharp eye
on the tradesmen's accounts.

As regards the porter, he should certainly be in the most friendly relationship with the traveller, but the sad fact remains that only too often he is not,

and this is in a great measure due to the different outlook of the two parties. The passenger acts on the assumption that the porter has been placed there by the railway company to minister to his wants, while the latter, starting out in life with a simple childish trust in all men, finds only too soon, alas, that his golden rule of minimum work and maximum tips has not been accepted by the traveller, who, with an almost incredible foolishness, seems to prefer the one of maximum work and minimum tips. It is from this cause that his faith in humankind is shattered, and from a careless heart-free whistling porter he, only too often, turns into a morose and discontented being.

The case of the guard, however, is very different. With the wisdom of experience he realizes that he exists for two objects, one being to take care of the luggage, and the other to father the oft times childish travelling public. He stands as regards the latter in a somewhat similar position to what is known at Army courts martial as 'Prisoners' Friend.' Moreover, unlike the porter, he expects no fee for his advice and labour, and when such does come his way he is correspondingly grateful.

Guards, it appears, are selected on account of their cheerfulness and amiability, coupled with the possession of a certain quiet dignity. Matriculating in the hard school of porterdom, unspoiled by the hard heartedness of the British public as regards tips, they pass through the intermediate stage of goods guard, until in consequence of their ability to take a cheerful view of life, even in the most depressing circumstances, they finally graduate as full blown passenger guards. Many, however, unable to reach the required Mark Tapley standard, fall by the way, and remain either as goods guards or drop once more into the ranks of porterdom. This accounts for the high standard of language used by the passenger guard as compared with his confrère of the goods, for while that of the one is measured and courteous, that of the other is – well, perhaps the following story will best illustrate my point. Auntie had been induced by her little nephew Peter to play trains. To her was allotted the part of engine driver, a row of chairs represented the trucks, and Peter himself was guard. When the time came for the departure of the train Peter, with his handkerchief tied to the poker to represent a flag, ran down the train shouting to the driver, 'Righto, Bill, it's all OK. Let her bloomin' well rip.' 'Peter, Peter, my dear,' screamed the scandalized aunt, 'wherever did you learn such language?' 'That's just like yer,' came the reply in the best goods-yard manner. 'Five minutes late already, and you start chewin' the blinkin' rag. Get a move on, can't yer!'

In any study of the characteristics of this admirable section of the great railway army there is one that stands out most markedly, and that is their placidity. It is very doubtful if even in the most unfavourable circumstances anyone has ever seen a guard 'rattled' or in any danger of losing his dignity. They realize fully that after all the travelling public are in the main but querulous spoiled children, and standing, as they do, *in loco parentis*, it is their duty to calm all fears by a quiet but firm demeanour. This trait is well illustrated in the following stories. It was a very foggy evening and the passengers in the train were loud in their complaints of the continuous stopping and also the rocking and jolting. Suddenly this ceased, and for a short while the passage was quite smooth. 'Ah, that's better,' exclaimed one of the grumblers. 'I should like to go all the way like this.' 'Would you really, sir?' said the guard, who at that moment came down the corridor, 'you might find it a bit awkward, seeing that we are off the rails.'

The guard had been very attentive to one of those fussy old ladies who seem to consider that the world only exists for their comfort, and after he had settled her down in her corner he found himself subjected to a perfect volley of questions. 'Had he seen the luggage put in the van?' 'Where was the van?' 'Had she her back to the engine?' 'Would the train start promptly to time?' 'Would it lose time on the way?' 'Were there many accidents on that line?' Patiently the guard answered the catechism until she came to the last question, when he quietly countered with, 'Not many, Madam, but in case of one, to what particular hospital would you like to go?'

Moreover, in justification of a very occasional outburst, it must be admitted that the questions asked by the travelling public are usually enough to try the temper of even a super Job. History unfortunately does not record what was said by the guard in the following case. A small boy travelling alone on a stopping train from London pestered the guard at every station with the question, 'Is this Reading?' At length, much to that official's relief, they arrived at the desired station, and going up to the carriage containing the enquiring small boy the guard said, 'Well, here we are at Reading at last, now perhaps you'll be satisfied.' 'Thank you,' replied the youngster, without making any effort to move. 'But ain't you getting out here?' said the astonished guard. 'Oh no,' said the boy, 'I'm going on to Swindon, but mother told me not to eat my sandwiches until I got to Reading.'

The second characteristic of our friend is his tact, a quality which often brings him in a pecunary recompense, as when he produces a key and locks in an obvious honeymoon couple, or, when addressing the shortskirted bobbed-hair would-be youthful mother travelling with her daughter, he asks if he can find seats for her and her sister. It is really wonderful to what trouble a guard will sometimes put himself in order to enhance the comfort of his passengers. One very hot summer's day as a train drew up to the station a very warm looking old gentleman put his head out of the window and asked the guard if there was time to have 'a quick one' at the refreshment room. The reply was favourable, but it was evident that the old gentleman still seemed to fear that the train might go on without him. 'Don't worry about that, sir,' said the obliging guard, noting his distress, 'I'll just slip in and have one with you.' What more tactful or soothing reply, also, could have been given than that of the guard to whom an old lady made the complaint at Vauxhall that a man in her carriage was mad? 'I wish you'd come to him,' she appealed, 'I'm sure he's mad. He's jibbering to himself in the corner, and keeps on saying that he's Napoleon.' 'Oh, don't you worry about that, mum,' replied the guard. 'The next station's Waterloo.'

There is one point, however, on which a guard can be very touchy, and that is the lateness or slowness of his train. Let anyone criticize on this point, and it is more than likely that our friend will display an entirely different side of his character, and one whose existence we had never suspected. His kindliness drops from him, and at the very least the questioner will get a sharp dose of sarcasm, nor can this be wondered at when one realizes that in attacking the train one is touching the guard's personal pride. A lady who was very anxious to reach her destination was travelling in a train that by no stretch of imagination could be called an express, and which indeed seemed to have formed a habit of making stops between stations. Unable to bear this any longer, she put out her head at the next stop and petulantly asked, 'I say, Guard, can't you really go any faster?' 'Well, perhaps I could, Ma'am,' was the reply, 'but you see, it's my job to stay with the train.'

Woe to the person who by any act holds up the train, if only for a few seconds, for on him assuredly will the wrath of the guard fall. It once happened that a train came to a stop between two stations, and a very worried looking little man, leaning out of the window, called to the guard, who was passing at the time, to know what was wrong. 'Why,' said the latter, 'somebody's pulled the alarm cord, and we can't find out who it is, and now we'll have to stop and let the express through, and that will make us at least twenty minutes late.' 'Twenty minutes late,' said the passenger in consternation, 'why, I'm to be married at eleven o'clock, and it's now ten and we're——' In an instant the guard turned to him. 'Here,' he said fiercely, 'you aren't the person who pulled the cord, are you?'

So deeply is this desire that the train should be a model of timekeeping implanted in the mind of some guards that they will take any risk in order to obtain the desired result, a fact which appears to be especially true in Ireland. A train was slowly wending its way along a west of Ireland railway when it pulled up outside a station. 'I say, Pat,' shouted the guard to the engine driver, 'what are yez stopping for? Get away out of it now.' 'How the devil can I?' yelled the engine driver. 'Don't you see the signals ag'in' us?' 'Signals ag'in' us,' came the contemptuous reply. 'Why, man alive, it's mighty particular you're getting all at once.'

This pride in his job, which shows itself in an objection to any criticism of his train, is frequently extended to everything pertaining to the company, and the guard becomes a strong upholder of all the bylaws, rules and regulations. When he reaches this stage the breaking of any one of these by a passenger becomes in his eyes a crime not far removed from high treason. 'Put your head in, sir,' once shouted a guard to a passenger who was leaning out of the window. 'I shall do as I like,' replied the passenger, who was one of those objectionable people who consider rudeness a form of independence. 'All right,' roared back the guard, 'do as you please, but don't forget that if your head does strike a bridge or tunnel you'll be liable for any damage done to the company's property.'

There was one occasion, however, on which the guard's adherence to the company's rules placed him in a very awkward position. An Irish passenger rushed on to the platform just as the train was moving, and naturally endeavoured to board it. 'Too late, sir,' said the guard, intercepting him, 'you're not allowed to enter a moving train.' 'Oh, ain't I,' said Pat, throwing his arms round the guard in a strong embrace, 'then if I don't catch it, faix, I'll take jolly good care that you don't,' and for once Pat was right.

The General Strike of 1926 produced a crop of good stories at the expense of the amateur railway man, and these are still told with joy by the regulars whose place he took for a brief period. Of these there is none to equal the story of the volunteer driver and guard who were placed in charge of a suburban train, that shortly after leaving town had to climb a very steep gradient. It was only with the greatest difficulty that the engine managed the task, and at the first stop the guard came running up to the engine to discuss the matter. 'My word,' said the driver, wiping his perspiring brow, 'I never thought we were going to climb that hill.' 'Yes,' said the guard, 'and you've got me to thank that we didn't run backwards. Thank goodness I had the presence of mind to ram the brakes on hard.'

Colonel Bogus in Wartime

Michael Barsley

The first thing to be noted about Colonel Bogus is his nickname. It is 'Boojum'. Admirers of *The Hunting of the Snark* will realize why.

Details about his origin and upbringing are scanty. 'Happy is the man that has no history,' he once remarked, when refusing to give away the prizes at an obscure school in a provincial town which made the bold claim to have had some hand in his education. 'Boojum' Bogus does seem in fact to have derived from the provinces, but some of his business rivals have declared that he is not actually British at all. Colonel Bogus remains politely silent. The fact that he makes no apology for a humble provincial origin shows how great is the contrast between him and the Blimps, who must all have been born in London, the Home Counties or Scotland, unless their families were Lords Lieutenant of a less fashionable county.

About his business career, Bogus is more explicit. His modest entry in *Who's What* lists a number of commercial houses which he helped to success, or failure. The entry 'Educ. privately' is thought to be a blind, but it is a known fact that from 1922-29 Colonel Bogus sat as Tory MP for Coalface, E, with a respectable majority even during the Labour Government. Bogus's considerable mining interests, gravely threatened in 1926 and again in 1931, have since passed into other hands. He has always been more anxious to derive income and position from munitions and from business abroad, particularly in Ruralitania and Capricornia.

Holder of the Black Star of the Order of St Stephanotis, with Vultures, the highest Ruralitanian decoration; friend and fellowshot of the notorious Prince Borzoi; chairman of the National Salt Mines and Armament Companies in that unhappy country, 'Boojum' Bogus has done much to maintain Ruralitania, through the peacetime years, in her traditional state of splendour and serfdom. He is now directing the Ruralitanian Post-War Recovery enterprises, and is ready to stage a comeback for Prince Borzoi when peace is declared.

His work in Capricornia, again associated with mines and also with every little tropical railway in the place, has been less spectacular but equally profitable. With the aid of industrial experts he has built up his 'Bedaux for the Blacks' system into a fine art. In the Empire he has been a close friend and financial adviser of the Rajah of Richistan, who, on his frequent visits to London before the war, occupied a suite specially designed for him in the Hotel Magnifico. Colonel Bogus also pursues certain interests in the neighbouring Indian state of Bloodipore, a highly promising field for industrial speculation, but dangerous politically.

Several minor concerns, such as the Patagonian Light Railway, an interest in Sir Maximus Merger's Restaurant and Milk Bar holdings, a chain of antique shops, fun fairs and dance halls, and now certain speculations in diamonds all testify to the width and catholicity of 'Boojum's' interests.

His social life has been on a rising scale of splendour. When MP for Coalface he rarely visited his grimy constituency, but divided his time between Cannes, Gleneagles, Palm Beach, Wannsec, and his present country home at Blackmarket. In 1914 he married his first wife, the Hon. Cynthia Stuckup, heiress to the Stuckup millions. The marriage was dissolved in 1921 when he chose the Marquise de Miramar el Sol, a Spanish-American beauty. The divorce took place at Reno in 1924. Subsequent wives not mentioned in *Who's What* are believed to include Gloria G. String, Ziegfeld showgirl, and the Grand Duchess Bessie of Bessierabia. At present 'Boojum' is a happy bachelor and fond of the ladies. Being director of so many companies, he can always offer one of his secretaries a seat on the board.

Colonel Bogus's general attitude and position can be summed up in a few sentences. He represents the Industrial Barony. He is a believer in the *mystique* of big business and the divine right of directors.

Common Man, who is a thinking sort of chap, is perhaps his chief enemy, even more dangerous that the unjust (shop) stewards and the minions of Marx House. God made so many common men, as Abe Lincoln pointed out, and therein may lie the danger to the Bogus Industrial Barony of Hardfaced Men.

The civil servant, or Whitehall warrior, is not so much Bogus's enemy as his stooge. Bogus will tell you that he is as irrevocably opposed to red tape as Beaverbrook or the editor of the *Daily Worker*. He asks, ironically, how long a business firm run on civil service lines would last; and is thankful that the controllers of war industry are nearly all business men. Towards trade unionists he is a little more polite, although pitying their lack of the business tycoon's dynamic fire: and following the orthodox Tory line, he believes that the trade unions must be protected from 'unfair political pressure'. He and his followers are only too willing to do the protecting themselves.

Colonel Bogus believes in preserving the Old School Tie. It has its place, and can always be used (to mix a metaphor) as a stalking horse for attacks by Common Man. He has no other loyalty to Toryism, or ties, or tiaras, or titles, and has himself refused a peerage on no less than three occasions. On the other hand, he likes to enjoy all the luxurious pleasures of the traditional ruling class. Hence his position as head of the Ritzkrieg.

Like others of his kind, he will support war in so far as he can benefit from it. When peace paid, he was a fervent Municheer. Now war pays, in position if not yet in actual net profits, and he is one of the V-men. As far as the future, it is hard to say. He is certainly irrevocably opposed to Hitler, but is glad that Mussolini has been replaced by Marshal Imbroglio and the Bankers.

Though not now a Member of Parliament, Bogus is an apparent champion of parliamentary democracy and has a small *claque* of MPs and parliamentary candidates. Sir Maximus Merger, his closest business associate and member for Ribbonville, expounds the Bogus-merger plan of Monopolitik in the House, assisted by Captain Umbrage, Lady Standaghast and others. As the celebrated Professor Haushofer expounded the science of *Geopolitik* to the awestruck Germans, so Bogus, Haushofer of the Ritzkrieg, is the recognized authority on the new Monopolitik. While, however, independent members remain so independent and socialist members still quote Keir Hardie, Colonel Bogus has to be very careful as to what pressure he exerts from outside on the jealous and watchful Mother of Parliaments.

'Boojum as the social figure is very different from Bogus the king of Monopolitik. He enjoys his relaxations, and his parties in Mayfair and Maidenhead have long been famous. He is popular with Press Lords who have found in his lavish junketings and in his celebrated maxims a ready source of copy. He has always been generous with his money, both for private and public purposes. As he once said, 'Give away possessions, if you keep your position. *Position is nine points of the war.*' About his own popularity, he remarked, 'A profiteer is not without honour saving his own country.'

The *Intimate Papers* were not begun until some time after the outbreak of the present war, since Colonel Bogus, ever since his return from holding a watching brief at the Wanglo-German Business Conference at Dusseldorf, had been consolidating his position and switching his interests to conform with the rapidly changing situation.

The fact that so much has been said about 'Boojum's' business dealings must not lead the reader to suppose that he is just a City Slicker with no interests outside the Stock Exchange. In *Who's What* an impressive list of publications appears. It includes such minor triumphs as *Easy Speeches, Wit Among the Wealthy, With Rod and Pole in the Corridor, The Marxist Muckheap, Let's Fight for Finland, Beware Bureaucracy,* and the recent *Light on our Leftist Fascists.* Those who knew the extent of Colonel Bogus's activities will tend to believe that, like Lady Standaghast, he employs a 'ghost' The *Intimate Papers,* however, are entirely his own. The book, as yet unfinished, is the pure distillation of his bright and nimble mind, and can only be compared with the brilliant collection of *Easy Speeches.* It abounds chiefly in the maxims, apothegms, and epigrams for which 'Boojum' is noted wherever smart society gathers. The Westminster Watchdogs and Sable-bodied Women alike enjoy his sallies, and as he himself has said 'debentures and debutants can both make a man happy, if they give him sufficient control.'

Perhaps the most interesting section of the *Intimate Papers* deals with the Ritzkrieg's attitude to what might be called, in general terms, the Left. There has been, naturally, some disagreement among diehards as to the correct Tory line, 'and', adds the Colonel, 'that line has not been toed'. His own attitude was conveyed in the maxim which won for him undying clubroom fame.

SOCIALISM MUST BECOME THE SOCIAL 'ISM'

But to delve further into the *Intimate Papers* is to reveal the real Bogus line towards Socialism:

BUY UP THE LEFT TODAY: BEAT UP THE LEFT TOMORROW

Meanwhile, 'Boojum' is very busy thinking out ways and means of dividing the Labour Party. He has recommended the extensive use of the word 'bureaucrat' and 'bureaucracy', and suggests that it should be applied more and more to labour planners and trade union officials. 'It is a title Englishmen detest. It suggests thoroughness without thought.'

He adds: 'Socialism used to be called communism. Now it is called bureaucracy. Already we hint that it might be called fascism.'

This is clever on the part of Colonel Bogus. He realizes that socialism must be called what the masses will dislike. It is therefore only necessary for the class observation workers of the Ritzkrieg to report that current dislike wherever they may find it.

'British communism we have no need to fear,' continues this chapter of the *Intimate Papers.* 'It has no mass membership, and it sounds too difficult.'

But the question of continental communism is different, and very hard to unravel. 'What if Germany goes communist?' asks Bogus, and wisely does not attempt an immediate answer.

So much for the negative, or anti-side of the Ritzkrieg plan. A further interesting section of the *Intimate Papers*, comprising a lecture read by Colonel
Bogus to a committee of the Westminster Watchdogs, gives the other side of
the picture. A profound study of the effect of Tory policy on the people led
Bogus to recommend, a few years ago, a complete swing over in midstream.

'We were once in favour of discipline, regimentation and planning. Now
we recommend individual freedom, and are against planning. Why is this? It
is because, by pursuing our policy of Monopolitik, we have actually secured
most of the planning and control we want. We have not only scrambled the
eggs of private enterprise: we have concentrated them as well. They would
be difficult to unscramble: they will be impossible to deconcentrate.

'Socialists, on the other hand, are only just beginning to plan. We are therefore against any extension of control or planning. *Our planning was Business.
Their planning is Bureaucracy.*'

Whether his hearers, and afterwards his readers, followed the argument, we
do not know. Certainly the Ritzkrieg is revelling in the recommendation of
freedom to Common Man. They find it goes down so well in suburbia. It also
helps to prevent the masses from organizing themselves, for as Bogus has himself said:

'An individual must have over £1,000 a year to be an individualist.'

Elsewhere in the *Intimate Papers*, on the subject of the people, occurs this
sparkling maxim:

'I do not believe in *vox populi*. I am a ventriloquist.'

On fascism, Colonel Bogus is uncommunicative. It is known that in the
early 'thirties he was a fervent admirer of Il Duce and the corporate state and
freely recommended it as a pattern which British democracy might have to
adopt if threatened by Bolshevism. The only reference to fascism the *Intimate
Papers* has to offer is one characteristic definition.

'Fascism: A form of government one stage worse than conservatism and two
stages better than communism.'

In the speech to the Westminster Watchdogs, quoted above, Bogus has
many criticisms to offer concerning orthodox Tory policy. Declaring that the
Tories have always promised too much in the post war world, he adds:

'After the war, we cannot meet the demands of both the FBI and the PBI.'

He is fond of quoting from the speech by the Independent MP for Rugby,
in which that forthright and entertaining gentleman summed up Tory
political methods in action.

1. *Do not move unless you are obliged to.*
2. *When you are obliged to move, move as little as you can.*
3. *When you do move, make it appear that you are doing a favour.*
4. *Never move forward but only sideways.*

On these points Bogus agrees only with 3. He is said, in fact, to have been the inventor of the famous Ritzkrieg slogan OUR RIGHTS ARE YOUR PRIVILEGES which he recommended to replace the original WHAT YOU HAVE WE HOLD. His rewriting of the other points for Tories in the *Intimate Papers* is illuminating:

1. *Move before you are obliged to.*
2. *When obliged to move, do not say where you are going.*
4. *Do not move sideways, but in a circle.*

He adds a fifth point which has proved encouraging to many a group of diehards faced with the unpleasant prospect of having to make a decision:

5. *When in doubt, never commit yourself. Committee yourself.*

This advice has been found invaluable through the years. It successfully staved off the embarrassing public outcry for enquiry into the private manufacture of armaments before the war and into the 'cost plus' system for government contractors during the war, and it is now successfully holding up the necessity for action in the case of the Average Report and the Ughwatt Report. ('Ugh what a report!' as Bogus exclaimed in the presence of the Press.) As for the famous Average Report, the fact that no less than twenty committees are considering it gives reasonable hope to the Ritzkrieg that it will only reach the legislature in an emasculated form.

On studying the *Intimate Papers of Colonel Bogus*, readers may wonder why the Ritzkrieg campaign still contains so much of the Old Guard element. Colonel Blimp is regarded as an unabashed sentimentalist, and so are his followers. 'Boojum' Bogus entirely eschews sentimentality, except where young women are concerned. But it must be admitted that Bogus, despite his genius for Monopolitik, has no monopoly of the Ritzkrieg's plans. He is content to be thought 'not quite a gentleman' and to keep his own private opinion of the genuine landed gentry. What he is anxious to avoid is a split in the Ritzkrieg ranks – and the possibility of such a split is about the only hopeful sign that Common Man can see at the moment.

Colonel Bogus's reputation as a wit has done much to make good his lack of family, education, etc, in the best circles. Supporters of Monopolitik and the managerial revolution are not, as a rule, witty or diverting in their speech, but 'Boojum' is the exception that proves the rule.

In a light moment at the *Foire Noire* restaurant, where his table is reserved night and day, he even spoke slightingly of the Spanish Caudillo, referring to his 'Sancho Panzer divisions'. He characterized a senior official in the Treasury, after unsuccessfully attempting to get a smart bit of business past him, as 'that inverted Micawber, waiting for something to turn down'.

The witty jests of Colonel Bogus are part of his stock in trade. They are the patter of the conjuror, intent on his 'now you see it, now you don't' activities. He tantalizes Common Man with half promises of a wonderful post war future – if he plays ball with the big shots. Our rights are your privileges. But Common Man is beginning to get the measure of him, and it may be that the *Intimate Papers* of Colonel Bogus will end up a worst seller after all.

Royal Mail

Arthur Marshall

19 Tregunter Crescent, W.8

Your Majesty,

After much hesitation I am taking the liberty of writing to you to ask a favour on behalf of my daughter, Penelope. Young Penny, a well developed 12 year old, has recently 'taken up' tennis and has visions of becoming a second Christine Truman! There are no courts at her Comprehensive, though promised, and she 'makes do' in the park.

On my way to and from work (at the Army and Navy Stores) my bus takes me between Victoria and Hyde Park Corner and past the Palace gardens. These have always intrigued me and from the top of the bus one gets a lovely view. With the leaves off the trees, your hard tennis court becomes very clear. It looks in perfect condition, with everything at the ready and the net up, but I have never seen anyone playing on it. Would it be possible, I wonder, for my Penny to make use of it?

Yours sincerely,
Pamela Johnston

From the Lady Jean Sidebotham
Buckingham Palace, S.W.1

Dear Mrs Johnston,

Her Majesty has commanded me to answer your letter and to say that she regrets that she does not feel able at the present time to agree to your request.

Yours sincerely,
Jean Sidebotham
Lady-in-Waiting to Her Majesty

Dear Lady Sidebotham,

There seems to have been some misunderstanding. I was not expecting that Her Majesty would be able to play with Penny, she is clearly much too busy.

My daughter would bring along one of her friends. Of course, if Her Majesty would care for a knock-up during a slack time in state affairs, that would be a marvellous bonus!

Penny and her friend would bring their own tennis balls. Their best days would be Tuesday or Friday about 2.30 p.m. They are both very excited at the possibility.

> Yours sincerely,
> *Pamela Johnston*

Dear Mrs Johnston,

Your further letter has been considered and it is regretted that no exeption can be made in this case.

> Yours sincerely,
> *Jean Sidebotham*

20 Tregunter Crescent, W.8

Dear Queen,

My good friend and neighbour, Mrs Johnston, has been telling me how you are planning to be throwing open your tennis courts to youngsters. This is being great good news. My daughter, Helga, 'caught the tennis bug' while staying with her Onkel Heinrich in Hanover last summer and would also like to 'join up' with the group.

> Hullo!
> *Gertrud Bauscher*

Dear Mrs Bauscher,

Her Majesty has commanded me to answer your letter and to say that she is sorry that you have been misinformed and that the tennis court cannot be liberated for public use.

> Yours sincerely,
> *Jean Sidebotham*

Dear Lady Sidebotham,

I understand that Mrs Bauscher has written – it was foolish of me to let her into our little secret. Of course if you extend the invitation to everybody the court would become impossibly overcrowded and this is the last thing we want. When would it be convenient for the children to start to play?

> Yours sincerely,
> *Pamela Johnston*

Dear Mrs Johnston,

I would very much like to me more helpful but it will be clear to you that the question of security is, in these sad days, of paramount importance and this, if for no other reason, prevents us giving your daughter access to the Palace grounds.

Yours sincerely,
Jean Sidebotham

Dear Lady Sidebotham,

You need have no fear about security Penny knows better than to damage any trees or shrubs in the garden. We have always brought her up to respect other people's property. Did I spot a side-door to the Palace which the children could use? It's in that wall near to where dear old Gorringes used to be. If the children were to use that there would be less chance of outsiders getting to know what was going on. They would be careful to stick to the path once inside the Palace grounds. What about next Friday?

Yours sincerely,
Pamela Johnston

Dear Lady Sidebottom,

I am not understanding why Helga's tickets for the court have not come through. Penny Johnston is cock-a-hop all over the Crescent and nothing for Helga! Is this being British Justice?

Hullo!
Gertrud Bauscher

Dear Mrs Bauscher,

I am afraid that you are under a misapprehension. No tickets are being issued to anybody for Her Majesty's hard tennis court. The question of security is, these sad days, of paramount importance.

Yours sincerely,
Jean Sidebotham

Dear Lady Sidebottom,

We Germans are not fearful persons. We mind little of security. A true German is as secure on tennis-court as on battle-field. Helga fears nothing She has her karate medal and can protect herself.

Hullo!
Gertrud Bauscher

Dear Lady Sidebotham,

I wonder if you can have received my last letter. The children are 'all set'
– and no news! Next week will be half term and an ideal moment for the
children's first visit. Please let me know soon.

Yours sincerely,
Pamela Johnston

From the Hon. Mrs J. C. B. Tynte
Buckingham Palace, S.W.1

Dear Mrs Johnston,

Lady Jean is away from duty at the moment with a complete nervous
breakdown and in her absence I am dealing with her letters. As the volume
of incoming correspondence is always very great, it is not the Palace practice
to retain many letters from the public, or our answers to them, and so I am
in some doubt about the 'first visit' to which you refer. Could you please
explain?

Yours sincerely,
Muriel Tynte
Lady-in-Waiting to Her Majesty

Dear Mrs Tynte,

Certainly . . . My daughter, Penelope, has recently 'taken up' tennis . . .

'Can You Come In and Do It Live?'

John Timpson

> It is amazing how often you can. On the debit side there is
> the early rise, the strange environment, the odd characters
> who are likely to receive you. On the credit side there is the
> cup of BBC coffee, you have beaten the rush hour, and if you
> have an axe to grind, a cause to promote or just a line to
> shoot, you have the biggest radio current affairs audience of
> the day. Be prepared, though, for the unexpected.

The radio and television critic, Chris Dunkley, one of our occasional contributors, described our old waiting room (or 'Hospitality Room' as it was ludic-
rously called) as having all the welcoming cosiness of a meat safe. He was
being too generous. Apart from the bleak furnishings and the claustrophobic
lack of windows, a large and menacing mirror covered the whole of one wall.
Few people look or feel their best at seven in the morning, but to have it
proved by that mirror that you are not one of them was an ordeal nobody
should have to endure. Fortunately the room became so congested at peak
times with guests, producers, studio managers and the occasional itinerant
electrician that there was little chance for any lengthy self-examination.

The only improvement on the average dentist's waiting room was that at
least the newspapers were up to date. On the whole, however, there must have
been for the uninitiated the same atmosphere of impending doom, the same
dread of the eventual summons to the room across the corridor, as they
grasped their plastic cups, avoided their own eyes in the mirror and tried not
to jog the arm of the Cabinet minister in the next seat.

For the entertainment of those who awaited our pleasure, there was for
many years the 'Today' ducking stool. This was an evilly-designed armless
sofa on which one set of legs was placed much too close to the centre, so that
any weight applied to the extreme end resulted in the legs acting as a fulcrum

and the sofa turning into a see-saw. This did not matter as long as somebody was already sitting on the other end, but as soon as that counterweight was removed, the whole contraption tilted sideways and the unfortunate victim was dumped ignominiously on the floor.

Some distinguished notches were carved on the ducking stool in its time: at least one Northern Ireland Secretary, a couple of bishops, a wide range of trade union leaders, top industrialists and backbenchers (or flatbenchers as we liked to picture them on these occasions). If they happened to be grasping a cup of tea at the time, that counted as bonus points. The enormous mirror, incidentally, was so placed that the victim could actually see himself descending, an added refinement which must have added vastly to his discomfiture.

Some spoilsport removed the sofa after a while, before any bones were broken or any egos too badly damaged. As I write there are plans to dispense with the Hospitality Room also, in favour of more elegant premises. We shall have to devise some other softening-up process for our guests.

Across the corridor in Studio 3E, the home of the 'Today' programme for many years, the chairs are more reliable but can often be in too great demand. There are only five around our D-shaped table – two along the straight side for the presenters, three on the curved side for everybody else. As the news bulletins are read in the same studio, this can cause considerable congestion at certain points in the programme. Interviewees have to lurk around the walls until chairs are vacated by the newsreader and the newsroom sub-editor who acts as 'minder', and when the introduction to the live interview is fairly brief there is a hasty bout of silent musical chairs as Pauline Bushnell or Peter Donaldson scrambles out and Sir Geoffrey Howe or Roy Hattersley scrambles in. The whole operation has to be carried out on tiptoe and in complete silence, giving it all a surreal and dream-like effect.

The traffic does not stop there. Sports reporters appear and disappear, the 'Thought for the Day' thinker manoeuvres for position, secretaries putter in with a motoring flash or a late headline or just a further supply of tea. Frequently a live interview has to continue throughout all these exits and entrances, and it must be very difficult for an inexperienced guest to concentrate on questions about the Green Pound or the economic recession in West Germany or the American nuclear missile programme while a ghostly army flits silently in and out.

Not that they are always that silent. There was the morning when the Deputy Editor of 'Today' fell heavily over a metal wastepaper basket during the course of a live interview. There was another when the newsreader and his colleague came into the studio, chatting cheerfully, while we were introducing the weather forecast. And how often has the studio door been opened just as the tea trolley is rattling past, or a great burst of laughter has gushed out from the Hospitality Room across the way.

If the professionals can slip up like this, small wonder some of our guests get caught out too.

It is not unusual at the end of an interview for the guest to be so relieved the ordeal is over that he leaps immediately to his feet and crashes out of the door. This can be much more disastrous on television, when not only can he be seen as well as heard, but he may also strangle himself with his neck mike. Even on radio, it can cause quite a disturbance.

My most memorable experience of this kind was with a distinguished professor, a great expert on some subject so obscure that I have quite forgotten what it was. He had arrived a little late and had been whisked out of his taxi, through the foyer, into the lift, along the corridor (by-passing the Hospitality Room) and straight into the studio. There was no time for explanation or preparation. As soon as he sat down we started the interview, and to his lasting credit he answered the questions with great clarity and aplomb. At the end of it I thanked him and led him to the door. Robert Robinson, the other presenter at that time, started to introduce the next item.

It had all happened in such a whirl, though, that I suspect the good professor had no idea he had actually been broadcasting. Perhaps he thought we had just been having a preliminary chat in some back room. I had got him as far as the door when suddenly he stopped dead, went back to the table, lent over Bob's shoulder and enquired, a few inches from the microphone, 'Excuse me. Did you see where I left my hat?' The whole nation started looking for it.

There are many more live interviews in the programme than there used to be. It gives the programme greater immediacy and spontaneity, but it creates a lot more problems as well. It is rare for a guest to dry up completely, though there have been occasions when the questions have had to get longer and longer as the answers got shorter and shorter. When the only reponse is a nod, you know it is time to give up. The more usual difficulty is getting people to stop.

It is not so bad if they are in the studio with you. You can make gestures and grimaces and as a last resort you can always put a bag over their head.

It is more tricky with interviews 'down the line', when the guest can be on the other side of the country or the other side of the world, not appreciating that vital seconds are ticking away and the nation is agog for the weather forecast.

In these cases the only device is a nervous cough or a grunt or even an impatient 'yes, yes', to indicate a certain restlessness at the receiving end. On only one occasion did we reach such desperate straits that we actually faded somebody out in mid-flow – a BBC correspondent at that. As so often happens, the final question was intended to produce only a crisp yes or no. Instead he embarked on a lengthy tirade which began to encroach further and further onto the space allotted to 'Thought for the Day'. Even blunt interruptions and cries of 'Thank you' and 'Splendid' and 'That's fine' failed to stop the flow. Looking back, we should probably have cut him off completely and pretended the line had gone down. As it was, he faded gradually into the distance. We could still hear him as we introduced 'Thought for the Day'. For all I know, he is talking still.

If a contributor cannot get to the 'Today' studio to be interviewed, various alternatives are available. He may be near one of our regional studios, where the local staff can look after him. Rather trickier are our unattended studios, which are scattered throughout the country in the most unlikely situations. There is one above a dentist's surgery, another at the back of a public library, a third in a town hall and so on. Each one has its printed set of instructions and everything is made as simple as possible, but it can still be a daunting experience to be tucked away in one of these isolated rooms, often in an otherwise deserted building, with only a disembodied voice in the headphones for company and knowing that whatever you say will be heard by millions.

There is one of these studios in particular which I shall always recall with a shiver. It was in the top room of an old country vicarage, close to the church but not much else. It so happened that the vicar and his family were on holiday and the house was empty. It was midwinter, a wild night with the rain pelting down and the wind howling. I crept up the creaking stairs to the little studio under the eaves, got the equipment working, made contact with Broadcasting House and started sending my report.

Mercifully it was not going out live, because in the middle of it, as I sat in my lonely eyrie, three shadowy storeys up in that deserted Victorian pile, there was a sudden loud bang on the window. 'Aaaah!' I cried, to the astonishment of the engineer at the other end, who thought I had pressed the wrong button and electrocuted myself. Indeed, the shock was very similar. The noise had been just a branch blowing against the window, but it was some time before I could get the quaver out of my voice to finish the report.

If our contributor lives within thirty miles or so of Portland Place but is still disinclined to make the journey, we can use the radio car, but this too presents its problems. Not unnaturally, casual passers-by can be quite fascinated by the sight of a government minister in his dressing gown and slippers, sitting in the back of what looks a cross between a taxi and a telegraph pole. The very high mast on the roof does rather attract attention, and it cannot be easy to concentrate on a conversation with an unseen interviewer while a crowd of spectators gathers around the windows.

At least these days they are not likely to suffer the same disaster that is said to have overtaken one of our earlier radio cars, which were just ordinary saloons with an expanding aerial on the boot. One such car was parked facing up a fairly steep hill. The distinguished contributor was ushered into it and the engineer wound up the heavy aerial to its full extent – whereupon the car gently toppled over backwards.

It is not only the outside end of an outside link that can have its problems. We once had a sports reporter, who shall remain mercifully nameless, who was in the 'Today' studio monitoring the progress of a Test match in Australia. He was listening to the commentry on Radio 3, so that at an appropriate moment he could announce the score and a few details about the state of play. However, he became so engrossed in following the game that he quite forgot where he was. All unsuspecting, I announced, 'Let's see how the Test match is going. What's the latest score?' Our listeners were treated to the crisp reply, 'Do shut up – I'm trying to listen!'

When a morning is really busy, one can run into another problem over interviews with unseen guests, the problem of mistaken identity. Often there is no time for a chat before the interview starts, and we can slip up over wrong Christian names, wrong titles, wrong designations – and very occasionally, wrong people.

The most famous incident fortunately happened off the air. We were to record a talented gentleman who was able to play tunes under his armpits. The action, we understood, was rather similar to playing the bagpipes, but without the bag. The sounds came like a series of burps, and apparently he could adjust the note by placing his other hand in the armpit. It all sounded as if it ought to be another 'Today' winner. We made an appointment with him to come into one of our regional studios during the evening to do his stuff, and in due course the reporter was called into our studio at Broadcasting House to record the interview. What he did not know was that another interviewee had been booked for the same regional studio, and had arrived first.

'Good evening,' said our reporter, blithely. 'Before we actually start the interview, would you just play us a tune under your armpit?'

There was the slightest of pauses at the other end, then a voice said apologetically, 'I'll do my best, but what does that have to do with the Common Market Fishery policy?'

Eccentric musicians are a favourite feature of live interviews on 'Today'. We always enjoy the chap who can make a wind instrument out of a kettle and a length of garden hose. We once entertained a man who could tap out the 'William Tell' Overture on his teeth, an agonizing performance which set less musical molars aching in mouths all over the nation. Even more painful was the RAF sergeant who played 'Rule Britannia' by hitting himself on the head with a nine-inch spanner. We took the precaution of interviewing him first in case he was a bit groggy afterwards, but as it turned out he even gave us an encore.

One expects problems with this sort of dotty performer, but the worst ones have actually occurred with more orthodox musicians. We ended the programme one morning with a Hungarian virtuoso who had little grasp of the English language, but a very firm grasp indeed on his violin. We had asked him to give us a short sample of his skill, but obviously he did not know the meaning of 'short' and unfortunately we did not know the Hungarian for 'stop'!

The closing headlines, the weather forecast, all the usual farewell civilities went by the board as our guest scraped away into the microphone, oblivious of the growing hysteria all about him. Long after we had been faded off the air and the next programme was well into its stride, he was still at it. He only stopped when we brought in his agent and told him that was as far as our money went.

Over the years we have managed to accommodate double basses, tubas, even a complete string quartet in our rather cramped studio. The one instrument that beat us was an alpenhorn. This monstrous device, some ten or twelve feet long, is admirably suited to an Alp but quite the wrong design for our studio. We compromised by having the bell end inside the studio with us, while the alpenhornist stood in the corridor to blow down the other.

This required a complex system of signals via an intermediary, as the player was actually out of our sight. Such a system was duly arranged, and after as many blasts on his alpenhorn as we thought the listeners could stand, we sent him the signal to stop. To our relief, he did – or so we thought. Only when we were halfway through announcing 'Thought for the Day' did he play his final deafening, Alp-shattering note, a combination of a trumpeting elephant and the siren on the QE2. It gave the thought for that day a most remarkable send-off.

It is very pleasant, incidentally, to have a live contributor so frequently these days in 'Thought for the Day'. There was a time when the 'Thought' was always sent over in advance by the Religious Broadcasting Department in the form of a tape recording, perhaps because in those days our religious broadcasters did not get up terribly early – rumour had it that they only just made it for Morning Service at half past ten. But in recent times we have welcomed a very distinguished selection of speakers to the studio: bishops and abbots, a lady Rabbi, a prison governer, welfare workers, charity organizers – and the charming Rosemary Hartill.

Rosemary is the BBC's religious affairs correspondent, and is one of our regular contributors. I always feel we have a sort of special relationship since we spent several hours early one morning closeted in a tiny commentary box in the middle of Gatwick airport for the arrival of the Pope. We spent a desperate ten minutes between the time the plane landed and the time it actually taxied to a halt, Rosemary giving the history of every Pontiff since St Peter and I describing each individual oil stain on the tarmac. That sort of experience must forge a lasting link.

Anyway, Brian Redhead thinks so, and he capitalized on it one morning in a way which nearly produced a broadcasting disaster. Rosemary had joined us in the studio a few minutes before 'Thought' was due, and while the tape was running, Brian announced suddenly, 'I had an amazing dream last night.'

'Tell us about it,' I said, knowing he would anyway.

'I dreamed,' he said, 'I had gone to Heaven. St Peter met me at the gate and checked his records and said, as a penance for my activities down here, I would spend the next seven years in Heaven shackled to a terrible old whisky-sodden crone. This didn't seem too severe, all things considered, so off I hobbled off with this crone attached to me – only to see Timpson wandering about Heaven, shackled to Rosemary Hartill.

'I forthwith went back to St Peter to complain, "Here I am," I said, "landed with this frightful smelly old crone, and there is Timpson shackled to Rosemary Hartill." Whereupon St Peter said, "You get on with your penance and let Rosemary Hartill get on with hers." '

Brian had just finished when the green light went on, the microphone was live, and I had to announce to the nation, 'Here is "Thought for the Day," with Rosemary Hartill.' I shall never know how I got through it.

A Motor Salesman Goes Crazy

(Being a manuscript found outside Olympia during the Motor Show)

Maurice Lane-Norcott

All day long I stand about in my canary-coloured waistcoat, and they come to me in their thousands and ask what the pistons are made of and how the valves work.

'Are the gears epicyclic?' they ask, 'and how many revolutions will the crankshaft do to a gallon of petrol?'

I tell them the pistons are tin, the gears are butter-churns, and every time the crankshaft revolves a fairy is born! Ha! Ha! Ha! They little know what *I* know, the fools! They never suspect me of being Einstein, the Human Magneto!

This morning I shut an old lady's head in the bonnet while she was peering into the works of the little Dobson Seven.

'Is it *quite* reliable on top gear in traffic, and *where* is the sump?' she asked.

'Put your head into my parlour and you shall see, pretty one,' I laughed back at her merrily.

Then when her head was in jeopardy I slammed down the bonnet and burst into peal after peal of shrill laughter. She appeared so odd protruding from the little Dobson Seven – so very odd, very odd.

It is now ten years since I attended my first Motor Show. I was a muff salesman for radiators then – a most charitable work. Poor things! They get so cold at night! I often feel sorry for them. Later I became a grease gunman, and many a wild shot I fired into the shackles and springs, thereby winning nut after nut and bolt after bolt. Today my name is Hispano and I am married to a girl called Suiza and have six dear little cylinders, all, alas, missing.

Yesterday I stood on a rival's stand and said to a farmer in leggings: 'Madam, can I interest you in reapers this morning? This machine is a self-hemmer and beats while it sweeps without once changing the needle. It breaks record after record in the well-known Fifty-Play-Way, and a plain van will bring it to your door in instalments.'

I wish you could have seen his face!

All day long I stand about in my canary-coloured waistcoat and they come to me in their thousands and ask fool questions. What can it mean to *them* where the flywheel is and if the back axle is floating? I think I will sit on the floor and pretend that I am an accessory.

No, sir, no! You mustn't ask *me* about camshafts! I do not know at what speed they revolve or how they are lubricated. I am a motor horn priced thirty shillings and sixpence. If you do not go away at once I shall blow at you suddenly and startle you beyond measure.

HONK! HONK!

Ha! Ha! Ha! What fun we accessories have!

Did I mention that in my spare time I am Exide, the World's Largest Accumulator, and can light my cigarettes at my own spark? My blood circulates at 2,000 revolutions per minute, and, unless I am well oiled, I knock before entering. You will find me under the show case on Stand 34, but do not look at me because I am hiding incognito now.

'Are you in charge of this stand, young man?' a bishop asked me this morning. 'If so, kindly show me the four-door Sedan, as advertised.'

'I am the four-door Sedan, as advertised,' I answered, bowing slightly. 'I am air-cooled, with fabric exterior, and I have a good watch and all accessories. As you can see, I am well shod and in perfect running order. If you will wait a minute I will give you a trial run.'

I then, to oblige him, ran at top speed all round Olympia, but when I got back again he had gone. Poor fellow! I expect he was mad, really.

Have *you* ever described an oiling system to a lady in a hat with large feathers? I had that pleasure quite recently. I was sitting at the wheel of an open tourer pretending to be Archie Compson driving off from the first tee at St Andrews, when this lady said to me: 'Will you kindly explain how the oiling system works?'

It really was a laughable moment.

'Well, sister,' I said to her, 'if you have any oil to spare you pour it in a hole in the front, and from what I know of this car, it runs straight out again through a crack in the back axle. And if you like to call that a "system" I don't.'

I then took two feathers out of her hat and stuck them on my shoulders with Fixo, the Perfect Puncture Cure.

'Tweet! tweet!' I said coyly. 'I'm an angel now!'

Needless to say, she didn't buy the car. I haven't sold a thing at this Show yet.

Sometimes I wonder why people stare at me so intently when I crawl from stand to stand on my hands and knees hissing quietly to myself. Plainly they can't know much about motoring. If they did they would realize at once that I had a puncture in my off-side shoe. I am only a little Pullman Four, looking for a foot pump, that's all. All day long I crawl about in my canary-coloured waistcoat, but they still come to me in their thousands and say: 'Is Twoxall the best lubricant for internal combustion engines?' or 'Are the bushes phosphor-bronze or steel?'

'Take away the registration number you first thought of and the answer is cellulose finish,' I always say to them, but they never understand.

Half an hour ago I hid my head in a silencer on Stand 352, but it has gone now. Alas, alas, I have lost my head: Two buns missing and a cup of tea! And to think that once I was Pyrex, the Famous Fire Extinguisher! Oh, it is hard, hard!

Are aluminium spokes better than mauve ones, and where do the gases go when they escape at last? What is the ratio of bottom gear, and why are the timing-wheels so late in chiming? These are terrible questions.

All day long I . . . No, madam, no! . . . the carburetter is rolled gold and . . . allow me, sir, to show you the way by the exhaust-pipe . . . you take the first turning to the left and then . . . ha! ha! ha! He's caught his nose in the piston! He's . . .

Mrs Magruder

Max Adeler

Mr Magruder is apparently a man of leisure and of comparative wealth; his social position is very good, and he has enough intelligence and cultivation to enable him to get along comfortably in the society of very respectable persons. Mrs Magruder, it seems, is rather inclined to emphasize herself. She is a physician, an enthusiast in the study and practice of medical science, and a woman of such force that she succeeds in keeping Mr Magruder, if not precisely in a state of repression, at least slightly in the background. He married her, according to report, shortly after her graduation; and as he was at that time an earnest advocate of the theory that women should practise medicine, a belief prevails that he became attached to her while under her treatment. She touched his heart, we may presume, by exciting activity in his liver. He loved her, let us say, for the blister she had spread, and demanded her hand because he had observed the singular dexterity with which it cut away tumours and tied up veins.

But if what Dr Tobias Jones, our family physician, tells me is true, the sentiments of Magruder upon the subject of medical women have undergone a radical change in consequence of an exuberance of enthusiasm on the part of Mrs Magruder. Dr Jones entertains the regular professional hatred for Mrs Dr Magruder, and so I have my private doubts respecting the strict accuracy of his narrative.

He said that a few years ago the Magruders lived in Philadelphia, and Mrs Magruder was a professor in the Women's Medical College. At that time Magruder was in business; and as he generally came home tired, he had a habit of lying on the sitting room sofa in the evening, for the purpose of taking a nap. Several times when he did so, and Mrs Magruder had some friends with her downstairs, he noticed upon awaking that there was a peculiar feeling of heaviness in his head and a queer smell of drugs in the room. When he questioned Mrs Magruder about it, she invariably coloured and looked confused, and said he must have eaten something which disagreed with him.

Ultimately the suspicions of Magruder were aroused. He suspected something wrong. A horrible thought crossed his mind that Mrs Magruder intended to poison him for his skeleton – to sacrifice him so that she could dangle his bones on a string before her class and explain to the seekers after medical truth the peculiarities of construction which enabled the framework of her husband to move around in society.

So Magruder revealed his suspicions to his brother, and engaged him to secrete himself in a closet in the room while he took his usual nap on a certain evening upon the sofa.

When that night arrived, Mrs Magruder pretended to have the 'sewing circle' from the church in the parlour, while her husband went to sleep in the sitting room with that vigilant relative of his on guard. About nine o'clock Mr Magruder's brother was surprised to observe Mrs Magruder softly stealing upstairs, with the members of the 'sewing circle' following her noiselessly in single file. In her hand Mrs Magruder carried a volume. If her brother-in-law had conceived the idea that the book might contain the tender strains of some sweet singer amid whose glowing imagery this woman revelled with the ecstasy of a sensitive nature, he would have been mistaken, for the work was entitled *Thompson on the Nervous System*; while those lines traced in a delicate female hand, upon the perfumed notepaper, and carried by Mrs Magruder, so far from embodying an expression of the gentlest and most sacred emotions of her bosom, were merely a diagnosis of an aggravated case of fatty degeneration of the heart.

I give the story literally as I received it from that eminent practitioner Jones.

When the whole party had entered the room, Mrs Magruder closed the door and applied chloroform to her husband's nose. As soon as he became completely insensible, the sewing in the hands of the ladies was quickly laid aside, and to Magruder's secreted brother was disclosed the alarming fact that this was a class of students from the college.

If Dr Jones is to be believed, Professor Magruder began her lecture with some very able remarks upon the nervous system; and in order to demonstrate her meaning more plainly, she attached a galvanic battery to her husband's toes, so that she might make him wriggle before the class. And he did wriggle. Mrs Magruder gave him a dozen or two shocks, and poked him with a ruler to make him jump around, while the students stood in a semi-circle, with note books in their hands, and exclaimed, 'How very interesting!'

Magruder's brother thought it awful, but he was afraid to come out when he reflected that they might want *two* skeletons at the college.

Mrs Magruder then said that she would pursue this branch of the investigation no further at that moment, because Mr Magruder's system was somewhat debilitated in consequence of an overdose of chlorate of potash which she had administered in his coffee upon the previous day for the purpose of testing the strength of the drug.

Mrs Magruder then proceeded to 'quiz' the class concerning the general construction of her husband. She said, for instance, that she had won what was called the heart of Mr Magruder, and she asked the students what it was that she had really won.

'Why, the cardia, of course,' said the class; 'it is an azygous muscle of an irregular pyramid shape, situated obliquely and a little to the left side of the chest, and it rests on the diaphragm.'

One fair young thing said that it didn't rest on the diaphragm.

Another one said she would bet a quart of paregoric it did, and until the dispute was settled by the professor, Magruder's brother's hair stood on end with fear lest they should go to probing around inside of Magruder with a butcher knife and a lantern, for the purpose of determining the actual condition of affairs respecting his diaphragm.

Mrs Magruder continued. She explained that when she accepted Mr Magruder he seized her hand, and she required the class to explain what it was that Mr Magruder actually had hold of.

The students replied that he held in his grip twenty seven distinct bones, among which might be mentioned the phalanges, the carpus, and the metacarpus.

The beautiful creature who was incredulous concerning the diaphragm suggested that he also had hold of the deltoid. But the others scornfully suggested that the deltoid was a muscle; they knew, because they had dissected one that very morning. The discussion became so exciting that thumb lancets were drawn, and there seemed to be a prospect of bloodshed, when the professor interfered and demanded of the girl who had begun to cry about the deltoid what was the result when Mr Magruder kissed her.

'Why merely a contraction of the orbicularis oris muscle; thus,' said the student as she leaned over and kissed Mr Magruder.

Magruder's brother, in the closet, thought maybe it wasn't so very solemn for Magruder after all. He considered this portion of the exercises in a certain sense soothing.

But all the students said it was perfectly scandalous. And the professor herself, after informing the offender that hereafter when illustration of any point in the lesson was needed it would be supplied by the professor, ordered her to go to the foot of the class, and to learn eighty new bones as a punishment.

'Do you hear me, miss?' demanded the professor, when she perceived that the blooming contractor of the orbicularis oris did not budge.

'Yes,' she said, 'I am conscious of a vibration striking against the membrana tympanum, and being transmitted through the labyrinth until it agitates the auditory nerve, which conveys the impression to the brain.'

'Correct,' said the professor. 'Then obey me, or I will call my biceps and flexors and scapularis into action and put you in your place by force.'

'Yes, and we will help her with our spinatus and infraspiralis,' exclaimed the rest of the class.

Magruder's brother in the gloom of his closet did not comprehend the character of these threats, but he had a vague idea that the life of that lovely young sawbones was menaced by firearms and other engines of war of a peculiarly deadly description. He felt that the punishment was too severe for the crime. Magruder himself, he was convinced, would have regarded that orbicularis operation with courageous fortitude and heroic composure.

Mrs Magruder then proceeded to give the class practice in certain operations in medical treatment. She vaccinated Magruder on the left arm, while one of the students bled his right arm and showed her companions how to tie up the vein. They applied leeches to his nose, under the professor's instructions; they cupped him on the shoulder blades; they exercised themselves in spreading mustard plasters on his back; they timed his pulse; they held out his tongue with pincers and examined it with a microscope, and two or three enthusiastic students kept hovering around Magruder's leg with a saw and a carving knife, until Magruder's brother in retirement in the closet shuddered with apprehension.

But the professor restrained these devotees of science; and when the other exercises were ended, she informed the students that they would devote a few moments in conclusion to study of the use of the stomach pump.

Dr Jones continued: 'I shall not enter into particulars concerning the scene that then ensued. There is a certain want of poetry about the operation of the weapon just named, a certain absence of dignity and sentiment, which, I may say, render it impossible to describe it in a manner which will elevate the soul and touch the moral sensibilities. It will suffice to observe that as each member of the class attacked Magruder with that murderous engine, Magruder's brother, timid as he was, solemnly declared to himself that if the class would put away those saws and things, he would rush out and rescue his brother at the risk of his life.

'He was saved the necessity of thus imperilling his safety. Magruder began to revive. He turned over; he sat up; he stared wildly at the company; he looked at his wife; then he sank back upon the sofa and said to her, in a feeble voice:

' "Henrietta, somehow or other I feel awfully hungry!"

'Hungry! Magruder's brother considered that, after that last performance of the class, Magruder ought to have a relish for a couple of raw buffaloes, at least. He emerged from the closet, and seizing a chair, determined to tell the whole story. Mrs Magruder and the class screamed, but he proceeded. Then up rose Magruder and discussed the subject with vehemence, while his brother brandished his chair and joined in the chorus. Mrs Magruder and the class cried, and said Mr Magruder was a brute, and he had no love for science. But Mr Magruder said that as for himself, "hang science!" when a woman became so infatuated with it as to chop up her husband to help it along. And his brother said he ought to put in even stronger terms than that. What followed upon the adjournment of the class is not known. But Magruder seems somehow to have lost much of his interest in medicine, and since then there has been a kind of coolness between him and the professor.'

'Yeo-Frightfully-Ho'

(A Tale of the Hi Seize)

Ralph Wotherspoon

The Admiral was seated in the charthouse when Bissit, the boatswain, entered.

'What is it, Bissit?' he inquired breezily.

The boatswain raised his peaked cap.

'Beggin' your pardon, sir—' he began. At that moment eight bells sounded. Then the Admiral signed to Bissit to continue.

'As I was about to say, sir,' resumed the boatswain, 'there's as odd a bit o' shipping' as ever I seed on the larboard bow.'

'Oh, is there?' mused the Admiral, keenly interested. 'What eyes you have, Bissit, to be sure.'

Bissit leant forward impressively.

'You should see 'er, sir. You really should,' he said.

'I should,' rejoined the Admiral, attempting to peer out of the porthole, 'but I don't,' he added.

'Nor you never won't, sir,' grunted the boatswain, 'till you looks in the right direction. She ain't that way – neaow.'

The Admiral laughed heartily.

'Come, come,' he chuckled. 'This will never do, will it, Bissit?'

His subordinate smiled grimly and held the door open. In less time than it takes to relate, the Admiral was on the bridge and his eyes were on a small semi-rigged schooner which, at a distance of several furlongs, appeared to be drifting backwards. A sharp glance through a prismatic glass confirmed his first suspicions.

'Ha – a derelict,' he exclaimed.

Simultaneously he switched over a dial pointer, rang a bell which communicated with the engine room, and spoke through a tube.

'Are you there, McCluskie?' he rapped.

'Phwat is it?' replied a phlegmatic voice.

'I want you to stop,' said the Admiral incisively.

'Is ut stop ye're after, yer honour?'

'It is,' said the Admiral, 'and at once, please.'

With these words he hung up the receiver and turned to re-survey the drifting ship.

'One does not often see a derelict,' he murmured, 'but when one does—'

'What orders, sir?' said Yelverton-Pink, the first lieutenant. (In private life, prior to joining the Navy, he had been the Hon. Lionel Yelverton-Pink, but this was not generally known.)

'Get off the survivors and blow her up,' the Admiral directed. At this moment the propeller ceased to churn and the '*Egg*' came promptly, yet carefully, to a standstill.

The Admiral nodded reassuringly to his first officer.

'McCluskie has his instructions,' he remarked.

'Shall I—?' began Yelverton-Pink. He paused.

'Shall you what?' said his superior encouragingly.

'Shall I fire a shot across her bows, sir?'

'Do, do,' said the Admiral. 'Bissit will arrange it. By the way, where *is* Bissit?'

''Ere I am, sir,' replied that worthy, appearing from behind the binnacle. 'Beggin' your pardon, sir, but do I understand as 'ow we're to open fire?'

'The Admiral wishes it, Bissit,' Yelverton-Pink said sternly.

'Then, in that case,' replied Bissit, 'I've no more to say. 'Ow many rounds would you like?' he continued.

'One will be ample,' said the Admiral. Eight bells sounded as he spoke. 'Ah, the bells, the bells,' the old seadog reflected. 'They always mean something. I wonder if they mean Pargiter is ready with my muffin? If you'll excuse me—'

The Admiral ran from the bridge, and, under the active direction of Yelverton-Pink, Bissit, Pringle, the underwriter, and H. Jones, the artificer-in-chief and man-at-arms, the after turret gun was trained over the derelict and loaded with a powerful projectile.

'When I give the word,' said Yelverton-Pink, 'let her go.'

He was palpably excited, a handsome fellow in the first flush of a recent promotion. Seizing a megaphone, the young officer raised it to his lips.

'FIRE,' he bellowed.

In less time than it takes to relate, the deck became an inextricable tangle of men and hosepipes, a heavy gong reverberated, an alarm signal sounded, a hydrant was brought into position, and the remorseless clank of pumps began to send a tremor through the ship from stem to stern. Bissit, Pringle and H. Jones were among the hardest workers.

The Admiral bounced out of his cabin as the first jet of water entered it.

'What's all this?' he inquired.

Yelverton-Pink attempted to explain.

'I'm sure I don't – I think – it may—' he began. His superior cut him short.

'Put the hose away and stop fooling, there's a good fellow,' he said. This was done. Then—

'Gun loaded, sir,' said H. Jones.

'Fire,' rasped the Admiral mechanically. 'Stoppit,' he continued as the spectacle of the hose being hastily unpacked and recoupled awoke him to the consequences of his command. 'Pipe all hands aft, Mr Bissit,' he added sharply.

The shrill whistle of the boatswain's instrument soon had the desired effect. The crew collected in the stern and, in a few well chosen words, their beloved commander acquainted them with the nature of the misunderstanding which had arisen. Rum was then served to all on board and gratefully appreciated. Conscious of their error the men did everything in their power to make amends.

In less time than it takes to relate, the pumps were dismantled, the hydrant removed, and the hose locked up. The key was given to Bissit, who passed it to Pringle.

Then the Admiral drew H. Jones's attention to the after turret gun.

'Gun loaded, sir,' H. Jones reminded him.

'I know,' said the Admiral. 'Unload it, will you? Fire – IT,' he added unexpectedly.

The man-at-arms applied himself to the ordnance with immediate and audible results. But there was no confusion on board the '*Egg*'. With the Admiral's exhortations fresh in mind, the crew pursued their various tasks with creditable calm. To judge from the expression on their faces the gun might not have been fired at all.

'Shall I—?' began Yelverton-Pink. He paused and saluted.

'We'll see, my boy,' responded the Admiral, as, with a kindly twinkle in his eye, he acknowledged the salute and swung himself on to the bridge.

From this eminence his practised gaze raked the horizon in all directions yet, seemingly, to no purpose. Incredible as it may appear the derelict was nowhere to be seen. It had completely vanished. The Admiral was hard put to it to conceal his displeasure. For there could be only one explanation. H. Jones had blundered.

'H——g,' he exclaimed testily. Eight bells sounded.

Re Helicopters

H. F. Ellis

To the Secretary of State for Air

Sir – I write to protest against the unwarrantable frequency with which I find myself rescued by your helicopters. On the first occasion on which I was snatched from the sea while enjoying a quiet float beyond the breakers I was prepared to make light of the incident. This is a normal holiday risk, which in my opinion it is the duty of members of the public to accept in the right spirit. But enough is as good as a feast. I have now three times been hoisted into the air and ferried to St Mawgan aerodrome, where everybody I have met has been most kind and attentive – too kind, if anything. Constant wrapping in warm blankets has brought my skin out in an irritating rash; nor am I a man who cares much for copious draughts of hot, sweet tea.

The pilot considers that my habit of floating very low in the water misleads holidaymakers ashore into thinking that I am waterlogged or in distress. That is as it may be. I cannot alter my centre of gravity or buoyancy coefficient to suit your convenience. Surely there is some alternative method of protecting the not so portly against the intrusive zeal of your Air Rescue Organisation?

August 5th.

Sir – It is no use saying that it is open to anyone not in immediate danger to refuse to be rescued. Quite apart from the question of good manners, if one attempts to ignore the machine or to brush the hoisting tackle aside the crew conclude that one is either unconscious or hysterical, and send a man down by rope ladder to see about it. Only yesterday, while sunbathing in a small deserted cove, I attempted to move out of the shadow created by one of your infernal contraptions and found myself suddenly seized from behind and forcibly buckled into a kind of surcingle made of harsh webbing. It is ludicrous to suggest that I was in any danger of being cut off by the tide; but the pilot – not the one who generally rescues me, by the way; this was an altogether more domineering and self sufficient type – would not listen to reason. He simply said that he had his orders and proposed to carry them out – with the result that I was late for lunch for the third day running, and dared not take my usual afternoon dip in case I missed a tennis engagement after tea.

I shall be obliged if you will take immediate steps to see that your rescue organization turns its attention to some other holidaymaker, preferably one who stands in need of it.

August 7th.

Sir – After a momentary respite (due in part, I think, to my practice of laying out warning 'KEEP OFF' notices with strips of sheeting whenever I seek seclusion on the rocks and coast hereabouts) the situation has again worsened. I am now constantly attended by a large yellow helicopter, hired I believe by a London newspaper to take photographs of any further attempts that may be made to rescue me by air. The noise is indescribable, and whenever I try to escape it by taking refuge in a cave or holding my breath under water some busybody can be relied on to ring up St Mawgan and bring a second helicopter on the scene. I have noticed, too, that I am now kept dangling in the air, before being hauled into the rescue machine, for a longer period than was the case at the beginning of my holiday. This (though I cannot prove it) is done at the request of the photographers who seem to be hand in glove with the authorities at St Mawgan. I shall hold you entirely responsible if any harm comes to me through the almost perpetual draughts to which I am now exposed.

I reopen this letter to add that my wife has just returned in an RAF truck and in a very highly strung condition from St Austell, of all places. It appears, so far as I can piece her story together, that she was violently scooped from the water *while actually sitting on an inflated horse* – an inexcusably careless mistake – and deposited, horse and all, on a makeshift aerodrome without any proper facilities for resuscitating people suffering from needless rescue. When I rang up St Mawgan to protest, they told me that their regular rescue craft was already out on a case (as if I needed to be told that!) when this second call came in. They had accordingly been compelled to ask Plymouth for assistance, and it might be that the pilot from there was *less experienced in rescue work than their own men* and had picked up the wrong bather by mistake. The italics are mine, but the responsibility, in my submission, remains yours.

August 8th.

Sir – You will see, from the enclosed cutting from a local paper headed 'HORSE RESCUED FROM SEA' something of the annoyance to which we as a family are almost daily subjected by the attentions of your rescue service. The very indifferent photograph of my wife does not help matters.

However, that is not the main purpose of this letter. I would like to inform you that, in a final attempt to obtain a little peace and privacy before returning to London on the 10th, I am tomorrow taking my wife, sister-in-law, two cousins, a Mrs Winworth, and most of our children to Lundy Island in a hired motorboat. We hope to be there by about 2.30 p.m. and have not, of course, thought it necessary to make any arrangements about the return journey.

We should like to reach St Mawgan not later than 7 p.m. If that would be convenient for you.

Yours faithfully,
H. F. Ellis

Noulded Into the Shake of a Goat

Patrick Campbell

When I was a tall sensitive boy at school I once sent up for a booklet about how to be a ventriloquist.

I was always 'sending up' for things – variable focus lamps, propelling pencils with choice of six differently coloured leads, air pistols discharging wooden bullets, scale model tanks with genuine caterpillar action, tricks in glass topped boxes, and so on – anything, I suppose, to vary the monotony of straight games and education.

The booklet arrived at breakfast time one morning in a large square envelope. I told the other boys it was a new stamp album, and got on with my shredded liver poached in water. I wanted the voice throwing to come as a real surprise.

We had twenty minutes after breakfast in which to get our things ready for first school. I had a quick run through the new book.

It was called *Ventriloquism in Three Weeks*. On the first page it explained that ventriloquism came from the Latin *ventriloquus* – 'a speaking from the belly'. There was also a drawing of a schoolboy smiling pleasantly at a railway porter carrying a trunk. From the trunk came hysterical cries of 'Help! Help! Murder! Police!'

It was just the sort of thing I was aiming at. I slipped the book in with my other ones, and hurried off to the first school.

In the next fortnight I put in a good deal of practice, sitting right at the back of the class, watching my lips in a small piece of mirror, and murmuring, 'Dah, dee, day, di, doy, doo.'

It was necessary, however, to be rather careful. Dr Farvox, the author of the book, suggested that it might be as well to perform the earlier exercises 'in the privacy of one's bedroom or den'. Dr Farvox was afraid that 'chums or relatives' might laugh, particularly when one was practising the 'muffled voice in the box'.

The best way to get this going, Dr Farvox said, was to experiment 'with a continuous grunting sound in a high key, straining from the chest as if in pain.'

He was right in thinking that this exercise ought to be performed in the privacy of the bedroom. It was inclined to be noisy – so noisy, indeed, that I was twice caught straining in a high key during practical chemistry, and had to pretend that I'd been overcome by the fumes of nitric acid.

But in the end, it was the easy, pleasant smile that terminated my study of what Dr Farvox described as 'this amusing art'.

It happened one Saturday morning, in the hour before lunch, ordinarily a pleasant enough period devoted to constitutional history. Bill the Bull, who took the class, was usually fairly mellow with the prospect of the weekend before him, and there was not much need to do any work.

As was by now my invariable custom I was seated at the back of the room with a large pile of books in front of me. I was working on the Whisper Voice, which had been giving me a considerable amount of difficulty.

'Lie down, Neddy, lie down,' I whispered, watching my lips closely in the glass.

'It's due in dock at nine o'clock.'

Not bad.

'Take Ted's Kodak down to Roy.'

There it was again – the old familiar twitch on 'Kodak.'

I sat back, relaxing a little. Dr Farvox was strongly in favour of the smile. 'What the young student,' he said, 'should aim at from the first is an easy and natural expression. He should smile.'

I smiled. Smiling, I whispered, 'Take Ted's Kodak down to Roy.'

To my absolute horror I found myself smiling straight into the face of Bill the Bull.

He stopped dead. He was in the middle of something about the growth of common law, but my smile stopped him dead in his tracks.

'Well, well,' said Bill, after a moment. 'How charming. And good morning to you, too.'

I at once buried my face in my books, and tried to shove the mirror and *Ventriloquism in Three Weeks* on one side.

Bill rolled slowly down the passageway between the desks. He was an enormous Welshman with a bullet head, and very greasy, straight black hair. He took a subtle and delicate pleasure in driving the more impressionable amongst us half mad with fear at least five days a week.

'Such pretty teeth,' said Bill. 'How nice of you to smile at me. I have always wanted to win your admiration.'

The other boys sat back. They knew they were on to something good.

I kept my head lowered. I'd actually succeeded in opening my constitutional history somewhere in the middle, but the corner of Dr Farvox was clearly visible under a heap of exercise books.

Bill reached my desk. 'But who knows,' he said, 'perhaps you love me too. Perchance you've been sitting there all morning just dreaming of a little home – just you and I. And later, perhaps some little ones . . .'

A gasp of incredulous delight came from the other boys. This was Bill at his very best.

I looked up. It was no longer possible to pretend I thought he was talking to someone else.

'I'm sorry, sir,' I said, 'I was just smiling.'

Suddenly Bill pounced. He snatched up Dr Farvox.

'Cripes,' he said. 'What in the world have we here? Ventriloquism in three weeks?'

'Scholars,' he said, 'be so good as to listen to this.'

He read aloud: 'To imitate a fly. Close the lips tight at one corner. Fill that cheek full of wind and force it through the aperture. Make the sound suddenly loud, and then softer, which will make it appear as though the insect were flying in different parts of the room. The illusion may be helped out by the performer chasing the imaginary fly, and flapping at it with his handkerchief.'

'Strewth,' said Bill. He looked round the class. 'We'd better get ourselves a little bit of this. Here am I taking up your time with the monotonies of constitutional history, while in this very room we have a trained performer who can imitate a fly.'

Suddenly he caught me by the back of the neck. 'Come,' he said, 'my little love, and let us hear this astounding impression.'

He dragged me down to the dais.

'Begin,' said Bill. 'Be so kind as to fill your cheek with wind and at all costs do not omit the flapping of the handkerchief.'

'Sir,' I said, 'that's animal noises. I haven't got that far yet.'

'Sir,' squeaked Bill in a high falsetto, 'that's animal noises. I 'aven't got that far yet.'

He surveyed the convulsed class calmly.

'Come, come,' he said, 'this art is not as difficult as I had imagined it to be. Did anyone see my lips move?'

They cheered him. They banged the lids of their desks. 'Try it again, sir,' they cried. 'It's splendid!'

Bill raised his hand. 'Gentlemen,' he said, 'I thank you for your kindness. I am, however, but an amateur. Am I not right in thinking we would like to hear something more from Professor Smallpox?'

They cheered again. Someone shouted, 'Make him sing a song, sir!'

Bill turned to me. 'Can you,' he said, 'Professor Smallpox, sing a song?'

It was the worst thing that had happened to me in my life. I tried to extricate myself.

'No, sir,' I said. 'I haven't mastered the labials yet.'

Bill started back. He pressed his hand to his heart.

'No labials?' he said. 'You have reached the age of fifteen without having mastered the labials. But, dear Professor Smallpox, we must look into this. Perhaps you would be so kind as to give us some outline of your difficulties?'

I picked up *Ventriloquism in Three Weeks*. There was no way out.

'There's a sentence here, sir, that goes "A pat of butter moulded into the shape of a boat".'

Bill inclined his head. 'Is there, indeed? A most illuminating remark. You propose to put it to music?'

'No, sir,' I said. 'I'm just trying to show you how hard it is. You see, you have to call that "A cat of gutter noulded into the shake of a goat".'

Bill fell right back into his chair.

'You have to call it *what?*' he said.

'A cat of gutter, sir, noulded into the shake of a goat.'

Bill's eyes bulged. 'Professor,' he said, 'you astound me. You bewilder me. A cat of gutter—' he repeated it reverently, savouring every syllable.

Then he sprang up. 'But we must hear this,' he cried. 'We must have this cat of gutter delivered by someone who knows what he is at. This – this is valuable stuff.'

He caught me by the ear. 'Professor,' he said, 'why does it have to be noulded into the shake of a goat?'

'Well, sir,' I said, 'if you say it like that you don't have to move your lips. You sort of avoid the labials.'

'To be sure you do,' said Bill. 'Why didn't I think of it myself? Well, now, we will have a demonstration.'

He turned to face the class. 'Gentlemen,' he said, 'Professor Smallpox will now say 'a pat of butter moulded into the shape of a boat' *without moving his lips*. I entreat your closest attention. You have almost certainly never in your lives heard anything like this before.'

He picked up his heavy ebony ruler. His little piglike eyes gleamed.

'And,' he went on, 'to make sure that Professor Smallpox will really give us of his best I shall make it my personal business to give Professor Smallpox a clonk on the conk with this tiny weapon should any of you see even the faintest movement of the facial muscles as he delivers his unforgettable message.'

Bill brought down the ruler with a sharp crack on my skull.

'Professor,' he said, 'it's all yours.'

I don't have to go into the next twenty-five minutes. The other boys yelled practically on every syllable. I got the meaningless words tangled up, and said 'A cack of rutter noulded into the gake of a shote.'

At times Bill was so helpless with laughter that he missed me with the ruler altogether.

When the bell went for the end of the hour he insisted on being helped out into the passage, wiping his eyes with the blackboard cloth.

After that, I gave it up, feeling no recurrence of interest even after reading Bill's observation on my end of term report. 'He ought to do well on the stage.'

The Step Ladder

Max Adeler

A step ladder is an almost indispensable article to persons who are moving into a new house. Not only do the domestics find it extremely convenient when they undertake to wash the windows, to remove the dust from the door and window frames, and to perform sundry other household duties, but the lord of the castle will require it when he hangs his pictures, when he fixes the curtains and when he yields to his wife's entreaty for a hanging shelf or two in the cellar. I would, however, warn my fellow countrymen against the contrivance which is offered to them under the name of the 'Patent Combination Step Ladder'. I purchased one in the city just before we moved, because the dealer showed me how, by the simple operation of a set of springs, the ladder could be transformed into an ironing table, and from that into a comfortable settee for the kitchen, and finally back again into a step ladder, just as the owner desired. It seemed like getting the full worth of the money expended to obtain a trio of such useful articles for a single price, and the temptation to purchase was simply irresistible. But the knowledge gained by a practical experience of the operation of the machine enables me to affirm that there is no genuine economical advantage in the use of this ingenious article.

Upon the day of its arrival, the servant girl mounted the ladder for the purpose of removing the globes from the chandelier in the parlour, and while she was engaged in the work the weight of her body unexpectedly put the springs in motion, and the machine was suddenly converted into an ironing table, while the maidservant was prostrated upon the floor with a sprained ankle and amid the fragments of two shattered globes.

Then we decided that the apparatus should be used exclusively as an ironing table, and to this purpose it would probably have been devoted permanently if it had suited. On the following Tuesday, however, while half a dozen shirts were lying upon it ready to be ironed, someone knocked against it accidentally. It gave two or three ominous preliminary jerks, ground two shirts into rags, hurled the flat iron out into the yard, and after a few convulsive movements of the springs, settled into repose in the shape of a step ladder.

It became evident then that it could be used with greatest safety as a settee, and it was placed in the kitchen in that shape. For a few days it gave much satisfaction. But one night when the servant had company the bench was perhaps overloaded, for it had another and most alarming paroxysm; there was a trembling of the legs, a violent agitation of the back, then a tremendous jump, and one of the visitors was hurled against the range, while the machine turned several somersaults, jammed itself halfway through the window sash, and appeared once more in the similitude of an ironing table.

It has now attained to such a degree of sensitiveness that it goes through the entire drill promptly and with celerity if anyone comes near it or coughs or sneezes close at hand. We have it stored away in the garret, and sometimes in the middle of the night a rat will jar it, or a current of air will pass through the room, and we can hear it dancing over the floor and getting into service as a ladder, a bench and a table fifteen or twenty times in quick succession.

Sport

Ned Sherrin

> 'I hate all sports as rabidly as a person who likes sports hates
> common sense'   *H. L. Mencken*

Witty parody of sports writing has done nothing, however, to stem its flow.
Nor did Bernard Levin's sceptical examination of the reaction of press and
public to World Cup fever in 1966. 'The Trophy, one of the most hideous arti-
facts Western Man has ever produced in his long history of bad taste, had
been stolen before the competition began, but unhappily recovered before it
ended,' remarked Levin. Then he went on to examine the patriotic frenzy
aroused in the breast of the leader writer for *The Times* – 'it being accepted
that in a fair contest England must either win the match or, in the parlance
that the sportsmen had picked up from the politicians, "gain at any rate a
moral victory".' Levin then considered the aftermath of soccer hooliganism:

> As the streets of London seethed and heaved with a marching, cheering,
> flag-waving, horn-blowing, rattle-wielding, bell-ringing, drum-banging,
> cymbal-clashing, traffic-jamming, glory-remembering, victory-celebrat-
> ing crowd, who at last had something to march, cheer, wave, blow,
> wield, ring, bang, clash, jam, remember and celebrate about . . . the
> nation that chooses to live by football shall perish by the trade gap, the
> sterling crisis, the failure of national purpose, the loss of identity, the
> cohesion and determination of her enemies and commercial rivals.

Perhaps this is the moment for the great World Cup chestnut inspired by
England's defeat by West Germany in 1970 – German fan: 'You see, we have
beaten you at your national game!' Disgruntled Englishman (remembering
two World Wars): 'Yes, well, we beat you twice at yours!'

Sports commentators are a relatively new and fertile source of laughter. The
wit involved here is often in spotting those inadvertent howlers and slips made

under pressure, the kind which have been immortally anthologized by *Private Eye* under the title *Colemanballs*. The Master, David Coleman himself, leads off:

> The pace of this game is really accelerating, by which I mean it is getting faster all the time.
> Football is football; if that weren't the case, it wouldn't be the game it is – Garth Crooks (LBC).
> The only thing Norwich didn't get was the goal they finally got – Jimmy Greaves (Central TV).
> Ian St John: Is he speaking to you yet?
> Jimmy Greaves: Not yet, but I hope to be incommunicado with him in a very short space of time. (ITV).
> There's been a colour clash: both teams are wearing white – John Motson (BBC).

Julian Barnes, when TV critic for the *New Statesman,* was vigilant regarding 'commentatese':

> Ron Pickering continued to overheat as usual. The mockery of my confrères had chided him out of saying, 'he's pulling out the big one,' and even, 'he's whacking in the big one.' But the National Viewers and Listeners Association will cut off his tail with a carving knife for his new and shameless variant: 'If she hits the board and bangs a big one, that'll put her in the bronze medal position.'

But we should spare some sympathy for the sports commentator. It can't be easy in the heat of the moment to speak proper English, and without sounding trite or even suggestive. As Russell Davies puts it in *The Sunday Times:*

> They know their stuff – even if David Coleman, in particular, has trouble in actually expressing it without mangling a couple of syllables per sentence. Living with the producer's voice permanently murmuring inside his ear is very gradually robbing him of his power of speech. But some things never change. Plainly no way has yet been found to stop long-jump commentaries sounding like naughty stories after lights-out in the dorm ('Oooh, it's *enormous!* it was so long!').

The most touching remark provoked by cricket came appropriately from the lips of W. G. Grace. In his last season the elderly Grace felt the need to apologize for his inept fielding – 'It is the ground,' he moaned, 'it's too far away.' The Oscar Wilde of cricket is Fred Trueman – again a magnet for apocrypha, a creator of chestnuts and a skilled reteller of other cricketers' wit. Batting with Cowan, a fine quick bowler, and appalling batsman, for Yorkshire against the West Indies, they were faced by a fast bowling onslaught. Wes Hall sailed in to Cowan. Cowan's bat prodded to leg, the ball rocketed past the off stump. 'I think this fella has found my weakness, Fred,' said Cowan. The next delivery encouraged Cowan to play to the off side. The errant ball shot over the leg stump. 'It looks to me he's found both of 'em now,' said Trueman. Reporting Emmott Robinson, Trueman evokes the era of Amateur and Professional when the two classes were required to converge on to the ground from the pavilion through different entrances. The occasion was an early appearance by A. E. R. Gilligan, future amateur captain of England – done up to the nines. As he approached the wicket a fellow professional came up to Robinson. 'What's this fella doing then?' he asked. 'I don't know,' said Emmott, 'but he smells nice.' He proceeded to bowl Gilligan comprehensively first ball. Gracious, gentlemanly and condescending, Gilligan deigned to speak to him on the way back to the pavilion. 'Well bowled, indeed, Robinson. That was a great ball.' 'Aye,' said Robinson, 'but it were wasted on thee.'

Trueman tells of the time when Washbrook and Wharton were opening for Lancashire, with Washbrook on 90 and Wharton on 99, and Washbrook called a quick single. Wharton refused to move and Washbrook barely regained his ground in time. 'It is a well known fact,' he snarled, the next time they met in the middle of the wicket, 'that I am the best judge of a single in all England.' 'Yes,' Wharton concurred, 'and it's a well known fact that when I'm on 99, I'm the best judge of a run in all the bloody world.'

On one occasion Trueman entered an opposing team's dressing room breathing fire and slaughter. 'I need nine wickets from this match,' he announced, 'and you buggers had better start drawing straws to see who I don't get.' Reproving Subba Row in the West Indies, after Subba Row had dropped a slip catch that led to four runs off his bowling, Trueman received the apology ungracefully and asked about the four runs. 'I'm sorry about that,' said Subba Row, 'it might have been better if I'd kept my legs together.' 'Yes,' Trueman agreed, 'it's a pity your mother didn't.'

The Definitive and Complete List of My Gaffes

Brian Johnston

At Headingley Test, 1961, as TV camera panned in to show Neil Harvey fielding at leg-slip: 'There's Neil Harvey, standing at leg-slip with his legs wide apart, waiting for a tickle.'

At Hove, Sussex *v* Hampshire, on radio, trying to describe Henry Horton's funny stance in which he crouches and sticks his bottom out: 'Henry Horton's got a funny sort of stance. It looks as if he's shitting on a sooting stick.'

At Southampton at close of play when handing over to Rex Alston at Edgbaston: 'It's close of play here but they go on till seven o'clock at Edgbaston. So over now for some more balls from Rex Alston.'

At Leicester on radio during a county match: 'As you come over, Ray Illingworth has just relieved himself at the Pavilion End.'

At Northampton in a match *v* Worcestershire, on radio: ' . . . a very disappointing crowd. In fact I would say there are more cars here than people.' (Who drove the cars in?!)

At Lord's during the Test in 1969, England *v* New Zealand. Alan Ward is playing in his first Test and bowling very fast from the Pavilion End. Off the *fifth* ball of one of his overs he hits Glenn Turner a terrible blow in the box. Glenn collapses in the crease, bat flying in one direction, his batting gloves in another. The TV camera pans in and shows him writhing in the crease. B.J. waffles away pretending Turner's been hit anywhere except where he has – as it's rude! At last, after a few minutes, Glenn Turner gets shakily to his feet, someone hands him his bat, someone else his gloves. B.J.: 'It looks as if he is going to try to continue, although he still looks very shaken and pale. Very plucky of him. Yes, he's definitely going to have a try: one ball left!'

At Old Trafford the Saturday of the Test between England and India. It's pouring with rain, and is cold and miserable. There are some Indian supporters huddled together looking miserable in the crowd. Radio 3 announcer cues over to B.J. at 11.25 a.m.: 'Any chance of a start, Brian?' B.J.: 'No, it's pelting with rain, and cold and miserable. No chance of any play at the moment. There's a dirty black crowd (cloud) here!'

At Worcester, Worcestershire *v* Hampshire, B.J.: 'Welcome to Worcester where you've just missed seeing Barry Richards hit one of Basil d'Oliveira's balls clean out of the ground.' (Loud laughter at the back of the commentary box.)

At Scarborough Festival, Peter Pollock has come over from South Africa to play for Rest of World, and is on his honeymoon. As he runs up to bowl, he slips and turns his ankle over, and lies in obvious pain on the grass. B.J., on TV: 'Bad luck on Peter. He's obviously in great pain and has probably sprained his ankle. It's especially bad luck as he is here on his honeymoon with his pretty young wife. Still, he'll probably be all right tomorrow, if he sticks it up tonight.' (Collapse of Denis Compton in the commentary box.)

A lady wrote to me after a Test at the Oval between England and the West Indies. She said how much she enjoyed my commentaries but that I must be more careful, as there were always a lot of young people listening. She asked if I realized what I had said when Michael Holding was bowling to Peter Willey. Evidently at the start of an over I had said: 'The bowler's Holding the batsman's Willey.'

When commenting for radio outside St Paul's Cathedral for the wedding of Prince Charles and Lady Diana I found myself saying: 'I can see the bride's procession coming up Ludgate Hill. When she arrives below me here at St Paul's she will walk with her father up the steps into the pavilion – er – I mean Cathedral.'

Clean Your Room

Art Buchwald

You don't really feel the generation gap in this country until a son or daughter comes home from college for Christmas. Then it strikes you how out of it you really are.

This dialogue probably took place all over America last Christmas week:

'Nancy, you've been home from school for three days now. Why don't you clean up your room?'

'We don't have to clean up our rooms at college, Mother.'

'That's very nice, Nancy, and I'm happy you're going to such a freewheeling institution. But while you're in the house, your father and I would like you to clean up your room.'

'What difference does it make? It's *my* room.'

'I know, dear, and it really doesn't mean that much to me. But your father has a great fear of the plague. He said this morning that if it's going to start anywhere in this country, it's going to start in your room.'

'Mother, you people aren't interested in anything that's relevant. Do you realize how the major corporations are polluting our environment?'

'Your father and I are very worried about it. But right now we're more concerned about the pollution in your bedroom. You haven't made your bed since you came home.'

'I never make it up at the dorm.'

'Of course you don't, and I'm sure the time you save goes towards your education. But we still have these old-fashioned ideas about making beds in the morning, and we can't shake them. Since you're home for such a short time, why don't you do it to humour us?'

'For heaven's sake, Mother, I'm grown up now. Why do you have to treat me like a child?'

'We're not treating you like a child. But it's very hard for us to realize you're an adult when you throw all your clothes on the floor.'

'I haven't thrown all my clothes on the floor. Those are just the clothes I wore yesterday.'

'Forgive me. I exaggerated. Well, how about the dirty dishes and the soft-drink cans on your desk? Are you collecting them for a science project?'

'Mother, you don't understand us. You people were brought up to have clean rooms. But our generation doesn't care about things like that. It's what you have in your head that counts.'

'No one respects education more than your father and I do, particularly at the prices they're charging. But we can't see how living in squalor can improve your mind.'

'That's because of your priorities. You would rather have me make up my bed and pick up my clothes than become a free spirit who thinks for myself.'

'We're not trying to stifle your free spirit. It's just that our Blue Cross has run out, and we have no protection in case anybody in the family catches typhoid.'

'All right, I'll clean up my room if it means that much to you. But I want you to know you've ruined my vacation.'

'It was a calculated risk I had to take. Oh, by the way, I know this is a terrible thing to ask of you, but would you mind helping me to wash the dinner dishes?'

'Wash dishes? Nobody washes dishes at school.'

'Your father and I were afraid of that.'

The Bad Back Problem

Art Buchwald

The biggest problem this country faces is not the economy, law 'n' order, the war, or revolution, but bad backs.

It turns out that everyone in this country has back trouble, and until a cure is found for it, we will never be able to solve any other difficulties.

I discovered this recently when my wife's back went out on her while she was playing tennis. I immediately sent her off to an orthopaedic surgeon, who told her she had a ruptured disc and would have to go in traction and wear a sponge collar around her neck.

It was her collar that gave us the tipoff on how many bad backs there are in this country. People rarely talk about their backs until they see someone else wearing a collar. Then they open up and confess about their own back troubles.

The first time I took my wife to a party with her collar around her neck a friend said, 'What are you doing about it?'

My wife said she was going to an orthopaedic doctor.

'They don't know anything,' the friend said. 'What you need for a bad back is a neurosurgeon.'

The next day we located one of the best neurosurgeons in the country. After careful examination, he concluded my wife had a ruptured disc and needed traction and advised her to wear a sponge collar around her neck.

Since this was the same diagnosis she got from the orthopaedic man, my wife was naturally disappointed.

But a few days later her spirits picked up. She told me when I got home, 'The man who rakes our leaves said that neurosurgeons don't know anything about backs. He said the best way to get rid of my bad back was to sleep on the floor.'

'Well, the guy who rakes leaves should know,' I said.

A week later she called me at the office. 'Anabelle knows a woman in Seven

Corners who can cure crooked spines with her fingernails. She has never worked on someone who didn't get better.'

Three days later my wife got wind of an acupuncturist who lived in Chinatown. Her friend Aggie said, 'Four gold needles and you'll be playing tennis in a week.'

Before she could look up the acupuncture doctor, her sister called from Cincinnati and told her the only way to get rid of her bad back was through yoga and meditation.

Several weeks went by, and while my wife did continue her traction, her heart wasn't in it.

'It seems so slow,' she protested to me. 'The hairdresser knows a spa in Italy that specializes in mud baths for bad backs.'

'If it doesn't work, you can always go to Lourdes,' I said.

But while she was getting her passport for Italy, a brother-in-law from West Virginia called in to tell about a new miracle cure for backs that some lady in the Blue Ridge Mountains had developed from herbs.

'It sounds better than mud baths,' I said.

The ointment arrived, and surprisingly, it had no effect on my wife's back.

Having tried everything, we decided to go back to the neurosurgeon on the off chance that he might know something about her problem that the hairdresser didn't.

The doctor said she was doing fine but would have to stay in traction for another month.

You can imagine her depressed state of mind when she left the office. But fortunately, on the way home the cabdriver recognized her symptoms and said, 'I know a hypnotist in Alexandria who specializes in nothing but ruptured discs.'

Christmas Cards Tell All

Art Buchwald

Christmas cards reveal a great deal more about America than one would like to admit. They show us as well as anything what a restless society we've become.

The other day my wife was opening cards, and she was puzzled by one from Hal and Virginia Lark.

'I thought Hal's wife's name was Frieda,' she said.

'So did I. Maybe she changed it to Virginia,' I suggested.

The next day the mystery was cleared up when we received a Christmas card from the McDowalls.

'We don't know any McDowalls,' my wife said.

'We must, or they wouldn't have sent us a Christmas card.'

'The handwriting looks familiar,' my wife said. 'As a matter of fact, it looks exactly like Frieda Lark's signature.'

'How could it be Frieda Lark's signature if it was sent by the McDowalls?'

'Maybe Frieda is no longer a Lark!' my wife exclaimed.

'Then that means Hal married a girl named Virginia, and Frieda married a guy named McDowall.'

'I wish people would tell me these things before I sent out *my* Christmas cards.'

She opened a few other cards and then came to one which she studied carefully. 'This photograph is very peculiar. I could swear it was Myrna Tuttle, but the card says it's from the Lindstroms.'

I looked at it. 'It sure does seem to be Myrna. Wait a minute. Aren't those Myrna's twins on the sailboat?'

'Yes,' my wife said. 'But I don't recognize the man at the wheel.'

'That's probably Lindstrom,' I said.

'I wonder what happened to Dick Tuttle?'

'Look through your cards. The answer is probably there.'

My wife went through the cards. 'You're right. Here's one from the Tuttles. It's Dick Tuttle, all right, but I don't recognize the woman or the children sitting on the lawn.'

'They're probably *her* children,' I said.

'Well, at least that takes care of the Tuttle problem,' she said.

The next day, when I came home from work, my wife was waiting for me with more cards.

'Helen Coates is now Helen Samovar, Marty Keeler has a new wife named Zelda, and we got separate Christmas cards from Lars and Margie Payne. His came from San Francisco, and hers came from Fort Lauderdale.'

'I got a few at the office,' I said. 'Apparently Bob Elmendorf got custody of the five children because his card shows him sitting on a fence with a new wife and eight kids.'

'Who are the other three?' my wife wanted to know.

'*Her* kids. I wonder why Lucy Elmendorf didn't get custody of the children?'

'This card,' my wife said, 'may explain it. It's from Lucy, and she says she's living in Guadeloupe with a fantastic penniless young artist whom she met when she went to visit her sister in Los Angeles.

'We also got a card from the Madisons,' she added. 'They still seem to be together.'

'Forget it,' I said. 'I just received a wire at the office from Bill Madison. It says DISREGARD CHRISTMAS GREETINGS. LETTER FOLLOWS.'

Marriage and the Gross National Product

Art Buchwald

For the first time, it has been conclusively proved that the United States loses 34,000,000 man-hours of work each week owing to fights between husbands and wives.

Professor Heinrich Applebaum of the Institute for Advanced Marital Development has just completed a study on marriage disputes and their effect on the gross national product.

'My study,' Professor Applebaum told me, 'indicates that production is affected even more by domestic fights than alcoholism.'

'How can that be?'

'For some reason, which we still have not been able to determine, the American wife prefers to start all fights with her husband at bedtime. These fights, which last on the average of two or three hours, prevent the man from getting any sleep. The next day he is completely useless at his job, causing accidents, grave errors in book-keeping, and making horrible decisions in a groggy state of mind.'

'That's serious,' I admitted.

'We suspected it all along,' Applebaum said. 'But now we have the data to back it up. This is a case history of a typical American couple in Detroit whom we followed through from dinnertime one evening to lunch the next day:

'Saxby came home at six p.m., had a dry martini, watched the evening news, and then shared a delicious dinner with his wife and three children. After dinner he took a bath, read the evening paper and watched the *Dean Martin Show*. The wife did the dishes, called her mother, took her bath, and read a chapter of *The Godfather*.

'Mr Saxby said, "Good night, dear. I have an early meeting tomorrow with some subcontractors to discuss a very important matter."

'Mrs Saxby said, "Good night, dear."

'Five minutes later Mrs Saxby asked, "Why don't you ever talk to me?"

'Saxby, who was just dozing off, responded, "Huh?"

' "You never talk to me anymore. You have an awful lot to say to your friends, but you don't have anything to say to me."

' "I talk to you," Saxby said, getting a good grip on his pillow. "We talk all the time."

' "But you never say anything. You don't talk to your children either. As far as we're concerned, you're just a boarder here."

'Saxby rolled over on his stomach. "You're right, I should talk more to all of you. Good night, dear."

' "That's typical of you," Mrs Saxby said, lighting a cigarette. "You think you can just end a discussion by saying I'm right. It doesn't wash anymore. You won't even talk to me now."

' "I'd love to talk to you," Saxby said, "but it's midnight, and I have this meeting with the subcontractors tomorrow."

' "Of course. Your work is so much more important than your home life. Why don't you just move into the office and forget about us?"

'Saxby started punching the pillow. "Look, I tell you what. Why don't I come home early from work tomorrow and we'll discuss it then?"

' "I want to discuss it now. Tomorrow it might not bother me." '

The case history said the Saxbys stayed awake until three o'clock in the morning discussing not only why Saxby didn't talk to his wife but also an old girlfriend that Saxby had before he was married, a questionable joke Saxby had told at a dinner party the previous week, a poker game Saxby had gone to a year ago, and the fact that he had missed his seventeen-year-old daughter's birthday party when she was three years old.

The next morning, according to the case history, Saxby was so sleepy he made a mistake on the subcontracting job, and three months later the Ford Motor Company had to recall 1,000,000 cars.

The Complete Naff Guide

Dr Kit Bryson, Selina Fitzherbert & Jean-Luc Legris

Naff Things to Do in a Restaurant

Go Dutch
Go drunk to table having spent too much time at bar
Order wine on sitting down
Address wine waiter as 'captain'
Say 'chop chop!' to Chinese waiter
Hang coat on back of chair
Smoke a pipe
Table-hop (see Camilla Horne)
Ask for celebrities' autographs
Send message via waiter to blonde in corner
Arrive with dogs, children etc.
Ask for separate checks
Knock off service charge
Squabble over disparities in joint bill
Ask management to turn the music up
Spend much time on telephone (incoming calls)
Strip off under the table (see Pamela Stephenson)
Be forced to surrender your table at eight-thirty
Have birthday cake brought to table
Order strawberries out of season and then complain about the price
Talk too loudly about your money, your sex life, your friends, your bowels
Call French waiter 'garc oɲ'
Offer owner protection
On being told to 'piss off, son,' threaten owner with solicitor's letter
Snap fingers at waiters to attract attention
Start a fight (see Peter Langan)
Insist on buying one cigarette (see Basil Seal)

Breast-feed your baby (see Esther Rantzen)
Drink spirits with food
Fold napkin
Use pengrip on knife
Cut Stilton down
Continually thank the waiter
Dunk moustache in soup and suck it
Take a line in the Ladies

Naff Restaurant Critics

All restaurant critics are naff except Basil Seal

Naff Food

Prawn cocktail
Melon and Parma ham
Avocado and prawns
Florida cocktail
Grapefruit cocktail
Escalope Milanaise
Chicken-in-the-basket
Scampi
Doner kebabs
Coupe Jacques
Chicken fried rice
All curries
Paella-in-the-packet
Beef-boil-in-a-bag
Duck à l'orange
Chilli con carne
Fish fingers
Gammon steak
Egg mayonnaise
Whelks
Duchess potatoes
Wiener Schnitzel
Pickled onions
Dips

Crisps
Cornish pasties
Mixed grill
Walls pork pies
Parsnip pie
Trifle
Compressed turkey in a tin
Eggs Florentine
Tomato soup (unless real)
Popcorn
Individual fruit pies

Naff Breads

Spanish
Russian
Mother's Pride

Naff Hotels

The Mayfair
The Piccadilly
The Penta
The Churchill
The Cunard International
The Cumberland
The Regent Palace
The Strand Palace
The Hilton
The Tara
The Ritz

Naff Behaviour in Hotels

Not pay the bill
Set fire to the furniture (see *Naff Dead Pop Stars*)
Sneak thieve
Solicit in the lobby
Supply own product – Allbran, decaffeinated coffee, etc. – at breakfast
Offer to pay bill in advance

Wash own clothes and hang them out of the window
Wash elaborately stained sheets in the bath
Fall down the laundry chute
Make own bed
Steal towels and coathangers
Tip the manager (paradoxically, it's not naff to tip Lord Matthews at the
Ritz – a mistake anyone could make)
Ask the night manager for girls
Ask the chambermaid if she'd ever thought of becoming a model
Ask the night manager if he'd ever thought of becoming a model
Sleep five to a room and when discovered claim that your guests are Equity
members auditioning for a musical
Claim, at the Ritz, that Lord Matthews is a personal friend of yours
Ask for a room without a bath at Claridges
Ask for second helping in restaurant
Insist on visiting kitchen to congratulate chef
Carry own luggage to room
Book in as Mr and Mrs Smith
Exercise dog in corridor
Sodomize the boots

When is a Joke not a Joke?

Rachel Ferguson

At a music-hall, the other night, one of the turns said to her partner: 'Do kippers swim folded or flat?' Whether this is a good sample of humour I don't know. All I know is that I was the only person in the vast hall who giggled, and I came home, lowered. For I could not but remember social occasions on which I was the only non-entertained person in the room. The leading occasions are apt (for they are ever with us) to be six in number, and I have recently made what is to me an important discovery about the matter: I have awoken to the fact that there is a form of humour current among the relatively limited circle of my friends which I have never previously suspected. It shall be dealt with last. It is, indeed, number six. The occasions, then, upon which I am progressively unable to be amused run as follows:

1. AT THE EXPERT'S JOKE

This is commonly used in reference to some sport or hobby, such as riding, golfing and motoring. It can only be appreciated by a fellow expert, or by one who has a smattering of spavins, stymies and magnetos. Unfortunately, the anecdote is not reserved by the retailer for fellow experts, but is related impartially to the totally ignorant, reducing the listener to civil but bewildered noises. It sometimes ends in his miserable exposure before a room full of people, to the braying delight of the retailer, or, if followed by his humble requests for technical points to be made clear, by the growing and imperfectly concealed impatience and rancour of the retailer. As: 'Hee-ha-ha-ha! He thought it was a mushroom on the ninth green and — hah! — told the caddie to pick it!! ha ha ha!' Or, ' "——" told him the mare's leg had filled and he said, "What with?" Ho Ho Ho! Good, eh?'

2. AT THE INFLEXION JOKE

This anecdote depends for its success, not upon the matter, but upon the manner of presentment. The concluding words are given with a roar (if by

a man) and (if by a woman) with a raising of the voice to a little scream. As:
'And, my dear, she'd kicked off her shoes IN THE TRAIN!'
The wave-length of the correct inflection is:
'And, my dear, she'd kicked off her shoes IN THE TRAIN!'

3. AT THE SENILE JOKE (By Those of Riper Years)

This bears a slight resemblance to number two, but with the substitution of repetition for inflection. The cream of the jest, in the Senile class, is always dwelt on twice, and often three times. As: 'I said to him – hech hech! – "Did you lay forks for the asparagus, Jervis? Did you lay forks for the asparagus?" and he said "No, Sir, but I won't forget to in future", hech hech hech. "I won't forget to in future." Hech! "Did you lay forks" – hech! "won't forget in future!" Hech hech hech.' (*Violent fit of coughing*.) 'Ergh, ergh, ergh . . . Oh ergh, ergh, ergh!'

4. AT THE AFTER DINNER, OR ELECTION JOKE

Is indulged in by the Guest of The Evening, or Professional Good Fellow. Is commonly rendered in some dialect, or with some characteristic accent. Is nearly always prefaced by the words, 'and that reminds me of the story——' Is seldom apposite to the particular occasion, but is given, more, to induce good feeling, and to set the Fair Sex at its ease. The joke, itself, need not be repeated. It can be picked up anywhere without difficulty. ('Hoots, mon,' said Sandy. 'Faith, then,' replied Pat.)

By the time the speaker, genially beaming, has got as far as Hoots and Faith, his audience, with luck, will already be primed with hypnotized titters.

5. AT THE BESOTTED MOTHER JOKE

This is only too familiar to us all. The point of this joke is not so much the point of the joke, as that it is about the children and/or grandchildren of (say) Mrs Masters. However modest Mrs Masters may sound, it should be borne in mind by the listener that she is not modest, and that to edge in a sample of the sayings of your own offspring is waste of time and breath, as it will not be listened to or, at best, will be dismissed with a hasty 'Did he? How quaint.' Also, it must be remembered that the Masters' children are models of health, and of uncommon beauty. You yourself will, perhaps, have only seen a boiled-looking toddler with stout, mauve legs, and a little beast with a spitcurl and a bulbous forehead.

So, she opens fire.

'My dear, you *must* come to tea soon and see the Babes. Lady Rennet was at lunch, yesterday, and simply couldn't *believe* Peter was only seven. I mean,

she simply said "nonsense!" I must say he was rather adorable. Lady Rennet
had just come in – and he walks straight over to her – you know! in our little
manly way, and he said, "Why are you a Lady when Mummy's only Mrs?"
She was simply enchanted! Couldn't forget it! "Why are you a Lady" – and
the other morning the car was at the door and Maurice looks up at me and
says, "It's the no-horse carriage, Mummy!" You see? . . . He'd seen Daddy's
hunters and the dog-cart, and noticed at once that the car went by itself. I
thought "no-horse-carriage" was rather wonderful. Alan says Maurice'll have
to be kept back for years yet, and not begin little lessons until he is quite six.
He's *too* observant, you know.'

6. AT THE HUMOURLESS JOKE

This, as I have hinted elsewhere, is, as far as I know, my personal and fairly
recent discovery. I think, however, that it will be widely recognized by those
who have dumbly suffered it, for I cannot believe that I hold the monopoly
in friends whose speciality it appears to be.

It may be asked can a 'joke' be 'humourless' in Law, as it were? I answer,
most unhappily, it can. The humourless joke can not only be without humour,
but minus point, into the bargain. It is always of purely personal application.
It is something that happened to the retailer. It is passed on with giggles; told
with vivacity and a certain worldliness. It suggests that the speaker is popular;
is one upon whom nicknames are bestowed, and who has a mass of doting
friends and adoring relatives. In the case of a young woman, you feel that she
has a mother who, when her daughter goes out to four dances in one week,
will exclaim, beaming, and in despair wholly feigned, 'Isn't Cynthia the *limit*!'
or, 'That terrible girl of mine!'

To me, this form of humour is easily the most frightful, and leaves numbers
one to five inclusive at the starting-post, because (1) It is apt to sound as
though the relation of it might be interminable, and (2) It leaves me almost
persuaded that my lifelong belief that I have a sense of humour must be drasti-
cally overhauled, since, without exception, it appears, according to the
retailer, that everybody else was convulsed by it.

Thus, Cynthia's recital:

'I went out in the car with Leo, this morning, and we got absolutely *stuck*
outside Australia House, and a policeman came up and said, "Come along,
your engine's running," and Leo was fooling about with the gears because he
doesn't really understand that car yet and he's had her for two months – it's
a perfect joke in the family, we were always chipping him about it, but he

never minds. He's a perfect darling – everybody adores him, and he grabbed at something and couldn't get the blessed thing to move and the policeman came right up – and I was laughing – and just then the car started with a frightful row and I said, "We shall have a crowd round us in two ticks" and he got her into top and we very nearly ran into a taxi, and you never saw anything so funny in your life. We were both in absolute fits!' . . . (etc.).

Or:

'Freddie gave me that umbrella – it's a tremendous joke in the family because, you see, I always used to forget to take one when it looked like rain – the boys simply roar at me because I won't even wear a mac, and once I came home in a new frock *abso*lutely drenched when Mummy had an At Home on and Freddie said I looked like a drowned puppy and I giggled so I couldn't say How do you do to anybody! and so he said, "You'd better have a brolly so large you can't forget it", and he went and bought me this awful thing. We simply shrieked. Whenever anyone says "umbrella" now we simply double up.'

The appropriate noises for the listener to number six I have not yet discovered.

Serpent's Teeth

Arthur Marshall

My father had a theory, not solidly based on any actual motoring experience on the road, that cars ran much better at night-time than by day. Returning from some outing and nearing home just as dusk was falling, he would listen appreciatively to the unchanging hum of the engine and say 'ah, it scents the evening air.' Whether this was a conscious but altered quotation from that sad spectre, the ghost of Hamlet's father and his 'But, soft! methinks I scent the morning air; Brief let me be,' I do not know and it was certainly not the kind of question that one would have put to him. A counter question would have resulted ('Why do you ask?'). I merely used to wonder if, in the unlikely and unwelcome event of a drive with my father right through the night, he would, when dawn came up, notice a sudden roughness in the engine's running.

From the 1920s on, the car we had was invariably a Morris (and during affluent years there were two), beginning with a bull-nosed Morris Cowley complete with hideously exposed and uncomfortable dickey seat, and progressing (wasn't there once a brand with a chassis rather daringly called a 'chummy body'?) through various models to a sedate Morris Oxford which had beige curtains to the windows, was painted a depressing dark brown and always seemed to me to be indistinguishable from a hearse. One felt one should be lying flat, embowered in blooms and deafened by sobs. But whatever sort we currently had, they were all alleged keenly to enjoy travel by night. As to the 'Brief let me be', this was never part of my father's creed. If a thing was worth saying, it was therefore worth saying at considerable length. Fortunately for him, he was quite unaware of both boredom and ruffled feathers in others ('Why did Miss Manning leave so early?').

For all trips by car we departed a full hour before we need, in case of accidents and unforeseen delays. There might, one never knew, be a puncture. There might be a nose-bleed requiring prostration and a cold key down the back. We might be witnesses of some exciting happening (murder, rape, robbery, regicide) and the police would need our names and lively recollections. Somebody might faint, and there was always a flask of brandy and some smelling-salts on board. Both of these emergency kit items led in their day, as did so many of the would-be kindly acts performed by my father, to misunderstandings and angry red faces and umbrage. We were once passing a pub and, seeing a man propped up, seated, against a wall with his eyes shut, my father instantly assumed that he had fainted. He leapt from the car, rushed forward with the smelling-salts and thrust them up the man's nose. But it was only a tipsy local who had been enjoying a quiet nap and who was understandably furious at being thus interfered with and so sharply recalled from the Land of Nod. My father had to make a somewhat hasty return to the car, pursued by a volley of exciting oaths which I did not at the time understand, and questions only produced 'Hush, dear.'

And another time, near Aldershot, we saw a trooper being unseated from his prancing horse, and, falling to the ground, lying motionless and as though dead. My father darted out with the flask and poured brandy down the man's throat (loud splutterings), only to be turned on by a wrathful officer who came galloping up. The trooper, he shouted, might have choked: he might have severe internal injuries for which brandy could be lethal, etc, etc. It took quite a lot to abash my father but the officer, accustomed by his profession to dispense abuse where needed, succeeded splendidly and my father, in a cricketing term, retired hurt ('I only wanted to help'). To lighten the occasion, my mother, a great soother and a calm presence during many of Life's turbulences, produced some patum pepperium sandwiches, that delicious salty and fishy substance that is also known as Gentleman's Relish (can the trade name now have been changed to Gentleperson's Relish?) and quite soon we all cheered up. Tomato soup and halibut (taken separately, I hasten to say) had also been known in their time to soothe my father when soothing was required at home, though at home it tended to be our visitors who needed the soothing.

There are, sadly, two things in life that can never be taught. One is 'timing' in acting, especially comedy. The other is tact. They are instinctive matters and are either present or not. The absence of tact in one or both parents was a subject that I frequently discussed in youth with my friend, Williamson, at our prep school on the Hampshire coast. Williamson was, if I may just remind you, the boy with whom I discovered the facts of life, more or less, with the aid of some striking wall drawings in the gentlemen's retiring-room of a rather scruffy and open air service rifle-range (much used in the First World War) and which lay within Sunday walking distance of our school. A few minor details were, I see now, missing but the drawings gave us the general spirit of the thing and indicated what to aim at in due course. The need constantly to refresh our memories and examine any fresh pictures made Sunday afternoons busier than ever. There was much to be done. Sunday letters home to dash off and cheer our loved ones ('Willoughby was sick in church'). Potatoes to be collected, sometimes with the cook's permission, from the kitchen (we used, permanently hungry, to make wood fires and bake them in the ashes). Then a quick look at Williamson's signed photograph of Dorothy Dickson and a discussion, fed on gossipy sections of the weekly *Sketch* and *Bystander*, as to how she might be spending her Sunday (brunch at Bray with Gerald du Maurier, we often assumed). Then a peppermint-cream or perhaps a pear-drop, after which it was heigh-ho for the range, two miles away but, like so many items in Baedeker, worth *le dètour*.

Boys in the two top forms were allowed on Sundays to wander abroad at will, provided that they went in twos, and at the range we lit, after a peep or two at the sensational graffiti, our twig fire and baked the potatoes. On the way back we used to call at a small shop, obligingly open on Sundays, which sold cigarettes and were usually able to persuade the proprietor to ferret about in the unsold packets in search of cigarette cards (Wildflowers of Britain, Characters of Dickens) that we needed for our sets. And so, exhausted, to tea (bread, margarine, jam and a bubbling urn, the ensemble presided over by Matron), followed by another peppermint-cream and a further glance at Dorothy Dickson (by now, we supposed, sipping champagne and having supper with Jack Buchanan).

We always referred, for some reason, to our parents as 'people'. 'My people are coming down on Saturday' one would say in an elaborately offhand manner, praying that one's mother's hat would not cause comment or that one's father would not be too ebullient with the headmaster ('How's the young man coming along?'). Williamson too had his worries – a charming but over-emotional mother who was given to embracing him publicly rather more often than we considered needful, and a delightfully round and bouncy dad permanently a-chuckle whom Williamson found bothersome but whom I thought, disloyally, to be the nicest kind of father. Did either Williamson or myself ever feel a spark of gratitude for the fact that we were being relatively expensively educated and, provided we worked reasonably hard, led a completely trouble-free life? No we did not. Did we ever pause to consider, as one passed slum dwellings in London and other towns, what our unhappy lot as children might have been? No we did not. Williamson, having an altogether nicer character than I, never actually criticized his parents but I, odious and fault-finding and whining, droned ceaselessly on about my father's border-line imperfections and the agitating nature of some features of my home life. One took food, houses, pleasures, clothes, warmth, holidays, cars, books, toys and even, I am very sorry to say, love as being merely one's right. I cannot imagine why my parents didn't, at least twice a day, take my horrid little head and bang it violently against the nearest wall.

A Likely Story

Keith Waterhouse

What knickers in what glove compartment?

It's not my car.

It may well be my car, now that I look at it from this angle, but those are not my knickers. Surely they're your knickers?

Yes, because don't you remember: when the dog chewed up my Kermit Squeezee-Sponge and I asked if you could spare me a bit of wash-leather or something to rub over the windscreen? And you said there was an old blue check duster in that biscuit tin under the sink where we keep the shoe-cleaning things?

I must have absent-mindedly gone to your dressing-table drawer and taken that pair of red satin knickers, then put it in the glove compartment thinking it was an old blue check duster.

Since you ask, now, I can't really see you wearing red satin knickers in a million years, especially that type. I'd qualify that even further and make it ten million years. Maybe that's one reason why we're not as close as we used to be.

However that doesn't alter the fact that the knickers were in your dressing-table drawer, where, not bothering to switch on the bedside lamp, I mistook them in the gathering dusk for a blue check duster.

How do I know? I expect you put them there yourself, after unwrapping them.

I know you have a short memory but surely you can remember getting a pair of red knickers for Christmas, among other perhaps more acceptable items? *I* certainly remember – I can remember your very words. 'Thank you very much but I couldn't wear these in a million years,' you said. 'I'll take them back to Janet Reger's when the shops open again and change them for a cardigan.' Then you must have popped them in your dressing-table drawer and not given them another moment's thought from that day to this.

All right. Joke over. Do you want to know what really happened?

You're not going to like this, I'm warning you.

Because it involves someone whose guts you hate.

Beresford, the office practical joker.

Of course you knew he was the office practical joker. That's why you hate his guts. Because he kept patting your bum at that dinner-dance we went to.

Well *he* thought it was a practical joke. Surely I'm not to be held responsible for my colleagues' offbeat sense of humour?

So. I can't prove anything, but I did notice when I set off home the other night that Beresford, the office practical joker, was hanging around the car-stack, where he's no right to be since he doesn't drive. As you know.

Let me just get this straight. You're saying that if I try to tell you that Beresford, the office practical joker, somehow got into the car, somehow forced open the glove compartment, without breaking the lock, planted a pair of red satin knickers that he happened to have in his pocket, then somehow managed to lock the glove compartment again, you're going to see a solicitor, right?

Then it's very fortunate indeed that that isn't what happened.

Beresford, the office practical joker, is only peripherally involved. The incident really centres on Carmichael.

Carmichael. I don't think you've met him. Has quite a reputation as the office conjuror. I've seen him do tricks with playing cards that would astound you. We all tell him he should take it up professionally. Listen: imagine, if you will, a bowl of goldfish, a wristwatch, an ordinary table napkin, the flags of all nations, an egg —

Did I mention tricks with glove compartments? Or sleight of hand with pairs of red knickers? Then until I do mention tricks with glove compartments and sleight of hand with pairs of red knickers, be so kind as to reserve judgement.

Where was I?

Good heavens.

You know that sensation one sometimes gets? Yes you do – the sensation that you know what someone's about to say? Déjà vu, isn't it? Well, I just had it then.

It was when I said, 'Where was I?' It suddenly brought something back to me. Sitting in the car and saying those very words. Well, not quite those very words but near enough. It wasn't 'Where was I?,' it was 'Where am I?' or 'Who am I?' or something of that kind. I must have temporarily lost my memory.

No, I know that's not the same thing as déjà vu, but you know what I mean. Of course you do. Don't tell me you've never temporarily lost your memory and come round hearing yourself saying, 'Where am I?' or 'Who am I?'

I don't think I like your tone. I wouldn't *dream* of asking you to believe that I came round saying, 'Where am I or who am I, and how did that pair of red knickers find its way into the glove compartment?' Had that been the case I would have mentioned it at the time.

The time I found myself sitting in the car asking, 'Where am I?' or 'Who am I?' as the case may be. The time I temporarily lost my memory.

Yes, well I was going to tell you about it but I forgot.

Red knickers don't come into it anywhere. I just got side-tracked by that moment of déjà vu or whatever it was.

I *am* getting back to the nitty-gritty. Beresford, the office practical joker, and Carmichael, the office conjuror, were how shall I put it, rather the worse for wear. Tired and emotional, as the phrase has it. Stinko. Three sheets in the wind.

You're right up to a point. Beresford, the office practical joker, didn't *used* to drink, but now he drinks like a fish. The only reason you don't know he drinks like a fish is because you won't have him in the house, because you hate his guts.

They were hanging around the car-stack. Beresford, the office practical joker, who doesn't drive, although he does now drink, was supporting Carmichael, the office conjuror, who both drives and drinks.

They'd been celebrating.

Does it matter what? Actually, since you ask, they'd been celebrating the news that Emerson, the office kleptomaniac, had just been appointed manager of the Bristol branch.

Didn't you know? Oh, yes, the company keeps it hushed up. We've been asked not to talk about it. It's an illness. He takes pills for it.

Yes, that's perfectly correct, he did take charge of the Bristol branch two and a half years ago – in order, I might add in confidence, to save him the humiliation of being kept under surveillance by officers from Bow Street who suspected him of purloining washing from clothes-lines. But it was only a temporary appointment until recently. As Emerson, the office kleptomaniac, will tell you if you ask him, he came back to Head Office to be confirmed as permanent Bristol manager. And promptly got pie-eyed with Beresford, the office practical joker, and Carmichael, the office conjuror.

Ring him up to congratulate him, if you know the Bristol STD code.

You may mention red knickers if you wish, but I cannot for the life of me see why you should want to. Have I accused Emerson, the office klepto-maniac, of stealing a pair of red knickers from Marks and Spencers and then stuffing them in the glove compartment of my car when he saw Beresford, the office practical joker, disguised as a policeman?

Very well then.

The only reason Emerson, the office kleptomaniac, comes into the story is that he was spending the night at the home of Carmichael, the office conjuror, before returning to Bristol by train. Carmichael, the office conjuror, was too drunk to drive. Beresford, the office practical joker, does not drive, as has been established. Foolishly, I volunteered to give them all a lift.

Now I am not going to weary you with the details of how Carmichael, the office conjuror, threw his latch-key out of the car window while we were cross-ing Chiswick flyover. He swore that when we arrived at his house he could produce it out of my glove compartment, and he is so damned clever – you know he's a member of the Magic Circle, don't you? Oh, yes. Vice-president – that we believed him, not knowing how sloshed he really was.

So. We arrive at Carmichael's, the office conjuror's, and I can see I don't have to tell you what's happened: we open the glove compartment and you've guessed it – no latch-key. Can't get in the house. Beresford, the office practical joker, has by now passed out cold and none of us knows where he lives, so I couldn't dump them all at *his* place. And I couldn't bring them back here, because you hate Beresford's, the office practical joker's, guts.

So.

I'm cruising along Chiswick High Road wondering whether to drive them to a hotel or what the hell to do, when what should I see reflected in my dip-lights but this ankle length ball-gown. Containing, as it turned out, one stun-ning blonde, thumbing one lift.

Are you sure I haven't told you this story? I thought I had.

So naturally, being the gent I am, I stop, and in gets this blonde and sits in the front passenger seat, where the glove compartment is. Beresford, the office practical joker, Carmichael, the office conjuror, and Emerson, the office kleptomaniac, were all in the back, sleeping it off.

Now as you know, there's a light in the glove compartment, which happened to be open because we'd been searching for Carmichael's, the office conjuror's, latch-key; so I was able to get a good look at her face. Hello, I thought, I've seen you before darling.

And do you know who it was?

I can see you're not going to get it. Of all people, it was none other than
Jamieson, the office transvestite. Not all that much of a coincidence, because
as you probably know he lives in the same street as Carmichael, the office conjuror, and Bates, the office security manager.

'Thank God it's you four,' says Jamieson, the office transvestite, 'because
I'm in dead trouble . . .'

All Creatures Great and Small

James Herriot

'The Reniston, eh?' I fidgeted uneasily. 'Bit grand, isn't it?'

Tristan lay rather than sat in his favourite chair and peered up through a cloud of cigarette smoke. 'Of course it's grand. It's the most luxurious hotel in the country outside of London, but for your purpose it's the only possible place. Look, tonight is your big chance isn't it? You want to impress this girl, don't you? Well, ring her up and tell her you're taking her to the Reniston. The food is wonderful and there's a dinner dance every Saturday night. And today is Saturday.' He sat up suddenly and his eyes widened. 'Can't you see it, Jim? The music oozing out of Benny Thornton's trombone and you, full of lobster thermidor, floating round the floor with Helen snuggling up to you. The only snag is that it will cost you a packet, but if you are prepared to spend about a fortnight's wages you can have a really good night.'

I hardly heard the last part, I was concentrating on the blinding vision of Helen snuggling up to me. It was an image which blotted out things like money and I stood with my mouth half open listening to the trombone. I could hear it quite clearly.

Tristan broke in. 'There's one thing – have you got a dinner-jacket? You'll need one.'

'Well, I'm not very well off for evening-dress. In fact, when I went to Mrs Pumphrey's party I hired a suit from Brawton, but I wouldn't have time for that now.' I paused and thought for a moment. 'I do have my first and only dinner-suit but I got it when I was about seventeen and I don't know whether I'd be able to get into it.'

Tristan waved this aside. He dragged the Woodbine smoke into the far depths of his lungs and released it reluctantly in little wisps and trickles as he spoke. 'Doesn't matter in the least, Jim. As long as you're wearing the proper gear they'll let you in, and with a big, good-looking chap like you the fit of the suit is unimportant.'

We went upstairs and extracted the garment from the bottom of my trunk. I had cut quite a dash in this suit at the college dances and though it had got very tight towards the end of the course it had still been a genuine evening-dress outfit and as such had commanded a certain amount of respect.

But now it had a pathetic, lost look. The fashion had changed and the trend was towards comfortable jackets and soft, unstarched shirts. This one was rigidly of the old school and included an absurd little waistcoat with lapels and a stiff, shiny-fronted shirt with a tall, winged collar.

My problems really started when I got the suit on. Hard work, Pennine air and Mrs Hall's good food had filled me out and the jacket failed to meet across my stomach by six inches. I seemed to have got taller, too, because there was a generous space between the bottom of the waistcoat and the top of the trousers. The trousers themselves were skin tight over the buttocks, yet seemed foolishly baggy lower down.

Tristan's confidence evaporated as I paraded before him and he decided to call on Mrs Hall for advice. She was an unemotional woman and endured the irregular life at Skeldale House without noticeable reaction, but when she came into the bedroom and looked at me her facial muscles went into a long, twitching spasm. She finally overcame the weakness, however, and became very businesslike.

'A little gusset at the back of your trousers will work wonders, Mr Herriot, and I think if I put a bit of silk cord across the front of your jacket it'll hold it nicely. Mind you, there'll be a bit of a space, like, but I shouldn't think that'll worry you. And I'll give the whole suit a good press – makes all the difference in the world.'

I had never gone in much for intensive grooming, but that night I really went to work on myself, scrubbing and anointing and trying a whole series of different partings in my hair before I was satisfied. Tristan seemed to have appointed himself master of the wardrobe and carried the suit tenderly upstairs, still warm from Mrs Hall's ironing board. Then, like a professional valet, he assisted in every step of the robing. The high collar gave most trouble and he drew strangled oaths from me as he trapped the flesh of my neck under the stud.

When I was finally arrayed he walked around me several times, pulling and patting the material and making delicate adjustments here and there.

Eventually he stopped his circling and surveyed me from the front. I had never seen him look so serious. 'Fine, Jim, fine – you look great. Distinguished, you know. It's not everybody who can wear a dinner-jacket – so many people look like conjurers, but not you. Hang on a minute and I'll get your overcoat.'

I had arranged to pick up Helen at seven o'clock and as I climbed from the car in the darkness outside her house a strange unease crept over me. This was different. When I had come here before it had been as a veterinary surgeon – the man who knew, who was wanted, who came to render assistance in time of need. It had never occurred to me how much this affected my outlook every time I walked on to a farm. This wasn't the same thing at all. I had come to take this man's daughter out. He might not like it, might positively resent it.

Standing outside the farmhouse door I took a deep breath. The night was very dark and still. No sound came from the great trees near by and only the distant roar of the Darrow disturbed the silence. The recent heavy rains had transformed the leisurely, wandering river into a rushing torrent which in places overflowed its banks and flooded the surrounding pastures.

I was shown into the large kitchen by Helen's young brother. The boy had a hand over his mouth in an attempt to hide a wide grin. He seemed to find the situation funny. His little sister sitting at a table doing her homework was pretending to concentrate on her writing but she, too, wore a fixed smirk as she looked down at her book.

Mr Alderson was reading the *Farmer and Stockbreeder*, his breeches unlaced, his stockinged feet stretched out towards a blazing pile of logs. He looked up over his spectacles.

'Come in, young man, and sit by the fire,' he said absently. I had the uncomfortable impression that it was a frequent and boring experience for him to have young men calling for his eldest daughter.

I sat down at the other side of the fire and Mr Alderson resumed his study of the *Farmer and Stockbreeder*. The ponderous tick-tock of a large wall clock boomed out into the silence. I stared into the red depths of the fire till my eyes began to ache, then I looked up at a big oil painting in a gilt frame hanging above the mantelpiece. It depicted shaggy cattle standing knee-deep in a lake of an extraordinary bright blue; behind them loomed a backcloth of fearsome, improbable mountains, their jagged summits wreathed in a sulphurous mist.

Averting my eyes from this, I examined, one by one, the sides of bacon and the hams hanging from the rows of hooks in the ceiling. Mr Alderson turned over a page. The clock ticked on. Over by the table, spluttering noises came from the children.

After about a year I heard footsteps on the stairs, then Helen came into the room. She was wearing a blue dress – the kind, without shoulder straps, that seems to stay up by magic. Her dark hair shone under the single pressure lamp which lit the kitchen, shadowing the soft curves of her neck and shoulders. Over one white arm she held a camel-hair coat.

I felt stunned. She was like a rare jewel in the rough setting of stone flags and whitewashed walls. She gave me her quiet, friendly smile and walked towards me. 'Hello, I hope I haven't kept you waiting too long.'

I muttered something in reply and helped her on with her coat. She went over and kissed her father who didn't look up but waved his hand vaguely. There was another outburst of giggling from the table. We went out.

In the car I felt unusually tense and for the first mile or two had to depend on some inane remarks about the weather to keep a conversation going. I was begnning to relax when I drove over a little hump-backed bridge into a dip in the road. Then the car suddenly stopped. The engine coughed gently and then we were sitting silent and motionless in the darkness. And there was something else; my feet and ankles were freezing cold.

'My God!' I shouted. 'We've run into a bit of flooded road. The water's right into the car.' I looked round at Helen. 'I'm terribly sorry about this – your feet must be soaked.'

But Helen was laughing. She had her feet tucked up on the seat, her knees under her chin. 'Yes, I am a bit wet, but it's no good sitting about like this. Hadn't we better start pushing?'

Wading out into the black icy waters was a nightmare but there was no escape. Mercifully it was a little car and between us we managed to push it beyond the flooded patch. Then by torchlight I dried the plugs and got the engine going again.

Helen shivered as we squelched back into the car. 'I'm afraid I'll have to go back and change my shoes and stockings. And so will you. There's another road back through Fensley. You take the first turn on the left.'

Back at the farm, Mr Alderson was still reading the *Farmer and Stockbreeder* and kept his finger on the list of pig prices while he gave me a baleful glance over his spectacles. When he learned that I had come to borrow a pair of his shoes and socks he threw the paper down in exasperation and rose, groaning, from his chair. He shuffled out of the room and I could hear him muttering to himself as he mounted the stairs.

Helen followed him and I was left alone with the two young children. They studied my sodden trousers with undisguised delight. I had wrung most of the surplus water out of them but the final result was remarkable. Mrs Hall's knife-edge crease reached to just below the knee, but then there was chaos. The trousers flared out at that point in a crumpled, shapeless mass and as I stood by the fire to dry them a gentle steam rose about me. The children stared at me, wide-eyed and happy. This was a big night for them.

Mr Alderson reappeared at length and dropped some shoes and rough socks at my feet. I pulled on the socks quickly but shrank back when I saw the shoes. They were a pair of dancing slippers from the early days of the century and their cracked patent leather was topped by wide, black silk bows.

I opened my mouth to protest but Mr Alderson had dug himself deep into his chair and had found his place again among the pig prices. I had the feeling that if I asked for another pair of shoes Mr Alderson would attack me with the poker. I put the slippers on.

We had to take a roundabout road to avoid the floods but I kept my foot down and within half-an-hour we had left the steep sides of the Dale behind us and were heading out on to the rolling plain. I began to feel better. We were making good time and the little car, shuddering and creaking, was going well. I was just thinking that we wouldn't be all that late when the steering-wheel began to drag to one side.

I had a puncture most days and recognized the symptoms immediately. I had become an expert at changing wheels and with a word of apology to Helen was out of the car like a flash. With my rapid manipulation of the rusty jack and brace the wheel was off within three minutes. The surface of the crumpled tyre was quite smooth except for the lighter, frayed parts where the canvas showed through. Working like a demon, I screwed on the spare, cringing inwardly as I saw that this tyre was in exactly the same condition as the other. I steadfastly refused to think of what I would do if its frail fibres should give up the struggle.

By day, the Reniston dominated Brawton like a vast mediaeval fortress, bright flags fluttering arrogantly from its four turrets, but tonight it was like a dark cliff with a glowing cavern at street level where the Bentleys discharged their expensive cargoes. I didn't take my vehicle to the front entrance but tucked it away quietly at the back of the car park. A magnificent commissionaire opened the door for us and we trod noiselessly over the rich carpeting of the entrance hall.

We parted there to get rid of our coats, and in the men's cloakroom I scrubbed frantically at my oily hands. It didn't do much good; changing that wheel had given my finger nails a border of deep black which defied ordinary soap and water. And Helen was waiting for me.

I looked up in the mirror at the white-jacketed attendant hovering behind me with a towel. The man, clearly fascinated by my ensemble, was staring down at the wide-bowed pierrot shoes and the rumpled trouser bottoms. As he handed over the towel he smiled broadly as if in gratitude for this little bit of extra colour in his life.

I met Helen in the reception hall and we went over to the desk. 'What time does the dinner dance start?' I asked.

The girl at the desk looked surprised. 'I'm sorry, sir, there's no dance tonight. We only have them once a fortnight.'

I turned to Helen in dismay but she smiled encouragingly. 'It doesn't matter,' she said. 'I don't really care what we do.'

'We can have dinner, anyway,' I said. I tried to speak cheerfully but a little black cloud seemed to be forming just above my head. Was anything going to go right tonight? I could feel my morale slumping as I padded over the lush carpet and my first sight of the dining-room didn't help.

It looked as big as a football field with great marble pillars supporting a carved, painted ceiling. The Reniston had been built in the late Victorian period and all the opulence and ornate splendour of those days had been retained in this tremendous room. Most of the tables were occupied by the usual clientele, a mixture of the county aristocracy and industrialists from the West Riding. I had never seen so many beautiful women and masterful-looking men under one roof and I noticed with a twinge of alarm that, though the men were wearing everything from dark lounge suits to hairy tweeds, there wasn't another dinner jacket in sight.

A majestic figure in white tie and tails bore down on us. With his mane of white hair falling back from the lofty brow, the bulging waistline, the hooked nose and imperious expression he looked exactly like a Roman emperor. His eyes flickered expertly over me and he spoke tonelessly.

'You want a table, sir?'

'Yes please,' I mumbled, only just stopping myself saying 'sir' to the man in return. 'A table for two.'

'Are you staying, sir?'

This question baffled me. How could I possibly have dinner here if I wasn't staying.

'Yes, I am staying.'

The emperor made a note on a pad. 'This way, sir.'

He began to make his way with great dignity among the tables while I followed abjectly in his wake with Helen. It was a long way to the table and

I tried to ignore the heads which turned to have a second look at me as I passed. It was Mrs Hall's gusset that worried me most and I imagined it standing out like a beacon below the short jacket. It was literally burning my buttocks by the time we arrived.

The table was nicely situated and a swarm of waiters descended on us, pulling out our chairs and settling us into them, shaking out our napkins and spreading them on our laps. When they had dispersed the emperor took charge again. He poised a pencil over his pad.

'May I have your room number, sir?'

I swallowed hard and stared up at him over my dangerously billowing shirt front. 'Room number? Oh, I'm not living in the hotel.'

'Ah, NOT staying.' He fixed me for a moment with an icy look before crossing out something on the pad with unnecessary violence. He muttered something to one of the waiters and strode away.

It was about then that the feeling of doom entered into me. The black cloud over my head spread and descended, enveloping me in a dense cloud of misery. The whole evening had been a disaster and would probably get worse. I must have been mad to come to this sumptuous place dressed up like a knockabout comedian. I was as hot as hell inside this ghastly suit and the stud was biting viciously into my neck.

I took a menu card from a waiter and tried to hold it with my fingers curled inwards to hide my dirty nails. Everything was in French and in my numbed state the words were largely meaningless, but somehow I ordered the meal and, as we ate, I tried desperately to keep a conversation going. But long deserts of silence began to stretch between us; it seemed that only Helen and I were quiet among all the surrounding laughter and chatter.

Worst of all was the little voice which kept telling me that Helen had never really wanted to come out with me anyway. She had done it out of politeness and was getting through a boring evening as best she could.

The journey home was a fitting climax. We stared straight ahead as the headlights picked out the winding road back into the Dales. We made stumbling remarks then the strained silence took over again. By the time we drew up outside the farm my head had begun to ache.

We shook hands and Helen thanked me for a lovely evening. There was a tremor in her voice and in the moonlight her face was anxious and withdrawn. I said goodnight, got into the car and drove away.

Doctor at Sea

Richard Gordon

It is remarkable what spiritual contentment can be obtained from washing your own socks. I soaped a pair in the basin and hung them to dry on a line Easter had stretched across my cabin. I glowed with a modest sense of achievement. This was the first time I had been obliged to do any washing, which I had previously looked upon as an esoteric feminine function comparable with giving birth.

The crew of the *Lotus* did their own laundering – even Captain Hogg, who appeared in the early afternoon on the strip of deck round his cabin with a bundle of white uniforms under his arm and a basket of clothes-pegs. The other officers hung their shirts over their bunks and smartened them afterwards in the bathroom with the Third Mate's travelling iron. Down aft, the crew set aside Sunday afternoon for the laundry, when it was usual to see large firemen and deckhands dressed only in underpants and tattoos scrubbing their singlets with bar soap in the fire-buckets. The clothes were then strung thickly round the winches and ventilators and flapped round the stern of the ship like some fantastic signal.

Drying was simple, for we had reached the Tropics and the ship's company was in white uniforms. I had only to fix a white cover on my Company's regulation cap, but the officers appeared unexpectedly one morning in white shorts and shirts like a crop of snowdrops. The other hands were less affected by the order. Easter changed his blue serge jacket for a white one, but the rest were permitted the informality of uniform usual in the Merchant Service and did no more than roll their dungaree trousers half-way up their calves and remove their shirts.

'We should have been in whites two days ago,' Hornbeam grumbled. 'It's the Old Man's fault.'

'Why? What's he done now?'

'The old bastard sunbathes every afternoon and keeps us in blues until his knees are brown.'

I felt I was becoming quite a sailor. I let my days pass uncaringly, carried away in the drift of the sea routine. In a ship everybody seems constantly to be getting up or going to bed. The watch changes every fourth hour, which brings one of the mates, warm from his bunk, to the bridge, and sends a couple of engineers scuttling down the complicated ladders into the engine-room and stokehold. As well as the officers, two A.B.s go on the bridge to take turns at the wheel, and a gang of greasers and firemen troop below. All this movement is set off by the ship's bell on the bridge, which rings through each watch an arithmetical progression of half-hourly strokes.

Members of the ship's company who had no watches to keep – people like Whimble, Easter, and myself – all arranged their days round the after-dinner siesta. In the afternoon the whole ship died. All hands, apart from those essential for the running of the vessel, tottered away from the saloon table and, encouraged by a weighty meal and the noon session of gin, crashed gratefully into their bunks. This was a habit I found condemnable, but irresistible. In medical school and practice the afternoon had been my busiest time, and I was determined to pass the hours between one and four studying *War and Peace*. At first I never drank before the meal and avoided the cook's suet roll, of which Captain Hogg must have eaten several fathoms every voyage. But – whether I was the subject of mass-suggestion or sea air contains some subtle narcotic – I was unconscious before I got the taste of the ship's cheese out of my mouth, and I stayed asleep until Easter shook me at four with a cup of tea and a small piece of confectionery known in the Merchant Service as a tabnab. This habit I regarded nervously as the first indication of moral degeneration.

At five-thirty every evening my bath was run by Boswell, the bath steward. Boswell, like Easter, had seen better days, and the courtly manners he had learned in big P. & O.s and Cunarders had not deserted him. Whatever the temperature, he wore a shining white jacket, a stiff wing collar, and a black bow tie. He would arrive at my cabin door at half-past five precisely, a clean blue-and-white towel folded over his arm, and announce 'Your bath awaits, Doctor,' as if it were an important delegation. He followed me to the officers' bathroom, which smelled like a seaside cave at low tide, spread the towel over the chair, and mixed the water with his skinny hand. He dipped in a foot-long thermometer with a little metal bucket at the end, anxiously inspecting the temperature, and made a careful adjustment to the taps (later I found the thermometer had not worked for several years). He then poured some fresh hot water from a large shining copper can into a small bowl for the feet, and laid on the white wooden rack across the bath my flannel, a long-handled scrubbing brush, a loofah, and a bar of sea-water soap.

'Would there be anything else you require, sir?' he asked every evening. I found it difficult to complicate such a simple act as taking a bath any further, and he would bow deeply and retire backwards through the steam. I knew he did so with disappointment, for a bath suggested to him as many variations as soup to a French chef. Every few days he would press me to take a few spoonfuls of mustard in it, or some washing soda, or a tumbler of rosewater. 'Might I recommend a little Sloan's?' he asked once. 'I used to put it in regularly for one doctor I looked after in the Cunard. Very good for the joints, I believe.'

Boswell's manners were unfortunately not sufficient to overcome the discomforts of the *Lotus's* bathroom. There were no portholes or ventilators, so water collected on the deckhead as efficiently as in the main condenser in the engine-room, and thence fell thickly in rusty brown drops. The deck was covered with some crumbling material that left potholes to trip the bather and make him catch his head or his shins against sharp projecting pieces of steel. The bath itself was shaped like a coffin, and was furnished with a pair of fearsome taps that gave between them hot and cold sea water and a disproportionate amount of steam. There was an alternative – the fresh-water shower outside Hornbeam's cabin, but owing to some subtle mechanical fault many feet below in the engine-room this emitted only ice-cold water or superheated steam, and after escaping a third-degree burn I decided to stick to the safe tepid waters under Boswell's supervision.

Boswell did not stop at baths: far greater was his pride in the officers' lavatories. These were not much more efficient than the bath, and in rough weather became alarmingly unreliable. But to Boswell they were a porcelain monument to his own calling. He spent the morning cleaning and polishing them, and on our arrival for inspection would bow low and flush each as we passed with the jaunty pride of the satisfied artist.

'There's more in lavatories than meets the eye, sir,' he explained to me one day, with a sigh. 'You've got to *understand* lavatories to do this job.' I gathered from Easter that as he contentedly did his morning task Boswell dreamed of his retirement in charge of a small underground nest of them at one of the quieter corners of Liverpool.

My professional duties were not exacting. I saw a couple of patients in the morning, perhaps half a dozen at five. The most common trouble was the constipation, doctor. This I first treated with pharmacopoeial doses of the usual remedies, but I soon found it was necessary to multiply the amount by three for most of the patients and by five for the Bos'n and firemen. There were boils and warts, a few burns from the engine-room, and several vague illnesses whose leading symptom was a disinclination to work. We had a few more cases resulting from careless choice of friends during our last nights in Liverpool. The approach to the medical attendant by sufferers from this embarrassing condition varied from the shifty request – with a sidelong glance at Easter – to "Ave a word wiv you a minute, Doctor,' to the full-blooded storming of the surgery by the experienced invalid with his 'Say, Doc, can you fix this for us by Friday?'

At eleven we inspected the ship. Hornbeam, Whimble, McDougall, and myself gathered outside the saloon door and saluted when Captain Hogg's boots appeared on the companionway from his cabin. This homage he returned with the grace of a publican handing back a counterfeit half-crown.

We lined up behind him and set off touring the decks, each of us trying to look as disagreeable as possible. We filed in and out of Boswell's lavatories with dignity, and zealously searched for dust under the coconut matting. The progress was broken only when Captain Hogg's eye was jarred by something that gave him displeasure, when he would turn his fury not only on the man responsible but on his parents as well. At first I shivered at the onslaught: then I grew to appreciate the range and power of the Captain's imagination and the felicity with which he turned his sentences, until I listened to him with fascination. As for the victims, they shrugged their shoulders and took no notice. Raving Captains were just like storms at sea: you had to put up with them until they blew themselves out, and not become unreasonably excited.

After inspection the Captain went on the bridge to supervize the daily ceremony of finding the noon position of the ship. I went up there only once, because Captain Hogg looked on visitors like a sour landowner spotting picnickers on his front lawn. It was a shady, restful place, lined with dark wood and brass, like an old-fashioned saloon bar. The sea was surprisingly far below, and the only sound was the irregular loud clicking of the gyro repeater, like the ticking of an arrhythmic clock. Abaft the bridge was the chartroom, where rulers, set-squares, and neatly sharpened pencils were arranged like a tidy school desk, and the chronometers nestled under thick glass like a pair of premature infants in an incubator. Hornbeam once offered me his sextant and let me work out our position, but I disgusted him by putting the *Lotus* within a few miles of Cleveland, Ohio.

I spent most of my time chatting to the officers off watch, leaning on the rail, playing quoits, or nosing round the deck. I was beginning to learn what everything was called. Ships have a distinct anatomy of their own, and our daily rounds were as confusing to me as my first demonstration in the dissecting room. I recognized fairly early on the difference between port and starboard, fore and aft, and a binnacle and a barnacle; but I was still uncertain where to find such obscure pieces of marine furnishing as the jumper stays, the monkey island, and the shrouds.

The tenth morning of the voyage I sat down resolutely in my cabin and took *War and Peace* from the locker. Somehow I had not yet found time to pass the first page. I opened it, smoothed down the paper, and began again the first paragraph. Hornbeam rattled the jalousie door and came in.

'Morning, Doc! Everything bearing an even strain?'

'Good morning, Chief,' I said. 'I think so, thanks very much.'

'Good.'

Picking up the first volume of *War and Peace* he neatly squashed a cockroach that was scuttling across the bulkhead.

'These damn roaches,' he said. 'Come out in families once it turns hot. Had any in bed with you?'

'No, not yet.'

He pulled a tobacco tin from his pocket.

'Would you like the makings?' he asked, offering it.

'No, thank you. I'm afraid it's a nautical knack I haven't picked up.'

'It's easy enough. Can't stand tailor-mades.'

He neatly rolled a cigarette between his fingers and thumbs. Whenever I tried the same manoeuvre I squeezed the tobacco out like the cream from an éclair.

'Wish you'd have a look at the Sparks, Doc,' Hornbeam continued affably.

'Why, what's the trouble?'

'I just saw him shake hands with a lifeboat.'

'Ah, yes. I was rather afraid something like that might happen.'

Our Wireless Operator was probably the luckiest man on the ship. He was one of those blithe people who live in a world of their own. He had been at sea for forty years, crouched over a telegraph key with the staccato song of Morse in his ears. This seemed to have induced psychological changes in him. For the rest of us, our universe was bounded by the steel and wooden limits of the *Lotus* – but not the Sparks. He passed his day in the company of soft-skinned maidens and amiable philosophers, with whom he could often be seen laughing, conversing, and singing while he walked round the deck or sat in the corner of his cabin. Sometimes he did a coy little dance with some of his companions, or played a simple game; and occasionally they would have a restrained tiff, which always ended happily in the way just observed by the Mate. The Sparks was by far the happiest person under Captain Hogg's command.

'I suppose he's quite harmless?' I asked. 'I mean, he doesn't send out dangerous messages or anything?'

'Oh, he's not in that stage yet,' Hornbeam assured me tolerantly. 'I've seen a good many worse than him. The Morse gets 'em in the end. I just thought you ought to know. I saw him kissing a ventilator yesterday,' he added darkly.

'We are all entitled to our little aberrations, I suppose.'

'You're right there, Doc. Life at sea wouldn't be possible without a bit of give and take. Old Sparks is all right. Just a bit dippy. Like some of these tanker types.'

'Tanker types?'

He nodded, lighting the cigarette and filling the cabin with smoke.

'Men in tankers. It's a dog's life. They run to places like the Persian Gulf and they can unload in a couple of days. That means the boys don't get much of a run ashore when they're home. Besides, you can't live on top of a few thousand tons of petrol all your life without getting a bit queer. Of course, they get the money . . . But is it worth it? Friend of mine went mate in a tanker to make a bit and ended up by cutting his throat. Made a hell of a mess of the chartroom, so they told me.'

From Hornbeam's conversation I gathered that suicide at sea had a panache not seen ashore.

'I think I'll stick to dry cargo,' I said. 'That seems dangerous enough for doctors.'

'Are you coming to the Third's do tonight?' Hornbeam asked. 'That's the reason I looked in.'

'I didn't know he was having one.'

'It's his birthday – twenty-first – and he's having a few beers. You're invited.'

'I don't drink much, you know.'

'Oh, don't be scared, Doc. None of us drinks while we're at sea. I'll say you're coming.'

The party was after supper, in the Third Mate's cabin. As I was anxious not to appear at all anti-social I was the first to arrive.

I had not been in his cabin before. It was smaller than mine, with just enough room for a man to stand between the bunk and the strip of settee on the opposite bulk-head. There was a porthole over the settee and a forced-draught vent in the deckhead that stabbed a narrow stream of cold air across the bunk. Opposite the door was a small desk covered completely with bottles of gin. The rest of the cabin was covered with girls.

They were everywhere – in frames over the bunk, pasted to the bulk-head, suspended from the pipes crossing the deckhead. There were plain photographs of ordinary girls, shadowy nudes from *Men Only*, taut scissor-legged girls in impossible brassieres from *Esquire*, a few bright beer advertisements from Australia of surprised but unresisting girls with their skirts caught in mangles, car doors, stiles, and dog leads, girls with no clothes playing on the beach, girls with all their clothes caught in a highly selective gale, even pictures of Chinese girls covered from neck to ankle.

'Come in, Doc!' the Third said. 'Have a peg.'

He pushed a glass into my hand and half-filled it with gin in one motion.

'Happy birthday,' I said faintly. 'You seem to have an eye for art.'

'Got to brighten the old cart up a bit. Here's to you.'

He pointed above the bunk to the photograph of a sharp-chinned young lady trying earnestly to look like Dorothy Lamour.

'That's a nice bit of crumpet. Met her in Hull last voyage. She's an intelligent bit, mind you,' he added seriously. 'Works in Boots' library.'

He indicated her rival next to her.

'Now there's a girl for you. Came across her in Adelaide. Last time we were there her brother came and socked me on the nose. She still writes to me, though.'

'I hope he didn't hurt you.'

'He did a bit. He's one of the wharfies. That one's from St John. But this Sheila here's the best of the bunch. Lives in Durban. Father's got pots of cash.'

'You seem to scatter your affections pretty widely.'

'They all love sailors. When a girl knows a fellow's going half-way round the world in a week's time she takes the brakes off a bit. Have a seat on the bunk.'

I sat down and rested my head uncomfortably on the paper bosom of a blonde.

The other guests arrived together. There was Hornbeam, the crazy Sparks, Whimble, the Second Steward, and the Chief, Second, Third, and Fourth Engineers. Archer was absent, keeping Hornbeam's watch on the bridge. The ten of us crammed ourselves into the tiny cabin. Hornbeam had his elbow in my face and his shoes on the Chief Engineer's knees. Whimble wedged himself behind the door and stuck his feet against the end of the bunk. The host struggled between everyone's legs, handing out drinks. I felt that something would shortly give way and project the lot of us into the sea.

The Third's health was drunk by all hands.

'Have another, Doc,' he said.

'No, really . . .'

'Come off it! It's only five bob a bottle.' He half-filled my tumbler again. 'How do you like the sea?' he asked.

'It is a very interesting form of existence.'

'Of course, you realize this is only part of it,' Hornbeam explained. 'It varies a good bit. As you know, British ships are in three classes.'

'Tankers . . .?'

'No. First of all there's the P. & O. Then there's the Merchant Navy, which is the set-up we're in. After that there's the Old Grey Funnel line.'

'Also known as the Royal Navy,' McDougall explained. 'It was nationalized years ago.'

'The P. & O. must not be confused with ordinary hookers,' Hornbeam continued. 'It's a sort of – well, a floating Horse Guards, if you get me. They hate to be called Merchantmen. If you make a noise drinking your soup . . .'

'They wear swords and spurs,' Trail said.

'I don't believe it.'

'Well, they ought to. Oh, very posh, very posh. Good shower of bastards on the whole, though. Have some more gin.'

'Not for . . . Oh, all right, as you've poured it out. It tastes better than the stuff you get ashore.'

'Everything does. By the way, you know the Second Engineer, Doc? Mr Macpherson.'

'Pleased to meet you.'

'Mr McPhail the Third and Mr Macintosh the Fourth.'

'What, are you all Scots in the engine-room?'

'We've a Taffy and a couple of Geordies,' Macpherson said. 'Had to have them in to do the dirty work.'

'You know what they say,' McDougall added proudly. 'If you open the engine-room hatch of any British ship and shout "Jock" someone'll be bound to come up.'

McPhail started singing 'I belong to Glasgow,' but petered out.

'Coming ashore with us in Santos, Doc?' Hornbeam asked.

'Certainly. I intend to take advantage of the voyage to broaden my education.'

'Santos will broaden it all right. Plenty of nice girls there.'

'I'm sure I should be pleased if you'd introduce me to them.'

This remark started everyone laughing.

'You don't need any introductions. It's keeping them away that's the trouble.'

'Well, I shall not be interested in meeting any of that sort.'

'Oh, you'll have to come with us to Madame Mimi's,' Hornbeam said reproachfully. 'It would be like going to London and missing the Houses of Parliament.'

'Are you suggesting,' I said coldly, 'that I should visit a brothel?'

'Where the hell else do you think there is to go in Santos?' Trail said testily. 'Anyway, Madame Mimi's is as respectable as the Liverpool Museum.'

'I wouldn't put that past suspicion,' Hornbeam said.

Trail cut the conversation short by pouring out gin all round and beginning a complicated story about two sailors losing their way in Lime Street station.

After an hour everyone was pretty cheerful.

'Don't make such a row,' Trail said. 'Father'll hear.'

'To hell with Father,' I heard myself say.

'Spoken like a sailor, Doc!' Hornbeam slapped me on the chest. 'Good old Doc! Best one I've ever sailed with.'

'I say, really . . .'

'You're the only one that's sane!'

This brought a round of applause.

'You're all mad at sea,' I said defiantly. 'The lot of you.'

The company immediately indicated their disbelief with the usual word.

'You are,' I said. 'Or you wouldn't be here.'

'Have some more gin,' Trail said.

'Thank you.' I swallowed another mouthful. 'As I was saying. I have made a diagnosis. From careful – not to say exacting – study of you in the past ten days I conclude that you're all suffering from the death wish.'

'What the hell's that?' McDougall asked angrily.

I held up a hand.

'Silence. As a disciple of Hippocrates I demand respect and silence. The death wish. When you are born all you want to do is die.'

This again filled the cabin with derision.

'Shut up, you blokes. Let the poor blighter speak,' Trail said.

I continued. 'That is what the psychologists say. Some people hang themselves. Others go into monasteries and . . . and things. Some climb mountains and live in caves. Others write poetry. Look at English poetry,' I demanded hotly of Hornbeam. 'Look at it! Redolent with the death wish!' I screwed up my eyes and struck an attitude of recitation.

> '. . . for many a time
> I have been half in love with easeful Death,'

I declaimed stumblingly.

> 'Call'd him soft names in many a musèd rhyme,
> To take into the air my quiet . . .'

I slipped off the bunk, but Hornbeam caught me.

'Death wish to the eyebrows, the lot of you! You withdraw – to sea. To sea! That's what it is!'

'You're full of prune-juice, Doc,' someone said.

'I will not have insults,' I cried. 'If you would care to defend yourself like a gentleman, I shall take you up on it. You have the death wish, by God! You've all got it. So had Nelson. I've got it as well.'

I fell over McDougall's feet and no one bothered to pick me up.

The UFO Menace

Woody Allen

UFOs are back in the news, and it is high time we took a serious look at this phenomenon. (Actually, the time is ten past eight, so not only are we a few minutes late but I'm hungry.) Up until now, the entire subject of flying saucers has been mostly associated with kooks or odd-balls. Frequently, in fact, observers will admit to being a member of both groups. Still, persistent sightings by responsible individuals have caused the Air Force and the scientific community to re-examine a once skeptical attitude, and the sum of two hundred dollars has now been allocated for a comprehensive study of the phenomenon. The question is: Is anything out there? And if so, do they have ray guns?

All UFOs may not prove to be of extraterrestrial origin, but experts do agree that any glowing cigar-shaped aircraft capable of rising straight up at twelve thousand miles per second would require the kind of maintenance and sparkplugs available only on Pluto. If these objects are indeed from another planet, then the civilization that designed them must be millions of years more advanced than our own. Either that or they are very lucky. Professor Leon Speciman postulates a civilization in outer space that is more advanced than ours by approximately fifteen minutes. This, he feels, gives them a great advantage over us, since they needn't rush to get to appointments.

Dr Brackish Menzies, who works at the Mount Wilson Observatory, or else is under observation at the Mount Wilson Mental Hospital (the letter is not clear), claims that travellers moving at close to the speed of light would require many millions of years to get here, even from the nearest solar system, and, judging from the shows on Broadway, the trip would be hardly worth it. (It is impossible to travel faster than light, and certainly not desirable, as one's hat keeps blowing off.)

Interestingly, according to modern astronomers, space is finite. This is a very comforting thought – particularly for people who can never remember where they have left things. The key factor in thinking about the universe, however, is that it is expanding and will one day break apart and disappear. That is why if the girl in the office down the hall has some good points but perhaps not all the qualities you require it's best to compromise.

The most frequently asked question about the UFOs is: If saucers come from outer space, why have their pilots not attempted to make contact with us, instead of hovering mysteriously over deserted areas? My own theory is that for creatures from another solar system 'hovering' may be a socially acceptable mode of relating. It may, indeed, be pleasurable. I myself once hovered over an eighteen-year-old actress for six months and had the best time of my life. It should be also recalled that when we talk of 'life' on other planets we are frequently referring to amino acids, which are never very gregarious, even at parties.

Most people tend to think of UFOs as a modern problem, but could they be a phenomenon that man has been aware of for centuries? (To us a century seems quite long, particularly if you are holding an I.O.U., but by astronomical standards it is over in a second. For that reason, it is always best to carry a toothbrush and be ready to leave on a moment's notice.) Scholars now tell us that the sighting of unidentified flying objects dates as far back as Biblical times. For instance, there is a passage in the Book of Leviticus that reads, 'And a great and silver ball appeared over the Assyrian Armies, and in all of Babylonia there was wailing and gnashing of teeth, till the Prophets bade the multitudes get a grip on themselves and shape up.'

Was this phenomenon related to one described years later by Parmenides: 'Three orange objects did appear suddenly in the heavens and did circle midtown Athens, hovering over the baths and causing several of our wisest philosophers to grab for towels?' And, again, were those 'orange objects' similar to what is described in a recently discovered twelfth-century Saxon-church manuscript: 'A lauch lauched he; wer richt laith to weet a cork-heild schonne; whilst a red balle lang owre swam aboone. I thank you, ladies and gentlemen?'

This last account was taken by medieval clergy to signify that the world was coming to an end, and there was great disappointment when Monday came and everyone had to go back to work.

Finally, and most convincingly, in 1822 Goethe himself notes a strange celestial phenomenon. 'En route home from the Leipzig Anxiety Festival,' he wrote, 'I was crossing a meadow, when I chanced to look up and saw several fiery red balls suddenly appear in the southern sky. They descended at a great

rate of speed and began chasing me. I screamed that I was a genius and consequently could not run very fast, but my words were wasted. I became enraged
and shouted imprecations at them, whereupon they flew away frightened. I
related this story to Beethoven, not realizing he had already gone deaf, and
he smiled and nodded and said, "Right." '

As a general rule, careful on-the-scene investigations disclose that most
'unidentified' flying objects are quite ordinary phenomena, such as weather
balloons, meteorites, satellites, and even once a man named Lewis Mandel-
baum, who blew off the roof of the World Trade Center. A typical 'explained'
incident is the one reported by Sir Chester Ramsbottom, on June 5, 1961, in
Shropshire: 'I was driving along the road at 2 a.m. and saw a cigar-shaped
object that seemed to be tracking my car. No matter which way I drove, it
stayed with me, turning sharply at right angles. It was a fierce, glowing red,
and in spite of twisting and turning the car at high speed I could not lose it.
I became alarmed and began sweating. I let out a shriek of terror and apparently fainted, but awoke in a hospital, miraculously unharmed.' Upon investigation, experts determined that the 'cigar-shaped object' was Sir Chester's
nose. Naturally, all his evasive actions could not lose it, since it was attached
to his face.

Another explained incident began in late April of 1972, with a report from
Major General Curtis Memling, of Andrews Air Force Base: 'I was walking
across a field one night and suddenly I saw a large silver disc in the sky. It
flew over me, not fifty feet above my head, and repeatedly described aero-
dynamic patterns impossible for any normal aircraft. Suddenly it accelerated
and shot away at terrific speed.'

Investigators became suspicious when they noticed that General Memling
could not describe this incident without giggling. He later admitted he had
just come from a showing of the film 'War of the Worlds', at the post movie
theatre, and 'got a very big kick out of it.' Ironically, General Memling
reported another UFO sighting in 1976, but it was soon discovered that he,
too, had become fixated on Sir Chester Ramsbottom's nose – an occurrence
that caused consternation in the Air Force and eventually led to General
Memling's court-martial.

If most UFO sightings can be satisfactorily explained, what of those few
which cannot? Following are some of the most mystifying examples of
'unsolved' encounters, the first reported by a Boston man in May, 1969: 'I
was walking by the beach with my wife. She's not a very attractive woman.
Rather overweight. In fact, I was pulling her on a dolly at the time. Suddenly

I looked up and saw a huge white saucer that seemed to be descending at great speed. I guess I panicked, because I dropped the rope on my wife's dolly and began running. The saucer passed directly over my head and I heard an eerie, metallic voice say, 'Call your service.' When I got home, I phoned my answering service and received a message that my brother Ralph had moved and to forward all his mail to Neptune. I never saw him again. My wife suffered a severe breakdown over the incident and now cannot converse without using a hand puppet.'

From I. M. Axelbank, of Athens, Georgia, February, 1971: 'I am an experienced pilot and was flying my private Cessna from New Mexico to Amarillo, Texas, to bomb some people whose religious persuasion I do not wholly agree with, when I noticed an object flying alongside me. At first I thought it was another plane, until it emitted a green beam of light, forcing my plane to drop eleven thousand feet in four seconds and causing my toupee to snap off my head and tear a two-foot hole in the roof. I repeatedly called for help on my radio, but for some reason could only get the old 'Mr Anthony' programme. The UFO came very close to my plane again and then shot away at blinding speed. By this time I had lost my bearings and was forced to make an emergency landing on the turnpike. I continued the trip in the plane on the ground and only got into trouble when I tried to run a toll booth and broke off my wings.'

One of the eeriest accounts occurred in August, 1975, to a man on Montauk Point, in Long Island: 'I was in bed at my beach house, but could not sleep because of some fried chicken in the icebox that I felt entitled to. I waited till my wife dropped off, and tiptoed into the kitchen. I remember looking at the clock. It was precisely four-fifteen. I'm quite certain of this, because our kitchen clock has not worked in twenty-one years and is always at that time. I also noticed that our dog, Judas, was acting funny. He was standing up on his hind legs and singing, 'I Enjoy Being a Girl'. Suddenly the room turned bright orange. At first, I thought my wife had caught me eating between meals and set fire to the house. Then I looked out the window, where to my amazement I saw a gigantic cigar-shaped aircraft hovering just over the tree-tops in the yard and emitting an orange glow. I stood transfixed for what must have been several hours, though our clock still read four-fifteen, so it was difficult to tell. Finally, a large, mechanical claw extended from the aircraft and snatched the two pieces of chicken from my hand and quickly retreated. The machine then rose and, accelerating at great speed, vanished into the sky. When I reported the incident to the Air Force, they told me that what I had

seen was a flock of birds. When I protested, Colonel Quincy Bascomb personally promised that the Air Force would return the two pieces of chicken. To
this day, I have only received one piece.'

Finally, an account in January, 1977, by two Louisiana factory workers:
'Roy and I was catfishing in the bog. I enjoy the bog, as does Roy. We was
not drinking although we had brought with us a gallon of methyl chloride
which we both favour with either a twist of lemon or a small onion. Anyways,
at about midnight we looked up and saw a bright-yellow sphere descend into
the bog. At first Roy mistook it for a whooping crane and took a shot at it,
but I said, "Roy that ain't no crane, 'cause it's got no beak." That's how you
can tell a crane. Roy's son Gus has a beak, you know, and thinks he's a crane.
Anyways, all of a sudden this door slides open and several creatures emerge.
These creatures looked like little portable radios with teeth and short hair.
They also had legs, although where the toes usually are they had wheels. The
creatures motioned to me to come forward, which I did, and they injected
me with a fluid that caused me to smile and act like Bopeep. They spoke with
one another in a strange tongue, which sounded like when you back your car
over a fat person. They took me aboard the aircraft and gave me what seemed
to be a complete physical examination. I went along with it, as I had not had
a checkup in two years. By now they had mastered my own language, but
they still made simple mistakes like using "hermeneutics," when they meant
"heuristic". They told me they were from another galaxy and were here to
tell the earth that we must learn to live in peace or they will return with
special weapons and laminate every first-born male. They said they would get
the results of my blood test back in a couple of days and if I didn't hear from
them I could go ahead and marry Clair.'

Acknowledgements

The Publishers acknowledge permission to reprint copyright material to the following: Alan Coren for *The Hangover in Question*. Michael Green and the Hutchinson Publishing Group Limited for an extract from *The Art of Coarse Sailing*. Hamish Hamilton Ltd for *The Night the Ghost Got In* by James Thurber, from *Vintage Thurber* © Hamish Hamilton Ltd, 1963. Miles Kington and Robson Books Ltd for *A la Douane* and *Dans le Health Food Shop*, from *Let's Parler Franglais* by Miles Kington, published by Robson Books Ltd. Gerald Durrell and the Curtis Brown Group Limited for *The King and the Conga*, from *The Bafut Beagles* © Gerald Durrell 1954. Basil Boothroyd and the Proprietors of Punch for *Why Dogs Bite Gardeners*. George Mikes and Andre Deutsch Limited for *Tea*, from *How to be An Alien*, first published 1946. Richard Stilgoe and George Allen & Unwin for *The Cricket Match*, from *The Richard Stilgoe Letters*. Lawrence Durrell for *Jots and Tittles*, reprinted by permission of Faber and Faber Ltd, from *Esprit de Corps* by Lawrence Durrell. Lady Ethel Wodehouse and the Hutchinson Publishing Group Limited for *The Rummy Affair of Old Biffy* by P. G. Wodehouse, from *Carry on Jeeves*. The Estate of H. E. Bates and Laurence Pollinger Ltd for an extract from *The Darling Buds of May*. Woody Allen and Elm Tree Books for *No Kaddish for Weinstein*, from *Without Feathers*. James Herriot and Michael Joseph Limited for an extract from *Let Sleeping Vets Lie*. John Lucas and the Hutchinson Publishing Group Limited for *Beggar your Neighbour*, from *Backs to the Garden*. Douglas Adams and Pan Books Ltd for an extract from *The Hitch Hiker's Guide to the Galaxy*. Richard Gordon for an extract from *Good Neighbours*, reprinted by kind permission of William Heinemann Limited. © Richard Gordon Ltd, 1976. Richard Ingrams, John Wells and Private Eye Productions Ltd for an extract from *The Other Half*. Lady Ethel Wodehouse and the Hutchinson Publishing Group Limited for *Pig-Hoo-o-o-o-ey!* by P. G. Wodehouse, from *Blandings Castle*. Douglas Sutherland and Debrett's Peerage Limited for *The Lady at Sport and Play*, and *The English Lady and her Wedding*, from *The English Gentleman's Wife*. *The Agony of Captain Grimes* is taken from *Decline and Fall*, reprinted by permission of A. D. Peters & Co. Ltd. *The Marx Brothers* by S. J. Perelman, from *The Last Laugh* is reprinted by

Acknowledgements

permission of A. D. Peters & Co. Ltd. Richard Gordon for an extract from *Dr Gordon's Casebook*. Reprinted by kind permission of the Curtis Brown Group Limited © Richard Gordon Ltd, 1982. Barry Took for *The Identikit Soap Opera*, from *Took's Eye View*, published by Robson Books Ltd. John Esmonde & Bob Larbey for chapter 5, from *The Good Life* (Penguin Books, 1976), pp 45–68, copyright © John Esmonde & Bob Larbey, 1976. Reprinted by permission of Penguin Books Ltd. *Oxford as I See It, Old Junk and New Money*, and *How to Borrow Money* by Stephen Leacock reprinted by permission of The Bodley Head Ltd, from *The Bodley Head Leacock*. Sphere Books Ltd for *When I first met Dr Hickey* by E. E. Somerville & Martin Ross, from *The Irish R.M.* Andrew McCall and Hamish Hamilton Ltd for *Weekends*, from *The Ghastly Guest Book*. Keith Waterhouse and Michael Joseph Limited for chapters 3 and 4 of *Office Life*. *Recollections of Notable Cops (1900–10)* by H. L. Mencken, copyright 1941 by Alfred A. Knopf, Inc. Reprinted from *The Vintage Mencken*, by H. L. Mencken, edited by Alistair Cooke, by permission of Alfred A. Knopf, Inc. First published in *The New Yorker*. *Are the Rich Happy?* by Stephen Leacock. Reprinted by permission of The Bodley Head Ltd, from *The Bodley Head Leacock*. *Preparing for the West*, from Swan Song of A. J. Wentworth by kind permission of H. F. Ellis © H. F. Ellis 1982, and the Curtis Brown Group Limited. Douglas Sutherland and Debrett's Peerage Limited for *The Gentleman and his Domestic Habits*, from *The English Country Gentleman*. The Executors of the Estate of W. Somerset Maugham and William Heinemann Limited for *The Three Fat Women of Antibes*, from *The Complete Short Stories of W. Somerset Maugham*. *A Terrible Worrier* by Joyce Grenfell, from *Stately as a Galleon* is reprinted by permission of Macmillan, London and Basingstoke. Mr D. C. Humphreys CMG, Mr R. M. L. Humphreys and Penguin Books Ltd for *How Will Noggin was Fooled, and Berry Rode Forth against his Will*, from *Berry & Co.* by Dornford Yates. The Estate of W. Heath Robinson and Duckworth and Company Limited for *Early Married Life*, from *How to be a Perfect Husband*. *The Eternal Combustion Engine* by Patrick Campbell, from *35 years on the Job*, is reprinted by permission of Blond & Briggs Limited. Compton Mackenzie and Robert Hale Limited for pp 239–254 of *Buttercups and Daisies*. *Cooper the Trooper* by Tommy Cooper, from *Just Like That!* is reprinted by permission of Jupiter Books. Peter Spence and the Hutchinson Publishing Group Limited for an extract from *To the Manor Born*. Dirk Bogarde and Chatto & Windus Ltd for an extract from *A Postillion Struck by Lightning*. John Mortimer for *Rumpole and the Case of Identity*, from *The Trials of Rumpole*, reprinted by permission of A. D. Peters & Co. Ltd. Keith Waterhouse for *Diary of a Child Guerilla*,

Acknowledgements

from *The Punch Book of Kids* published by Robson Books Ltd. Paul Jennings for *Dear Electricity Board*, from *I Must Have Imagined It*. Harry Chance and the Hutchinson Publishing Group Limited for *Talking Your Way to the Top*, from *The Bounder's Companion*. Jilly Cooper and Methuen, London for *The Seven Deadly Virtues*, from *Supercooper*. John Wells for *On Ilkley Moor b'aht Frog* and *Not My Day*, from *Masterpieces*, reprinted by permission of A. D. Peters & Co. Ltd. Dr Northcote Parkinson for an extract from *Mrs Parkinson's Law* by C. Northcote Parkinson © C. Northcote Parkinson, 1968. Lady Ethel Wodehouse and the Hutchinson Publishing Group Limited for *Happy Christmas and Merry New Year* by P. G. Wodehouse, from *Louder and Funnier*. *Ear, Nose and Throat* by Cornelia Otis Skinner is reprinted by permission of Dodd, Mead & Company, Inc., from *Dithers and Jitters* by Cornelia Otis Skinner. Copyright 1937, 1938 by Cornelia Otis Skinner. Copyright renewed 1965, 1966 by Cornelia Otis Skinner Blodget. First published in *The New Yorker*. *A Visit to London* by Frank Sullivan, from *Sullivan By Bay*, is used by permission of the Historical Society of Saratoga Springs, Saratoga Springs, New York. *How to Swot a Fly*, from *How to Attract the Wombat* by Will Cuppy is copyright 1935, 1945 by Will Cuppy. Copyright © 1942, 1943, 1945, 1946, 1947, 1948, 1949 by The Curtis Publishing Co. Reprinted by permission of Holt, Rinehart & Winston. *Sporting Life in America: Dozing* by Robert Benchley is taken from *The Treasurer's Report*. Copyright 1930 by Robert C. Benchley; renewed 1958 by Gertrude D. Benchley and reprinted by permission of Harper & Row Publishers, Inc. *The Cricket Match* by A. G. Macdonell, from *England Their England* is reprinted by permission of A. D. Peters & Co. Ltd. Art Buchwald for *Flying with Child* and *Breaking the Ice at St Moritz*, from *I Chose Caviar*. Hamish Hamilton Ltd for *The Pleasure Cruise, and How to Survive It*, and *My Own Ten Rules for a Happy Marriage*, by James Thurber, from *Vintage Thurber* © Hamish Hamilton Ltd, 1963. *Yoga Attempted* and *Business Party* by Cornelia Otis Skinner are reprinted by permission of Dodd, Mead & Company, Inc., from *Dithers and Jitters* by Cornelia Otis Skinner. Copyright 1937, 1938 by Cornelia Otis Skinner. Copyright renewed 1965, 1966 by Cornelia Tos Skinner Blodget. *Mr Pumpenstempel's Orchestra* by Eric Linklater, from *Juan in America* is reprinted by permission of A. D. Peters & Co. Ltd. Richard Boston and Elm Tree Books for *Parlez-vous Franglais?*, from *Baldness Be My Friend*. *Child-Holding*, from *My Ten Years in a Quandary* and *How They Grew* by Robert Benchley is reprinted by permission of Harper & Row Publishers, Inc. Copyright 1936 by Robert C. Benchley. Dennis Rooke and the Proprietors of Punch for *Unhappy Meeting*. Tim Brooke-Taylor and J. M. Dent & Sons Ltd

Acknowledgements

for *Advice to Beginners*, from *Rule Britannia*. The authors and Methuen, London for an extract from *1066 And All That* by W. C. Sellar & R. J. Yeatman. Denis Norden for *The Faux Pas*, from *Robert Morley's Book of Bricks*, reprinted by permission of Weidenfeld (Publishers) Limited. Frank Muir for *On Remembering Names* from *Robert Morley's Book of Bricks*, reprinted by permission of Weidenfeld (Publishers) Ltd. Jasper Carrott for *The Big Yin and Tonic*, from *Sweet and Sour Labrador*, reprinted by permission of Hutchinson Publishing Group Limited. J. B. Morton for *Straight Bat Department*, from *By the Way*, reprinted by permission of A. D. Peters & Co. Ltd. *On Having a Cold* is reprinted by permission of the Bodley Head Ltd from *And the Next* by R. S. Hooper. E. V. Lucas for *The Double*, from *Urbanities*, reprinted by permission of Methuen and Co. Peter Fleming for *On Being Mean*, from *Goodbye to the Bombay Bowler*, reprinted by permission of Nicholas Fleming. Tom Wolfe for *The Mid-Atlantic Man*, from *The Pump House Gang*, reprinted by permission of the author and the author's agents.

Adam and Colonel Blount is reprinted by permission of A. D. Peters & Co. Ltd, from *Vile Bodies* by Evelyn Waugh. Arthur Marshall for *Royal Mail*, from *I Say!* reprinted by permission of Hamish Hamilton Ltd. John Timpson for *Can you come in and do it live?*, from *The Lighter Side of Today*, reprinted by permission of George Allen & Unwin (Publishers) Ltd. H. F. Ellis for *Re Helicopters* reproduced by kind permission of Curtis Brown Ltd. *Noulded into the Shake of a Goat* by Patrick Campbell, reprinted by permission of Lady Glenavy. Ned Sherrin for *Sport* from *Cutting Edge*, reprinted by permission of J. M. Dent & Sons Ltd. Brian Johnston for *The Definitive List of My Gaffes*, from *Chatterboxes: My Friends the Commentators*, reprinted by permission of Methuen, London. Art Buchwald for *Clean Your Room, The Bad Back Problem and Christmas Cards Tell All* from *I Never Danced at the White House*. Kit Bryson, Selina Fitzherbert and Jean-Luc Legris for *Naff Things to Do in a Restaurant* from *The Complete Naff Guide* reprinted by permission of Hutchinson Publishing Group Limited. *When is a Joke not a Joke* from *Nymphs and Satires* by Rachel Ferguson is reprinted by permission of the Executors of the Estate of Rachel Ferguson. Arthur Marshall for *Serpent's Teeth*, from *Smile Please*, reprinted by permission of Hamish Hamilton Ltd. James Herriot and Michael Joseph Limited for an extract from *All Creatures Great and Small*. Keith Waterhouse and Michael Joseph Limited for *A Likely Story* from *Funny Peculiar*. Richard Gordon for an extract from *Doctor at Sea*, reprinted by kind permission of Curtis Brown Ltd © Richard Gordon 1961. Woody Allen for *The UFO Menace*, from *Side Effects*.

Acknowledgements

Every effort has been made to trace the owners of the copyright material in this book. In the case of any question arising as to the use of any such material, the Publishers would be pleased to receive notification of this.